Biotechnology 1996–2000

the years of controversy

edited by George Gaskell and
Martin W Bauer

This book has been produced as part of the
project Life Sciences in European Society
(contract QLG7-CT-1999-00286) of the
European Union Fifth RTD Framework.

Science Museum

Published 2001 by NMSI Trading Ltd, Science Museum,
Exhibition Road, London SW7 2DD.

British Library Cataloguing-in-Publication Data
A catalogue record for this publication is available from the British Library

Set in Postscript Monotype Plantin Light by Jerry Fowler
Printed in England by the Cromwell Press
Cover design by Jerry Fowler

ISBN 1 900747 43 X

Website: http://www.nmsi.ac.uk

Contents

List of contributors

Pedro Alcântara
(Portugal)
Research assistant at the Instituto de Ciências Sociais (ICS), University of Lisbon. He studied sociology and is enrolled in a masters programme on communication, culture and technologies. His particular research interests include science and technology, health studies, theory of journalism and mass media, immigration, methodology and social statistics.

Agnes Allansdottir
(Italy)
Lecturer in the psychology of communication at the University of Siena. She trained as a social psychologist and her research interests concern the relationship between science, mass media representations and public perceptions, with a special focus on reasoning over ethical and risk issues in health communication. Since 1996 she has been working on public perceptions and representations of biotechnology.

Nick Allum
(UK)
Research officer and doctoral student at the Methodology Institute, London School of Economics and Political Science, where he focuses on the relationship between risk perception, trust and knowledge with regard to controversial technologies. Other special interests include computer-assisted textual analysis methodologies and philosophies of science and probability.

Laura Angotti
(Italy)
Graduated in humanities from the University of Siena, and works as a technical collaborator on research projects in the Department of Communication Sciences.

Sebastiano Bagnara
(Italy)
Professor of Psychology at the University of Siena and the Director of the Department of Communication Sciences. His research interests are in the field of human–technology interaction. Over the last two decades he has published extensively on human factors, risks and new technologies.

Martin W Bauer
(UK)
Senior Lecturer in Social Psychology and Research Methodology at the London School of Economics and Political Science. Research centres on issues of science and society, including the functions of resistance in social processes, media indicators of science since the nineteenth century and a comparative study of the BSE/CJD controversy.

Siv Frøydis Berg
(Norway)
Researcher at the Centre for Technology, Innovation and Culture (TIK-Centre), University of Oslo. Her main areas of interest are concepts of disease and health, and the history of medicine.

Marie-Louise von
Bergmann-Winberg
(Sweden)
Professor of Political Science at the Department of Social Science, Mid Sweden University, and Dean of the Faculty of Interdisciplinary Research. Her doctoral degree at the Swedish School of Economics in Helsinki, Finland, was in political science, especially comparative politics and welfare theory. She is also President of the EU Institute for Federalism Research.

Heinz Bonfadelli
(Switzerland)
Professor at IPMZ – Institute of Mass Communication and Media Research, University of Zurich. He researches the use and the effects of mass media, risk communication, mass media and children.

Daniel Boy
(France)
Director of research at the Centre d'Études de la Vie Politique Française (Cevipof), Paris, specialising in the study of public attitudes to science and of Green movements in Europe. Recent projects include 'Attitudes of the French public towards science and technology', 'French attitudes to animal experimentation' and 'Evolution and structure of the ecology movement in France'.

Aglaia Chatjouli *(Greece)*	Studied molecular cell biology at Kings College London and human biology at the University of Oxford. She is currently working at the Bioethics and Communications Office of the National Hellenic Research Foundation, Athens, and is a doctoral student at the Department of Social Anthropology, University of the Aegean.
Suzanne de Cheveigné *(France)*	Sociologist specialising in the study of the relations between science, media and society at the Laboratoire Communication et Politique, Centre National de la Recherche Scientifique (CNRS), Paris. Recent projects include 'Science information in the European media', 'An analysis of environmental news on French TV', and 'A study of the reception of science programmes by the general public, scientists, and producers'.
Susana Costa *(Portugal)*	Research assistant at the Centre for Social Studies and a graduate student in sociology at the School of Economics, University of Coimbra. She has recently completed a study of forensic DNA profiling in Portugal.
Urs Dahinden *(Switzerland)*	Lecturer and researcher at IPMZ – Institute of Mass Communication and Media Research, University of Zurich. His research interests include science and risk communication, public participation procedures and the Internet.
Carmen Diego *(Portugal)*	Research assistant and doctoral student at the Department of Sociology, Instituto Superior de Ciêntas do Trabalho e da Empresa (ISCTE), University of Lisbon, where she holds a scholarship from the Portuguese Foundation on Science and Technology. Her main fields of interest are sociology of science, culture and communication, qualitative research methods and communication and social representations.
John Durant *(UK)*	Professor of Public Understanding of Science at Imperial College of Science, Technology and Medicine, London. He is Chief Executive of @Bristol, a new science and discovery centre in the west of England, prior to which he was Assistant Director of the Science Museum, London, and chairman of the European Federation of Biotechnology Task Group on Public Perceptions of Biotechnology.
Caroline Egger *(Austria)*	Studied psychology at the University of Innsbruck and is in the final stages of writing her thesis. Her main focus of interest is social psychology, especially social representations.
Edna F Einsiedel *(Canada)*	Professor of Communication Studies at the Faculty of Communication and Culture, University of Calgary. She has served on several federal biotechnology committees including the National Biotechnology Advisory Committee. Her research interests include communication issues around, and public participation on, biotechnology.
Björn Fjæstad *(Sweden)*	Adjunct Professor of Science Communication at the Department of Social Science, Mid Sweden University, Östersund and Docent of Economic Psychology at the Stockholm School of Economics. He is also editor and publisher of the Swedish popular science journal *Forskning & Framsteg*.
George Gaskell *(UK)*	Professor of Social Psychology and Director of the Methodology Institute of the London School of Economics and Political Science. Chair of the International Research Group on Biotechnology and the Public and coordinator of 'Life Sciences in European Society'.
Alexander Görke *(Germany)*	Researcher at the Department of Media Science, Friedrich Schiller University, Jena. His main research focus is on risk communication, theory of journalism and international communication. Current projects include 'Evaluation of teleteaching' and 'Gene technology in the media – between information and entertainment'.

Petra Grabner *(Austria)*	Assistant Professor at the Department of Political Science, University of Salzburg. Her research interests include biotechnology policy in comparative perspective, EU policy-making and European integration studies.
Jan Gutteling *(Netherlands)*	Social psychologist at the Department of Communication Studies, University of Twente. His research focus is on the planning, design and evaluation of risk communication, on which he has published various articles and a monograph.
Jürgen Hampel *(Germany)*	Senior researcher and coordinator of the research group on public understanding of science at the Centre of Technology Assessment of Baden-Württemberg. His research interests include public understanding of science and technology, and the analysis of conflicts on new technologies.
Trond Haug *(Norway)*	Researcher at the Centre for Technology, Innovation and Culture (TIK-Centre), University of Oslo. His main area of interest is the history of technology and science.
Erling Jelsøe *(Denmark)*	Associate Professor at the Department of Environment, Technology and Social Studies, Roskilde University. His current research includes: 'Consumer aspects and policy issues of food biotechnologies'; 'Technology assessment in relation to new biotechnologies and food production'; 'The consumer as an agent in relation to R&D in food technology'; 'Sustainable development in Latvian agriculture' and 'Biotechnology and the Danish public'.
Jorge Correia Jesuíno *(Portugal)*	Professor at the Instituto Superior de Ciências do Trabalho e da Empresa (ISCTE), Lisbon.
Mercy Wambui Kamara *(Denmark)*	Doctoral student at the Department of Environment, Technology and Social Studies, Denmark, where she also received a masters degree in technological and socio-economic planning. Her main fields of interest include the relationship between policy-making, science and politics, with particular reference to modern biotechnology.
Sandra Knickenberg *(Switzerland)*	MA student at IPMZ – Institute of Mass Communication and Media Research, University of Zurich. Her thesis focuses on public perception of biotechnology in Switzerland.
Matthias Kohring *(Germany)*	Lecturer in the Department of Media Science, Friedrich Schiller University, Jena. His main research interests are journalism and public communication and he is currently working on the projects 'Trust in media' and 'Science communication – university public relations'.
Nicole Kronberger *(Austria)*	Lecturer at the Department of Social and Economic Psychology, University of Linz. Her research focus is on group processes, public understanding of science and qualitative analysis.
Jesper Lassen *(Denmark)*	Associate Professor at the Department of Human Nutrition, the Royal Veterinary and Agricultural University, Copenhagen. He is currently working at the Centre for Bioethics and Risk Assessment and has participated in projects addressing the interaction between technology and society, technology assessment of modern biotechnology and policy analysis of the reception of the modern biotechnologies in Europe.
Martina Leonarz *(Switzerland)*	Researcher at IPMZ – Institute of Mass Communication and Media Research, University of Zurich. She studies cultural anthropology, film theory and communication science and has a particular interest in media content, risk communication and gender studies.

Nicola Lindsey (UK)	Doctoral student in the Department of Science Communication, Imperial College of Science, Technology and Medicine, London. Her research interests include the symbolic significance of genetics in everyday discourse, public understanding of science, and the role of science in policy-making.
Julia Lueginger (UK)	Former research manager of the project 'Life Sciences in European Society'.
Marisa Matias (Portugal)	Research assistant at the Centre for Social Studies and graduate student in sociology at the School of Economics at the University of Coimbra. She is completing a study on scientific controversy, citizen movements and environmental issues in Portugal.
Jennifer E Medlock (Canada)	Masters student in the Communication Studies Program at the University of Calgary. Her thesis is on the use of the citizen jury on the issue of xenotransplantation.
Cees Midden (the Netherlands)	Professor of Psychology at the Department of Technology Management, Eindhoven University of Technology. His research focus is on human–technology interactions as these become apparent in the development of new products and systems, in societal and market introductions and in the consumption and use of products.
Anneloes Meijnders (the Netherlands)	Assistant Professor of Human–Technology Interaction at Eindhoven University of Technology. Her research concentrates mainly on consumer attitudes and behaviour. She is especially interested in the antecedents and consequences of emotional responses to technological developments
Arve Monsen (Norway)	Researcher at the Centre for Technology, Innovation and Culture (TIK-Centre), University of Oslo. His main research interest is the history of science and genetics.
Lorenzo Montali (Italy)	Researcher in the Faculty of Psychology, University of Milan, Bicocca. He collaborated with the University of Siena in conducting qualitative analysis of public concerns that served as material for his doctoral thesis on social representations of biotechnology in Italy. His research interests relate to public understanding of science, social representations and everyday reasoning.
Arne Thing Mortensen (Denmark)	Professor of Philosophy at the Department of Communications, Roskilde University. His recent projects include: 'A study of public perceptions of biotechnology in connection with an information campaign' and 'Hearings and consensus conference on assessment and public perception of modern technology'.
Torben Hviid Nielsen (Norway)	Professor at the Centre for Technology, Innovation and Culture (TIK-Centre), University of Oslo. He is a member of the Bio TIK Expert Group and the Norwegian Biotechnology Advisory Board.
João Arriscado Nunes (Portugal)	Associate Professor of Sociology at the School of Economics, University of Coimbra, and researcher at the Centre for Social Studies (CES). His main interests are in social studies of biomedical research, forensic biology, public participation in issues involving science and technology, and in social and cultural theory.
Anna Olofsson (Sweden)	Doctoral student of sociology at the Department of Social Science, Mid Sweden University, Östersund. Her thesis is on the framing of genetic technology by the Swedish mass media over the past 25 years.
Susanna Öhman (Sweden)	Doctoral student of sociology at the Department of Social Science, Mid Sweden University, Östersund. Her thesis is on public perception of technology and the environment.

Uwe Pfenning (Germany)	Professor at the Centre of Technology Assessment in Baden Württemberg.
Susanna H Priest (USA)	Associate Professor at the Department of Journalism, Texas A&M University. Her research interests are in public understanding of science, risk communication and the nature of public controversies involving science and technology.
Andrzej Przestalski (Poland)	Assistant Professor of Sociology at the Institute of Sociology, Adam Mickiewicz University, Poznań. His research interests include the theory of social differentiation and history of sociology.
Georg Ruhrmann (Germany)	Chair of Media Communication and Media Effects at the Department of Media Science, Friedrich Schiller University, Jena. Currently he is working on the following projects: 'Attitudes towards television in Western and East Germany', 'Foreigners in German newspapers', 'Evaluation of teleteaching', and 'Gentechnology in the media – between information and entertainment'.
Maria Rusanen (Finland)	Researcher in the Department of Social Sciences, University of Kuopio. She studied animal sciences, biotechnology, public health, social sciences and administration, specialising in multidisciplinary research, animal biotechnology, safety issues and insecurity in a social context.
Timo Rusanen (Finland)	Researcher at the Department of Social Sciences, University of Kuopio. He studied social sciences, public health, education, cultural studies and science communication and is involved in several international collaborative research programmes. His research focuses on social issues about biotechnology, public assessment of insecurity, risks in society and disability.
George Sakellaris (Greece)	Senior Researcher at the Institute of Biological Research, National Hellenic Research Foundation, Institute of Biological Research, Athens, Greece.
Michael Schanne (Switzerland)	Director of AGK Communication Consulting which specialises in applied social research. Recent projects include 'Communication aims for biotechnology' and 'Handbook for risk communication'. His research interests include scientific journalism and risk communication.
Colette Schneider (Switzerland)	MA student at IPMZ – Institute of Mass Communication and Media Research, University of Zurich. Her thesis focuses on the media coverage of biotechnology in Switzerland.
Nina Seger (Sweden)	Researcher at the Department of Social Science, Mid Sweden University, Östersund.
Franz Seifert (Austria)	Studied biology at the University of Vienna and Political Science at the Institute of Advanced Studies, Vienna. His research focuses on democracy theory and social conflicts on technology. He is currently writing a book on the history of the biotechnology conflict in Austria and Europe.
Carla Smink (The Netherlands)	Researcher and project manager at the SWOKA Institute for Consumer Research. Her main fields of interest are food and biotechnology. In the field of biotechnology, she has performed studies on: the labelling issue; consumer information about the use of biotechnology in foodstuffs; organisational aspects of round-table discussions about biotechnology; and the public acceptance of genetic engineering of animals.
Bolesław Suchocki (Poland)	Professor at the Institute of Sociology, Adam Mickiewicz University, Poznań.

Contributors

Toby A Ten Eyck *(USA)*	Assistant Professor in Sociology at the National Food Safety and Toxicology Center, Michigan State University. He received partial research funding from the National Food Safety and Toxicology Center and from the W K Kellog Foundation, and would like to thank Melissa Williment for her contributions to the research.
Paul B Thompson *(USA)*	Distinguished Professor of Philosophy and holder of the Joyce and Edward E Brewer Chair in Applied Ethics, Purdue University, Indianapolis. Professor Thompson is the author or editor of seven books and many articles on ethical issues associated with food and agriculture. His 1997 book *Food Biotechnology in Ethical Perspective* deals closely with the issues of this volume.
Helge Torgersen *(Austria)*	Researcher at the Institute of Technology Assessment of the Austrian Academy of Sciences. His research interests include biotechnology policy and safety regulation, the relation between risk assessment and public acceptance, and participatory technology assessment.
Tomasz Twardowski *(Poland)*	Professor at the Institute of Bioorganic Chemistry, Polish Academy of Sciences, Poznań, and Professor at the Institute of Technical Biochemistry, Technical University of Lodz. He is chairman of the Interministerial Experts Team for GMO and Poland's delegate to OECD and UNEP. He is also editor-in-chief of the Polish journal *Biotechnologia*.
Wolfgang Wagner *(Austria)*	Professor of Psychology at the Institut für Pädagogik und Psychologie, Johannes-Kepler-Universität, Linz. He is editor of *Papers on Social Representations* and on the editorial boards of *Culture and Psychology*, *Asian Journal of Social Psychology* and the *British Journal of Social Psychology*.
Patrizia Weger *(Austria)*	Studied psychology at the University of Salzburg. Her masters thesis was on evaluation of education programmes. She is currently working at the University of Linz, where she is collaborator in the project 'Biotechnology in Austrian public discourse'.
Atte von Wright *(Finland)*	Professor of Nutritional and Food Technology at the University of Kuopio. He is also a member of the EU Scientific Committee on Animal Nutrition, taking part in the safety evaluation of microorganisms and plant GMOs.

Acknowledgements

Many of the contributors to this book have been working together since 1996 in a stimulating, productive and collegial atmosphere, and over the years have welcomed in others, who share their interest in studying the social, ethical and legal aspects of modern biotechnology. At the same time, some have left the international group to pursue other avenues. In particular, a special mention should go to John Durant, one of the early initiators of the research, who reluctantly left the group last year after taking up the position of Chief Executive at @Bristol. His enthusiasm, broad interests and wide knowledge are greatly missed. Thanks also to our research managers, Eleanor Bridgman and subsequently Julia Leuginger, who have since moved to new responsibilities.

This book is the third volume from the group now called 'The International Research Group on Biotechnology and the Public'. The core funding for the research has come from the European Union Fifth RTD Framework Programme, for the project 'Life Sciences in European Society' (contract QLG7-CT-1999-00286), and also from a variety of national funding agencies. We acknowledge with gratitude the support of the European Commission. In particular, our thanks go to Maria Theofilatou, Alessio Vassarotti, Maurice Lex and Mark Cantley of DG Research.

For the production of this book we owe a debt of gratitude to Ela Ginalska and Lawrence Ahlemeyer of the Publications Department at the Science Museum and to Giskin Day and Jerry Fowler who have done a splendid job on the text and the layout.

Finally, thanks to all our colleagues in the project team. It is a privilege and a pleasure to work with you. The genuine synergy arising from the different academic cultures and disciplinary backgrounds is reflected in this book. It is a lasting symbol of the dedication, inspiration and openmindedness of all members of the research group and proof of the value of European and international collaboration in the social sciences.

George Gaskell

Martin Bauer

Abbreviations used in the text

BSE	Bovine spongiform encephalopathy
Bt	*Bacillis thuringiensis*
CJD	Creutzfeldt-Jakob disease
DG	Directorate General
DNA	Deoxyribonucleic acid
EC	European Community
EEC	European Economic Community
EU	European Union
FDA	Food and Drug Administration (USA)
GM	Genetically modified
GMO	Genetically modified organism(s)
GDP	Gross Domestic Product
INRA	International Research Associates
IT	Information technology
IVF	*In-vitro* fertilisation
LMO	Living modified organism(s)
MEP	Member of European Parliament
MP	Member of Parliament
NGO	Non-governmental organisation
OECD	Organization for Economic Cooperation and Development
R&D	Research and development
rBST	Recombinant bovine somatotropin
rDNA	Recombinant DNA
UN	United Nations
UNEP	United Nations Environment Programme
UNESCO	United Nations Educational, Scientific, and Cultural Organization
vCJD	Variant Creutzfeldt-Jakob disease
WHO	World Health Organization
WTO	World Trade Organization

Part I
Introduction

Biotechnology in the years of controversy: a social scientific perspective

George Gaskell and Martin W Bauer

The controversy in context

In a substantial and scholarly review of the history of regulation of biotechnology in 1995, Cantley described public opinion as the 'major uncertainty for investors and government alike'.[1] More recently, public opinion has been described as the 'second hurdle', after regulation in the process of introduction of a new technology.[2] This second hurdle is increasingly visible. At a committee of the European parliament in July 2001, Mr Philippe Busquin, the EU Commissioner for Research (formerly DGXII), called for a wide-ranging and pluralist debate in order to agree a common basis for European Community rules on biotechnology. He emphasised that the introduction of any new technology requires public acceptance. He also said that by the end of the year 2001 the Commission would set out a strategic vision for the life sciences to the year 2010 which would include measures for launching a pluralist debate on biotechnology. Mr Busquin is not alone in his concerns about the current position of biotechnology and its future prospects. Across Europe the biotechnology industry laments the prospects for the agrifood sector as the de facto moratorium on the commercial exploitation of GM crops stays in force, debates rage over stem-cell cloning in Germany, France, Canada and the USA, and a EU–US Biotechnology Consultative Forum recently 'urged the EU and US to promote a transatlantic process for engaging a broad range of stakeholders to examine ongoing issues in biotechnology'.[3]

What is it that continues to make biotechnology so controversial? This is a new technology, born in the 1970s and launched with exuberant visions in the 1980s. So why is it necessary to launch a pluralist debate when many thousands of patents on 'forms of life' have been granted, and after the introduction of a wide range of biomedical and agrifood applications of biotechnology? One of the reasons is that biotechnology is living up to its early description as a strategic technology and, as such, likely to have an impact on many areas of contemporary life. The pace of biotechnological

R&D and the developing range of applications continues to accelerate. With the completion of the sequencing of the human genome, proteomics is now the focus of basic research. The breakthough of nucleic transfer for cloning that led to the first cloned mammal, Dolly the sheep, has been found to be inefficient and new techniques of stem-cell cloning have been developed. Genetic testing is bringing the genetic information society closer as forensic, insurance and other uses of gene banks are identified. Transgenic animals are now ready for xenotransplantation and, in the pharmaceutical and agricultural areas, modern biotechnology continues to challenge traditional methods.

Alongside these developments, biotechnology has initiated a number of debates and been sucked into others. Perhaps the central debates have been around regulation, safety and the moral status of particular applications of modern biotechnology. Beyond these, biotechnology enters into discussions about world trade, intellectual property rights and trade, the patenting of life forms, privacy and the uses of genetic information, the funding of research and development, the role of science in society, public participation in science and technology, animal rights, biodiversity and environmental conservation, the future of the Common Agricultural Policy, organic farming, agriculture in developing countries, the vertical integration of the food chain and global capitalism, consumer safety, product labelling and source identification, and the 'Risk Society' – to name but a few. Biotechnology it seems has become a platform for discussions and conflicts over a wide range of issues, involving many stakeholders.

The research reported in this volume seeks to put the controversies over contemporary biotechnology into an international and comparative context. It is the product of the ongoing research of social scientists in 21 laboratories in 16 countries who came together under the auspices of an EU-funded project: Life Sciences in European Society. European research teams from Austria, Denmark, Finland, France, Greece, Germany, Italy, the Netherlands, Norway, Poland, Portugal, Sweden,

Switzerland and the United Kingdom, joined by associates in Canada and the USA, designed and conducted this international and comparative project investigating biotechnology in the public sphere.

This book focuses on biotechnology in the public sphere during the years 1996 to 2000, updating earlier work in which we analysed the representation of modern biotechnology within the three arenas of policy and regulation, mass media coverage, and public perceptions. It is a sequel to an earlier volume which reported the trajectory of the European debate over biotechnology from 1973 to 1996.[4]

The years 1996 and 1997 turned out to be a 'watershed' for biotechnology. Around that time, Monsanto's Roundup Ready Soya was imported into Europe and Dolly the sheep, cloned from an adult cell at the Roslin Institute in Scotland, was presented to the world's mass media. This volume is also complementary to another publication in which the research group takes an analytic perspective on the emerging biotechnology movement, placing the events of the watershed years in historical context.[5]

Conceptualising technological innovation

Before outlining our concept of the public sphere in relation to the trajectory of technology we comment on the traditional social scientific call of engagement, the diffusion model of technology. This is based on the work of Ryan and Gross on the introduction of hybrid corn in Iowa,[6] research that was later formulised by Rogers and Shoemaker in 1973 in the theory of the diffusion of innovations.[7] This programme of research is predicated on the assumption that technological innovations are 'a good thing' and that the role of social science is to use the understanding of social change, as distinct from scientific or technological change, to speed up public acceptance. Amongst the public, those who take up innovations as they come on stream are the 'early adopters' and are typically well-educated and cosmopolitan types. Conversely the 'laggards', for a variety of personal and contextual deficiencies, ignore or resist the innovation.

The diffusion paradigm suggests a number of activities for social scientific research. First, to distinguish 'early adopters' from 'laggards' as a diagnostic task. Secondly, it has as its objective the speeding up of the diffusion process. Thirdly, as the means to this end, it seeks to devise effective communication strategies, of which the identification of 'the gate-keeper', a prestigious and therefore credible group member, is a key resource. Fourthly, and fundamental to diffusion research, the innovation – the technological design itself – is beyond critique. The black box is a *fait accompli*. If diffusion of innovations brings together the technical and the social, the former is the fixed entity; it is the latter, the public and communication strategies directed at the public, that are subject to manipulation and social engineering. There is no place in this analysis for an enlightened and critical response to the challenge offered by the innovation.

The success of the diffusion paradigm[8] in many fields of innovation and marketing has informed strategies and policy-making, and as such it has become part of the conventional wisdom of what can be expected from the social sciences. This is simultaneously a blessing, as it demonstrates the utility of social sciences, and a constraint, because it frames the problem solely in terms of public responses to an innovation. Many of the themes of early diffusion research continue to inform social scientific thinking about new technology. For example, strategies for risk communication are in demand to persuade the public that their anxieties have no foundation in reality. Diffusion research comes with an implicit rule about the attribution of problem. Those who do not innovate quickly are the problem, and they need to be worked on. As such, sections of the public appear to be deficient, either through lack of information or by their inadequate processing of the available information. So for example this deficit model of the public, which has found its way into the analysis of the public understanding of science, argues that lack of public support for science is a product of a knowledge deficit. And to counter this, a dose of knowledge is the recommended remedy.

The corollary of this is that the technological design is exempt from scrutiny; in other words the black box is white-washed. Only recently has it been recognised that most social scientific disciplines lack an adequate conceptualisation of things, artefacts and technological developments. Our approach by contrast views the trajectory of a technology, in our case biotechnology, as social process. The technology and those engaged in it, either as active supporters or critics, represent the technology as variously offering opportunities and constraints, hopes and fears for the future and as such constitute a mutual challenge. We conceptualise this process of challenge and counterchallenge in the dynamic of the 'biotechnology movement'. The idea of a technology movement highlights the issues of mobilising support for particular representations of the technology (the use of ideology to construct particular futures), and the technological trajectory as a process without a pre-determined teleology. In this sense, the future is open, not determined. Far from being an integrated system of unified command, the technology movement is held together by various conflicts. The threads linking these various actors are the common reference to biotechnology as something having good or bad prospects for the future, and the competition to mobilise wider public support for their particular vision (for an extended discussion see Bauer and Gaskell)[9]. In this sense counter-challenges in the form of informal or organised public resistance to new technology may come to influence the trajectory of the technology.[10]

The technology movement operates in various arenas: for example in the markets of investors and consumers, and in the public sphere of politics and citizens. The market is a source of venture capital and consumer revenue; the public sphere the source of regulation and legitimisation through public opinion. To make progress the biotechnology movement has to make inroads in these arenas. Making inroads is manifested through a portfolio of visible and invisible actions in a particular arena, which may have an impact on activities in another arena. For example, the entrepreneurial logic may lead to lower visibility in regulation and public opinion, both being seen as constraints on innovation,[11] while at the same time increasing visibility in the capital and consumer markets. Because of the increasing overlap between the consumer and capital markets, in which the public appear as investors, consumers and citizens, contradictions and dilemmas of strategy may occur. However, our present concerns are not with the market arena of biotechnology, but rather with the dynamics of the public sphere. Our working model of the public sphere is depicted in Figure 1.

In the middle of the triangle, the circle represents the movement that is engaged with 'biotechnology', either for or against, unconditionally or conditionally stated. This movement both observes and is observed by the public arena, the public sphere. The three dimensions of the public sphere, government and regulation, mass mediation and public conversations and perceptions, are represented by the three sides of the triangle. This we refer to as a triangle of mediation as each constituent element of the public sphere also observes, and is observed by, the other two. Just as policy-making takes cognisance of the content of the mass media and public sentiment on an issue, so, albeit on the basis of

different logics, are the other two enmeshed in a process of dynamic mediation.

At the bottom of this triangle of mediation is government and regulation. By regulation, modern states assure publics that the uncertainties of new developments are contained. The regulatory frame-work serves as a negotiated social contract which specifies the terms under which societies come to agree the costs and benefits of a new technology.[12]

The other two sides of the triangle represent public opinion. Public opinion, conceived as a communication system,[13] is a process as well as an outcome, which can be observed in the various arenas as speakers, media and audiences. It may be informal, in the sense of public perceptions and conversations, or formal in the sense of mass-media coverage. Two major features of public opinion are salience, a scarce resource in the context of issue competition, and framing, the lines of argumentation and imaginations that prevail.

In our research we systematically 'observe' the 'observers of biotechnology' in the public sphere, rather than its actors in the sense of actor-network theory. The objectives of the research are first, to understand the form and content of challenges and counterchallenges extending into the public sphere. Second, to analyse the interrelations between the representations of biotechnology in the three constituent arenas of the public sphere, for example changes in the regulatory arrangements in response to public opinion. Finally, we have a keen interest, but no systematic data, in identifying influences of the public sphere that may have come to change the technology. This amounts to an exercise in counterfactuals: would X (a change in the

Figure 1. The biotechnology movement and the public sphere

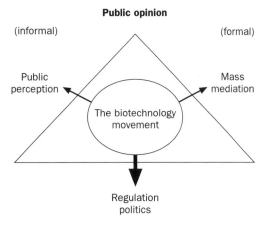

Public opinion

(informal)   (formal)

Public
perception

Mass
mediation

The biotechnology
movement

Regulation
politics

technology) have happened without Y (a counter-challenge in the public sphere)? For example would the 'terminator gene' have been dropped without mobilisation in the public sphere?

To gain access to the public sphere we investigate the historical development of 'public discourses' about biotechnology. Public discourses comprise rules and regulations, debates, written reports, media coverage and conversations (research interviews and the social survey are forms of conversation), that embody one or more representations of biotechnology.

Researching the public sphere

The objective of the empirical research is to build and interpret an integrated body of internationally comparable data in the three arenas of public discourse on biotechnology: public policy, media coverage, and public perceptions, in order to derive empirically warranted observations and conclusions about biotechnology in the public sphere, and to do so in the public domain. This work has its origins in 1994, when the founding members of the current research group met to design a research programme on what was a technology that had yet to capture the public imagination. Continuing and developing on our past activities this programme of research includes three key empirical foci.

First, participating countries conducted a longitudinal (historical) analysis of public policy for biotechnology over the period 1996 to 2000. The period from 1973, the date of the patenting of rDNA technology, to 1996 was analysed in the previous project. Second, participating countries conducted a longitudinal analysis of media coverage of biotechnology in the opinion-leading press, also from 1996 to 2000. Third, in 1999, all participating countries undertook a series of individual or group interviews to explore representations of biotechnology in depth. This qualitative research also informed the development and analysis of a representative sample survey of public perceptions of biotechnology. This survey was fielded in 1999 in each member state of the EU, together with Norway, and in 2000 Switzerland. The Eurobarometer survey was also conducted in Canada in 1999 and in the USA in 2000 by our North American associates.

No one of these perspectives would be sufficient to characterise the public sphere conceptually or empirically. In our model the public sphere is the outcome of the intersection and mutual influence of the three constituent arenas. In this sense we do not privilege any one perspective in our analyses or interpretations, nor do we reduce public opinion to results of either surveys, focus groups and media analysis or rules and regulations.

The policy arena

The analysis of the policy arena extended the previous research which had charted the development of policy debates and regulations from 1973 to 1996.[14] This period was characterised in a policy template showing the timing and development of policy initiatives in ten areas of biotechnology from reproductive technologies through GM foods to intellectual property rights.

For the period 1996–2000, the contours of the policy arena were mapped under three headings. First, the key policy initiatives or events in the period were documented. These 'policy events' include, for example, the creation of new committees and regulatory mechanisms and the establishment of new regulations. Second, for each 'policy event' the background context was explored with interviews, media analysis and the existing policy database and the key 'trigger event' or events identified. These 'trigger events' are taken to be the catalyst for the initiation of the policy event. Third, again using a variety of source materials, the relatively direct 'policy outcomes' are identified. Such outcomes might include further policy initiatives, developments in procedures for consultation or implications that impact upon other institutions, for example industry.

While the distinction between policy triggers, events and outcomes is somewhat arbitrary it serves to represent the policy process in a temporal dimension, relating policy events to the wider context of the activities in and around biotechnology. Thus it links the policy events, for example, to debates and regulatory developments at a European level, new R&D in biotechnology, the activities of NGOs, and aspects of media coverage and public perceptions.

Media representations

The mass media constitute a major forum of the public sphere in modern societies. The mass media may be viewed as 'channels' of communication both from government to the public and from the public to government. It is the complex inter-relationships between media discourses, policy discourses and public perceptions on biotechnology that is the focus of our attention. We treat the media as a 'cultural indicator' that documents the emerging social representation of genes and genetics in late twentieth-century Europe.[15] Our media analysis comprises two dimensions of the representation of biotechnology: these are salience, and the framing of the coverage of biotechnology. Salience is taken as an indicator of the attention given to an issue. As this changes over time it demarcates phases in the life history of the debate, and at the same time it stands as a measure of public controversy. The second dimension of the representation is that of the framing of the content of coverage. This shows what types of arguments, hopes and fears are being mobilised and how these change over time.

The two dimensions of media coverage are established empirically via an intensity index of the amount of coverage over time, and a formal content analysis of the coverage of biotechnology from 1996 to 2000. This builds upon earlier research which covered the period 1973–96. Our analysis of the media focuses largely on the elite or opinion-leading press in each country. This we assume can be taken as a good proxy for the tone of the wider media arena in the country. It is the press that is read by decision takers and by journalists working in other media outlets. Pragmatically these newspapers make relatively convenient and accessible sources for purposes of data collection and analysis.

Intensity as an index of salience

Using keywords (DNA, genetic*, biotech* genome and cloning) to search online media databases, the absolute number of articles published in each year in the chosen newspaper was established. In some countries, opinion leadership covered more than one outlet and in these cases an appropriate weighting was applied to create a single outlet equivalent.

Content analysis of media coverage

A corpus of media material was sampled from the population of articles identified in the intensity index. In different countries this was implemented pragmatically to suit local needs and preferences, but within the criterion of achieving international comparability.[16] The corpus was analysed using classical content analysis. This allows for systematic and replicable comparisons on the basis of a common coding frame; it is a practical way of analysing large amounts of material, and it is sensitive to symbolic material albeit through a

process of simplified interpretation. Content analysis transforms media texts into 'objectified' traces of the complex communication process in each country (see appendix 1).

For each article, the coding frame assesses: the section of the newspaper in which it appears; the size of the article, as an indicator of news importance; the format of the article; and whether the article appears as controversy. The news event is also characterised by authorship, the actors identified with biotechnology, the theme, its location, and its attributed consequences in terms of risks and benefits. An indication of the evaluation tone is gained by convenient 'negativity' and 'positivity' ratings. A key feature of the coding is the identification of 'frames' of coverage. As in the policy analysis, here a frame constitutes the dimension on which disagreements are elaborated. For our purposes, we adopted the set of frames observed by Gamson and Modigliani[17] in the context of nuclear power and added further frames identified in the course of pilot work, including 'nature/nurture', 'ethics' and 'globalisation'.

In our previous research focusing on the cultivation of biotechnology from 1973–96 we identified national phase structures on the basis of the peaks and troughs of coverage over time. Different countries reported different numbers and timings of phases on this basis. Each phase was characterised by the relative structure of coverage on five key variables: frames, themes, actors, locations, and risk and benefit. For the present study we summarise the media data on these variables contrasting the period before the watershed 1992–96 and after the watershed 1997–2000.

Public perceptions

The third constituent of the public sphere is that of public perceptions, explored in depth through a series of focus-group and individual interviews, and measured by means of random sample social survey, Eurobarometer 52.1 of October/November 1999. We employ the term 'pubic perceptions' as a generic category embracing awareness and interest in, understanding of and attitudes towards biotechnology. It also covers the images, hopes, fears, expectations that people may entertain when they think about biotechnology. On occasions we use the term 'representation' as a synonym for perception, reflecting a particular theoretical preference of the current authors, which has provided both concepts and a practical epistemology for aspects of the wider research into biotechnology in the public sphere.[18]

Qualitative research

The qualitative research was motivated in part by some curious findings from the 1996 Eurobarometer survey. Here, moral considerations appeared to be more influential than perceived risk in the formation of judgements about applications of biotechnology. To understand the resources or representations that people draw upon in making such judgements and opinions, it is necessary to explore common sense or the lay knowledge that people bring to the issues in question. To do this calls for in-depth qualitative social research.[19] Hence in 1999 and 2000 a series of group and individual interviews were conducted in two phases. To facilitate comparative analysis across a number of European countries the inter-view topic guide, the selection of interviewees, the structure for analysis of the transcripts and the final interpretation were a collaborative exercise within the group of qualitative researchers. In the nature of qualitative inquiry, the interviewees were not selected to be statistically representative. Rather, we recruited respondents with the aim of maximising the range of currents of opinion on biotechnology. The topic guide drew on results of the 1996 Euro-barometer, relevant literature and on pilot inter-views. To open up the underlying 'representations' a variety of indirect questioning techniques were designed, for example, free associations to keywords and card-sorting tasks based on different applications of modern biotechnology (see appendix 2). The qualitative team worked together on the analysis and interpretation of the corpus of interview material and, having described the currents of opinion in each national context, explored the extent to which these were idiosyncratic to countries or shared between particular countries or even across Europe as a whole.

Quantitative research

In 1996 the team had the opportunity to design Eurobarometer 46.1 on biotechnology. The design of the next survey in 1999 maintained key time-series questions and question sets, updated the set of applications of biotechnology to take account of new developments, and introduced some new questions to address some of the lacunae that we recognised during the analysis and interpretation of the 1996 survey. The survey was conducted in October and November in 1999 in each member state of the EU. Respondents were interviewed face to face and were selected using a multistage random sampling procedure providing a statistically representative sample of national residents aged 15 and over. The sample size for each country was approximately 1000. In addition, similar samples were achieved in Norway and Canada (1999) and in Switzerland and the USA in (2000). The US and Canadian surveys used a slightly modified version of the Eurobarometer questionnaire to meet the requirements of telephone interviewing.

The revised questionnaire included items on the following topics (see appendix 3):

- optimism/pessimism regarding several techno-logical developments, including biotechnology;

- knowledge biology and genetics;

- awareness of selected applications of biotechnology;

- judgements of seven applications of biotechnology measured on four dimensions: usefulness, risk, moral acceptability and support;

- specific questions on the risks associated with animal cloning and GM foods;

- consumer intentions and public participation;

- confidence in different actors associated with biotechnology;

- religious and other value orientations;

- sociodemographic characteristics.

A caveat on time-series comparisons

For the analyses reported in the chapter entitled 'In the public eye',[20] those respondents saying 'don't know' to a question are excluded. However, for time-series comparisons, for example monitoring changes in the extent of support or opposition to applications of biotechnology from 1996 to 1999, the exclusion of 'don't know' responses is insufficient. When analysing the 1996 survey we suspected that some respondents with little or no awareness of certain applications of biotechnology were, nevertheless, prepared to give a response. This is a result of the implicit demands of the survey interview. Such responses, so-called non-attitudes, could be expected to be unstable over time and to add 'noise' to analyses attempting to model perceptions of biotechnology. Hence in the 1999 survey, a filter question was introduced asking respondents whether or not they had heard about the particular application before. The result of this was that far more respondents than in 1996 said 'don't know' to the key questions about a set of applications of biotechnology. By implication, had this awareness filter question been asked in 1996, the percentage of 'don't know' responses would have been substantially higher. Hence, the different form of questioning leads to non-comparable subsamples of respondents for the 1996 and 1999 surveys, a bias that cannot be countered by merely excluding the 'don't know' responses from the analyses.

In the light of this we used a procedure based on the concept of 'response logics' to investigate changes in public perceptions over the period 1996 to 1999. We assume that the more informed respondents explicitly or implicitly adopt a stance on a particular application of biotechnology, that involves a coherent relationship among the four dimensions of use, risk, moral acceptability and encouragement. For each respondent their judgements on the four dimensions were each collapsed into dichotomies, useful/not useful, risky/not risky, morally acceptable/morally unacceptable and to be encouraged/not to be encouraged. Excluding all those with any 'don't know' responses, the remaining respondents can fall into one of 16 possible combinations of the four dimensions, what we call response 'logics' In practice only three of the 16 'logics' were widely used (meeting a criterion threshold of around 10 per cent). The three are as follows: *logic 1*, supporters (those who say that the application is useful, not risky, morally acceptable, and should be encouraged); *logic 2*, risk-tolerant supporters (those who say that the application is useful, risky, morally acceptable, and should be encouraged); and *logic 3*, opponents (those who say that the application is not useful, risky, not morally acceptable, and should not be encouraged). Logics 1 and 2 are similar in being supportive, but they display different perceptions of risk. For the 'supporter', risk is not an issue. By contrast the 'risk-tolerant supporter' perceives risk but then discounts it. Opponents, those using logic 3, take a position exactly opposite to that of supporters.

To investigate changes in public perceptions from 1996 to 1999, we assess the extent to which changes have occurred in the percentages of supporters, risk-tolerant supporters and opponents on four applications of biotechnology: GM foods, GM crops, medicines and genetic testing. It is important to bear in mind that estimates of change in public perceptions based on these three logics use a relatively small subgroup of the overall sample of the Eurobarometer survey. Only those respondents with a full set of judgements on a particular application and, in addition whose judgements fall into one of the three common logics are included. Hence it would be invalid to treat the percentage distribution for the three logics

for a particular application as an estimate of the balance of support and opposition in any one country or in Europe as a whole. Such percentages represent the views of a relatively small group of what we call the 'decided public'.

The structure of this volume

Following this introduction, Part II presents a series of international and comparative perspectives. While all these comparative perspectives are attributed to the researchers responsible for their preparation and writing, the source materials, in the form of the integrated database of policy, media and public perceptions, are the collective product of all the researchers in the project group. Without this effort, commitment and genuine collaborative spirit this volume would not exist.

The first analysis is of the European and national policy responses to the challenge of regulating the multitude of areas affected by developments in biotechnology. It highlights a series of tensions affecting policy-making on biotechnology, many of which have instigated controversy, which is yet to be resolved. For example, the tensions between visions of biotechnology as a major commercial and economic opportunity as against a technology that has generated unexpected opposition from public opinion; tensions in the search for pan-European policy and regulation in a context of national sensitivities and diverse national policy responses; tensions resulting from the opening up of the debate to address ethical issues associated with medical applications and with consumer and citizen concerns over the agrifood applications; and tensions across the North Atlantic.

The following chapter concerns the cultivation of biotechnology and the changes in its representation in the elite press. It analyses the dramatisation of biotechnology and shows that after the watershed years the national dramas have become increasingly synchronised into an international theatre. Based on intensity of coverage and framing, a typology of five different dramas is constructed and associated with particular groups of countries.

We next present an analysis of public perceptions of biotechnology drawing on the Eurobarometer survey (52.1) of biotechnology fielded in 1999, with time-series comparisons to earlier Eurobarometer surveys for selected questions. Beyond a description of public perceptions at the end of the 1990s, the chapter builds on a number of social scientific concepts to analyse the bases of differing national and individual profiles of responses to biotechnology. These include an exploration of a subgroup of the European population that is more 'engaged' with the topic of biotechnology, the ways in which trust in key actors interacts with risk perception and support for biotechnology, and public representations of risk with a particular emphasis on those risks that capture uncertainties about the future, so-called 'dread risks'. It also looks at different bases of opposition to biotechnology, the traditional 'blue' or conservative stance vs the modern 'green' stance.

The next chapter presents the findings of our qualitative and in-depth analysis of the representations of biotechnology and related issues. The extended conversations, mainly conducted in group settings, explore lay knowledge, or common sense, and how people use common sense to come to terms with the challenge of the new technology. This is captured in the form of the significant currents of opinion as expressed in words and images, hopes and fears. Across ten European countries it is striking that the similarities are much greater than the differences. On the issues of nature and life, the globalisation of technology, trust and democratic participation, Europeans draw upon common cultural roots, although these may be discussed using examples drawn from local experience. While biotechnology is not well understood in the technical sense, the respondents show sensitivity, sophistication and some ambivalence in their wide-ranging consideration of what are fundamental issues confronting European society as a result of the development of the technology.

Following these European comparative perspectives colleagues from Europe and North America present an analysis of the transatlantic biotechnology divide. Are Europe and North America worlds apart, and if so how can this be explained? Indicators of science policy and R&D funding show that the USA is ahead of Europe. But to what extent is this due to differences in the public sphere? The analysis subjects a range of frequently cited explanations for the transatlantic divide to critical scrutiny. As might be anticipated it is a complex picture, and even the characterisation of a transatlantic divide over biotechnology is not without problems. Those explanations that attribute the differing trajectories of biotechnology in North America and Europe to a single and systemic difference in the respective public spheres are, as often as not, found wanting.

The final chapter of Part II examines three broader issues arising from the research: public trust in the technoscience of biotechnology; the structure and dynamics of the national public spheres as they relate to biotechnology; and the roles of bioethics and public consultation in regulation and policy-making.

Part III presents the national profiles, which provide a synoptic account of the development of biotechnology in the public domain within each participating country during the 1990s. Each profile outlines the historical development of the biotechnology debates, the key developments in regulation and policy-making in recent years, an analysis of the elite media reporting of biotechnology before and after the watershed years, an account of public perceptions and an integrative commentary.

Finally, more details and technical information regarding the research can be found at http://www.lse.ac.uk/lses

Notes and references

1 Cantley, M, 'The regulation of modern biotechnology: a historical and European perspective', in Brauer, D (ed.), *Biotechnology, vol. 12* (New York: VCH, 1995), pp505–681.

2 Gaskell, G, Allum N and Bauer M *et al.*, 'Biotechnology and the European public', *Nature Biotechnology*, 18 (2000), pp935–8; Von Wartburg, W and Liew, J, *Gene Technology snd Social Acceptance* (Lanham, Maryland: University Press of America, 1999).

3 EU–US Consultative Forum on Biotechnology, *Final Report* (Brussels: European Commission, 2000).

4 Durant, J, Bauer, M W and Gaskell, G (eds), *Biotechnology in the Public Sphere: A European Sourcebook* (London: Science Museum, 1998).

5 Bauer, M W and Gaskell, G (eds), *Biotechnology: The Making of a Global Controversey* (Cambridge: Cambridge University Press, in press).

6 Ryan, B and Gross, N, 'The diffusion of hybrid seedcorn in two Iowa communities', *Rural Sociology*, 8 (1943), pp15–24.

7 Rogers, E M, *Diffusion of Innovation*, 4th edn (New York: Free Press, 1996).

8 Valente, T W and Rogers, E M, 'The origins and

development of the diffusion of innovations paradigm as an example of scientific growth', *Science Communication*, 16 (1995), pp242–73.

9 Bauer, M W and Gaskell, G (eds), (see note 5).

10 Bauer, M W, 'Towards a functional analysis of resistance', in Bauer, M W (ed.), *Resistance to New Technology – Nuclear Power, Information Technology, Biotechnology* (Cambridge: Cambridge University Press, 1995), pp393–418.

11 Ernst & Young, 'Integration', *8th Annual European Life Sciences Report* (London: Ernst & Young, 2001).

12 Jasanoff, S, 'Product, process or programme: three cultures and the regulation of biotechnology', in Bauer, M W (ed.) (see note 10), pp311–31.

13 Neidhardt, F, 'The public as communication system', *Public Understanding of Science*, 2 (1993), pp339–50.

14 Gaskell, G, Bauer, M W and Durant, J, 'The representation of biotechnology: policy, media, public perception', in Durant, J, Bauer, M W and Gaskell, G (eds) (see note 4), pp3–14.

15 Bauer, M W, *et al.* (see note 5); Bauer, M W, Durant, J and Gaskell, G, 'Biology in the public sphere: a comparative review', in Durant, J, Bauer M W and Gaskell, G (eds) (see note 4), pp217–27.

16 Details of the coding procedures can be found in appendix 1.

17 Gamson, W and Modigliani, A, 'Media discourse and public opinion on nuclear power: a constructionist approach', *American Journal of Sociology*, 95 (1989), pp1–37.

18 Bauer, M W and Gaskell, G, 'Towards a paradigm for the study of social representations', *Journal for the Theory of Social Behaviour*, 29 (1999), pp163–86.

19 Bauer, M W and Gaskell, G (eds), *Qualitative Researching with Text, Image and Sound – a Practical Handbook* (London: SAGE, 2000).

20 Wagner, W, Kronberger, N and Gaskell, G, *et al.*, this volume, pp80–95; Gaskell, G, Allum, N and Wagner *et al.*, this volume, pp53–79.

Address for correspondence

George Gaskell, Department of Social Psychology, London School of Economics, Houghton Street, London WC2AE, UK. E-mail g.gaskell@lse.ac.uk

Part II
Comparative perspectives

Biopolitical diversity: the challenge of multilevel policy-making

Petra Grabner, Jürgen Hampel, Nicola Lindsey and Helge Torgersen

Introduction: the watershed years, 1996/97

At the beginning of a new millennium, the way governments regulate modern biotechnology is still far from homogeneous. Recent developments point to deep differences, for example in the perception of the role of scientific advice, on both sides of the Atlantic. The US government seems eager to push various applications, including those in agriculture. The EU, in contrast, revised their directive on deliberate releases and the marketing of products (2001/18 EC) in a direction contrary to expectations. They made explicit reference to the precautionary principle in its new interpretation, apparently paying tribute to a period of heated public debate, stalling every regulatory activity for a while.

Although such a turnabout is not unique, and European regulatory policy-making and controversies therein have undergone various changes before, the period from autumn 1996 to spring 1997 appears, in retrospect, to have been a watershed. Since 1996 a tendency towards Europeanisation and globalisation of the controversy has emerged, primarily triggered by the first imports of a GM crop and the first appearance of a clone from an adult animal. These key events marked the beginning of years of controversy, while the announcement of the completed sequencing of the human genome and the revision of the deliberate-release directive in March 2001 can be interpreted as the ending of this period. The struggle over biotechnology, however, is far from over.

Within this time, a number of important and unforeseen developments changed the landscape of European biotechnology. Most influential for the developments, on the supranational level, was the swing to a more critical public and, consequently, political attitude in formerly biotechnology-friendly European countries. The debate became 'Europeanised' as, for the first time, there were key events with a continental impact that prompted actors to perform differently at a European level.

Furthermore, medical and agricultural applications increasingly became separated both in terms of public esteem and of political responses. The integrative concept of 'life sciences' was challenged when public opposition to agricultural biotechnology put the growth prospects of the whole commercial sector in jeopardy. Finally, both national governments and the European Commission found themselves forced to institutionalise mechanisms for dealing with new issues such as ethical questions, especially regarding medical applications, and consumer interests, focusing on mainly food issues. This apparently indicated a trend towards greater inclusiveness of actors and arguments.

The background for these developments was the slow process of building a European identity across national idiosyncrasies at different levels. While in the period 1996–2000, as was the case before, national responses to new challenges showed a picture of a fragmented mosaic, transnational stimuli played a decisive role. Paneuropean food scandals, such as BSE, provided for 'public-policy disasters'[1] and provoked reactions that fused with general antiglobalisation attitudes. The fragility of traditional national as well as EU policy-making with respect to scientific uncertainty opened up new opportunity structures, in particular for NGOs but also for other stakeholders, for crossnational cooperation and a synchronisation of mobilisation. Simultaneous media reporting in many European countries created a European audience for the issues at stake, being driven by similar concerns and demands. In the case of GM food especially, Europeans as consumers became decisive for policy-making both on the national as well as the supranational level.

From the outset there were tensions between the harmonisation and the diversity of policy initiatives. This chapter traces the lines of European biotechnology policy-making between national diversity and supranational developments and trends in the past years of controversy, towards a multilayered system of technology regulation.

Science, global competitiveness and harmonisation

Since the 1970s the debate about biotechnology has undergone profound changes, both in terms of the diversity of issues discussed and in terms of its societal underpinnings. Looking across Europe, countries differ in the amount of public and political attention that biotechnology has received at any one time.[2] For countries in the north and the west of Europe in the vanguard of technological development, political debates and regulation of biotechnology have been underway since the early 1970s and have been responsible for setting the agenda in others. However, there was considerable heterogeneity in the type of regulation adopted during this time, and this complexity was deepened by the EU harmonisation attempts. Moreover, developments on the other side of the Atlantic have had a marked effect on the direction of the debate in Europe. More recently, the tables have turned as controversies activated in Europe had a visible impact on the debates in the USA and Canada. This 'globalisation' of the debate became visible, for example in NGO actions at the WTO meeting in Seattle in 1999 and at other events.

Scientific research (1973–78)

During the early 1970s, biotechnology was viewed principally as a promising area of research. Despite early concerns raised by American scientists about laboratory safety (which led to the widely known Asilomar conference and later a self-imposed moratorium), risks at this time were perceived purely in technical terms and their significance was soon downplayed. In the USA at least, the debate waned once scientists had reassured the public that the risks were both marginal and manageable. Nevertheless, a need for some kind of regulation was acknowledged, and in 1976 National Institutes of Health guidelines took effect that handed the locus of control to the scientific community itself. This form of regulation was also quickly adopted by the forerunner European countries, as it was perceived to provide both a flexible and sufficient means of ensuring acceptable safety levels for the handling of recombinant DNA. At this time, awareness of biotechnology amongst the European public was not considered to be significant. Moreover, any concerns that fell outside the rubric of technical risk were either dismissed because they were 'unscientific' or were dealt with separately. This arrangement served to effectively assuage any emerging public debate in most countries for the next few years, and for the regulators at least, the problem appeared to be under control.

Competitiveness, resistance and regulatory responses (1978–90)

Over the ensuing decade, biotechnological techniques began to be applied in various fields and contexts, and as a result the arguments diversified and a debate arose. In an increasingly competitive world, the technology was primarily seen in terms of its enormous economic importance and, as such, policy manoeuvres were aimed principally at defending it from the slowly increasing resistance that was fuelled by concerns about its risks. As the applications of biotechnology left the scientific laboratories and entered the technological marketplace, the content and societal base of the debate expanded. Critical NGOs took up counterarguments developed by scientists from other fields and placed biotechnology, together with nuclear energy, on the list of contentious technologies characterising the 'risk society'.[3] Indeed, from an early stage, opponents identified links in the biotechnology debate with other contested sociopolitical issues such as environmental protection, the future of agriculture or IVF. In addition, the very essence of the technology itself – the manipulation of the building blocks of life – was questioned, giving rise to moral concerns.

At this point, it became clear to many European governments that self-regulation was not enough. Some governments imposed national regulations in an attempt to both balance the arguments about possible or perceived risks with those of the promising economic opportunities, and to confine the issues at stake. This was spurred on by pressure from industry demanding a defined legal framework to protect them from obstruction against their R&D activities. At the same time, the European Commission was beginning to recognise that the applications of biotechnology would need some unified conditions (indeed, Scandinavian countries and Germany had established special laws), and that compromise was necessary if the growing critique was to be contained.

European harmonisation (1990–96)

Emphasis on global competitiveness intensified in the early 1990s as the political elites in Europe continued to frame the debate surrounding biotechnology in mainly scientific and economic terms. The Common Market project drove the EU to harmonise its rules in order to overcome the regulatory divergence in its member states. However, this proved to be more difficult than expected, since regulatory styles and the history of the debate across Europe varied profoundly. As a result, initiatives such as the directive on deliberate release of 1990 (90/220), did not entirely resolve national differences and left inconsistencies (e.g. in risk-assessment regimes).[4] Nevertheless, it did succeed in providing policy-makers in EU member countries with a compulsory framework for regulation, as well as a useful reference point for non-member countries. One effect of the shifting of decision-making competence to Brussels was a new power balance that was tipped heavily in favour of industry. When coupled with the once again waning public debate about biotechnology in most of the European countries in the mid-1990s, this resulted in the rapid growth and spread of the technology.

Although the European integration process and the establishment of the Common Market was introducing greater complexity and a European element into the political debate, controversies surrounding biotechnology appeared almost exclusively on a national level. Debates and policy-making were shaped chiefly by national regulatory styles, political cultures, historic experiences and general attitudes towards technological developments in the different countries.[5] Hence, up until this time the emergence of new controversies and the consequent shifts in national policies and debates on biotechnology were primarily triggered by national key events. Often, such focusing events[6] provided the opportunity for interest groups – and in particular, NGOs – to encourage mobilisation amongst the public, and consequently, to pressurise for policy change.

The years of controversy

This phenomenon of nationally confined key events changed fundamentally in the period of autumn 1996 to spring 1997 when two unrelated events sparked global controversies that were to change the way that biotechnology was to be perceived from then onwards. The first of these events was the import in autumn 1996 of the first GM soya-beans to European shores. The introduction of this product marked a watershed in debates about biotechnology, for it provided the opportunity for NGOs to launch unilateral strategies of opposition to genetically modified foods (later coming to be

known as 'GM foods') across Europe, which in turn had the effect of sparking transnational media debate. Most significantly, in contrast to the exclusively national protests that had occurred in previous years, these actions were targeted at both national governments and the European political institutions. Although public and policy reactions to the imports differed both in their nature and timing across Europe,[7] the actions of these NGOs demonstrated a shift in focus towards the EU that was symbolic of the process of Europeanisation itself. Table 1 shows a summary of key events.

The second event to mark a watershed in national and international debate about biotechnology occurred within a few months of the soya imports, when the existence of the world's first ever cloned mammal, Dolly the sheep, was announced in February 1997. This technological achievement came to be the 'first real global and simultaneous news story on biotechnology'.[8] Although in the beginning, it appeared to be purely a media event, it soon initiated significant policy outcomes and had a strong impact on future debates. Indeed, in countries like France and Italy, it was the cloning debate that opened up new channels for a debate about GM food as well. Together, the importation of GM soya and the advent of Dolly the sheep provided the platform from which the years of controversy would lift off.

Medical progress and public outcries

Medical applications proceeded in a generally positive social and political climate, under the auspices of significant medical benefits and economic gains in the future. While applications such as genetic fingerprinting have become mainstream, others have been temporarily stalled in the research stage due to technical problems, for example gene therapy and xenotransplantation. It was the medical research community itself that halted such applications, thus curbing the intensity of public debate from the outset.

A sheep is born and the world talks ethics

In February 1997, the advent of Dolly the sheep raised worldwide attention. The reaction in the media and in the European policy communities to the announcement was swift and unanimous: almost everywhere, the use of cloning techniques for the purposes of human reproduction was condemned. This sentiment was reproduced at many levels, from churches to the European

Table 1. *Key international events*

Date	Trigger	Description	Outcome
March 1996 onwards	BSE (along with other food scandals, e.g. dioxin in Belgium).	Link between BSE and CJD admitted by UK officials; adverse responses by the EU, its member states and their publics.	Distrust in conditions of food production and regulation; food safety, labelling, consumer choice are paramount; EU ban on British beef and beef products.
Autumn 1996	First soyabean imports from the USA to Europe.	EU labelling rules not yet in place; protests in many European states.	Launch of Greenpeace campaign in Europe and other NGOs nationally; Monsanto demonised.
1997	*January:* Novel food directive.	After ratification by the European parliament in January, directive is enacted in February 1997; regulation is late and incomplete; in force only after first imports.	Italy, Luxembourg, Austria ban marketing and cultivation of maize ('import bans') in February; EU regulates products not included in novel food directive; eventually mandatory labelling for GM maize/soya produce is introduced.
	February: Report of Dolly the sheep.	Unanimous rejection of human cloning; ethical questions brought to the fore; trigger for wider debate on biotechnology in some countries.	Churches, European Commission, European parliament, WHO articulate rejection; ethics committees worldwide issue advice; European legal text on biomedicine (Convention on Human Rights and Biomedicine) ratified by the Council of Europe in January 1998.
1998	French government refuses to authorise cultivation of Bt maize.	General shift in French policy; citizens' conference; heavy NGO activism.	France becomes one of the most restrictive countries with respect to agricultural biotechnology within the EU.
1998–99	Pusztai case: international scientists support unpublished work on GM potatoes.	In Britain, unease growing from 1996 explodes into furious media debate and NGO activism.	Case attracts international attention. Britain forced into a more cautious approach to agricultural biotechnology.
1999	Monarch butterfly study.	Reports on unintended side-effects of Bt maize on Monarch butterfly breeding intensifies resistance to GM crops in Europe and in the USA, widely cited by NGOs as evidence against GMOs.	USA issues stricter conditions for growing Bt crops.
	August: Deutsche Bank report advises against investment in agricultural biotechnology.	Monsanto fusion (initially announced in June 1998) fails in late 1999, agro biotechnology shares down, US farmers sue Monsanto (December 1999).	Biotechnology industry and particularly Monsanto in financial distress; public relations campaign in the USA; pharmaceutical companies start shedding agro divisions.
	June: EU Council.	After policy shifts in several member states, EU-level reconsideration.	EU issues temporary suspension of approvals on GM products.
Winter 1999–2000	Intermittent reports of GM ingredients detected in food products.	NGOs and retail chains form coalitions, food producers and distributors decide not to sell/use GMOs.	GM food disappears from European market shelves.

Table 1 (continued). Key international events

Date	Trigger	Description	Outcome
2000	*January:* Death of a patient in gene therapy trial in the USA.	After several failures, review of gene therapy protocols in USA.	FDA stops gene therapy experiments at University of Pennsylvania.
	January: Biosafety Protocol.	After start of negotiations in Aarhus (1996) and failure in Cartagena (February 1999), process comes to an end.	Biosafety Protocol as signed in Montreal includes 'precaution'.
	February: European Patent Authority issues patent to University of Edinburgh for human embryos 'by mistake'.	Series of promising human stem-cell research results raise questions about embryo research, gene therapy and cloning; renewed ethics *vs* research debate.	NGOs demand patent regulation amendment (spring); German government considers EU patent directive inadequate, seeks renegotiation (October).
	June: First draft of complete sequence of the Human Genome announced.	After racing to complete, the private firm Celera and public consortium HUGO join forces.	Achievement is widely acclaimed, but overshadowed by issues of intellectual property rights.

Commission to the WHO. From February 1997 onwards, public advisory bodies and ethics committees in many nations produced reports recommending that human cloning be prohibited. The existence of Dolly has brought ethical questions to the fore in policy-making on biotechnology. The answers from officials all over the Western world summed up to something like a common moral standard.

In this way, the cloning case has been the key precipitator for initiatives in the institutionalisation of ethics in many countries.[9] At the same time, ethical statements from institutionalised bodies – such as the national ethics committees in France, Italy and the USA – have accompanied almost all prohibitions of cloning. In most countries new legislation has had to be drafted, as existing laws on reproductive technologies have proved to be inadequate. Among the few countries with legislation strict enough to cope with developments associated with cloning (such as Norway) was Germany, since the German Law for the Protection of Embryos prohibits all consuming use of human embryos. As a result, no cloning debate was triggered by the advent of Dolly initially. However, in the further course of events, a more general debate was kicked off by a lecture by the philosopher Peter Sloterdijk in mid-1999, which was particularly delicate owing to Germany's history. Finally the strict law itself came to be the cause of controversy, as scientists had been pressurising the government to relax its regulations on the protection of the embryo. They argued that research into the therapeutic uses of embryos was being hindered and Germany's international competitiveness in the field was being compromised.

Thus, while many countries had a regulatory debate surrounding cloning, this was soon followed by a debate on deregulation in Germany. In contrast to this, human reproductive cloning did not invite much serious political consideration in Sweden[10] or Finland, but contrary to countries with strict regulation, this was for pragmatic reasons: its likelihood was seen as remote. In the case of Finland, the absence of any upheaval over Dolly was basically due to public policy promoting biotechnology and to the fact that public opinion is very favourable towards the technology as well. In Sweden there was some debate on human cloning for a few months, because it was regarded as being rather hypothetical, and because questions of reproductive medicine are dealt with less emotionally and religion is less salient. This is in sharp contrast to southern European countries, where debates on reproductive technologies have never been fully resolved and consequently the exploitation of the pre-embryo has been prohibited mostly on religious grounds. In Italy, for instance, in March 1997 a decree was issued banning all forms of cloning, which has since then been re-enacted every 90 days. Hence, although there is no national regulation of reproductive technologies, cloning is prohibited.

The initial, swiftly agreed upon moral standard in official statements in the wake of the advent of

Dolly eroded over time into more nationally diverse preoccupations. It is no wonder that debating ethics in a pluralistic society may result in diverging opinions. Ethics committees, installed as expert-oriented bodies in order to arrive at a viable moral consent, often highlighted divergent reasoning rather than providing a unanimous 'expert' opinion about the legitimacy of the issues at stake that would resolve possible conflicts. Such differences added to the moral and ethical uncertainty, and hence to the erosion of the initial gross moral outcry over cloning.

In particular, the use of cloning techniques to produce embryos for stem-cell research and for future therapeutic purposes became contested. As a result, legislation has been delayed in most countries while cloning is still high on the political agenda. Old ethical debates on the status of the embryo and the morality of scientists researching in this field have been reawakened and systematically countered by the argument that such research could have numerous medical benefits, including the treatment of degenerative neurological diseases.

December 2000 was a turning point. The British parliament voted to pass, with a significant majority, the necessary changes to the Human Fertilisation and Embryology Act of 1990[11] to allow for research on human embryos up to 14 days old to be carried out. In the same month, the French government also proposed a bill to lift its ban on human embryo research and to update its own bioethics legislation, passed in 1994. However, Britain and France's pro-science attitudes have met with some hostility in Europe, and in September 2000 the European parliament passed a resolution calling for a ban on all forms of human cloning throughout Europe.

Ethics takes centre stage

Over the years, the use of ethical argumentation in the design of policy on medical biotechnology has become increasingly widespread, for example through the establishment of national bodies in nearly every country. Indeed, as events over the last few years have unfolded, ethical perspectives on the development of the technology have increasingly taken centre stage.

In April 1997, after ten years of difficult negotiations, 22 countries signed the European Council Convention on Human Rights and Biomedicine, prohibiting the creation of human embryos for research purposes.[12] This Convention marks a culmination in the institutionalisation of bioethics across Europe. It is an internationally binding, legal text designed to 'protect people against the misuse of biological and medical advances' through a series of principles and prohibitions with implications for many areas of medical biotechnology beyond embryo research.[13] The aim of the Convention was to establish, beyond rhetorical statement, a common standard for bioethics across Europe and internationally. Indeed for many countries, especially those in Eastern Europe, its assimilation will represent the first instance in which issues of bioethics have been addressed in legislation on medical biotechnology. However, it soon turned out that such a common standard is hard to achieve. Pro-science countries have had problems with the Convention, and Britain did not sign because its prohibitions were seen as too stringent; conversely, Germany and Austria refused to sign because the prohibitions were considered not stringent enough.

In addition to cloning, the Convention has implications for genetic testing, and this is another area that has been at the centre of intense ethical debate across Europe during this period. Whereas genetic testing of consenting adults for disease-related genes, for both diagnostic and predictive purposes, is currently well supported and indeed fairly widespread across Europe,[14] great concern has been shown for the social and ethical implications of the genetic testing of children, prenatal testing and pre-implementation diagnosis. The last two cases could potentially allow parents to choose some of the traits of their child and to intervene either through abortion (in the case of prenatal genetic testing) or through selection of the desired embryo (in the case of pre-implantation genetic diagnosis). This practice is naturally most sensitive in Germany, where several bioethics institutions have been set up to deal with the issue. The main fear expressed by opponents to genetic testing is one of a 'slippery slope' towards 'designer babies' and the spread of negative attitudes towards undesirable traits (and therefore those people living with such traits) throughout society. Critics, as in the opposition to the use of human embryos in stem-cell therapies, apply the Kantian ideal that human lives, at any stage in their development, should not be used as a means to an end. In countries with a more positive attitude towards genetic testing, discussion has been centred on which traits would be acceptable to test for prenatally. However, although there are strict rules in many European as well as in some US states, the technology is still largely self-regulated by its practitioners in many countries, and there have been widely publicised rumours about Italian doctors offering sex selection to couples both at home and abroad.

Safety: a precondition throughout

Thus, ethics has played a pivotal role in policy debates surrounding medical applications of bio-technology. Interestingly, whilst risk is a pertinent issue in agricultural biotechnology, it played a much smaller role in the debate on medical applications. This appears paradoxical but it is a reminder that any consideration of risk is contingent on and implies a parallel assessment of the benefits. Medical benefits are obviously desirable, so the question of risk may take second place. This is not to say that risk arguments did not play a role both in expert assessments and in public debate on medical biotechnology. Ethical argumentation, however, often concealed risk discourses.

Xenotransplantation, like cloning, has been shrouded in ethical controversy since its inception, while progress has been hampered by problems of safety.[15] So far, no country has gone beyond consideration of the technical and theoretical issues and, as a result, clinical trials involving xenotransplantation have yet to be permitted anywhere in Europe. Indeed, the future of xenotransplantation is currently uncertain, since the precaution that is exercised over it has prompted many commercial developers to abandon their programmes. Consequently, public debate has also been fairly limited, although many governments have organised forms of public consultation on the issue[16] and there has been some interest from the media. Moreover, religious organisations have taken an interest in the topic as well, notably the Greek Orthodox Church and the Vatican, which has organised conferences on the matter, and the Pope has issued statements supportive of xenotransplantation.

Meanwhile, gene therapy has also been mired in controversy over safety, despite a fairly positive start. The change followed the death of a patient who had been taking part in a clinical trial in the USA in 1999. As a result of the ensuing FDA investigation, both scientific and political institutions in the USA demanded a temporary halt on all gene-therapy trials. Ironically, US agencies appear to be more cautious than their European counterparts when it comes to disputes over medical developments for, although widely publicised in Europe, the American controversy did not trigger any similar reactions. Indeed, although

gene therapy has not been without its controversies[17] and debates on its efficacy, clinical trials have been continuing to progress slowly across Europe within a fairly positive political and media climate.

The genetic information society

Biotechnology is fast becoming, not only an applied technology, but an information technology. This is signified most notably by the efforts of researchers worldwide to identify and sequence the DNA of the human genome as part of the internationally funded Human Genome Project.[18] In September 1999, the Project was challenged by the American firm Celera Genomics, headed by the sequencing entrepreneur Craig Venter, who announced that it had also begun sequencing the genome (using the new 'shotgun' technique) and would complete it within two years. Moreover, it transpired that access to Celera's sequence data would be by sub-scription only and that patents would be filed out on some of the genes identified, thus undermining the public achievements of the Human Genome Project. This announcement prompted the Project to release their results daily on the Internet and to race to complete their own sequencing publicly before Celera.

Finally, on 26 June 2000, in an unprecedented move, the two sides joined forces to announce the completion of the sequencing two years ahead of schedule in a televised satellite link-up between the US president and the UK prime minister. The announcement was broadcast internationally and widely acclaimed as 'biology's Apollo landing' (President Clinton) and 'the first great technological triumph of the twenty-first century' (Prime Minister Blair). However, although it was undoubtedly a great scientific achievement, in terms of public admiration it was not comparable to the first landing on the moon. Instead, the accomplish-ment was overshadowed by debates about the merits of privately vs publicly funded research.

The race between the publicly funded group of researchers and the private-enterprise group high-lighted an issue of general importance. How should science be organised, and what is its purpose: the pursuit of knowledge as an end in itself, or a means to make a profit? Is there a role for publicly funded research, or is this an outdated and inefficient model. Should science be commercialised? If so are research results a commodity that can freely be traded or are there restrictions where results concern human-kind's common heritage? And who should profit:

only those who pay for the work, or is there such thing as a 'common good' that everyone should be able to take advantage of? Hence, the race for the human genome sequence has flagged up some of the basic questions of today's science policy.

Intellectual property rights

Together with the promise to revolutionise medicine, the Human Genome Project's success has caused concern over intellectual property rights and the use and storage of individuals' genetic information. Whether living material, such as plants and animals, or naturally occurring substances, such as genes, may constitute the subject of an invention – and therefore a patent – is highly controversial. This is not simply because of the ethical questions concerning who 'owns' genes, but because of the research and economic implications that restricted access to gene sequences may hold. In July 1998, the European directive on the legal protection of biotechnological inventions finally came into force after more than ten years of debate in the European parliament. Under the directive, which effectively brings plant, animal and human biotechnologies together, genes could in fact become the subjects of patents, provided that they have been characterised in isolation of the human genome.[19]

The implications of the directive are enormously complicated, and while the biotechnology industry has welcomed it, it has been met with much opposition both in the policy arena[20] and from interest groups (ranging from medical associations to farmers, environmentalists, animal welfare groups, religious groups and development organisations) who have orchestrated demonstrations outside the European Patent Office. Conversely, in Switzerland, scientists were mobilised against the Gene Protection (Gen-Schutz) Initiative, that proposed to prohibit patents on GM plants and animals and was later rejected in a referendum in 1998. However, despite resistance to the directive, by the beginning of 2001 most member states were well advanced in their preparations to implement it, and most governments have not seen the need to consult publicly on the issue.

The generation and storage of genetic information

The identification of specific genes has the potential to reveal a great deal of information about individual genetic makeup. The use of genetic technologies for the purposes of identification, for example genetic

fingerprinting, has become a mainstay in tools for solving crime in Europe. In many countries, massive public and media support have backed high-profile criminal investigations using this technology.[21] Moreover, DNA analysis is now seen as a routine procedure in paternity testing, and the use of genetic testing in the clinic for prediction and diagnosis of disease is becoming increasingly common. Although there are currently no widespread adult genetic screening programmes in operation in Europe, the possibility raises the question for policy-makers of how to store the growing mass of genetic information (genetic databases) and genetic material (gene- or biobanks).[22]

Proposals for different types of genetic databases have been met with varying levels of controversy in Europe. In 1998, the Icelandic parliament passed a bill which allows the whole population's individual health (including genetic) information to be passed on to a large database that is being created, without patients' explicit prior consent.[23] Iceland's case has been widely reported in the media of other European countries, and has prompted reactions in many of its policy communities. In Sweden, officials stressed that individual patients should be able to give consent for whether their information could be accessed in this way. A proposal for a large-scale database in the UK has also raised concern in the media, where it has been suggested that access and control over genetic information could be abused. At an international level, both the WHO and the World Medical Association (WMA) have identified large-scale DNA collection projects, particularly in developing countries, as an area of great concern, and the WMA is in the process of drawing up its own ethical guidelines on the matter.

Access to genetic information

One of the main concerns about genetic databases is not simply the storage of genetic information, but who should have access to it and, more importantly, how it might be used. It has been questioned whether insurance companies should be allowed to know the results of genetic tests before underwriting policies. Whilst insurance companies have maintained that genetic information should be treated like any other kind of medical information, those opposed have argued that genetic tests differ in two respects. First, they are often predictive rather than diagnostic, and whilst they can predict the likelihood of a particular disease developing, they can not predict the severity of the disease or when it will occur. Consequently, those wishing to purchase insurance with a positive test result are often 'presymptomatic' with no knowledge of when the disease may develop. Second, genetic tests do not only reveal information about an individual, but potentially about their families too, raising complex issues of confidentiality and privacy.

This issue has been highlighted in the policy arena across Europe and the USA, generating very similar outcomes despite varying levels of visible public unease. In Europe, overall attitudes towards genetic testing are positive due to its expected medical benefits. However, in the USA where health insurance and pensions are largely privately funded, genetic tests are perceived more ambiguously since their implications in terms of additional costs, loss of coverage and access to employment, are more tangible. Consequently, genetic testing and insurance has been a salient issue in the USA for longer than it has been in Europe and has prompted action at both the state and the federal levels, resulting in either prohibition or severe restrictions on the use of genetic test results for any non-therapeutic purposes.

Policy reactions have been similarly heavy handed in Europe, where there is either legislation[24] or moratoria[25] that prohibits insurance companies from obtaining and using genetic test results. For the rest of Europe, some guidance has come from the European Council Convention on Human Rights and Biomedicine. Although its implications for insurance are unclear, the Convention does place a ban on all forms of gene-based discrimination and states that predictive genetic tests are only permissible when used for medical purposes.

Prolonged promise and national variety

As a direct result of the accomplishment of the sequencing of the human genome, genomics research has received increased national funding from many governments (as in the UK, Germany and Italy), who now see it in terms of its growing economic potential. As a landmark achievement, the Project has instilled wonder over the sheer volume of sequence information it has generated. In spring 2001, the announcement that the human genome nevertheless contains far less genes than anticipated – perhaps less than 30,000 – has added to its mystery. The gradual analysis of the data has apparently generated new scientific puzzles about the 'nature of the gene' faster than it has solved other ones.

Thus, it is becoming increasingly clear that the genome, and study of genetics as a whole, may be significantly more complicated than optimistic researchers had originally anticipated in their depictions of its future possibilities and in their search for venture capital. Ironically, its implications for 'everyday use' appear more distant now than before the establishment of the genome sequence, as the surprisingly low number of genes highlights its complexity. Major breakthroughs will have to wait for the age of so-called proteomics when more data at the level of the protein will be available. The promise remains and practical implications – both negative and positive – will be subject to future debate. Thus, the era of promise in the 'genetic information society' remains on hold.

The ways to proceed for the realisation of this promise, however, are likely to diverge significantly. The example of stem-cell research gives a taste of national variation. While France and the UK have been severely criticised for their pro-science and permissive policies, at the time of writing, stem-cell research, pre-implementation diagnostics and related therapeutic purposes are heavily debated in other countries such as Germany and Austria. Thus, the issue of the status of the embryo, already salient in previous controversies on reproductive medicine, has become paramount again.

Agricultural biotechnology: Europeans as consumers

Earlier controversies concerning GM crops, having emerged in countries like the Netherlands, Sweden and Denmark had virtually faded away by the mid-1990s. Even in Germany, where the destruction of experimental test sites continued, other issues such as the consequences of the country's reunification had reduced the importance and visibility of the biotechnology controversy. Indeed, in some parts of Europe, GM food had already entered the market without appearing to raise any social or political controversy: after so-called vegetarian cheese[26] had been introduced to the British market from 1995 onwards British supermarkets retailed Zeneca's tomato paste made from GM fruit and, although not legally required, labelled it voluntarily as such. It seemed to be only a matter of time before such products would be a normal part of everyday life.

Yet, when the first ships carrying GM soyabeans reached European harbours in August 1996, this event led to massive protests in most of western and northern Europe, reopening those apparently settled debates. Moreover, it was not long before GM maize, which had received market approval following EU regulation, became closely interlinked with the soya case and added another layer of dispute to the rising controversy. In contrast, for southern and eastern Europe, GM soyabeans were not initially a topic of general concern and protests did not find much response.

The introduction of GM crop plants into the Common Market raised alarm over agricultural biotechnology to an unprecedented level, even in countries where people had previously been fairly positive towards biotechnology. In fact, evidence from the Eurobarometer surveys of 1991 and 1993 suggests that the seeds of rejection had already been sown in the early 1990s. In 1996, the Eurobarometer 46.1 survey (fielded shortly before the first GM soya imports) showed that a majority of Europeans were against the use of genetic engineering in food production,[27] and by 1999, when the Eurobarometer 52.1 was carried out, it was clear that the rejection had intensified in all but a few European countries, thus reflecting the controversy resulting from the first imports.

European diversity: national reactions

Although the emerging controversies were not surprising, their origins varied considerably through-out Europe. In some countries, as mentioned, the GM debate fell on the fertile ground of already existing debate about agricultural biotechnology, whilst in others, new social actors mobilised the public. In France, Germany and the UK, con-servative administrations had been replaced by centre-left governments which included, in some cases, representatives of Green parties. However, it seems that changes in biotechnology policies were more often due to public mobilisation than to pro-grammatic changes of governments. Countries also varied in the speed at which the debate escalated; for example in Austria, Denmark and the UK, the debate took off relatively quickly and was directly interlinked with the imports, whereas in Germany, France and Italy, the debate was delayed and eventually modulated by other events. At the same time, there were other countries where the ship-ments were initially ignored by the public, as was the case in Finland, the Netherlands and Norway.

National political reactions also differed in the direction they took, ranging from complete U-turns to re-emphasis of established ways to cope with challenges from biotechnology. In some cases, reactions often perceived to be mostly driven by public opinion, added up to drastic changes of domestic policies. Moreover, as will be shown, they also initiated a reformulation of the EU's approach to agricultural biotechnology.

Exporting and reinventing resistance

The soya case triggered resistance against GM food in all but a few countries. In Austria, an exclusively national event had already kicked off an earlier dispute: the first and 'illegal' release of a GM plant had raised severe public controversies in the spring of 1996 (approximately six months before the European imports), putting a country that had just become an EU member in a European 'forerunner' position only by historic coincidence. Austrian NGOs had recognised that agricultural biotechnology would serve well as a new topic for mobilisation. Over the following year, by the time Greenpeace introduced its international campaign, several national NGOs had already joined forces, linking both the 'blue' and 'green' critiques of biotechnology.[28] By spring 1997, massive NGO mobilisation had engendered widespread public support, and Austria joined the club of countries 'traditionally' taking a critical position at the European level. Moreover, the Austrian debate was the first in Europe to closely link general questions of agricultural policy (with a strong domestic organic sector) with those of food safety, consumer protection and labelling of GM foods, introducing unprecedented collaborations between NGOs and other actors, such as retailers.

Even before EU membership was enacted, Austrian negotiators in the relevant EU committees had always been rather critical of agricultural biotechnology. Thus, although the public debate and resistance was a new phenomenon, Austria's reaction was essentially to re-emphasise an already restrictive official policy. In contrast, Denmark had been experiencing significant public controversies since the 1980s. Indeed, in response to rising public concern it had already held a consensus conference on gene technology in industry and agriculture in 1987, setting an example to the rest of Europe. After a period of relative calm during the early 1990s, the import of GM soyabeans from the USA reopened the debate and the advent of Dolly the sheep led to its intensification. As in Austria, labelling, consumer choice and the role of biotechnology in agricultural production became salient. In Denmark, the collection of more than 75,000 signatures against GM foods outspokenly followed the Austrian example, and close cooperation between NGOs as well as their joining forces with retail chains was a further similarity.

Both countries have also been influential at the EU level – together with Italy, France, Greece and Luxembourg – in their attempts to block new permissions for marketing of GM products.

U-turns on resistance

For a long time, scepticism towards biotechnology was restricted to highly industrialised countries in northern and central Europe, whilst those in southern Europe appeared both supportive of biotechnology and indeed of new technologies in general. During the years of controversy this changed considerably. For example, when the first imports of GM soya arrived in Europe, Italy was fairly unresponsive. Yet, when the existence of Dolly the sheep was announced, there was a huge public outcry, which served in turn to spark mobilisation against GM foods. The discussion was less about the risks of the technology than about the perceived quality of biotechnologically modified food. Such produce was seen as the exact opposite of regional products from organic agriculture that appeared much more favourable. This additional framing of the issue was not unique to Italy, but was also common in other countries.[29] Until 1996, Greece had stood out as one of the most supportive countries of biotechnology, but the shift in survey results since then has been dramatic: in 1999, Greece overtook Austria as the most critical country in Europe.[30] This shift coincided with the actions of Greenpeace, who in the midst of contradictory signals from the state authorities with regard to GM field trials, succeeded in mobilising the public. Consequently, GM food became one of the dominant topics in the media. In France, and to a certain degree in the UK, policy as well as measured public opinion profoundly changed since the mid-1990s. Whereas they were formerly biotechnology-friendly or at least relaxed countries, pursuing a regulatory strategy that favoured scientific expertise, technocracy, and specific boards, the picture has now completely changed.[31]

As in Italy, the first imports of GM soyabeans into Europe did not initially provoke much interest in France. However, the conservative government had already initiated a consensus conference on agricultural biotechnology, which took place in mid-1998. The situation changed when the French government constellation turned into 'cohabitation', with the president and the prime minister representing different parties. The new government made a U-turn with respect to GM crops,[32] but French authorities continued to be uncertain about

how to handle such matters. Public opposition had grown meanwhile, although the trigger for this was mostly Dolly the sheep. Indeed, the latest Eurobarometer results confirm that France has since become one of the countries most opposed to transgenic food in Europe. Moreover, the French case highlights another facet to the new debate, which is that resistance to GM food is closely linked to arguments against global-isation,[33] and in this case the increasing control that American biotechnology companies are claiming over the European food market. This is a theme that has been reiterated at demonstrations outside different international assemblies, such as the WTO meeting in Seattle in November/December 1999, and the World Bank meeting in Washington in April 2000.

For the UK biotechnology community, the first imports of GM soya could not have been more badly timed, as public controversy on GM food also flared up in Britain. In the wake of the BSE scandal, the country experienced a collapse of trust in the regulatory system and in food-sector scientists. After the first shipments of GM soyabeans reached British harbours, a rainbow coalition of environmental groups such as Friends of the Earth, consumer associations and high-profile individuals, notably Prince Charles, argued against GM food. In February 1999, the debate exploded across the newspaper headlines, when controversial unpublished experiments by the researcher Arpad Pusztai were publicly supported by a group of 22 scientists in a letter to a leading newspaper. What followed was a furious media campaign that was to have repercussions across the globe. Meanwhile, the crisis in trust faced by the food industry, and by the regulatory authorities in Britain, led the government to establish a new Food Standards Agency[34] and to overhaul the entire advisory system on biotechnology.

Upholding support and channelling unease

In Germany, a country with a long history of continuous public biotechnology controversy, the media closely observed the GM soya imports. Surprisingly though, despite organised resistance from NGOs such as Greenpeace, the event did not trigger developments to the same extent that it did in other countries. In fact, it was first an emerging alliance of NGOs and retailers[35] that resulted in tangible results and the withdrawal of GM produce; a ban did not become official policy until 1999. Instead, it seemed that both the industry and the politicians were following a 'duck and cover' strategy in order to head off public controversy and to avoid endangering the economic prospects of the technology. Moreover, the general aim of the German government to support a biotechnology boom was not shaken even when the Green Party joined the coalition in 1998. Thus, the German government has managed to continue supporting biotechnology, despite public controversy.

There were a few countries, though, that did not experience heightened public debate after the soya imports. This is due to a variety of reasons. In Portugal, which lags behind with respect to implementation of EU regulation of biotechnology, the autumn of 1996 did not trigger an intense domestic GM food debate, and only towards the end of 1998 did NGOs start to pay more attention to the topic. Governmental policies were ambiguous during these years. New initiatives were taken in late 1999 and early 2000, such as the suspension of market approval for two seed varieties as well as a parliamentary debate on the precautionary principle and a five-year moratorium. This, however, has to be seen in the context of the Portuguese EU presidency in the first half of 2000 and thus can be interpreted as owing more to an alignment to trends in EU policies than as being the result of intense controversy within the country itself. Also in Poland, which is a young democracy with NGOs still in a relatively early stage of development, biotechnology has not caused intense political and public debate. Biotechnology in Poland has, so far, been more or less restricted to the laboratory. However, debate on its implications has recently been gaining in importance, both in public debate and with respect to regulatory initiatives, so the picture might change in the future.

In Sweden, the Netherlands and Norway, potential public unease was successfully channelled by the respective governments through the adoption of proactive and integrative policies. As a response to the soya and maize debate of 1996–97, several commissions on topics related to biotechnology were established, for example in Sweden, and a consensus conference on human genetic diagnosis was held in autumn 2000. Overall, the most recent years may be described as a fairly calm period of enquiry and preparation for future regulatory steps. As in the past, regulation is seen to contribute to the maintenance of this calmness. In Norway, a balance between technology push-and-pull strategies has been sought. Norwegian regulation of biotechnology is very strict, and concerns articulated during the years of controversy all over Europe had been addressed previously. Hence, although public

opinion has been sceptical before and this scepticism increased to a similar extent as the European average, it was channelled by the traditional regulatory approach in the country.

Finally, the Netherlands and Finland may be said to be those countries in which the period from 1996–97 did not come to be watershed years as they did in other European countries. In the Netherlands in particular, the cooption of critical voices allowed the government to take on the role of a facilitator. Cooperation and consensus hence proved to be an adequate means of dealing with high risk awareness, and societal conflict surrounding biotechnology was deflected. In Finland, with public opinion still very favourable towards biotechnology and a promoting public policy, neither the soya case nor Dolly caused any upheaval or public debate. As recently as May 2000, the first NGO outspokenly critical towards biotechnology was founded, but it remains to be seen whether this will change the Finnish biotechnology landscape in the years to come.

Swimming against the European tide?

In Switzerland, developments were rather different. The national referendum on biotechnology of 1998 was the most important event during the years of controversy. The so-called Gene Protection Initiative (Gen-Schutz Initiative), originally dating back to 1992, was an attempt to ban genetic modification of animals, the release of GM organisms and 'patents on life'. In previous years, the Swiss government had pursued a laissez-faire strategy, but this could no longer be maintained and so it decided to accept regulatory measures. Consequently, parliament issued a bill for a Gene Law in March 1997. Moreover, in an unprecedented move, scientists and industrialists were mobilised to support the so-called Gene Lex Package. The Initiative was finally rejected after a concerted campaign by industry and scientists concentrating on medical issues, and the Swiss government continued work on the Gene Lex Package. Since then, the agricultural aspects have come under strict regulation in Switzerland. However, in contrast to the majority of European countries, the Swiss debate crucially focused on medical rather than on agricultural aspects of biotechnology. Thus, differences in the German-speaking countries alone are symbolic of the variations in debate across Europe. So whereas Austria, for example, reacted with emphasis of resistance, German authorities managed to re-emphasise their support, and Switzerland experienced one of the most positive swings in both public and regulatory attitude in Europe.

Divergence and convergence of domestic and supranational policies

Despite key developments taking place at a European and even global level, debates in different countries depended very much on national idiosyncrasies. Factors that shaped the course of the debate included political changes (such as a change of government or changes in roles that different institutions play), the existence of long-standing food controversies, the advent of Dolly the sheep, and different governments' sensitivity and perception of public opinion. Whereas some governments were proactive in their policies on agricultural biotechnology, others seemed simply to respond to tides in public mobilisation.

However, a general feature across Europe was the formation, during the years of controversy, of new alliances with international connections. NGOs organised networks with food retailers and producers to convince (or coerce) them to ban GM foods from their shelves. At the same time, consumer groups encouraged citizens to 'vote with their feet', in order to reinforce the assertion that food produced using biotechnology was not wanted. As consumers, they demanded the right above all to be able to choose what they ate, safety and environmental issues aside. Slowly, GM food disappeared from European markets and the economic potential of agricultural biotechnology could no longer stand up as the dominant political frame. Under increasing public opposition, both national governments and EU institutions were forced to seek new solutions to growing problems, such as labelling and the need for harmonisation across the increasingly different interpretations of product assessment in member countries.

The European struggle I: labelling

By the time the controversy over the soya case broke out, GM food had already entered the European market through the backdoor (indeed some products had been on sale for a number of years in Britain, for example). There were conflicts amongst European institutions over the novel food directive and in particular the issue of labelling, which had still not been reconciled by the time the imports arrived. The main line of conflict ran between the European Commission and the European parliament who distinguished itself as the advocate of public concerns and consumers' interests by demanding strict regulation and extensive labelling. In addition, various Directorates General took different positions on the issue, and this had the combined effect of allowing GM food to reach the market in the absence of any of the demanded regulation.

The novel food directive was eventually passed in January 1997, requiring that GM food be labelled if the modification is 'substantial'. However, this did not serve well to quell the controversy, since the main objects of concern – GM soya and maize – had already been approved for market before the directive came into force. In the meantime, some member states decided to enact their own national bans on the marketing and cultivation of GM maize in antecedence of the EU's provisional regulations (1813/97), which came to be known in the media as 'import bans' deriving from their factual repercussions. Indeed, it was only after massive disputes within the Commission (between the Directorates General for Environment and Consumer Protection versus Industry) that additional mandatory labelling for food stuffs and additives produced from GM soya and maize could be enacted at the EU level (1139/98).

By 1996, food safety had become an issue of paramount concern in Europe. After a series of scandals in Europe (in particular, the case of BSE in the UK and of dioxins in Belgium), there was sharp critique of the structures, practices and control of food production by the public, and this combined to introduce a new dimension to the dynamics and framing of the debate on agricultural biotechnology. Consumer protection and labelling, closely interlinked with questions of accountability, became central issues, and prompted the establishment of food agencies both within some member states and at the EU level (in the form of a European counterpart of the FDA).[36]

The labelling debate and the controversy over GM food also created significant transatlantic tensions, as the USA accused Europe of protectionism. The threat of a trade conflict added yet another layer to the increasingly global debate.[37] In fact, Canada and the USA continued to attempt to export biotechnology food products to the European markets even after the soya debacle. At the WTO meeting in Seattle in late 1999, debate centred on the relationships between the USA, Canada and other major crop-exporting countries with Europe and developing countries. The American-led consortium saw biotechnology simply in terms of world trade and protested against elements of the Biosafety Protocol, arguing instead for a strictly 'science-based' form of regulation. The political position of their governments stood in stark contrast to the emerging debate on agricultural biotechnology arriving from Europe. In the USA, GM food had rarely been disputed before, but gradually US farmers started to wonder whether they should be sowing GM seeds, since the market for them in Europe had dried up. Meanwhile, by autumn 1999, the controversy had spread to Canada, forcing large American companies such as McCain and Gerber (one of the main producers of baby food) to cease using GM ingredients.

The European struggle II: banning

The debates of 1996 changed agricultural biotechnology in Europe irrevocably. The next issue to come under scrutiny was Bt maize, a crop containing genes from soil bacteria.[38] Austria took the lead when it, together with Italy and Luxembourg, imposed an 'import ban' on Bt maize, referring to article 16 of the 90/220 directive on deliberate releases. The so-called 'safeguard clause' stipulated that any member country may issue temporary restrictions on a product, even if it has already been approved, provided that they provide evidence of scientific assessment within a limited period of time. Although the reasons given by the Austrian government were not necessarily consistent with this criterion, the Commission was unable to force it to lift its ban. This was partly because other countries – even those that had formerly promoted the technology, such as France – were also adopting restrictive policies. By the time the BSE crisis had reached its climax, article 16 had in fact become a major obstacle to the rationale for the directive 90/220 (and indeed the Common Market itself), i.e. that all countries should permit a product once it had been approved by another member state.

Thus, as a wave of scepticism flowed over Europe, the process of product approval ground swiftly to a halt. It seemed senseless for producers to try to market GM seed when retailers refused to stock GM food. The Commission had no choice but to accept the situation as a fait accompli. In fact, it used the pending revision of directive 90/220 as an opportunity to rationalise the decision that no more marketing proposals would be accepted – until the revision was complete. Thus in June 1999, the Commission was able to implicitly legitimise what

had already been developing: a moratorium on the production and sale of GM crops in Europe.

The revision of directive 90/220

The 1990 directive on deliberate releases and marketing of GM organisms retained traditional elements of process regulation, since it required that all GM organisms should undergo a risk assessment before their release. However, its principle concern was the sheer novelty of GM products, rather than the inherent risks of the modification technique itself. Consequently, calls for a revision appeared almost immediately after its issue, and these were intensified as GMO releases became more widespread.

At the same time, pressure was mounting from across the Atlantic. US agencies and industries pushed for a more 'streamlined' procedure of approval for GM products, involving the replacement of European case-by-case assessment methods by a simplified procedure in which new crops were classified according to the properties they shared with those that had already been approved. Indeed, the OECD made several attempts to establish a basis for the mutual acceptance of data in this respect. However, although the basic requirements for a risk assessment on either side of the Atlantic were not dissimilar, European governments did not always come to the same conclusions as their US counter-parts about the acceptability of a particular GM crop.

Not only were there disagreements across the Atlantic, but there were also marked differences in the conclusions from risk assessment results within the EU, despite the guidance of a regulation that meticulously prescribed the criteria for how assessments should be made.[39] Obviously, it was the interpretation of these questions by different countries that gave rise to the variance. For example, in Austria the directive was taken to include the possible effects of the product on agricultural practice, but this was not accepted by the majority of officials from other member states. In Denmark, assessments included consideration of the future options for sustainable agriculture, but this was often not an issue elsewhere. On the other hand, France was quite unique in its rationale that an exact molecular characterisation of the genetic construct could be taken as a proxy for the predictability of the respective organism. Later, British authorities decided that antibiotic-resistance markers were unacceptable, although other countries considered them to be relatively harmless as antibiotic resistance is already widespread in soil microbes. Thus, despite harmonisation attempts among national experts, differences remained unresolved for years; and a revision of the directive appeared to be the only way that a clearer framework for assessment could be reached.

Further complexity was added by the so-called comitology, i.e. the decision-making procedure within and among European institutions themselves.[40] Owing mostly to the unanimity rule, the shared responsibility between the Commission and the Council of Ministers often created *Catch-22* situations, particularly when member countries could not agree on the interpretation of a risk assessment.

By the time American modified maize and soya imports were pending in 1996, a revision of the directive 90/220 was expected to significantly relax the requirements. However, after years of controversy the opposite was the case. NGOs intensified their pleas for more stringent rules, and the European parliament took up the issue of consumer protection. Since the Novel Food Regulation was not yet in place, products intended for food purposes received market permission according to 90/220. With the issue of GM food products, the procedure for placing them on the market again came under scrutiny. In an attempt to balance the demands of consumers with the interests of industry, both the Commission and the parliament developed new and more restrictively phrased regulations.[41] The new directive 2001/18 EC, issued in March 2001, included a phasing-out of antibiotic-resistance markers and made explicit reference both to the precautionary principle and to the need to take into account the indirect and long-term effects of the product in its assessment. Moreover, product approvals were to be issued for a limited time only, post-marketing monitoring was made mandatory and products had to be labelled in such a way that their origins were traceable. Finally, advice on approval could be sought on demand from an ethics committee, which in itself is an unprecedented development in the regulation of agricultural biotechnology.

One area that was neglected in the new directive, much to the chagrin of NGOs, was the issue of liability. According to the Commission, this was to be covered by a general ('horizontal') regulation on environmental liability; however, although this had been discussed for years, it was yet to provide a satisfactory solution. In addition, new comitology rules, independently issued in the Treaty of Nice by the end of 2000, promised to streamline decision-making through more majority votes.

Thus, despite the apparent severity of the new directive, it was clear that the intention of the Commission was to open channels for new products to enter the regulatory system. However, first reactions from member countries proved that for some of them the directive had not gone far enough. Instead of lifting their bans, France, Italy and other countries declared that they would uphold their bans, because the provisions laid out in the directive could not guarantee the traceability of GM produce, and hence the effective separation of GM from non-GM foods.[42] Consequently, rather than resolve the controversy over GM crops, the revisions simply opened up a new round of debate.

The precautionary principle

Over recent years, the so-called precautionary principle has gained precedence as a tool for handling possible risks in the face of scientific uncertainty in policy-making across Europe. First proposed in 1976 by the German Minister of the Environment at an international conference on the North Sea, it was later adopted as European environmental policy and has since been taken up by several international treaties. Meanwhile, the EU has adopted precaution as a guiding formula in related areas of policy, such as food safety, and has repeatedly tried to anchor it as a legal principle in international treaties. Indeed, it has been included in regulations ranging from the 1994 Cartagena Protocol on biological diversity, to the safeguard clause of the EU directive 90/220 and the Agreement on Sanitary and Phyto-Sanitary Measures of the WTO.

The precautionary principle is often misleadingly interpreted in a common-sense meaning according to maxims such as 'safety first' or 'if in doubt, don't'. More sophisticated versions emphasise the necessity to be on the safe side especially if there is a possibility of a severe adverse impact. The most common official understanding implies that preventive action may be taken in the absence of full scientific demonstration of the existence of a risk. An important aspect is the question of who has to bear the burden of evidence, and whether or not it is possible to show the absence of a risk. The most contested aspect pertains to its relationship with scientific evidence. While the USA repeatedly stressed that there has to be a demonstration of a cause–effect relationship according to 'sound science', the precautionary principle acknowledges that action may be taken in the face of uncertainty.

So far, all attempts by international organisations like OECD to reconcile these differences (for example in a report to the G8 leaders entitled 'Biotechnology and other aspects of food safety' in summer 2000) have been futile. Since scientific risk assessment is considered to be absolutely necessary, international protocols have had to include a compromise, and various derivatives have been developed in order to introduce precaution but without calling it a 'principle'. In February 2000, the European Commission issued a semi-official statement on their latest understanding of the principle.[43] It defined precaution as a tool for risk management where the scientific risk assessment has established uncertainty. Moreover, it emphasised that proper risk communication should take on board the interests of various stakeholders; indeed it was framed as the most coherent policy approach for adequately addressing risk and uncertainty in modern society.

Nevertheless, US officials have claimed that the principle is simply a loophole designed by European governments to enable arbitrary trade restrictions and encourage NGO-staged public pressure. In fact the EU has invoked the precautionary principle against the USA in two other food disputes, unrelated to biotechnology. In the 'hormones in beef' case, the import of products into the EU was banned, despite the fact that no direct adverse health effects could be demonstrated. Indeed the WTO conflict resolution panel ruled that the EU's evidence was insufficient to uphold a ban, but rather than lift it, the EU retaliated. When it later announced its refusal to import GM crops, it was widely argued in the USA that the EU should be taken to court. However, not only does such a procedure take a long time, but its outcome is doubtful and even if the USA went ahead and imposed trade restrictions on the EU, it would directly conflict with the quest for free trade that is the major tenet of US international policy.

Future prospects

Over the recent years of controversy, public debate on both agricultural and medical biotechnology has heavily influenced not only political developments but also debate in related areas. Indeed, both the survey and media data over the period, as recounted in this volume, reveal that national differences were greater on those issues where there was intense public debate. This shows that the representation of issues, and hence the way they are dealt with in different countries, depends heavily on underlying cultural and political complexities. In general, however, it may be said that agricultural biotechnology has, in public esteem, been more controversial than medical biotechnology (with the exception of cloning and stem-cell research), and thus their future prospects currently lie at tangents.

Medical biotechnology

It is reasonable to assume that debate on – and perhaps even rejection of – certain aspects of medical biotechnology will become more significant once tangible products and treatments evolve. The case of agricultural biotechnology has shown that public opinion can shift rapidly and persistently to the negative if there is a perceived lack of benefit, or perceived misbehaviour of those responsible, and if there are any concerns about moral acceptability and risk. In contrast, the short history of cloning has revealed that categorical rejection might also quickly wane if there are medical benefits to be reaped. Dolly the sheep swiftly raised fears about human reproduction for doubtful purposes that resonated across the globe. Today, although therapeutic cloning is by no means uncontested, the initial overwhelming rejection because of the 'slippery slope' argument has since been replaced by a conditional argument that balances medical benefits with redefinition of moral standards. The power of such reasoning highlights that where the potential medical benefit is perceived to be great, resistance to even the most contested technology can eventually weaken.

A look across the Atlantic reveals that such benefits will not go undisputed, however, if they entail societal consequences in daily practice. Genetic testing has advantages not only for the individual but also for medical insurance companies and employers. Consequently, there has been public resistance against genetic testing somewhat greater than that displayed in Europe. In the light of ever more sophisticated testing technologies, and of those European public social security systems that, in jeopardy of breakdown are undergoing re-organisation, the issue of genetic testing will also become a topic of more widespread debate in Europe. Like the agricultural system, the health system is also prone to major change. It is conceivable that a powerful modern technology may be taken as a proxy in future debates for changes that increase social disparities.

Under such conditions, will the traditional system of safeguarding standards in medical research and development be sustainable? A variety of internal standards and institutions secure, in a parallel way, proper performance and keep fraud and malpractice at a tolerable level. This, however, strongly depends on professional ethics, and less on transparency. Food biotechnology has shown that, in the case of a scandal, a system highly dependent on professional expertise is vulnerable under challenges to its trustworthiness. There is no watchdog in the medical realm that is accountable to civil society other than the medical community itself. It remains to be seen whether or not such institutions will emerge and what their role will be in the future.

Agricultural biotechnology

The agricultural system of the EU is bound to change profoundly. Many of the possible newcomers to the EU depend heavily on their agricultural produce, and if not revised this will create tensions within the European agricultural system.

A constant row over animal diseases and food scandals, widely publicised by the media, threw light during this period on the vulnerability of a system that is dependent on high productivity and industrialised production. GM products became identified with high-input high-technology agriculture. Thus, the soya case had a particular role in highlighting GM crop plants as part of a seemingly antiquated regime rather than of the new agriculture to come. Retail chains in fear of consumer boycotts obviously do not think that this will change in the near future.

As a result of the controversies in Europe, seed companies have been slow to promote their GM varieties. After pressing hard initially, they have since adopted a 'wait and see' strategy, hoping that second-generation varieties, with more tangible consumer benefits, will break the ice. In the meantime, they are trying to encourage the market in preaccession countries like Hungary, Romania and Bulgaria where agricultural and climatic conditions are more favourable to those GM varieties that were originally bred for the USA. Opposition in these countries is low, as they have other problems to cope with. While international NGOs have been trying to export the protest, their success will depend on whether they can establish a base within the local population. To date, they have yet to succeed.

In western European countries, categorical resistance to GM crop plants is slowly weakening even amongst NGO activists. Instead, arguments have turned to the reshaping of the agricultural system in the direction of enhanced sustainability, and some organisations now find themselves in an unexpected alliance with parts of the European Commission. Under the heading of 'science and governance', the Commission has promised to renew the relationship between research and the public, by taking closer account of the views of stakeholders other than industry and academic science, a policy that up until now has been contrary to common practice. Above all, the Commission endorsed the precautionary principle as a means of guiding risk management and the dealing with scientific uncertainty.

So will GM crops be grown in the future in Europe? In the short term, the probability is low in most countries. However, in the longer run, their future does not look so dim. NGOs are no longer directing their resistance against the technology per se, but the aims for which the technology is being used. Thus, as soon as these aims are deemed acceptable, then the technology may be reconsidered. Indeed, it is not impossible to conceive that a restricted market may emerge for enhanced products that consumers perceive to have benefits (apart from lower price). This will not affect bulk production but create special niche markets, eroding the anti-GM phalanx. Crops for industrial productions of bulk chemicals – where arguments about food safety do not play any role – are on their way, and arguments about environmental safety are not likely to have similar salience. Finally, it is no longer a particular crop that is subject to investigation but a certain 'event' of introducing a trait (i.e. a gene or a couple of genes) into a crop plant. Hence, a whole range of varieties adapted to different conditions and demands will come to possess such a trait and it will be more difficult to identify, and demonise, any particular GM variety.

At the same time as genetic modification has become a routine tool in plant breeding, industry has become accustomed to consumer demands for non-GM food, labelling and traceability. Indeed some companies may switch to GM varieties as it becomes more convenient to do so, and the change may even go unnoticed. Nonetheless, the fading of consumer rejection will depend on the successful reconstruction of the EU agricultural system. As long as consumers continue to react to the ever increasing stream of food scandals over 'perceived' or 'real' threats, agricultural biotechnology will remain in the state of flux.

Consumers or citizens?

Finally, a debate to come could emphasise either the consumer or the civil rights aspect. The future prospects of the technology and surrounding debate will depend on whether individual economic benefits and disad-vantages are to the fore, or whether discussion is framed in terms of more general issues like equity, privacy and the protection of the vulnerable. In addition, governments will be forced to cope with challenges from various national publics in an increasingly globalised environment. Although debates are likely to become more syn chronised across countries, they will retain their national flavours and idiosyncrasies. Consequently, whilst national strategies to contain debate may orient themselves around successful examples, they will still have to be different. For example, the Dutch government's model of openly coopting critical voices, and thus framing its own role as that of a facilitator, was successful in containing the debate on GM crops. In contrast, the German government kept the volume of debate to a minimum by silently permitting spontaneous coalitions of NGOs and industry to implicitly regulate this field. Although the ends may appear similar, diversity inevitably prevails. However, one factor that may be expected to spread, in the light of the European Commission's recent emphasis on reframing the relationship between science and governance, is a more open and pluralistic attitude towards debating, as well as regulating, biotechnology throughout Europe.

Acknowledgement

We would like to express our thanks to our colleagues in the 'policy' group who contributed ideas and comments to the development of this chapter: Urs Dahinden, Edna Einsiedel, Erling Jelsøe, Mercy Wambui Kamara, Jesper Lassen, Arve Monsen, George Sakellaris, Tomasz Twardowski and Atte von Wright.

Notes and references

1 Baggott, R, 'The BSE crisis. Public health and the "risk society"', in Gray, P and T'Hart, P (eds), *Public Policy Disasters in Western Europe* (London: Routledge, 1998).

2 Torgersen, H, Hampel, J and von Bergmann-Winberg, M-L, *et al.*, 'Promise, problems and proxies: twenty-five years of European biotechnology debate and regulation', in Bauer, M W and Gaskell, G (eds), *Biotechnology: The Making of a Global Controversy* (Cambridge: Cambridge University Press, in press).

3 See Beck, U, *Risk Society: Towards a New Modernity* (London: Sage Publications, 1992).

4 Levidow, L and Carr, S (eds), 'Biotechnology risk regulation in Europe', *Science and Public Policy* (special issue), 3 (1996).

5 Jasanoff, S, 'Product, process, or program: three cultures and the regulation of biotechnology', in Bauer, M (ed.), *Resistance to New Technology: Nuclear Power, Information Technology, Biotechnology* (Cambridge: Cambridge University Press, 1995).

6 Birkland, T A, 'Focusing events, mobilization and agenda setting', *Journal of Public Policy*, 18 (1998), pp53–74; Kingdon, J W, *Agendas, Alternatives, and Public Policies* (New York: Harper Collins, 1995), pp94–100.

7 Lassen, J, Allansdottir, A and Liakopoulos, M, *et al.*, 'Testing times: the reception of Round-up Ready Soya in Europe', in Bauer, M W and Gaskell, G (eds) (see note 2).

8 Einsiedel, E, Allansdottir, A and Allum, N C *et al.*, 'Brave new sheep: the clone named Dolly', in Bauer, M W and Gaskell, G (eds) (see note 2).

9 This may be witnessed in the establishment of, for example, BIOSAM in Denmark (1997), the Platform for Medical Biotechnology and the Forum for Genetics and Healthcare in the Netherlands (1998) and the Reference Centre for Ethics in the Bio-Sciences in Germany (1999).

10 However, several commissions have been created to deal with biotechnology in recent years.

11 In the USA, the National Bioethics Advisory Commission has given approval for embryo stem-cell research. Similarly, in the UK, two prominent ethics advisory bodies have also recommended during this period that stem-cell research should be approved. However, the British government hesitated in their acceptance of the recommendations through fear of sparking further controversy over biotechnology at a time when public and media opposition to GM foods was fierce. When the row over GM foods finally weakened, the moratorium was overturned.

12 In January 1998, an additional protocol to the

Convention on the Prohibition of Cloning Human Beings was signed by a further 19 countries.

13 For example, the Convention bans germ-line gene therapy and IVF where it is used for sex selection (except where it would avoid a serious hereditary condition), and it also prohibits genetic discrimination. The regulations also extend to cover issues of consent, organ donation, the conducting of medical research and public consultation.

14 However, there has been debate over the implemen-tation of genetic testing services (whether they are to be accompanied by adequate counselling of patients and because of this, whether they should be available 'over the counter'), as well as debate over the use and storage of genetic test information.

15 Although not scientifically proven to occur, viruses dormant in donor animals could 'awaken' when tissue is grafted to another species, thus creating new and devastating diseases in humans.

16 For example in Canada, the Netherlands and Denmark.

17 For example in Denmark, where patients in a liver cancer trial were being treated illegally.

18 The Human Genome Project, formally established in 1990, consists of a consortium of over 1000 research-ers, funded largely by public money (especially in the USA) and by heavy investment from the British medical research charity, the Wellcome Trust.

19 The directive states that any invention that is new, involved an inventive step and is applicable for industrial purposes is patentable 'even if they concern a product consisting of or containing biological material or a process by means of which biological material is produced, processed or used'.

20 In particular in the Netherlands, France, Norway and Italy. The Netherlands did not agree to the directive at the Council, and filed a plea of nullity at the European Court in December 1998, which was later supported by Italy, but did not result in a suspension. The German government has also remained deeply split over the directive, and pushed for a renegotiation at the European level in October 2000; the parliament has since refused to implement it in German law.

21 As has been the case in Austria and Germany, for example.

22 The UK holds one of the largest databases of DNA profiles from charged suspects in criminal cases, and there is evidence to suggest that in other countries, such as Finland, this would also be welcomed. However, in Britain, a recent change in the law that will allow the database to be extended to include suspects who have not been charged, has raised concerns amongst civil liberties groups and the principle ethics advisory body, the Human Genetics Commission.

23 Access to this information is then controlled by the company deCODE, who will use it in conjunction with extensive publicly available written records of Icelandic family histories and donated genetic material, to identify genes involved in simple and complex genetic diseases.

24 In Austria, Denmark and Norway.

25 In the Netherlands (1990), France (1997) and Sweden (1999). In the UK, the government rejected pleas for a moratorium in 1998 in favour of a voluntary agreement with the industry that no applicant would be required to undergo a genetic test. However, companies have been permitted to request the disclosure of genetic test results, for some health-related insurance products and for life insurance where this exceeds a specified amount, provided that the test in question has been approved by a new independent body. At the time of writing, one such test – that for Huntington's disease – has been approved for use in life insurance.

26 Cheese that had been prepared with the help of rennin produced by GM bacteria instead of being extracted from calf stomachs.

27 Durant, J, Bauer, M W and Gaskell, G (eds), *Biotechnology in the Public Sphere. A European Sourcebook* (London: Science Museum, 1998).

28 Nielsen, T H, 'Behind the colour code of "no"', *Nature Biotechnology*, 15 (1997), pp1320–21.

29 As in Italy, also in France and Austria the rejection of GM food made reference to claims of national and regional identity and notions of traditional food production. As an act of political symbolism, this led to the announcement of 'genetic-engineering-free areas' such as Tuscany or few Austrian municipalities. However, at least in Austria, in the meantime this has turned out to be legally impossible.

30 If one is prepared to regard Austria as a country in a sense exporting resistance to agricultural biotech-nology, then one might take Greece as an exemplary country for considerable import of the controversy.

31 Marris, C, 'Swings and roundabouts: French public policy on agricultural GMOs since 1996', *Politeia*, 60 (2000), pp22–37.

32 As for instance with the prohibition of import and growing of GM rape-seed, which had been declared to be absolutely unobjectionable only two years before; later on, three GM maize varieties were forbidden.

33 In France, this opposition was mainly driven by the Confédération Paysanne and José Bové, who symbolises and personifies the resistance against biotechnology in a comparable way to Jeremy Rifkin in the USA.

34 Similarly, in Greece the National Authority of Food was founded in March 2000, with the task of ensuring food safety and the protection of public health and consumers.

35 This regime can be interpreted as the strongest parallel to Austria or Denmark. In Austria, NGOs established a working group together with three supermarket chains in order to establish a label for 'genetic-engineering-free food'. Indeed, this was also mirrored also in other countries, for example in France and the UK.

36 However, unlike the FDA, the new European authority is an advisory body to the Commission, and so its influence is likely to be weaker.

37 GM food was only one issue in the context of transatlantic trade conflicts; such tensions between the USA and the EU also broke out over hormones in beef, the banana regime and the use of bovine somatotropin (rBST).

38 Strains of the soil bacterium *Bacillus thuringiensis* are used as an 'environmentally friendly pesticide'. They contain proteins directed against certain major crop plant pests. If the genes for these proteins are introduced into plant genomes, they can convey resistance against the pest.

39 Levidow, L and Carr, S (eds), 'Precautionary regulation: GM crops in the European Union', *Journal of Risk Research* (special issue), 3 (2000).

40 Toeller, A E, 'Die Komitologie. Funktionsweise und Reformperspektive', paper presented at the conference *Europa zwischen Integration und Ausschluss*, University of Vienna, 5–7 June 1998.

41 EU officials frequently claim that there is, in essence, nothing new, but that regulation has just become more explicit.

42 Resistance from various European regions, wanting to sustain bans of GM crops from their areas, remained as well. Only lately has this view been supported by European Green parties.

43 COM (2000) 1, Communication from the Commission on the precautionary principle (Brussels: European Commission, 2000).

Address for correspondence

Mag. Petra Grabner, Institut für Politikwissenschaft, Universität Salzburg, Rudolfskai 42, A-5020 Salzburg, Austria. E-mail: petra.grabner@mh.sbg.ac.at

The dramatisation of biotechnology in elite mass media

Martin W Bauer, Matthias Kohring, Agnes Allansdottir and Jan Gutteling

In this chapter we will characterise the cultivation of biotechnology in the European, Canadian and US public spheres during the 1990s as a drama. Drama involves a background of scenery and sound, and a foreground of plot, actors, reasoning and, on occasion, tragic outcomes. Classical drama theory argues that dramatic representation is rule based (rather than a simple stroke of intuition and genius), it focuses on actions rather than personality and makes a positive contribution to the conduct of life outside the theatre.[1] The Aristotelian idea of 'katharsis' or 'purification' suggests that dramatic representation of events raises laughter, fear and pity among the audience and thereby regulates such emotions towards a 'level of passion' that is adequate to the issues in reality. The adequacy of passions is difficult to judge *a priori*. However, classical drama theory suggests that in a world where passions are absent, they need to be raised, and where they are too high or overwhelming, they need to be contained. In this manner, drama cultivates human virtues and prepares for effective collective action. This is achieved by the 'homeo-pathic living-through' of these passions in the vicarious reality of reading, watching scenes and images, and listening to arguments about issues.

This classical point of view offers some advantages. First, it steers a middle way between assuming that mass media is either objective information or only misleading and despicable entertainment. Secondly, it avoids the alternative error of relegating mass media coverage to irrelevance and thereby ignoring its power on one hand, or endowing it with overwhelming powers on the other. The latter gives rise to moral panic and 'media bashing' over alleged misinformation or propaganda. Viewed from the perspective of classical drama, media discourse over biotechnology contributes to the regulation of collective passions over an issue, which influences the manner in which we think about it and how we come to solutions for future actions.

In our research, we systematically compare the press coverage of biotechnology in 15 countries over two periods, 1992–96 and 1997–99, using a random sample of newsprint in each country, and a common coding frame. The coding frame identifies the scenes that are set, the actions, the actors, their reasoning and the outcomes, as these are associated with biotechnology in the 1990s. We define these two periods as the years before and after the 'watershed years' of 1996/97, which mark a clear turning point in this drama, where heroes turn into villains, and villains into heroes. The two episodes of Monsanto's export of Roundup Ready Soya (from late autumn 1996) and of Dolly the sheep (February 1997) changed the symbolic landscape of biotechnology in Europe and worldwide.

Mass media and, in particular, the daily press, provide one of several arenas in the modern public sphere, which itself has a protracted history.[2] They offer a public space where various actors present a drama of public significance to a wider audience in order to entertain, to alert and focus attention, to raise passions, to inform, to distract and mislead, and to argue in order to educate.

Many theories on the media's role in society have been formulated, some of which have reflected a 'realistic approach' of telling how the world is. This is based on the assumption of an existing set of events, which can be reported 'objectively' and balanced by competent, fair and unbiased journalists. According to this realistic approach, journalism's role in society is seen to mirror reality. The ideal-typical ethos of this kind of journalism is 'objectivity and dispassion'. By contrast, others have stated that the media offer meaning and orientation by presenting a 'constructed world' using understatement, exaggeration, elaboration and foremost, selection and framing. This is a 'constructive' activity, akin to dramatisation according to the rules of drama, rather than simply mirroring a 'reality out there'. In the mediated reality, processes of news selection play a role, in particular in the theoretical notions of news value and framing. The framing of news can be understood as the process through which complex issues are given shape along journalistically manageable dimensions, resulting in a particular focus on an issue. This reasoning implies that journalistic framing may also lead to journalistic selection, for example by relying heavily on information from particular sources. Differences in perceptions between those sources due to selectivity or conflicting values, in particular regarding the risks and benefits of modern biotechnology, may motivate journalists and editors to further emphasise their role of watchdogs or as extra-parliamentary opposition, highlighting neglected issues and framing the news as danger and controversy. These processes may encourage media outlets to highlight some aspects of biotechnological innovations at particular times, but also encourage the media to ignore other biotechnology issues. The construction of meaning necessarily involves selection and framing. The ideal-typical ethos of this kind of journalism is guided by advocacy, investigation and fulfilling the role of the fourth estate in society.

To the analytical eye it appears paradoxical that what is called the 'realistic approach' is very much a normative stance, highlighting how journalists ought to report the world by appealing to the ethos of 'objectivity' as a self-regulatory professional standard. The function of such an analysis is the critical assessment of journalistic practice measured against an external standard of reality that is 'misrepresented'. On the other hand, the constructive approach is more realistic from the empirical point of view; in daily practice objectivity may not be achieved, and may not be a guiding principle. Constructive analysis includes 'realistic' analysis as a special case. It attempts to understand how news is produced as a matter of actual practice according to operative rules, such as news values and framing. Normative expectations may or may not be part of the analysis. The media representations are assessed comparatively with reference to their functions in a context. For this purpose, the defense or diagnosis of the violation of professional standards, such as 'objectivity and dispassion', is secondary, albeit with juridical implications at particular times and in particular cases.

Public opinion *qua* elite press: salience and framing

We focus on the opinion-leading press. The press informs the wider public about important issues that are relevant for a country. It equally informs policy-makers and also serves as an indicator of what the wider public may think about the issues at hand. The selection of events to be reported, the amount of coverage given to a particular issue

(salience) and the way events are portrayed may have an impact on public perception of these events. However, they are more likely to influence policy processes, by indirectly pointing to what public opinion may be about.

Among the many types of mass media, the press serves a key function. Across Europe, certain newspapers and news magazines are considered to be opinion-leading sources of information for other media, as well as for the public and decision-makers such as politicians, civil servants, experts and industrialists. Therefore, newspapers are very suitable for studying journalistic selection and framing by proxy. By analysing the opinion-leading press, we can get a reasonably robust impression of how society processes meaning about modern biotechnology, as well as an insight into the development of these information flows over time. The choice of the opinion-leading press in the participating countries leads to a diverse set of print media: in some countries large-circulation dailies, in others small-circulation newspapers, and in others news-weeklies.

We consider elite media as addressing an elite audience and their concerns in the public sphere. These representations are characterised in aggregate by inference from a sample of observations. Beneath this observable and aggregate order is the fractal nature of media coverage. In the reality of events, each news item (in research terms, each item of coding), has a 'natural history' that, in principle, is traceable to various sources; for example the occasion of attention of a particular journalist whose motives and inspiration are translated into text, or the editorial negotiations that turn it into a published piece that must then compete with other news items in a confluence of luck and local competence. Here we observe the aggregate patterns that emerge from a myriad of local battles in the newsrooms between source, writers, editors and the contexts of the hour or the day. We assume that these emergent patterns, once abstracted from random elements, are indicative of a climate of opinion outside the newsrooms. Newsrooms have particular sensitivities to the world by reference to virtual readers, or in our case elite publics, who are most likely configured as advertising profiles. In the context of increasing competition in the information market, journalists – like everybody else in that market – need to get ever closer to the pulse of society in order to hold their audience and consumers to attention.

The main focus of our analysis is journalistic salience and framing which, considering the sensitivity of journalists to the pulse of society, can be considered as indicators of wider societal concerns and as representing public opinion. Our method is classical content analysis,[3] which is particularly useful for longitudinal and comparative analyses.[4] The purpose is to construct aggregate indicators of discourse that are sensitive to variation across time and contexts. This is a particularly effective approach for characterising the long-term trends, the 'longue duree' of the development, rather than the short-term perturbations in the media coverage. The index of the topicality of biotechnology in the public sphere is, however, predicated on the observers' analytic framework. What the questionnaire provides for the pollster, the content analytic frame provides for the media analyst: it gives an explicit framework of data construction, comparison, and interpretation. For the observer, mass media contents are traces; their context of production and reception is a matter of inference. Thus, inferences about public opinion are based on differentials in salience and framing.

For the present purpose we focus on the period from 1996 to 1999. The period from 1973 to 1996 has already received a detailed analysis.[5] The press material was sampled according to an annual random regime and retrieved online from databases of national opinion-leading newspapers or news magazines. Articles were coded on a coding frame that was developed for this purpose and which has already been documented in detail.[6] The present study follows those established procedures with minor changes. All quoted figures refer to elite newspapers only and to articles with clear focus on biotechnology (see appendix 1).

Our argument unfolds in several steps. First, we focus on the synchronisation of public spheres by analysing the background 'scenery and sound' of the biotechnology drama through various indicators of selection: salience, format, focus and size of reportage in the various countries. Next, we explore the plotting of biotechnology through various indicators of journalistic framing. We analyse the themes of biotechnology including notable absences, the degree of controversy in the coverage, the frames that are mobilised and the actors appearing in the coverage, as well as the consequences of biotechnology in terms of risks and benefits. Most features are compared by country and over time. The analysis culminates in a typology of different dramas of biotechnology across Europe and North America. Results are presented in the form of relative frequencies and correspondence analyses.

Salience: setting the scene and the rhythm

Every drama has a background of scenery, sound and rhythm, which make up its quantitative elements. We characterise these elements of the biotechnology drama in terms of four indicators: salience of the topic, the average size of the articles, the journalistic formats that are mobilised and finally, the degree of focus in the reference to biotechnology. Salience and size describe the background scenery, shifts in salience its rhythm and, to complete the analogy, journalistic formats and their focus suggest the type of 'sound'.

Synchronising the debate

Figure 1 shows the aggregate yearly coverage of biotechnology in the elite press across 12 European countries from 1973 to 1999. In the online retrieval we used the following four keywords (appropriately translated to local languages): biotech*, genetic*, genome, DNA. The figure indicates that in terms of media events, biotechnology went through a number of phases: from a slow start after Asilomar of 1975, to its recognition as a 'strategic technology for the twenty-first century' in the early 1980s, to the European regulations of crop biotechnology in 1991, and finally to the events after 1996/97 around Monsanto Roundup Ready Soya, GM crops and foods, and Dolly the sheep in February 1997. The years 1996/97 are a clear watershed, indicated by the step rise in coverage. While our previous reports have shown much diversity in the phasing of biotechnology,[7] the watershed 1996/97 marks a break across all of Europe and in Canada. The years 1997–99 saw a veritable explosion of coverage of biotechnology. Overall, 1999 sees three times the coverage of 1996, whilst 1996 was only twice that of 1992. There does not seem to be any reason to believe that in recent years the intensity of coverage has abated, considering the various national debates over stem-cell research in 2000 and 2001. Until 1996, the debates over biotechnology followed separate timings and different agendas in the various countries; after 1997, the debates went into a joint rhythm. Here we are documenting two of Luhmann's hypothetical contributions of mass media to society, namely to irritate society and to synchronise attention.[8] It is clear that the levels of salience have reached the threshold of irritation at various points across Europe. The watershed events of 1996/97 created a step function bringing biotechnology to public attention as never before.

Figure 1. The coverage of biotechnology in the elite press across 12 European countries from January 1973 to December 1999. Annual counts of newspaper articles are aggregates based on a single opinion leading newspaper outlet in each country. The bars show the total annual counts, the line shows the moving three-year average

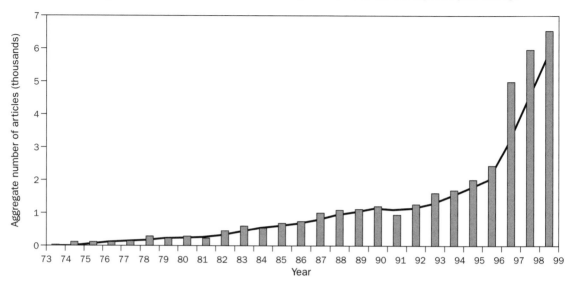

However, one should not overstate the unity of this aggregate picture, since the pace of events has been different across the regions and countries of Europe. Despite synchronisation, the countries vary both in terms of overall salience and in the rate of change. Figure 2 shows a comparison of the yearly coverage for the two waves (wave 1 and wave 2) before and after the watershed years, 1992–96 and 1997–99. The countries are ordered by the salience in the first wave. The UK remains the one country with extraordinary attention to biotechnology with a single daily paper carrying more than 1000 articles per year, or three to four articles per day. This remains a puzzle. Possible explanations could include the relative significance of the biotechnology sector for the economy and the City of London; or the particular cultural significance of all things 'genetic', anchored in the status of Charles Darwin as a national hero; or simply the cutthroat competition for readership attention between four quality newspapers in roughly the same market segment. With such competition, no newspaper would want to lose out on a gene or biotechnology story for fear that the others might make a story out of it.

Austria, Italy, France and Germany are all countries that have experienced a 'wake-up call' with respect to biotechnology after the watershed years. These countries approached the threshold of 1000 articles in 1999. Their coverage increased three to four times from the pre-watershed years, and they have now moved into serious coverage.

Here, Monsanto's soya and Dolly the sheep were major catalysts for the whole area. Biotechnology as a whole is now covered by more than 600 articles per year, the equivalent of two to three daily articles per newspaper. For other countries, such as the Netherlands, Finland, Sweden, Switzerland, Denmark and Greece, coverage has at least doubled, although overall levels remain modest. What this indicates is a synchronisation over biotechnology after 1996/97. The clocks on the issue finally tick in time with each other, albeit with different intensity.

Figure 2 also includes data from Canada and the USA. The coverage in Canada can be seen to increase to the same degree as Switzerland, the Netherlands and the European average. On the other hand, while the level of media attention in the USA remains high, the increases have been small. This indicates that the salience of biotechnology in the USA remains as high as it already was during the early 1990s. While the debates over GM food and cloning did not impact south of the big lakes, further north, Canada tuned in with Europe. Public attention over biotechnology has been synchronised across Europe and Canada, but not with the USA.

Scenery and sound: size, format and focus

The length of text that is dedicated to a topic is an indicator of editorial importance. However, it is

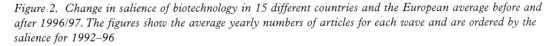

Figure 2. Change in salience of biotechnology in 15 different countries and the European average before and after 1996/97. The figures show the average yearly numbers of articles for each wave and are ordered by the salience for 1992–96

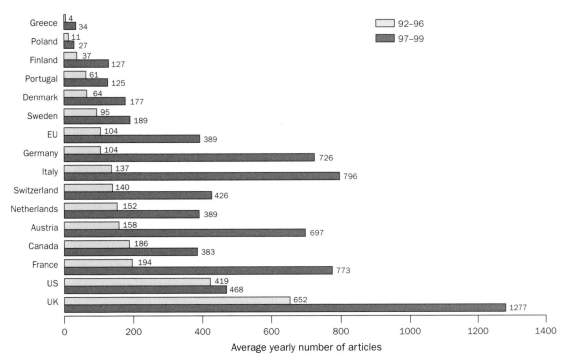

also a matter of journalistic practice, which may change as newspapers get thicker or thinner over time. The faster the pace of life, the smaller the average media 'bite'. The average reader is no longer expected to have the leisure to digest long arguments. Under these changing circumstances (low expectations of the reader and sound-bite styles of reporting), increased length of writing indicates a more serious elaboration of a topic. Since the period we are considering here is only eight years, changes in the length of articles during this time are taken as indicators of journalistic importance, rather than of a change in practice. Each article is coded according to a national criterion of 'small', 'medium' and 'large'. By this criterion, the scenery of biotechnology after 1996/97 is getting more elaborate in Finland, Poland, Sweden and Austria, and less elaborate in Denmark, Greece and France. In contrast, in Canada, the UK, Germany, Italy, the Netherlands and Switzerland there is no detectable change in the length of reporting.

Biotechnology can be reported in a series of different journalistic formats. We distinguish eight different journalistic genres or writing formats in our coding: latest news; investigative reporting;

interview; column; editorial; outside commentary reviews of books, films, etc.; and others. Each of these can be considered as a particular means of dramatising biotechnology for the reader. In analogy to a musical commentary the delivery can enhance or tone down the significance of a piece of news. The distribution of journalistic formats across the different countries shows an increased range of 'music'. Over the watershed years, elite newspapers show a diversification of journalistic scenery. We see a move from the initially dominant 'latest news' format into column writing, editorials and outside commentary. However, Canada is the exception where no such change is observed and the 'latest news' item continues to dominate.

Another feature of the dramatic scenery is the degree of specific focus on biotechnology. For each article we code whether biotechnology is the focus of the argument, whether it is mentioned only in passing while the article follows other issues, or whether it is used as a metaphor or by allusion. In dramaturgical terms, the last-mentioned indicates the number of 'episodic', irrelevant and purely ornamental elements in the plot. From the point of view of biotechnology, these references are 'irrelevant' writings; however, from the point of view of popular culture, these are highly significant cross-references. We have noted earlier, for example in the UK, that genes and genetics have become topics to which other issues become attached.[9] For example, making reference, either in pictorial form or in text, to genes in the context of an evolutionary analogy for technical designs, such as cars, has become a common feature of advertisements in the UK since 1996/97. It appears that with increasing societal salience, the topic has developed news value in itself. As the references to biotechnology increase, they are elaborated to various degrees of foci. We observe across the contexts an increase in articles with passing or metaphorical cross-references to biotechnology. This indicates that genes, genetic engineering, biotechnology and the like have increasingly become a resource for the popular imagination. However all the analyses reported here exclude the most marginal references. We fade out some of the music to come to a clearer picture of the plot.

In summary we can say that after 1996/97, articles on biotechnology in all the considered contexts get longer, use a wider range of journalistic formats, and have a greater number of passing cross-references to genes and biotechnology. The watershed years of 1996/97 shift the coverage in all countries, including Canada, but with the exception of the USA, into a clearly upward trend. The drama of biotechnology expands the journalistic 'scenery' over the 1990s, thereby diversifying its 'sound' while synchronising its rhythm, and keeping to a different tempo in different countries. What this shows is the emergence of a 'European theatre of biotechnology': the drama expands, synchronises, and gains a richer scenery. While Canada assimilates Europe's scenery, the US media continue to play a different tune. The watershed years mark the reversal of fortunes in an ongoing drama of biotechnology, where the conclusion is not yet defined, but where many authors are working on the unfolding plot.

Plotting biotechnology: actors, activities, reasoning and outcomes

The qualitative elements of drama are those of activities, actors and reasoning. For our analysis we examine activities in terms of the fields of applications of biotechnology that come into the media focus. Reasoning is analysed as frames of argumentation and controversy, while actors are coded in terms of those public actors and agencies that cut through the threshold and reach the media stage.

Activities and reasoning – themes and frames

Besides salience, a second major dimension of the drama of biotechnology is its framing. What kind of activity is biotechnology? The metaphor of 'frame' plays on the image of a picture that is demarcated at the edges, thereby putting a drawing or a photograph into a defined cotext. The same picture can be presented in different frames, giving it a different perspective. In other words, the meaning of the picture depends on the cotext that is opened up by the frame. By analogy, a press article on a particular theme of biotechnology is elaborated within a particular frame of discourse which presents biotechnology in a particular light and perspective. A frame in this sense has several characteristics. First, it offers a discursive space within which disagreement and controversy over the topic is elaborated. Second, it is often illustrated by a root metaphor that condenses the main point into a succinct image. Finally, a frame is often associated with an actor who favours a particular frame because it offers an argumentative advantage in the public debate. Frame analysis shows that public controversies are as much about how to argue a topic as about disagreements within a particular frame. With different framing the topic appears in a different light, hence sponsors compete in elaborating frames which show their take on a topic most clearly. Our analysis distinguishes eight frames of biotechnology as shown in Table 1.

These eight different frames were carefully developed to capture the argumentative discourse of biotechnology over the whole period of investigation. Table 1 gives a short characterisation of these frames. For some of the following analyses we classified the frames into two main arguments. Firstly, the *argument of prospect* which combines descriptions of biotechnology as scientific, technical or cultural progress and as a prospect for economic advance of a nation. Secondly, the *argument of concerns* combines most other frames, for example ethical arguments, which remind the reader that biotechnology is 'too important to be left to the scientists and the engineers'; Pandora's box arguments, which warn that caution is required; arguments of nature/nurture with regard to human characteristics such as homosexuality, female empathy and so on, which proliferate in news about genetic breakthroughs; arguments about the lack of, or the functioning of, public accountability with

Table 1. *Biotechnology framing in the press*

Frame	Dimension	Key images
Prospects		
Progress	Progress/old wine in new bottles	Scientific breakthrough
Economic prospect	Profitable/loss-making investment	Technology of the twenty-first century
Concerns		
Ethical	Morally sound/immoral	Slippery slope
Pandora's box	Open the box/warning: keep locked in	'Frankenfood', thalidomide
Nature/nurture	Genetically determined/environment	Gene for X, Y and Z, e.g. intelligence, female empathy, aggression, etc.
Public accountability	Public involvement/public exclusion	For example, consensus conference
Globalisation	International competition/isolation	The country is falling behind
Runaway	Too late to do something/never too late	The train has already left the station

Table 2. *Basic frequencies (based on multiple coding for themes and actors) of frames, themes, actors, and risk and benefits for two waves of coverage*

	Wave 1: 1992–96	Wave 2: 1997–99
Frame (%)		
Progress	50	42
Economic prospects	17	14
Ethical	12	10
Pandora's box	4	6
Runaway	2	3
Nature/nurture	4	8
Public accountability	10	16
Globalisation	2	2
Risks and benefits (%)		
Both	23	25
Risk only	9	15
Benefit only	44	39
Neither	25	21
Main theme[a] (%)		
Biomedical ('red')	28	23
Agrifood ('green')	15	20
Generic research	12	9
Economics	12	8
Moral issues	2	2
Public opinion/policy	4	7
Regulation	6	6
Genetic identity	15	12
Cloning	0	9
Other	6	4
Main actor[a] (%)		
Independent science	45	39
Interest groups, NGOs	4	5
Politics	16	15
Moral authorities	2	2
Media/public opinion	6	7
Business	21	20
International	1	2
EU	2	4
Other	4	6
N	3871	5580

a Multiple coding

regard to these new developments; arguments of globalisation concerned with the position of the nation in global markets for research and development; and finally runaway arguments pointing to a fait accompli, behind which the public debate is helplessly lagging, leaving little freedom of choice. Table 2 shows the basic frequencies of these frames from the first to the second wave, and the overall shift in public discourse from arguments of prospects to those of concern, in particular in the areas of public accountability and nature/nurture.

Table 2 also shows the frequencies of basic classes of application of biotechnology as themes of reportage. The most important are biomedicine, agrifood, general genetic research, and issues of assessing genetic identity through either genetic fingerprinting or genetic testing. Through the 1990s, agrifood becomes more important, biomedicine less so, while cloning gains in salience. These reflect the impact of the debate over GM food and cloning after 1997. The distribution of themes by country shows some characteristic patterns. Whereas some countries pay more attention to cloning, for example Greece, Sweden, Portugal, Austria, Poland and Italy, other countries pay more attention to 'red' biotechnology (biomedicine), in particular Poland and Portugal, but also Germany, Canada and Finland. Still in others, it is 'green' applications (agrifood) that are most in focus, for example Denmark, UK, France, Netherlands, Austria and Switzerland.

Figure 3 shows the correspondence between the framing of three biotechnology applications in agrifood ('green'), biomedical ('red'), and cloning. Closer proximity of the points in the figure indicates characteristic, but not exclusive covariation between themes and frames across the different countries. Hence, we can say that biomedical applications are

Figure 3. Correspondence between frames and themes over the period 1992–99 in a two-dimensional space with very good fit. Thematic clusters by frames

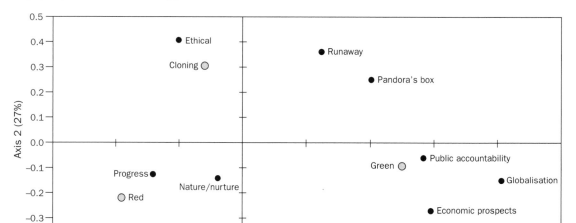

relatively more associated with a discourse of progress and nature/nurture. Many developments in medicine are celebrated as progress, or they elaborate the uncertainties over how to attribute dispositions, either to the environment or to genetic endowment. Cloning is relatively closely associated with the ethical argument, making the point in public that the development is too important to leave to the specialists. Green applications are framed mainly in terms of economic prospects, globalisation or public accountability. Agrifood biotechnology provides business opportunities and responds to a global imperative. These issues are clearly presented as matters for publicly accountable regulation. The two frames of 'Pandora's box' and 'runaway' do not have a clear association with any of the key applications, although they are between cloning and 'green', indicating that for both themes admonition of caution and recognition of fait accompli have salience. 'Tampering with the forbidden' raises ethical questions and urges circumspection; however, it seems that little choice is left when too many facts are already on the ground.

An analysis across the two waves shows little shift in these associations between themes and frames over time, with the exception that 'runaway' and 'Pandora's box' become more closely associated with 'green' applications. The framing of agrifood biotechnology has shifted, whilst medical biotechnology has remained in the progress frame. Not surprisingly, this reflects the focus of controversy over GM food and crops after 1997, offering a sense of fait accompli as well as admonition to the readers.

These patterns of associations between themes and frames show some variation across countries. After the watershed years we find a diversification in the frames. Before 1996/97, most countries mainly celebrated biotechnology in terms of progress and economic prospects. This changed after 1997 when arguments over biotechnology diversified in all countries and characteristic patterns of discourse emerged. For example, the UK and Finland are more concerned with nature/nurture than other countries; issues of public accountability are particularly prevalent in Denmark and Switzerland; progress remains the dominant discourse for Germany; the economic prospect is an important argument in France, Germany and Canada; and ethical framing is most prevalent in France and Denmark.

Actors: dramatis personae

Every drama has a number of persons who perform the actions on stage, whose 'characters' explain their contribution to the plot, and who reason about their predicament. The mass media are the stage upon which different actors perform. When, in what company and on what pretext do the various actors of biotechnology enter the media stage? From the point of view of particular actors, visibility through media attention is often a strategic objective and therefore a criterion to evaluate the success of their own public-relations activities. A public profile in terms of media coverage is an actor's achievement, which indicates, at least potentially, that a particular voice is heard in public debate. The various actors may ask: what are the topics on which we are likely to find an opening to enter the stage of public debate? In our analysis we coded for around 40 different actors. These 40 actors are reduced to independent science and research, moral authorities such as ethics committees, the media and the general public, business enterprises, political parties, interest groups, international actors, and the EU. These are the actors and agencies implicated in the drama over biotechnology in the different countries.

Table 2 lists the actors, of which science and scientists, business and industry, and politics and politicians are the most important, figuring in about 80 per cent of the articles. There is little overall shift during the 1990s in this pattern. The common notion that interest groups have been given disproportionate visibility in the GM food debate or over cloning is not supported by our observations, for they stay at around 5 per cent. Also, little attention is dedicated to international actors such as the EU or the World Health Organisation, etc., and there is little national variation in this pattern of staging the actors over biotechnology. There is, however, the important distinction between working behind the scenes and acting on stage. Our analysis can reveal little in that respect. Many of the actors who have little visibility in our analysis, could be very active behind the scenes. An actor can get 'editorial', which means one brings in a journalist to write about oneself, or

'position' an article, meaning one writes an article and has it published under one's name. Our analysis picks up both these cases of publicity seeking. However, finally, there is also the case where an actor 'plants' an argument with a journalist, where their names are not mentioned, but the issue is framed in their terms. It is likely that NGOs, such as Greenpeace, were successfully planting arguments by way of press releases in many countries, while their visibility remained low. Another significant absence among the stage actors are the military. Over the whole period of monitoring actors, the military are mentioned in relation to genetic engineering in less than 0.2 per cent of all articles. Considering the international concern over biological warfare and the opportunities arising from genetic engineering for this activity, this is a rather surprising finding.

Figure 4 shows the discursive association between the actors on the media stage and the main themes of biotechnology. The applications of biotechnology are relatively clearly associated with actors, and there is little variation in these associations over time and across countries: 'red' is a matter for science, *cloning* a matter of ethics and public opinion, and 'green' a matter for private business, interest groups and the regulators. If anything, this seems to show the emergence of an international plot in the theatre of biotechnology, with clear assignments of who is playing which role.

The correspondence between frames and actors is much less clear. In general, the progress and nature/nurture frames tend to be associated with independent science and research. Not surprisingly, economic prospects are close to business and industry, whilst arguments over globalisation and public accountability tend towards international actors, NGOs, the EU, the mass media and the

Figure 4. Correspondence between actors and themes with a very good fit in two dimensions. Themes are reduced to green, red and cloning. Raw profiles and column profiles on axes 1 and 2

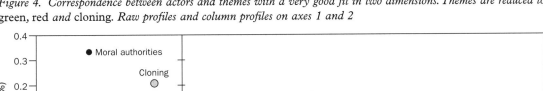

general public. Political parties and residual actors are associated with the Pandora's box, runaway and ethics arguments. However, in the drama over biotechnology overall, the various actors show considerable flexibility in their use of arguments, which is why a statistical analysis has difficulty in identifying consistencies and correspondences.

Controversy and conflict

Part of the comparison of the dramas is to assess the degree of conflict and controversy, and here we consider two indicators: salience and the proportion of controversial reportage. Salience, the level of coverage, seems a necessary but insufficient measure of public controversy. Public controversy generally results in media reportage, but media reportage does not always indicate controversy. High levels of media coverage, such as over the death of Diana, Princess of Wales, may indicate other news values such as human feeling, rather than public conflict (although an implicit controversy over the British Royal family undoubtedly contributed to the public mourning over Princess Diana). Media generally operate under limited capacity selecting news items from a number of candidate topics. It is likely that it is only those scientific and technical topics that signify deviation from the normal course of expectations, and therefore are likely to concern the public, that are selected. Considering the functions of the media as

catalyst, purifier or mirror of public passions, salience may be an indicator of controversy, although not in all circumstances.

Given this uncertainty, intensity of coverage needs to be validated by another indicator to qualify as a controversy index. Our second indicator considers whether the articles make explicit reference to public controversy, for example by mobilising contradictory sources and arguments, or by explicitly advocating sides in the writing. For each article we coded whether the writing is controversial or not, and if it is controversial, in which ways: by advocating one side of the controversy, or by reporting in a balanced manner. This leaves us with two indicators of controversy: the ratio of controversial writing and the overall intensity of coverage.

Figure 5 shows these two indicators before and after the watershed years. This gives us a picture of how salience and controversy over biotechnology combine and shift. The emerging picture is complex. Looking at the individual countries, we can say, as shown below, that salience generally increases over the two periods. This is shown by all the lines pointing in the direction from left to right in Figure 5. At the same time, the level of controversy moves in different directions. This is indicated by the line pointing either from bottom to top, indicating an increase, from high to low indicating a decrease, or on the horizontal, indicating stable controversy. Controversy over biotechnology decreases in the

Figure 5. Salience of and controversy over biotechnology in wave 1 (1992–96) compared to wave 2 (1997–99) in 15 countries. Salience is on a log scale; intensity is measured as average number of articles per year in wave 1 and wave 2. Controversy is measured by the proportion of articles that are coded as controversial reportage

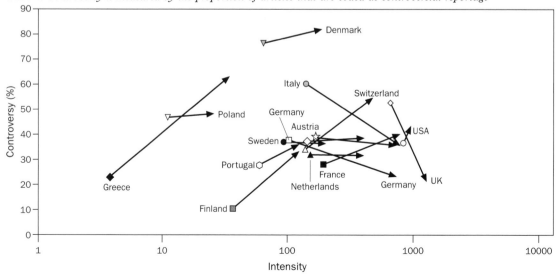

UK, Germany, Italy and Austria; stays the same in Sweden, Canada, Switzerland, Poland and the Netherlands; and increases in Greece, France, Portugal, Denmark, Finland and, to a lesser extent, the USA.

To explore further the complex relationship between salience and controversy we look at the reportage across different applications of biotechnology. Controversy is measured by the proportion of articles that refer to a controversy over biotechnology, for example by citing different experts or by alluding to contradictory arguments over an issue. We compare the level of controversy for the two types of biotechnology applications.

Figure 6 shows the levels of controversy for 'red' biotechnology by country comparing the period before and after 1996/97. The countries are ordered from left to right according to the level of controversial reporting in wave 1. Before 1996/97, Denmark, Italy, Switzerland, Poland and the Netherlands had higher levels of controversy; Canada, Sweden, Greece, the UK, Portugal and Finland had lower levels of controversy; and the USA, France, Austria, and Germany may be said to occupy the middle ground (since the average level over the two phases is 35 per cent). The picture changes slightly after the watershed years. Most countries see a reduced level of 'red' controversy, while USA and Canada, and to some extent France and Sweden move in the opposite direction. 'Red' biotechnology has become more of a controversial

drama in North America in the 1990s than it has in Europe.

Figure 7 shows the controversial reportage over 'green' biotechnology. Given that the average controversy across the two phases was 59 per cent, the ranking shows again that those countries with high levels of conflict before 1996/97, were Denmark, Poland, Sweden, the UK, Canada, Austria and the Netherlands, and those with lower levels of conflict were Germany, France, Finland and Greece. After the watershed years, seven countries show stable or increasing controversy over 'green' biotechnology (the USA, France, Switzerland, Portugal and, more dramatically, Finland and Greece); and only two countries, the Netherlands and Poland, show a significant decrease in controversial reportage; all others remain level.

In summary, although salience is not a direct indicator of controversy over biotechnology, it does give an indication of the level of attention in the public sphere. There is only a tenuous correlation between salience and controversial reporting. In dramatic terms, this means that a larger scenery does not necessarily mean more fighting on stage. More reportage does not come with more controversy. For some countries, such as the USA and France, a general increase in salience is accompanied by an increase in controversy. In others, the controversy shifts from 'red' to 'green', as in Switzerland and Italy. However, for Austria, Germany and Sweden there is little shift.

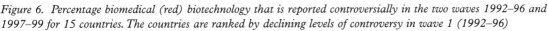

Figure 6. Percentage biomedical (red) biotechnology that is reported controversially in the two waves 1992–96 and 1997–99 for 15 countries. The countries are ranked by declining levels of controversy in wave 1 (1992–96)

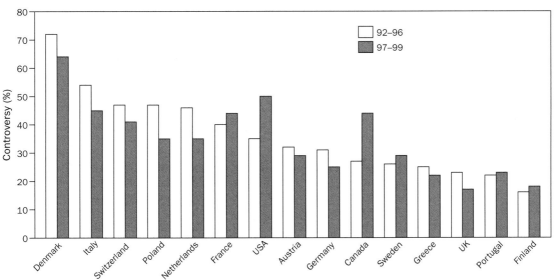

Figure 7. Percentage agrifood (green) biotechnology that is reported controversially in the two waves 1992–96 and 1997–99 for 15 countries. The countries are ranked by declining levels of controversy in wave 1, 1992–96

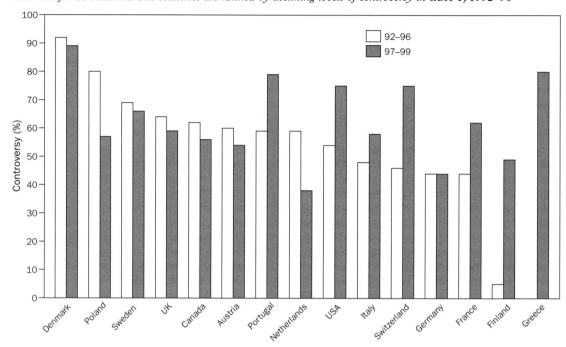

The watershed years 1996–97 have affected the drama over biotechnology: levels of controversy over 'red' are decreasing, while those over 'green' are increasing. During the 1990s, the drama of biotechnology splits into two distinct plots, one over agrifood and one over biomedical applications. The question arises, how is this crystallisation of two different plots in the mass media reflected in public perceptions? This is not a question which we will address here, but clearly invites further investigation.

Sensitivities and outcomes

Another element of the biotechnology drama is the extent of reporting of good or bad outcomes of biotechnology, and the kind of sensitivities that are at stake. Does the drama point towards a happy or an unhappy ending? Are the consequences of biotechnology presented in terms of benefits and risks or costs? What kinds of consequences are considered in terms of risk and benefits? We coded each article on whether potential consequences of biotechnology are mentioned, whether these are elaborated in terms of risks and benefits, and what type of consequence is sensitive in each country. We interpret consequences as either dreaded or desired outcomes of action. From this we defined an

indicator of four possible discourses of consequences: biotechnology is only risky, biotechnology is only beneficial, biotechnology is risky and beneficial, and biotechnology is neither of these – it is 'beyond good and evil' as other possible consequences apply. An emphasis on risk discourse might reflect more concerned public opinion towards biotechnology while a discourse of benefit might reflect one that is embracing this new technology.

Figure 8 maps the associations for the two waves between biomedical and agricultural or food applications on the one hand, and discourses of risks and benefit on the other. It clearly indicates a substantial shift in press coverage from the wave of 1992–96 to the wave of 1997–99. In wave 1, 'red' applications were both associated with risk-and-benefit discourses and with benefit-only discourses. But in the later wave, 'red' applications are more clearly and uniquely associated with the discourse of benefit only. In other words, the European press perceives such applications as more promising now than in the past. The changes are even more substantial for the 'green' applications of biotechnology to food and agriculture. In the earlier wave, such applications were perceived either ambiguously in terms of risks and benefits or outside the context of hopes for benefits and fears over risks, while in wave 2 they become closely associated with risks

Figure 8. Correspondence of green and red biotechnology and risk or benefit discourses for the two waves of media coverage

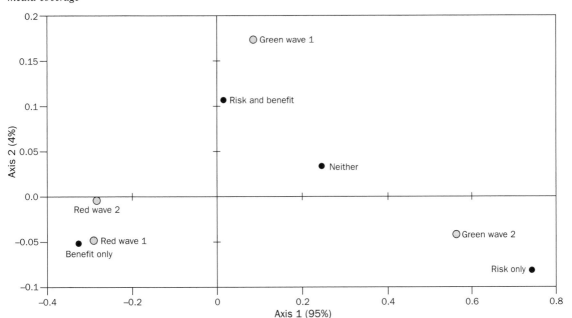

only, far removed from potential benefits. In other words, the European as well as the North American press increasingly differentiates between biotechnology applications, and presents medical applications as promising and agrifood applications as posing risks and threats. The European press clearly locates different applications in different discourses: 'red' is beneficial and good, 'green' is risky and problematic. Again the question arises, how is this long-term split in the media drama over biotechnology reflected in public perceptions?

There are two further issues to consider. Firstly, the balance between risk and benefit might indicate a culturally dependent mode of reasoning and/or manner of reporting on such issues. Overall, as shown in Table 2 above, risk-only discourse increases from 9 per cent in wave 1 to 15 per cent in wave 2, risk-and-benefit discourse remains at around 25 per cent, benefit-only decreases slightly from 44 to 39 per cent, and 'beyond good and evil' discourse declines slightly from 25 to 21 per cent. There are, however, clear differences in the way the countries endorse these arguments in 1997–99. Canada and Greece largely balance risks and benefits in their reportage. For these countries the drama of biotechnology seems open-ended. For the USA, Poland, Portugal, Austria, Finland, Italy and Germany the drama is mainly one of 'happy endings' with 40 per cent of benefit-only arguments;

these represent an optimistic outlook. Denmark, Switzerland and France are the sceptical countries with 20 per cent benefit-only and more risk-only arguments on biotechnology. In the Netherlands, the UK and Sweden, risks and benefits are not the main concern over biotechnology.

Discourses of risk and benefit are always content specific. Concerns and promises have a double reference to 'for whom' and 'in what respect'. Therefore, we distinguish different types of consequences that are mentioned: economic growth, 'third world' development, health, legal, social equality, moral and ethical, ecological, war and peace, research, and consumer. These indicate the specific hopes and fears which are associated with biotechnology. Health, economic growth and research are the most frequent types of benefits, and moral/ethical, health and ecological fears represent the main types of risk.

Figure 9 shows the associations between countries and the types of consequence of biotechnology, both risky or beneficial, for the second wave of media coverage in 1997–99 . After the watershed years, the moral and ethical issues, the 'natural boundaries' or 'playing God' type arguments, show no variation across the countries: their position is at the centre of the figure. The salience of these concerns are similar in all countries. Sweden, Switzerland, Canada, the USA and Germany tend

Figure 9. Correspondence of countries with the types of risks and benefits for the second wave 1997–99 only. The fit is 61 per cent suggesting that more than two dimensions are necessary to depict the full complexity of the distribution. Types of risks and benefits, wave 2, 1997–99

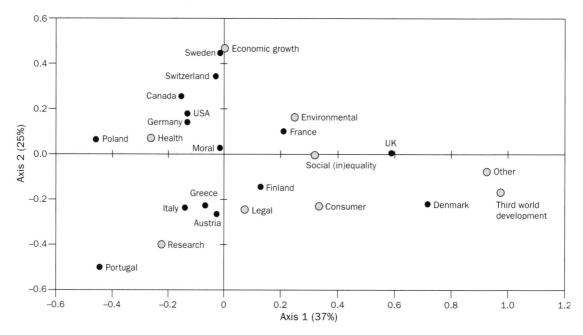

towards the upper end associated with high salience of economic benefits; similarly, Poland, Germany, the USA and Canada are also associated with high salience of health-type consequences. Portugal, Italy, Greece and Austria see prospects in the area of research, while Denmark is characteristically sensitive to consequences for the developing world. The French drama of biotechnology is characteristically argued on ecological grounds, and that of the UK on issues of social equality.

In summary, we observe that the representation of consequences of biotechnology clearly polarises into two discourses after the watershed years: 'red' biotechnology is beneficial, and 'green' biotechnology is problematic. Overall the risk-only discourse gains in ground, while benefit-only discourse loses ground. There are particular sensitivities in the various countries in terms of which risks and benefits are in focus; however, the picture is far from clear cut.

Different dramas over biotechnology

We have considered the similarities and differences across the various countries in terms of salience and journalistic features – the scenery and the sound of the drama; and in terms of actors, themes, frames, sensitivities and outcomes – the plot of the drama.

We will now attempt to construct a typology of dramas over biotechnology across the 15 countries. The question is: can we identify a small number of distinct ways in which the drama over biotechnology unfolds in the various national contexts?

For this purpose we focus on wave 2 from 1997 to 1999, when there was a considerable increase in media attention, which we referred to earlier as the synchronisation of the dramas. We focus on biomedical applications on the one hand, and the agricultural and food applications on the other, a split we have already observed in the discourses on several of our variables. The coverage of 'red' and 'green' amounts to about 38 per cent of the whole media coverage of biotechnology during the period, compared to 44 per cent in the period before from 1992–96. These two clusters of applications cover about two-fifths of all references to biotechnology.

To define the typology we include the following variables as shown in Table 3 from left to right: first, the intensity of the coverage 1997–99, which measures the salience of the topic; secondly, the shift in salience, measured by the relative increase or decrease of the topic from wave 1 to wave 2; thirdly, we consider the frames of the stories. For this purpose we distinguished between prospect frames and concern frames, as defined in Table 1 above. Across all countries three quarters of all

Table 3. Country typology of biotechnology coverage (relative percentages)

	Red						Green					
	A	**B**	**C**	**D**	**E**	**F**	**A**	**B**	**C**	**D**	**E**	**F**
Type I. All prospects, few concerns												
Poland	43	–19	58	20	82	18	14	10	64	31	71	29
Italy	18	–19	47	23	62	38	17	–12	35	36	67	33
Germany	18	–6	50	24	64	36	14	–2	41	26	62	38
Canada	25	–2	88	48	73	27	20	4	64	70	51	49
USA	25	5	50	27	75	25	11	–2	35	37	49	51
Type II. Prospects and concern												
France	19	–10	38	19	44	56	37	24	23	28	45	55
Netherlands	15	–1	38	22	65	35	14	–9	24	20	41	60
Finland	31	4	68	19	62	38	26	6	53	48	39	61
Type III. Forget green, run red with caution												
UK	10	–3	54	25	58	42	25	13	36	50	21	79
Sweden	9	–35	54	31	67	33	29	19	23	27	23	77
Greece	20	–3	89	22	72	28	28	25	40	72	28	72
Switzerland	12	–5	43	34	46	55	18	5	22	52	28	72
Austria	10	–6	81	21	75	25	15	7	38	39	32	68
Type IV. Red: yes please, green: no thanks												
Portugal	59	–13	82	16	84	16	11	4	54	69	12	88
Type V. Risky business												
Denmark	4	–56	55	73	64	36	47	36	18	89	12	88

A = Intensity 1997–99, B = Shift, C = Benefit, D = Risk, E = Prospect, F = Concern

'red' articles frame this topic as prospect, with no change between the two periods. In comparison, articles dealing with 'green' applications are framed less frequently as prospect, around 50 per cent, decreasing in the period from 1997–99 from the period before. Finally, we consider evaluation in terms of the discourse of consequences. 'Risk' corresponds to either risk and benefit or risk only, 'benefit' corresponds to risk and benefit or benefit only, as shown in the previous section.

The analysis reveals five distinctive patterns of framing and evaluation of these applications. In all countries 'red' biotechnology is framed mainly as prospect and is more likely to be evaluated as benefit than as risk. Across all countries benefit arguments and prospect framings are much more salient than risk discourses and concern framings. 'Red' receives a consensual plot with some variation, but no reversal of the drama. By contrast, the framing and evaluation of 'green' shows various features, varying considerably on the plot. There are some countries where the mass media coverage draws more heavily on concerns and paints a more risky image, and there are others where the media coverage is framed in terms of prospects and the benefit arguments exceed those of risk. It should be noted however, that above-average frequencies in

both risk and benefits indicate high salience of the risk-and-benefit type discourse.

The first drama is enacted in Germany, Italy, Poland, Canada and the USA. In these countries the reasoning on the prospects of 'green' applications far exceeds that of concerns, while the benefit discourse is equal or more salient than the risk discourse. These countries tend to have decreasing or lower salience of 'green' coverage overall. This drama is called 'biotechnology: all prospects, few concerns'.

The second drama runs in France, the Netherlands and Finland. Here, 'green' biotechnology is relatively salient overall; in Finland 'red' is very salient. Here the reasoning is ambiguous. For 'green' neither prospects, nor concerns, nor risk nor benefits are clearly dominant. On 'red' they show a relatively high level of concern. The drama in these countries is 'biotechnology: prospects and concerns'.

The third drama includes the UK, Sweden, Greece, Switzerland and Austria. In these countries, 'green' biotechnology is highly salient and increasingly so, and comes with a predominantly sceptical reportage. Concerns far exceed prospects, and risk discourse exceeds benefits discourse. The salience of 'red' biotechnology is declining after the watershed years, and this is particularly dramatic in Sweden where it declines by 35 per cent. Considering that many of these countries have a strong medical and pharmaceutical research basis, the low salience of biomedicine and the focus of controversy on agrifood biotechnology is a curious phenomenon. Overall, most of the public concerns focus on 'green' biotechnology, while 'red' biotechnology receives below-average concern (with the exception of the UK and Switzerland). This drama may be called: 'biotechnology: forget 'green', run 'red' with caution'.

Finally, our exercise in typology creates two interesting exceptions. Firstly, there is Portugal where there is very high salience of biomedical bio-technology, that is seen in terms of benefits and prospects, but very low salience of agrifood biotechnology, which is regarded with great concern through a discourse of risk. Considering that Portugal is a newcomer to the debate over bio-technology and has only recently woken up to it, the drama may be called 'biotechnology: 'red' yes please, 'green' no thanks!'. This is in contrast to Denmark, where the coverage comes with low salience of biomedical applications and very high salience of agrifood applications. 'Green' applications are seen as very concerning and are discussed through a discourse of risk. Danish 'red' applications also have high-risk coverage with considerable levels of concern. Thus, Denmark seems to make little difference between 'red' and 'green' biotechnology, but to consider them as one unified development. The Danish drama is therefore: 'biotechnology, a risky business'.

When considered together, our typology reveals a crucial feature of the public drama of biotechnol-ogy in the new millennium. While the biomedical applications have hitherto had a generally good press, agrifood applications have encountered a mixed press, particularly after the watershed years. The media coverage of the opinion-leading press increasingly makes a clear distinction between 'red' and 'green' applications both in their framing and in their evaluation. The age of biotechnology is entering into a new phase, in which several dramas are unfolding. While the overall dramatic scenery has many similarities, the dramaturgy diversifies into a small number of different plots serving different contexts.

Conclusions

In this chapter we characterise the cultivation of biotechnology in the European, Canadian and US public spheres during the 1990s through the looking-glass of the mass media. The main focus of our analysis is the representation of biotechnology in the press during the 1990s in two dimensions: salience and framing. This representation contributes to a characterisation of trends in public opinion over biotechnology in each country. We consider these representations in terms of a classical drama and explore the analogy between the elements of classical drama including scenery, sound and a plot that comprises actors, actions, reasoning and outcomes. Thus we consider the features of mass media reportage of biotechnology such as salience, journalistic features, actors, themes, frames and risk-and-benefit discourse. Speculatively, we adopt the Aristotelian idea of 'katharsis' or 'purification'. This suggests that dramatic representations regulate the passions of the audience, who are actors in real life and, in so doing, facilitate the finding of adequate solutions to societal problems. Virtues are thus cultivated by drama. In this sense, drama prepares for collective action by the 'homeopathic living-through' of particular passions in reading, watching and listening to ideas and arguments about biotechnology. Here, we content ourselves with analysing the drama over biotechnology. Its cathartic effects remain speculative. However, the drama analogy moves us to consider the media as part of the solution rather than as part of the problem in the controversy over biotechnology.

The salience of biotechnology considerably expands during the 1990s and after the watershed years of 1996/97. Articles on biotechnology get longer, use a wider range of journalistic formats, and the rate of passing references to 'genes' or 'biotechnology' increases. The watershed years synchronise the coverage across many countries – with the exception of the USA – into an upward trend. Biotechnology becomes a daily news item. In dramatic terms one could say that biotechnology expands its scenery, diversifies its 'sounds', synchronises the rhythm, but keeps different tempo.

The watershed years clearly mark a reversal in the coverage of biotechnology. Different biotech-nology activities are associated with different forms of reasoning. The frame of progress, which equates new technology with social progress, is in long-term decline and losing ground. Overall, 'red' biotechnology remains a matter of progress and mobilises concerns related to the issue of nature/ nurture. Cloning raises ethical concerns that may be too important to be left to the technocrats and scientists alone. And finally, 'green' biotechnology becomes a matter of public accountability and economic prospects where the problem of global-isation comes to bear.

Different episodes bring different actors on stage. Cloning gives visibility to moral authorities such as the Vatican or national or international ethics committees. 'Red' biotechnology gives independent science a voice, and 'green' biotechnology brings business, politics, NGOs and international organisations into the picture. The watershed years 1996/97 affect the drama over biotechnology: levels of controversy over 'red' are decreasing, while those over 'green' are increasing. The drama of biotechnology splits into two distinct plots during the 1990s, one over agrifood and one over biomedical applications. Increased salience does not always mean higher levels of controversy. A larger stage may or may not bring more conflict or drama. In the USA and France general controversy is increasing with increased salience, whilst in Switzerland and Italy the controversy is shifting from 'red' to 'green'. Meanwhile in Austria, Germany and Sweden, there is more attention to biotechnology but little shift in the conflict before and after the watershed years.

During the 1990s, the reasoning over consequences of biotechnology polarises into two discourses: 'red' biotechnology is beneficial, and 'green' biotechnology is problematic. Overall the risk-only discourse gains ground, while the benefit-only discourse loses ground. Different countries have their particular sensitivities in terms of types of consequences. Scientific research is a sensitive area for Portugal, Italy, Greece and Austria, whereas economic growth is sensitive in Switzerland, Sweden, Canada, Germany and the USA. At the same time, developing countries concern the Danish press, whilst social inequality concerns the British. In addition, we have identified a typology of five different dramas that are played over biotechnology in different contexts. This is testimony to the diversity in treatment that 'red' and 'green' biotechnologies are given in the elite press of the various countries. Biotechnology comprises an ongoing dramaturgy where the end is not yet defined, but where many authors are working on the plot for different audiences.

After all this, we ask ourselves, can we predict future trends in the media representations of biotechnology? Considering the process of globalisation and its discontents, and the protracted process of EU regulation, it seems reasonable to expect that agrifood applications will remain controversial for some time to come. However, the big question is for how long the public enthusiasm over 'red' biotechnology will carry on? Will the controversy that was unleashed over Monsanto's Roundup Ready Soya carry over into biomedical applications? The short but sharp controversy over Dolly the sheep may have given a taste of things to come. The signs are indeed already visible. The enthusiasms for genomics, post-genomics and proteomics with which the new millennium started, are confronted by regulatory uncertainties and controversies over patenting rights, the access to genetic information, and most recently, the use of stem-cell cloning in medical research. Are these cells more like fetuses or corpses? This is a question that German courts and law professors have been asking themselves recently, and it is likely to draw the developments of biomedical biotechnology into the established confrontations over abortion. This alignment of old and new issues is likely to mobilise larger sectors of the public than food issues were able to in the past. And this is also likely to unfreeze the established arguments, which had seemed previously to settle the issues.

Considering the trends in media coverage, we can expect a revival of the debate over genetic determinism in terms of nature/nurture. The increase in this frame of arguing is visible in many countries, in particular in the UK. This may be a more middle-class debate than that over abortions, but it is capable of mobilising strong passions through historical analogies with the eugenics movements of the early twentieth century. This again seems an old issue. The lawyers are uncertain on how to classify and contain it, and old debates over abortion and eugenics are drawn into the controversy. One looks ahead to interesting times for biotechnology.

However, one things seems clear: the salience of biotechnology is likely to increase even further in the public spheres across Europe and the world. Hence, the dramaturgy over biotechnology will continue to unfold. There is a need to investigate how the drama played out in the mass media has influenced the trajectory of biotechnology as we witness it. This answer can only be given with hindsight: what would have happened to biotechnology if the drama had been different?

Acknowledgement

We would like to express our thanks to our colleagues who contributed their data files to the common data corpus and allowed us to use them in this chapter: Edna Einsiedel, Toby Ten Eyck, Franz Seifert, Patrizia Weger, Arne T Mortensen, Timo Rusanen, Suzanne de Cheveigné, Anne Berthomier, Aglaia Chatjouli, Andrezj Przestalski, Anna Olofsson, Martina Leonarz and Pedro Alcântara.

Notes and references

1 Janko, R, *Aristotle Poetics* (Cambridge: Hackett Publishing Company, 1987).

2 Habermas, J, *The Structural Transformation of the Public Sphere: An Inquiry into a Category of Bourgeois Society* (Cambridge: Polity Press, 1989).

3 Krippendorff, K, *Content Analysis. An Introduction to its Methodology* (Beverly Hills: Sage, 1980); Holsti, O R, *Content Analysis for the Social Sciences and Humanities* (Reading, MA: Addison-Wesley, 1969).

4 Bauer, M W, 'Classical content analysis: a review', in Bauer, M W and Gaskell, G (eds), *Qualitative Researching with Text, Image and Sound* (London: Sage, 2000), pp131–51.

5 Gutteling, J M, Olofsson, A, Fjæstad, B, Kohring, M, Goerke, A, Bauer, M W and Rusanen T, 'Trends and dynamics in the opinion-leading press', in Bauer, M and Gaskell, G (eds), *Biotechnology: The Making of a Global Controversy* (Cambridge: Cambridge University Press, in press).

6 Durant, J, Bauer, M W and Gaskell, G, *Biotechnology in the Public Sphere: A European Source Book* (London: Science Museum, 1998).

7 Durant J *et al.* (see note 6).

8 Luhmann, N, *Die Realitaet der Massenmedian* (Opladen: Westdeutscher Verlag, 1996).

9 Bauer, M W, Durant, J, Gaskell, G, Liakopoulos, M and Bridgman, E, 'United Kingdom', in Durant, J, Bauer, M W and Gaskell, G (eds), *Biotechnology in the Public Sphere: A European Source Book* (London: Science Museum, 1998), pp162–76.

Address for correspondence

Dr Martin W Bauer, Department of Social Psychology, London School of Economics, Houghton St, London WC2A 2AE, UK. E-mail Bauer@lse.ac.uk

In the public eye: representations of biotechnology in Europe

George Gaskell, Nick Allum, Wolfgang Wagner, Torben Hviid Nielsen, Erling Jelsøe, Matthias Kohring and Martin Bauer

Introduction

In 1997 we reported that the European public was ambivalent on biotechnology.[1] In what was the third Eurobarometer survey on public perceptions of biotechnology in 1996 we found broad support for medical applications of gene technology, opposition to the use of transgenic animals in medical research, and signs of concern about agricultural and food biotechnologies.[2] Since then, agricultural and food biotechnologies in particular have been beset by controversy.

The period from 1996 to 1999 has been a 'watershed' in the development of biotechnologies. The industrial prospects led to the integration of agrichemicals, GM foods and pharmaceuticals. The integrated life sciences company became one of the industrial and scientific visions for the twenty-first century. In parallel, however, European governments, the European Commission and the European Parliament struggled, and sometimes clashed, over regulatory arrangements. The public domain saw an explosion of media coverage, episodes of mobilisation in protest against field trials of GM crops, consumer resistance to GM foods, supermarket boycotts and finally a moratorium on the commercial planting of GM crops in the European Union in 1999. While governments and interest groups legitimated their positions on the basis of representing public opinion, there were few if any attempts to find out what the European public actually thought. Hence the vital role of the European Commission's Eurobarometer surveys on biotechnology, providing a systematic, comparable and dispassionate assessment of public perceptions across Europe.

In the autumn of 1999, the European Commission conducted the fourth in a series of Eurobarometer surveys of public perceptions of biotechnology.[3] The survey was designed by the same team that had worked on the 1996 Eurobarometer survey (EB 46.1), an independent team of researchers from 11 countries whose investigation of biotechnology in the public sphere is featured in this book. The new survey in 1999 included some key trend questions designed to assess the stability or change in particular aspects of public perceptions, together with some new questions devised to capture more recent issues and developments in the field of biotechnology (see appendix 3). The survey was conducted in the 15 European member states in the autumn of 1999. In addition it was fielded in Norway in 1999, and in Switzerland, Canada and the USA in 2000, as part of the research programme of the International Group on Public Perceptions of Biotechnology.

Here we provide an overview of the key findings for the European countries, the 15 European Union member states plus Norway and Switzerland, drawing contrasts with the earlier surveys in the series in 1996, 1993 and 1991 on the selected time-series questions. A comparison of the European, Canadian and American findings from the surveys are presented elsewhere in this volume.[4] The chapter complements the description of public perceptions given in the national profiles by presenting the picture for Europe as a whole, and by bringing together the national data in particular tables allowing for country comparisons to be made.

It must be said at the outset that survey research has both strengths and weaknesses. Surveys provide an indication of the distribution of opinions and attitudes in the public at large, and evidence of changes in public perceptions over time. With appropriate formative research of a qualitative nature it is possible to ensure that the questions tap into issues of relevance to the public and do so in familiar words. In the analysis of survey results we can explore the linkages between clusters of attitudes on different issues, and between such clusters of attitudes and the sociodemographic characteristics of the respondents. With appropriate sampling methodology, as achieved in the Eurobarometer survey, we can be reasonably confident in making generalisations to the wider population.

But there are limits to survey research. Responses to survey questions are relatively superficial and, unlike qualitative inquiry, we cannot explore what ideas lie behind such attitudinal responses. For a survey we need to make assumptions about a shared basis of understanding of words and issues that are shared across the public, a bold assumption in one country and an even bolder in the context of 17 European countries. In the nature of the survey the response alternatives are framed by the researcher; there is no opportunity for the respondents to rephrase the question in their own terms, or to finesse an answer. And, whatever is believed, the results of surveys do not speak for themselves. Like any social research, the survey provides polysemic data that invites a number of different interpretations. Contextual information from other sources, whether the research literature, the social scientific imagination, or general knowledge of the area is always important in the interpretation of survey results.

For these reasons our research into biotechnology has always followed a multimethod approach, combining qualitative and quantitative inquiry and the understanding of the wider context of public debate in terms of the media coverage and policy making. As described elsewhere in this volume,[5] qualitative research reveals a core of common concerns about modern biotechnology across the publics in a number of the European member states, and from this research we can begin to understand the representations that give meaning to the responses to the survey questions. To employ a

cartographical metaphor, the survey provides a map of the wider area at low resolution, while the qualitative research focuses in on particular areas at higher levels of resolution. To orient oneself in the landscape of biotechnology requires both types of maps. In this chapter we focus on the wide perspective on the basis of the Eurobarometer survey.

Expectations of the impact of technologies on our way of life

Since 1991 the Eurobarometer surveys have charted the public's general attitudes to science and technology. For each of seven technologies (solar energy, computers and information technology, telecommunications, new materials and substances, space exploration, the internet, biotechnology and – asked for the first time in 1999 – nuclear power) respondents were asked, 'do you think it will improve our way of life in the 20 years, it will have no effect, or it will make things worse?' For biotechnology a split ballot was used with half the sample asked about 'biotechnology' and the other half asked about 'genetic engineering'.

Figure 1 shows that Europeans are less optimistic about biotechnology and genetic engineering than any other technology with the exception of nuclear

Figure 1. Impact of technologies on way of life (Europe)

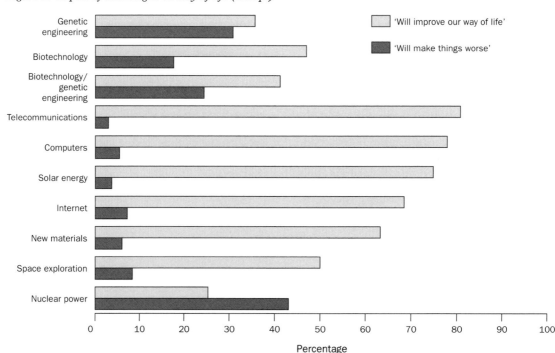

Figure 2. European optimism about technologies, 1991–99

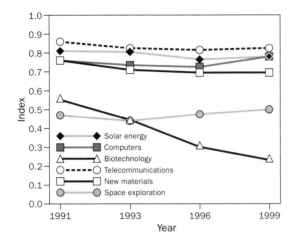

power. The contrast between the three so-called base technologies of the post Second World War years is strikingly varied. For modern biotechnology (combining responses for biotechnology and genetic engineering) 41 per cent are optimistic and 23 per cent are pessimistic. The comparable figures for nuclear power are 28 per cent optimistic and 40 per cent pessimistic; and for computers 79 per cent optimistic and 5 per cent pessimistic. It is notable that, notwithstanding the relative notoriety of biotechnology over the last three years, as many as 26 per cent of Europeans said 'don't know' to this question. By contrast 'don't know' responses for computers were 8 per cent and for nuclear power 17 per cent.

The terms 'biotechnology' and 'genetic engineering', as in 1996, continue to have different connotations. Some 12 per cent more Europeans see 'biotechnology' as likely to improve their way of life in the future, than those asked the same question about 'genetic engineering'. The more positive connotation of biotechnology, perhaps a result of the association of 'bio' with healthy and natural foods, holds across much of Europe with the exception of Italy, Spain, Portugal, UK and the Netherlands where the terms genetic engineering and biotechnology lead to very similar response patterns.

To assess the changes in optimism and pessimism over space (countries) and time (1991 through 1999) we have constructed a summary index (Figure 2). For this we subtract the percentage of pessimists from the percentage of optimists and divide this by the combined percentage of optimists, pessimists and those who say the technology will

have no effect. In excluding the 'don't know' responses, this index is based on only those respondents who expressed an opinion. A positive score reflects a majority of optimists over pessimists, a negative score a majority of pessimists over optimists and a score around zero more or less equal percentages of the two. As the percentage of 'no effect' respondents increases, so the index shrinks towards zero. This index has the following merits. First it is an economical way of presenting the time-series and country comparative data; secondly with substantial differences in the 'don't know' responses across countries the raw scores can be misleading; and thirdly it weights the balance of optimism and pessimism in relation to all the respondents who expressed an opinion on the question.

The index of optimism show a clear trajectory for the six technologies that have been included in the time series. Apart from biotechnology, all the other technologies have a stable score on the index. With the highest score on the index, telecommunications has the highest ratio of optimists over pessimists. In 1991 biotechnology had a higher index of optimism than space exploration, but since then biotechnology has steadily declined. This reflects a fall in optimism from 50 per cent in 1991 to 40 per cent in 1999, and a rise in pessimism over the same period from 11 per cent to 25 per cent. Notwithstanding the change in opinion over the last decade, there is still a majority of optimists over pessimists.

It can hardly be argued that Europeans are technological Luddites or technophobic and that the relative lack of enthusiasm for biotechnology is the product of declining support for technology in general. Biotechnology, like nuclear power (see Figure 1), appears to be a special case. Interestingly, this was identified by Fischoff, Slovic and colleagues as early as the late 1970s.[6] Their study of the qualitative dimensions of risk perception in the USA showed that nuclear power and DNA technology were characterised by the combination of 'dread' and 'unknown' risks. Such a combination leads to what they termed 'signal potential'. Problems or accidents with such hazards are likely to be taken as warnings of worse to come.

Turning to the European country level, Table 1 shows the index of optimism for the period 1991 to 1999. The countries are ranked in terms of optimism in 1999. On one hand, the majority of countries follows the wider European trend of declining scores on the index of optimism, while the balance is still with the optimists. However, in the case of Denmark and Greece, and for Norway in 1996–99, the outcome of this decline results in a

Table 1. Index of biotechnology optimism 1991–99

	1991	*1993*	*1996*	*1999*	*Mean 'don't know'*
Spain	0.82	0.78	0.67	0.61	32
Switzerland	–	–	0.07	0.50	–
Portugal	0.50	0.77	0.67	0.50	41
Netherlands	0.38	0.20	0.29	0.39	21
Belgium	0.53	0.42	0.44	0.29	25
Luxembourg	0.47	0.37	0.30	0.25	23
France	0.56	0.45	0.46	0.25	22
Germany	0.42	0.17	0.17	0.23	24
Italy	0.65	0.65	0.54	0.21	26
Ireland	0.68	0.54	0.40	0.16	35
Finland	–	–	0.24	0.13	21
UK	0.53	0.47	0.26	0.05	27
Austria	–	–	–0.11	0.02	23
Denmark	0.26	0.28	0.17	–0.01	19
Norway	–	–	0.03	–0.07	24
Greece	0.70	0.47	0.22	–0.33	46
Sweden	–	–	0.42	–	24
Mean (%) 'don't know'	32	28	25	27	

majority of pessimists. Interesting exceptions are the Netherlands and Portugal where optimism has held relatively constant over the decade. Finally, in Germany, following a decline in the early 1990s, the index of optimism shows an upward movement. Table 1 also shows average percentage of 'don't know' responses by country and by year. While 'don't know' responses fall from 32 per cent to 27 per cent overall, there is almost no change since 1993. Even in countries with a long history of biotechnology, for example the Netherlands, Germany, Denmark and the UK, around 20 per cent of respondents are unable or unwilling to express a view. Overall, while there has been virtually no change in the levels of optimism for a range of technologies during the 1990s, in the majority of countries levels of optimism about biotechnology have fallen and levels of pessimism risen. It is notable that the decline in optimism from 1991 to 1999 is fairly consistent, and that the 'watershed' year of 1996 is not associated with a sudden crisis in confidence. It would appear that as biotechnology has become more visible so have more Europeans become more concerned about it. Only in Germany and the Netherlands do we observe an increase in optimism over the last three years.

Evaluating applications of biotechnology

How, if at all, has this decline in optimism about biotechnology affected public perceptions of particular applications of biotechnology? Respondents were asked whether they thought each of seven biotechnologies was useful for society, risky for society, morally acceptable and whether it should be encouraged. The response alternatives for these questions were four-point scales (definitely agree +2, tend to agree +1, tend to disagree –1 and definitely disagree –2). The seven applications were described as follows:

- Genetic testing: using genetic tests to detect inheritable diseases such as cystic fibrosis.

- Medicines: introducing human genes into bacteria to produce medicines or vaccines, for example to produce insulin for diabetics.

- Bioremediation: genetically modified bacteria to clean up slicks of oil or dangerous chemicals.

- Cloning human cells: cloning human cells or tissues to replace a patient's diseased cells that are not functioning properly.

- GM crops: taking genes from plant species and transferring them into crop plants to increase resistance to insect pests.

- Cloning animals: cloning animals such as sheep to get milk which can be used to make medicines and vaccines.

- GM food: using modern biotechnology in the production of foods, for example to make them higher in protein, keep longer or change the taste.

Figure 3 shows the mean scores on a scale ranging from –2 to +2 for the assessments of use, risk, moral acceptability and willingness to encourage for each application. It is clear that the European public distinguish between different applications of biotechnology. Europeans are neutral about GM crops, and opposed to both GM foods and the cloning of animals. By contrast, and despite the opposition to GM foods, perceptions of medical biotechnologies (genetic testing and the production of medicines) and environmental biotechnologies (bioremediation) are positive. Note that this should not be read as implying strong support for all applications of genetic testing, for example in the areas of employment or insurance. The question wording points to solely medical uses of genetic testing

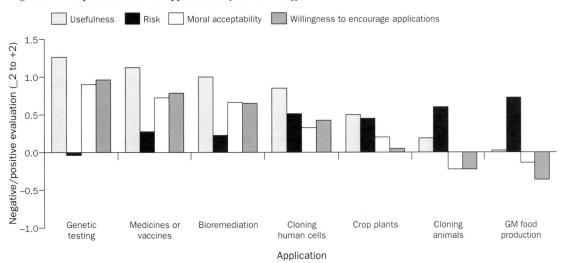

Figure 3. European attitudes to applications of biotechnology, 1999

There are two further striking findings. The first is that while the cloning of animals for medical purposes is widely rejected, the cloning of human cells and tissues for similar purposes receives moderate support. This suggests that the public are making judgements beyond specific techniques, such as cloning, to take into consideration the scope of the intervention – whole vs part cloning – and its intended uses. Secondly, the greater opposition to GM foods over GM crops suggests that 'consumer traits' are more worrying than 'agronomic traits'. In other words, it appears that Europeans are more concerned about food safety than possible environmental impacts.

The figure shows a consistent pattern in the structure of public perceptions across the seven applications. As the perceived usefulness of applications declines so is there an increase in perceived risk, and a decline in moral acceptability and support. Usefulness, the 'Achilles heel' of the first generation of GM food products, is a precondition for support. Indeed the absence of consumer benefits from GM foods may accentuate perceived risks and moral concerns. By contrast, where people perceive biotechnologies to have substantial benefits, for example in health care, they are willing to tolerate risks (e.g. medicines and cloning human cells). However, where biotechnologies are perceived to have only modest benefits, which come with modest levels of risk, there is no positive support (GM crops).

In 1999, as in 1996, perceptions of moral acceptability appear to act as a 'veto'. Thus, cloning of human cells is generally regarded as useful, risky

and morally acceptable; and the overall response of Europeans is that this technology should be encouraged. By contrast, while the cloning of animals is also regarded as useful and risky, crucially it is seen as morally unacceptable; and the overall response of most Europeans is that this technology should not be encouraged. Perhaps for the public, as was evidenced in much of the media coverage, the cloning of Dolly the sheep opened 'Pandora's box'; cloning people and eugenics would be coming next.

Support for biotechnology

Turning from Europe as a whole to the individual countries, Table 2 maps the relative levels of support for the seven applications and an indicative ranking, based on optimal scaling,[7] of the countries from most supportive (Spain) to most opposed (Greece). In the table the single '+' or '–' represents a mean score between 0 and +0.49 and 0 and –0.49 respectively, while '++' and '– –' represent scores of 0.50 and above and –0.50 and below.

In all countries, public attitudes towards genetic testing, medicines and bioremediation are supportive. With the exception of Greece, across Europe there is support for the cloning of human cells and tissues. Animal cloning is viewed negatively in all countries except Portugal and Spain. For GM crops there is a mixture of weak support and opposition. Finally, of the seven applications, GM foods are the most sensitive. While they attract moderate support in Finland and Spain, all the other countries are opposed and in six countries there is strong opposition.

Table 2. Level of support and opposition for seven applications: 1999

	Genetic testing	Medicines	Biomediation	Human cell cloning	Crop plants	Cloning animals	GM food
Spain	++	++	+	++	+	+	+
Finland	++	++	++	+	+	−	+
Ireland	+	+	+	+	−	−	−
Portugal	++	+	+	++	+	+	−
Belgium	++	++	+	+	+	−	−
United Kingdom	++	+	+	+	−	−	−
Netherlands	++	++	++	+	+	−	−
Italy	++	++	++	+	+	−	−
Luxembourg	+	+	+	+	−	−	−
Germany	++	++	++	+	+	−	−
Sweden	++	++	+	+	−	−	−−
Switzerland	++	++	++	+	−	−−	−
Denmark	++	++	++	+	−	−	−−
Norway	+	+	+	+	−	−	−−
France	++	++	+	++	−	−	−−
Austria	+	+	+	+	−−	−	−−
Greece	++	+	+	−	−	−−	−−

++ Strong support + Weak support − Weak opposition −− Strong opposition

Modelling encouragement for the applications

A simple model to explain the differential levels of encouragement, or support, is based on the assumption that the support for an application is judged on a combination of their perceived usefulness, moral acceptability and risk. Multiple regression offers a test of this model and also indicates the relative importance or predictive power of each of the attributes. For the seven applications the model performs well statistically, accounting for around 70 per cent of the variance in each case. Of the three attributes 'moral acceptability' is the best predictor across all seven applications with unstandardised regression weights (ßs) ranging from 0.44 to 0.57, followed by 'useful' with ßs in the range 0.31 to 0.36 and then 'risk' with ßs from 0.06 to 0.12. This pattern is very similar to the 1996 survey result. Apparently perceived risk, while a significant predictor of support, is far less influential than either usefulness or moral acceptability. This surprising finding from the 1996 survey led us to ask some further questions about risk perception in the 1999 survey, the results of which are presented later in this chapter.

Have attitudes changed since 1996?

Four of the seven applications of biotechnology – medicines, genetic testing, GM crops and GM foods – were included in both the 1996 and the 1999 Eurobarometer surveys and provide a basis for mapping changes in attitudes. However, making simple comparisons between the mean scores is not possible as the format of the questionnaire changed from 1996 to 1999. In the 1996 survey a large percentage of people gave 'don't know' responses to the questions about the applications and indeed some 51 per cent of Europeans said that they 'had never talked to anyone about biotechnology before'. Hence it may be assumed that in 1996 a sizeable proportion of the respondents were giving 'off the top of the head' responses, what Converse has described as non-attitudes,[8] created by the demands of the survey. Hence in the 1999 survey respondents were additionally asked whether or not they had heard about each application before giving judgements of usefulness, risk, moral acceptability and encouragement. This filter question provides a basis for distinguishing between those respondents who were more likely to have an attitude formed before the survey, or at least some prior knowledge of the topic, and those who formed a judgement on the spot, presumably without much relevant information. Differences in perceptions and attitudes between these two groups are explored in a later section of this chapter.

A consequence of this prior question concerning awareness of the particular applications is a significant increase in the percentage of 'don't know' responses in 1999 as compared to 1996. This increase in the 'don't know' responses complicates time-series comparisons of attitudes based on the entire sample. By implication, many who answered the questions in 1996 would not have done so had the form of questioning used in the 1999 survey been employed. Hence a simple comparison of the mean scores for 1996 and 1999 would be based on non-comparable samples. In the light of this, the following analysis of change over time uses only those respondents who gave a full set of responses

to the key attitude questions (i.e. no 'don't know' responses). These people, whom we call the 'decided public' may be assumed to have better formed opinions and to constitute comparable subsamples for 1996 and 1999. Judgements of use, risk, moral acceptability and encouragement were each collapsed into a dichotomy (useful/not useful, risky/not risky, etc.) in order to model patterns of response (henceforth 'logics') over the four dimensions of attitude. This produces 16 possible combinatorial 'logics', of which in practice only three were widely used, i.e. offered by more than 10 per cent of respondents (Table 3).

Logics 1 and 2 are similar in being supportive, but they display different perceptions of risk. For the 'supporter', risk is not an issue. The 'risk-tolerant supporter' perceives risk but then discounts it. Opponents take a position exactly opposite to that of supporters. Table 4 shows the logics of support for each of the seven applications in 1999, and time-

Table 3. Three common logics

Logic	Useful	Risky	Morally Acceptable	Encouraged
1 Supporters	YES	NO	YES	YES
2 Risk-tolerant supporters	YES	YES	YES	YES
3 Opponents	NO	YES	NO	NO

Table 4. The logic of judgements for seven applications of biotechnology

		1996 (Base = 60%)	1999 (Base = 49%)
Genetic testing	Supporters	56	53
	Risk-tolerant supporters	37	38
	Opponents	8	10
Medicines	Supporters	48	43
	Risk-tolerant supporters	43	44
	Opponents	9	13
Crops	Supporters	44	34
	Risk-tolerant supporters	33	30
	Opponents	23	36
Food	Supporters	30	23
	Risk-tolerant supporters	29	23
	Opponents	41	54
Bioremediation	Supporters	–	43
	Risk-tolerant supporters	–	42
	Opponents	–	15
Cloning human cells	Supporters	–	32
	Risk-tolerant supporters	–	46
	Opponents	–	22
Cloning animals	Supporters	–	24
	Risk-tolerant supporters	–	30
	Opponents	–	46

series comparisons with the 1996 Eurobarometer in the four applications selected for analysis.

It is very important to bear in mind that the figures in the two columns are based on only those respondents who held one of the three common logics. As such column 1, 1996, is based on approximately 60 per cent of the sample. Column 2, perhaps as a result of the new filter question, reflects only about one half of the sample. Thus it would *not* be appropriate to say that 56 per cent of Europeans support genetic testing. Rather it is valid to conclude that 56 per cent of the 'decided' Europeans, with one of the three common logics, do so. On this basis we can be reasonably confident about observed changes in support and opposition from 1996 to 1999. Over the past three years, support and risk-tolerant support for the two medical biotechnologies has held roughly constant. Amongst the 'decided' Europeans, and combining the two supporting logics, genetic testing remains at over 90 per cent support in 1999, with GM medicines falling marginally from 91 per cent in 1996 to 87 per cent in 1999. In contrast, however, there has been a moderate decline in support for the production of GM crops and a sharp decline in support for GM foods. In 1996, for example, 61 per cent of Europeans opting for one of the three common logics were either supporters or risk-tolerant supporters of GM foods, and 39 per cent were opponents; but three years later, 47 per cent

were supporters or risk-tolerant supporters, and an overall majority of 53 per cent were opponents of this technology. Overall it appears that the secular trend in declining optimism about biotechnology reflects growing opposition to specific applications of biotechnology, in particular GM foods, and not to wholesale rejection of modern biotechnology.

Of the three applications introduced into the 1999 Eurobarometer survey bioremediation enjoys comparable support to the medical applications. The contrast between the two cloning applications is rather striking. While both have majority support amongst the 'decided' Europeans, the supporters of cloning human cells and tissues outnumber opponents by almost 4:1, while the comparable ratio for animal cloning is close to 1:1. That there are twice as many opponents of animal cloning as for the cloning of human cells and tissues, suggests that the former is likely to be a highly controversial application of biotechnology.

How support, risk-tolerant support and opposition has changed in the European countries

Further insights into changes in public perceptions over the past three years can be seen by comparing shifts in attitudes to particular applications across the European countries. Table 5 is based on the

Table 5. *Support, opposition and change of support from 1996–99 for the four applications genetic testing, medicines, crop plants and GM food (numbers indicate the % of supporters and opponents within the 'decided' public)*

	Genetic testing			Medicines			GM crops			GM food		
	Support	Opposition	Change	Support	Opposition	Change	Support	Opposition	Change	Support	Opposition	Change
Belgium	90	10	−6	86	14	−9	74	26	−16	47	53	−25
Denmark	91	9	−0	90	10	−3	58	42	−10	35	65	−8
Germany	90	10	3	89	11	2	69	31	−4	49	51	−7
Greece	91	9	−6	72	28	−17	45	55	−32	19	81	−31
Italy	95	5	−2	88	12	−3	78	22	−8	49	51	−11
Spain	94	6	−2	96	4	2	87	13	1	70	30	−10
France	94	6	−2	85	15	−8	54	46	−25	35	65	−20
Ireland	94	6	−2	87	13	−4	67	33	−17	56	44	−17
Luxembourg	85	15	−7	85	15	−7	42	58	−27	30	70	−26
Netherlands	96	4	3	94	6	0	82	18	−4	75	25	−3
Portugal	96	4	−1	89	11	−5	81	19	−9	55	45	−17
UK	96	4	−1	94	6	0	63	37	−21	47	53	−20
Norway	78	22	0	82	18	−1	48	52	−7	35	65	−9
Finland	91	9	−4	84	16	−6	81	19	−6	69	31	−8
Sweden	92	8	−1	90	10	−3	61	39	−12	41	59	−1
Austria	78	22	4	77	23	−1	41	59	2	30	70	−1
Switzerland	87	13	−2	88	12	3	49	51	−15	47	53	3

Figure 4. Correspondence analysis, by country, for supporters (sup), risk-tolerant supporters (rts) and opponents (opp) of crops (C), food (F), medicines (M) and genetic testing (T)

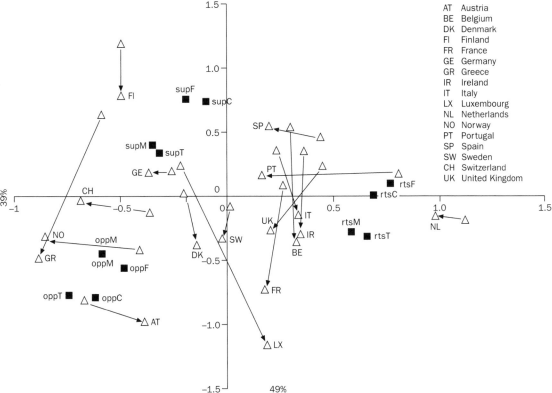

logics analysis described above. For each application there are three columns. The first combines the two types of support (supporters and risk-tolerant supporters) for 1999; the second shows the percentage of opposition in 1999, and the third column shows the percentage change in support from 1996 to 1999. A positive score indicates more support in 1999 than 1996 and a negative score a decline in support over the three-year period. Note that this analysis is based only on the 'decided public' as previously defined and in this sense the percentages should not be read as population estimates.

Across the European countries we observe rather similar patterns of responses for the 'red biotechnologies' and separately the 'green biotechnologies'. Support for 'genetic testing' and 'medicines' was high in 1996 and remains so in 1999, although in most countries, with the exception of Greece, there are a small declines in supporters. In the case of GM crops and foods, overall we find a larger decline in support over the period 1996 to 1999, but there is an interesting contrast between a group of countries (Germany, Netherlands, Austria,

Sweden and Switzerland) showing moderate declines and another group (Belgium, France, Greece, Luxembourg and the UK) showing substantial decline. In this latter group there is a sizeable drop in support of around 25 per cent.

The differential fortunes of the red and green biotechnologies suggests that public discrimination between different applications has increased over recent years, and that by the same token the high-profile public debate about agricultural and food biotechnology has had little impact on European attitudes toward medical biotechnologies.

Another way of mapping the contours of change across the 17 countries from 1996 to 1999 is based on a statistical procedure known as correspondence analysis.[9] The input to this correspondence analysis is a cross-tabulation of countries by the percentages of the three groups (supporters, risk-tolerant supporters and opponents) for each of the four time-series applications (C = crops, F = food, M = medicines and T = genetic testing). The output (Figure 4) depicts the information in the matrix in a visual form. The interpretation has

61

two steps. First, points that are close to each other represent similar responses across countries. It can be seen that support is clustered in the top left quadrant, while opposition falls in the bottom left quadrant. Support and opposition are the anchor points of the vertical dimension. Risk-tolerant support is clustered on the right-hand side of the horizontal axis, which contrasts risk-tolerant supporters from both supporters and opponents.

We observe that within the support area the medical applications are very close to each other and somewhat apart from food and crops, which in turn are themselves relatively close. When countries cluster together in the same area this signifies similar responses with regard to all the applications. The relative change of countries from 1996 to 1999 is indicated by the arrows, which start at country position for 1996 and point to 1999. From this we can see that, for example, for Greece, the arrow moves from the upper left into the lower left quadrant, indicating a change from support to opposition for all the four applications.

Some general points are evident. The arrows for a number of countries are pointing downwards in a direction more or less parallel to the vertical axis, indicating a change from the supporting pattern to the opposition pattern. Countries with the most pronounced changes in this direction are Greece, Luxembourg and France. By contrast Austria, Germany, the Netherlands, Spain and Sweden show relatively little change over the period 1996–99, albeit from different positions. For example, in the Netherlands risk-tolerant support remains dominant, while in Spain support and in Austria opposition holds constant. By contrast Portugal, moving from the right towards the left, shows a decrease in risk-tolerant support over the time period, but no change in the relative distribution of supporters and opponents.

In the non-changing countries it might be argued that the public perceptions were relatively unaffected by events of the watershed years. Austria for example had taken its stand against biotechnology in 1996–97, the issue was closed and there was no further controversy. The small increase in risk-tolerant support indicates the emergence of more discriminating opinions, beyond the yes/no vote. In Germany and the Netherlands there has been relatively little controversy over the period, with an apparent normalisation of biotechnology. For Spain, a country in the process of modernisation, the project of biotechnology is still seen as an opportunity and it has not experienced the periods of coping that characterise the history of biotechnology in many

of the other European countries. But for France, Greece and Luxembourg the response to the events of the watershed years has been a dramatic shift towards opposition.

The engaged public

There has been a long-standing interest in the role of 'scientific literacy' as a factor implicated in public understanding of science.[10] A more literate public, it is argued, is a prerequisite for effective democratic participation on issues of science and technology; all the more relevant in contemporary times as governments are increasingly taking up the idea of public participation and consultation about the direction of new technological developments.[11] The long history of 'scientific literacy' appeals to a widely held belief among scientists and regulators that an informed public will tend to be more supportive of science and technology.[12] This view, supported by findings of moderate correlations between scientific knowledge, and interest in and support for science[13] has been called the 'deficit model'.[14] Two implications follow from this model. Firstly, that opposition to new technologies is grounded in ignorance or misinformation, sometimes presumed to be the result of biased media reporting. And secondly, that information campaigns to inform the public about the 'facts' and methods of science will be effective in cultivating greater public confidence in science and technology.

This public relations approach to fostering public acceptance of science and technology is misguided. That those who have greater scientific knowledge are more supportive of science and technology does not mean that scientific knowledge *per se* is the crucial determinant of attitudes to science and technology. It might be just the reverse. Supporting science, for example in the belief that it will bring progress, may make people more interested in matters scientific, prompt them to be attentive to media coverage of science and encourage them to find out more about it. And the same could be true for the opponents of particular applications of science and technology. Their critical position may well motivate them to take an interest in new scientific developments, which they see as a threat to contemporary society. Hence, the deficit model of the public as an explanation of public attitudes to science and technology is open to question. Perhaps the most that can be claimed, and it is not an unimportant claim, is that scientific literacy, like knowledge of the political system for example, is a resource with which citizens may understand scientific developments and contribute to public debates on such issues.

Here we pursue a complementary approach based on the concept of 'issue publics' that has been developed in political science.[15] This concept is used to explain differential interest in politics and information-seeking behaviours. The 'issue public' are more likely to be better informed and to seek out new information on political issues, to have a coherent belief system, more resistant attitudes, and to be more likely to participate in political processes such as elections. Using the data from the Eurobarometer survey we explore whether it is possible and useful to talk of the 'issue public', or what we shall call the 'engaged public', of biotechnology. The exploration is based on a number of measures of involvement with and personal salience of biotechnology. The indictors are: past and intended behaviours, awareness of biotechnological applications, and knowledge of biology and genetics.

Reported and intended behaviours

Respondents were asked three questions:
1 'Before today had you ever talked about modern biotechnology with anyone?' (response categories: frequently, occasionally, once or twice, never)
2 'I would take the time to read articles or watch TV programmes on the advantages and disadvantages of developments in biotechnology' (response categories: tend to agree, tend to disagree and don't know)
3 'I would be prepared to take part in public discussions or hearings about biotechnology' (response categories: tend to agree, tend to disagree and don't know).

Those responding either 'frequently' or 'occasionally' to the first question were given a score of one, as were those responding 'tend to agree' to the second and third questions. We would expect that these three behavioural indicators would be intercorrelated. For example, those who had talked about biotechnology before would be more likely to be interested in a television programme on the topic. And this is confirmed by a test that shows that the items form a cumulative scale with adequate statistical properties (Cronbach's alpha = 0.50). Hence we create a summary score of behavioural involvement for each respondent.

Awareness of biotechnologies

Following the concept of the issue public in political science, we expect that those who are behaviourally

involved with biotechnology would be likely to have heard more about the subject and, as such, be aware of a greater number of applications of biotechnology. Before respondents gave their judgements on each of the seven applications of biotechnology they were asked the question: 'Have you heard of this application of biotechnology before, or not?' These seven items form a reliable scale (Cronbach's alpha = 0.67) and provide an index of awareness of biotechnologies for each respondent, with a range from 0 to 7.

Knowledge of biology and genetics

The 1999 Eurobarometer survey included a set of questions about basic biology and genetics, many of which were also asked in the 1996 survey. Respondents were asked to say 'true' or 'false' in answer to each (a 'don't know' option was also available). The questions were of two types. First, there was textbook knowledge – the kind of facts that a person might learn at school or from a popular science magazine or television programme. Seven such items were included in the survey.

The second type of knowledge question, while factual in nature, was designed to assess what can be best described as menacing images of food biotechnology. For these image items, which were developed from qualitative research prior to the 1996 Eurobarometer survey, an incorrect answer reflects a lack of scientific knowledge, but also an inclination to assent to the idea that food biotechnology is associated with adulteration (Q3), infection (Q4) and monstrosities (Q8). Table 6 shows the knowledge questions and the percentages of correct answers for Europe as a whole.

Before proceeding with the exploration of knowledge as a characteristic of the engaged public of biotechnology, we make some comments on the knowledge items. First, the questions about basic biology (Q1 and Q6) and prenatal screening (Q7) are answered correctly by the greater majority of Europeans. By contrast, with the exception of Q3 on cloning, the smaller percentage correct for the questions about genetics (Q5, Q9 and Q10) indicates that this area is not very familiar. This is not surprising, as many Europeans will have completed formal education before genetics entered the school curriculum. That 64 per cent gave the right answer to Q3 on cloning probably reflects the extensive media coverage of the cloning of Dolly the sheep. Second, on the three questions tapping menacing images (Q3, Q4 and Q8), about 40 per cent of Europeans correctly reject each of

Table 6. Percentage correct answers for the knowledge quiz

	1996	1999
1. There are bacteria which live from waste water	83.9	85.0
2. Ordinary tomatoes do not contain genes, while genetically modified tomatoes do	35.8	37.4
3. The cloning of living things produces genetically identical offspring	45.7	64.0
4. By eating a genetically modified fruit, a person's genes could also become modified	48.6	42.0
5. It is the father's genes that determine whether a child is a girl	N/A	44.9
6. Yeast for brewing beer consists of living organisms	68.2	67.0
7. Can Down's Syndrome be detected in the first few months of pregnancy	79.6	78.1
8. Genetically modified animals are always bigger than ordinary ones	36.1	35.4
9. More than half of human genes are identical to those of chimpanzees	50.0	50.9
10. It is impossible to transfer animal genes into plants	27.7	28.1

the statements. But, asked whether ordinary tomatoes do not have genes but GM ones do, 32 per cent of Europeans said the proposition was true. In addition, the other two menacing image questions were considered true by around 25 per cent of respondents. That about 25 per cent of Europeans assent to these menacing image propositions does not necessarily mean that they actively held such views of biotechnology before being asked the question in the survey interview. It is likely that many would not have thought about the issue before. Hence, a more realistic interpretation is that when asked these questions about the unfamiliar area of genetics, their general unease and possible anxieties about the technology leads them to assume the worst when asked about specific issues. This is much the same process as stereotyping. If a stereotype as a general evaluation is negative, then the holder is likely to impute negativity to all specific attributes of the object in question, including those of which they were previously unaware.[16]

Returning to knowledge as a possible characteristic of the engaged public of biotechnology we find that taken together the ten knowledge items form a reliable scale (Cronbach's alpha = 0.74). The total number of correct answers is used as an index of knowledge of biology and genetics for each respondent.

Is there an engaged public of biotechnology?

Thus far we have established reliable scores for each individual on three separate measures of engagement with biotechnology – reported behaviours, awareness and knowledge. These three constructs were selected to function as indicators of an 'issue public' for biotechnology. We can now determine whether it is empirically plausible to define an issue or engaged public of biotechnology in this way. We operationalise this concept by

carrying out a principal components analysis of the three indicators. This shows that they combine well into a single component accounting for 59 per cent of the variance. Each indicator has loadings on this single factor of around 0.75. This provides evidence that it is justifiable to talk of the engaged public of biotechnology. The engaged public report higher behavioural involvement, are aware of more different applications of biotechnology and are more knowledgeable of biology and genetics. A score for each respondent was computed from this principal component and this we take as our index of engagement.

Returning to the political science literature, we know that issue publics are more likely to have strong opinions on the particular issue for which they have been identified. For the engaged public of biotechnology, a measure of this would be giving fewer 'don't know' responses to the questions about use, risk, moral acceptability and encouragement for the seven applications. This is clearly shown in the data. The correlation between the level of engagement and the number of 'don't know' responses is –0.47. In other words, the more engaged with biotechnology Europeans are, the less likely they are to offer 'don't know' responses to judgements about applications of biotechnology.

Engagement in the European countries

Given that the index of engagement is a derived score, which in absolute terms has no external 'real life' referent, the following procedure was adopted to compare levels of engagement across the 17 European countries. We define the engaged public of biotechnology as those people falling in the top quartile (25 per cent) of the distribution of engagement scores for all the countries. This categorisation is to some extent arbitrary and is not meant to convey the idea that only the top 25 per cent are engaged in biotechnology and the remaining 75 per cent of the European public are completely unengaged. But with this arbitrary criterion we can make comparisons between the countries based on the percentage representation of the engaged in each country. All things being equal we would expect to find 25 per cent in each country, but clearly all is not equal as shown in the final column of Table 7. This table also shows the percentages and mean scores for each country on the measures that make up the index of engagement.

As can be seen, the countries with the highest percentages of engaged public are Denmark, Switzerland, Finland, Sweden and the Netherlands. At the opposite extreme are Portugal, Greece, Belgium and Spain. The overall European pattern is something of a 'north–south' divide, with the Scandinavian countries having the greatest engagement with biotechnology and the southern member states the least. This pattern would appear to reflect with both the onset of media coverage and of regulatory activities in the different countries. But there are exceptions to this 'rule'. France, Germany and the UK have a long history of regulation and of media reporting on biotechnology, yet there are within plus or minus 3 per cent of the European mean. One explanation for this is that the measure of engagement is a snapshot at a point in time – November 1999, and

it would be inappropriate to assume that levels of engagement are constant over time. While levels of engagement may reflect a longer term underlying cultural interest in biotechnology it must also reflect the extent to which, in different countries and at different times, biotechnology emerges as a controversial issue in the public sphere, while at other times it is recedes into the background as other public concerns take centre stage.

The profile of the engaged public

A further question concerns the sociodemographic characteristics of the engaged public of biotechnology. For this analysis we contrast the group of respondents whose engagement score falls in the top quartile, with the other respondents. A logistic regression analysis was carried out, regressing engagement on to age, gender and education. The results show that the engaged public of biotechnology is significantly more likely to be male and better educated. The effect of education on engagement is not significantly different for men and women. Overall, age is not a predictor of engagement after taking education level into account. However, respondents who are over the age of 55 and have a university degree are more likely to show engagement in biotechnology.

Table 7. Engagement with biotechnology

	Have talked about frequently or occasionally (%)	Would attend a public meeting (%)	Would watch a TV programme (%)	Number of applications heard about (mean 0–7)	Number of correct answers to knowledge quiz (mean 0–10)	Engaged (%)
Denmark	46	53	83	4.81	6.3	46
Switzerland	63	43	73	3.63	5.5	35
Austria	41	54	74	3.46	4.9	33
Finland	44	40	76	3.62	5.8	32
Germany	40	50	72	3.65	5.1	31
Luxembourg	35	47	80	3.72	5.3	30
France	31	51	82	3.74	5.6	29
Norway	39	31	82	4.32	5.4	25
Sweden	27	30	83	3.96	6.7	24
Netherlands	29	24	77	4.20	6.4	24
Italy	28	39	66	3.20	4.9	22
United Kingdom	27	37	73	3.41	5.3	21
Ireland	20	38	72	3.28	4.7	21
Belgium	22	28	69	2.90	5.5	16
Spain	21	26	60	3.14	4.8	16
Greece	14	55	67	2.98	4.8	13
Portugal	13	36	55	2.09	3.8	11
Europe	32	40	73	3.53	5.4	25

Engagement and attitude

While issue involvement in politics predicts that particular people will be more likely to take a position on particular political issues, not surprisingly it makes no prediction about the position, pro or anti, that a person will take. Only in totalitarian states would all people be expected to vote in the same way. But, in the context of scientific issues it has often been argued that the more engaged will be more likely to be supportive of science and technology.

To investigate the relations between engagement in and attitudes towards biotechnology we contrast the attitudes of those Europeans in the lowest quartile of engagement with those in the highest quartile. Table 8 shows the judgements of usefulness, risk, moral acceptability and overall encouragement of seven applications for the high and low engaged respondents. The percentages represent respondents who either 'agree strongly' or 'agree' with each of the statements (see previous section for question wording). Those who did not express an opinion, by answering 'don't know' are excluded from the analysis.

In the lowest quartile of engagement around one third of the respondents answered 'don't know' to the attitude statements. In the highly engaged quartile the mean percentage drops to around 10. However, sufficient numbers of the unengaged respondents took the opportunity of expressing views on attitudinal items (use, risk, moral acceptability and support) for us to be able to compare the attitudes of respondents with low and high engagement. The overall pattern across all applications is remarkably consistent across the seven applications. Compared to less engaged respondents, those with higher engagement are more likely to judge it to be useful, morally

acceptable and to agree that it should be encouraged. This is best captured by means of odds ratios, the ratio of positive to negative opinions for the lowest and highest quartiles of engagement.

The greatest differences in encouragement between the two groups are for GM medicines, genetic testing and the cloning of human cells and tissues. For each of these applications, the odds of a highly engaged respondent holding a positive attitude rather than a negative one are just over twice as high as they are for a less engaged respondent. From the table it can be seen that 57 per cent of the less engaged respondents say it should be encouraged. Amongst the most engaged, the proportion saying it should be encouraged rises to 74 per cent. A similar pattern emerges for GM medicines where 66 per cent of the less engaged say it should be encouraged, contrasted with 81 per cent of the engaged group. The smallest differences in attitudes between the two groups are in relation to GM food and crops, the so-called 'green biotechnologies'. In the case of GM foods, 34 per cent of less engaged respondents signalled approval, contrasting with 45 per cent of the engaged group. For GM crops the corresponding proportions are 46 per cent and 56 per cent. For these two applications the odds ratio shows that the engaged are one-and-a-half times more likely to give encouragement than the less engaged. These results, based on Europe as a whole, are consistently replicated across the 17 countries. There are a few exceptions, often in cases where there are small sample sizes, in the low engagement group. But the overall trend is so striking that the finding can be confidently recognised as a general phenomenon across countries and different applications of biotechnology.

The pattern for judgements of 'risk' across the seven applications is intriguingly different in two

Table 8. European judgements about seven applications of biotechnology by awareness (% in agreement)

	Usefulness		Risk		Moral acceptability		Willingness to encourage	
	Unengaged	Engaged	Unengaged	Engaged	Unengaged	Engaged	Unengaged	Engaged
GM food	45	57	71	72	39	51	34	45
Crop plants	58	70	65	65	49	62	46	56
Medicines	77	89	61	58	65	80	66	81
Cloning human cells	68	84	68	64	53	71	57	74
Cloning animals	48	64	72	66	37	52	38	52
Genetic testing	81	91	54	48	71	83	72	84
Bioremediation	73	86	58	56	65	79	65	77

crucial respects. First, by comparison with the judgements of usefulness, moral acceptability and support, the level of engagement with biotechnology only marginally influences the judgement on risk. The odds ratio comparing the lower and upper quartiles of engagement is close to one. In other words, the differences between more and less engaged Europeans concerning judgments of risk are small. In percentage terms the largest difference is for cloning animals where there is a mere 6 per cent difference between the lower and upper quartiles of engagement. The second striking finding in relation to judgements of risk is that for medicines, genetic testing, bacteria and the two cloning applications, engagement is associated with the perception of slightly lower risk to society. But for GM foods and GM crops there is no difference at all. Could it be that food safety and food scares are so salient in contemporary Europe that even those who are relatively unengaged in biotechnology arrive at similar judgements to the engaged public? Or maybe it is because the controversies over GM foods and crops have been so intense that the impact has been rather uniform across most sections of the European public.

Why judgements of risk in general should be so weakly related to levels of engagement, and in the case of GM foods and crops unrelated, is not clear, but given the consistency of these findings across applications and countries they merit further exploration.

A final observation about the attitudes of the engaged public of biotechnology takes us back to the shortcomings of the deficit model of public understanding of science. Although we find that the more engaged are more likely to judge applications of biotechnology to be useful, morally acceptable and to merit support, there are still substantial percentages of the engaged public who hold negative views on these issues. For medicines and genetic testing the percentages are low: 19 per cent and 16 per cent respectively. At the other extreme, a majority of the engaged public, 55 per cent, are not prepared to give their support to GM foods.

To conclude this section we find persuasive evidence for the existence of an engaged public of biotechnology. The membership of this 'issue public' is more likely to be male and better educated, to have more behavioural involvement in biotechnology, to have heard about more applications of biotechnology and know more about biology and genetics. In contrast to the less engaged public they are more likely to judge our examples of biotechnology as useful, morally

acceptable and worthy of support. However, they are no more likely to see these applications as having lower risks for society. Finally, even among the engaged public of biotechnology there are those who hold negative attitudes, and in the context of GM foods a majority of them are not prepared to offer support.

Our use of the concept of the issue public from political science has proved to be of value. The issue public, or as we have called them, the engaged public of biotechnology show many of the characteristics that were predicted from research in the political domain. It also underlines one of the limitations of the 'deficit model' of the public in relation to science and technology. It is too simplistic to attribute opposition to science merely to a lack of knowledge. Engagement in science is a combination of a number of personal and contextual characteristics. To be knowledgeable about science is for many people to have been socialised into a culture that has positive regard for science. In this sense, giving people a 'dose' of scientific information will not cure their scepticism. To be engaged in science is to have stronger views and more resources upon which to arrive at a view. In absolute terms, these resources may lead to both supportive views, for example on the 'red biotechnologies' and to opposition, for example for the 'green biotechnologies'. Nevertheless, it is also the case that the engaged public is, on average, always more supportive than the less engaged. Future research will need to be more sophisticated about the role of interest in and knowledge of science, along with other attributes of issue engagement in the explanation of attitudes towards science and technology.

Risk perception: GM foods and animal cloning

In the 1996 Eurobarometer we found that judgements of 'risk to society' were not strongly correlated with overall encouragement for applications of biotechnology. This was somewhat surprising as conventional wisdom would lead us to expect that the perceived risks associated with new technologies would act, along with other aspects such as usefulness, as good predictors of people's support for such technologies. In 1999, we explored this finding further with a set of questions designed to tap a much wider range of risk beliefs. The approach taken draws on the work of Slovic and the Oregon Group, and is known as the 'psychometric' approach to the perception of risk. In this approach, risk is taken to mean much more to people than an esti-mate of the severity of harm weighted by the prob-ability of its occurrence. Different types of risks are associated with different qualitative characteristics.[17] A robust finding from this research is that hazards are 'dreaded' if they are perceived as uncontrollable, with consequences of a global or catastrophic nature, are fatal, or carry a high risk for future generations. Hazards that score highly on this risk dimension are, amongst others, nerve gas, nuclear weapons, terrorism and DNA research.

A series of items in the Eurobarometer survey were designed to tap this 'dread risk' dimension using a split-ballot procedure in which half of the sample was administered items relating to GM food and the remaining half the same items relating to cloning animals. These two contexts were chosen because GM foods (e.g. Monsanto's soya) and animal cloning (e.g. Dolly the sheep) have been widely debated biotechnologies of recent years. Perhaps not surprisingly, Table 9 shows that a substantial majority of those who oppose these applications believe that GM foods and cloning animals 'threaten the natural order', and that it would be a 'global catastrophe' if they went wrong. Even more notable and surprising are the views of the supporters. Here, an outright majority have the same beliefs about the two applications. That the two most prominent applications of biotechnology are troubling, even to those who have expressed overall support, can hardly be ignored. A similar overall pattern of responses is present for both applications but there is a notable difference. Whilst a similar percentage of opponents have negative beliefs regarding threats to the natural order and global catastrophe relating to both GM food and cloning animals, for supporters the pattern is more differentiated. Some 70 per cent of supporters believe that cloning animals threatens the natural

order, while only 59 per cent believe the same about GM food. It appears that, even for supporters of the technology, the prospect of cloning animals raises more concern about threats to the natural order than does GM food.

In order to test that these items measure Slovic's 'dread risk' construct, a confirmatory factor analysis (CFA) was carried out. After allowing for correlated measurement error between items 1 and 2 (the wording of both items includes a reference to natural/unnatural), the model fits acceptably well (chi sq 22, df = 4; RMSEA = 0.03, TLI = 0.99).[18] The factor loadings are shown in Table 9.

As can be seen, the highest factor loading is that for item 4, 'I dread the idea of GM food'. This increases our confidence in the validity of the scale, as it is anchored on the item that is closest in meaning to the 'dread risk' factor in the psycho-metric literature. Following this analysis, a sum-mated score from the items was computed and then linearly rescaled to range from 0 to 100. The resulting variable, called 'dread' (mean 74.2, SD 21.3, skewness −0.7, kurtosis −0.1) was used in the proceeding analyses as a measure of 'dread risk'.

Next, the relationship between 'dread risk' and the judgements of usefulness, risk to society, moral acceptability and overall encouragement was examined. The bivariate correlations between dread risk and the other judgements for GM foods are as follows: useful −0.43; risky 0.36; morally acceptable −0.44; encouraged −0.48. A similar pattern of correlations was found for cloning animals. It is notable that the correlation between dread risk and risk to society is smaller than the correlation between dread risk and encourage. This suggests that dread risk is tapping into aspects of risk perception that do not come to mind when respondents think about the question 'is it risky for society?'. To explore this further, dread risk was added as a predictor in the

Table 9. *Dangers seen by supporters and opponents of GM foods and animal cloning*

	Supporters (%)		Opponents (%)		Factor loadings
	GM foods	Clone animals	GM foods	Clone animals	GM foods
Threatens the natural order	59	70	85	88	0.67
Global catastrophe if it went wrong	54	53	76	72	0.66
Even if had benefits it is fundamentally unnatural	62	76	87	90	0.64
I dread the idea	40	50	74	76	0.81
Poses no danger for future generations	47	55	78	79	0.58

Figure 5. Path diagram for stuctural equation model

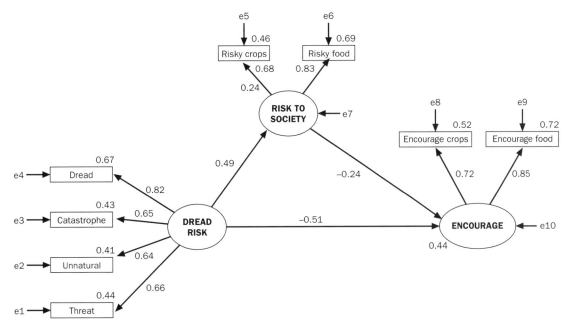

regression model described earlier (see section on support). This time the dependent variable used was encouragement of GM food. The multiple regression supports the contention that 'dread risk' and 'risk to society' are not synonymous. The standardised regression weights are risk −0.07 (down from 0.09 in the original model); dread −0.12. In other words, both risk and dread risk independently predict encouragement of GM food. Risk is clearly a multidimensional variable and is not fully captured in either 'risk to society' or 'dread risk' items. It seems likely that people's beliefs about the possible consequences of using GM food and crops, the 'green biotechnologies', not only have a direct effect on how much they approve or disapprove of the technologies, as shown in the regression results, but also act as a predictors of how much people consider them as 'risky for society'. This raises some doubts about the construct 'risk to society' at least in the sense of how it is understood by our respondents.

As noted above, we performed a one-factor CFA on the risk belief items. The model fitted well and we interpret the latent construct measured as 'dread risk'. Rather than form a summated scale, structural equation modelling allows us to use the latent variables themselves in regression models. This means that we control for measurement error in individual items and the regression coefficients more accurately measure relations between under-

lying constructs, partitioning out the error associated with responses to single items. The path diagram for the model is shown in Figure 5. Dread risk (for GM food) is measured using four of the five items described above. The question about 'danger for future generations' was dropped as it had the lowest factor loading on the latent variable and had residual correlations with other items in the model. Given the high correlation between responses to judgements about food and crops, and their logical interdependence (GM foods are manufactured by and large from GM crops), we assume that judgements about them are part of overall judgements towards 'green biotechnologies'. We measure people's judgements of 'risk to society' and 'encouragement' with pairs of items for food and crops as indicators of two latent constructs relating to green biotechnologies.

With a sample size of 4074 (one-half of the split ballot), the model fits well (chi sq 62, df 14; RMSEA 0.03; TLI 0.99).[19] Standardised regression weights are shown on the path diagram. The path diagram shows that 'dread risk' has a significant path to 'risk to society' indicating that risk beliefs play a part in the construction of people's views about risk to society. In turn, both risk to society and dread risks have significant paths to encouragement. What is interesting, however, is that the path from dread risk to encourage is double that of 'risk to society'. Hence we may conclude that risk to society does not capture the full scope of perceived risks of 'green biotechnologies'. While dread risk quite strongly influences people's perceptions of 'risk to society', societal risk is only a moderately good predictor of overall encouragement. Other factors such as perceptions of personal risk may play a role too. In any case, we may assume that the wording of the question of 'risk to society' leads to a non-exhaustive framing of the risk issue; only with the more specific form of questions embodied in dread risk are we able to elicit a more comprehensive perspective on risk, and even this is probably far from being exhaustive.

This analysis provides a possible explanation for the counterintuitive finding from the 1996 survey that 'risk' played only a modest role in the determination of overall support for applications of biotechnology. Essentially, the form of the question, perhaps even the use of the word 'risk', did not bring to mind people's concerns relevant to their overall judgement of support for the technology. Interestingly, in our recent qualitative analysis of public concerns,[20] spontaneous uses of the term 'risk' were few and far between. In this sense, risk may be a useful and often-used (but not always defined) abstract category, but not one that is familiar or brings to mind people's actual concerns.

Trust in key actors and sources of information

In an increasingly complex world people cannot be experts or even reasonably well informed about every situation or decision they confront. For example, how many air travellers know how the air-traffic-control system works? As such, people have to rely on others in many areas of life, and in so doing they act on trust. To trust is to transfer responsibility for the future into the hands of another or others. Trust reduces the uncertainty of the future and provides a basis for action. The function of trust is to make this transfer of responsibility tolerable, and in this sense, trust replaces information.[21]

To be regarded as trustworthy the trustee has to take care of three different types or levels of trust-relevant expectations. First there is a general trustworthiness based on common social rules and values; second there is structural/institutional trustworthiness based on the technical competence of the experts, evidence of institutional learning and risk-management strategies, and finally there is specific trustworthiness, referring to expectations about the obligations and responsibilities of

particular actors – what Barber calls 'fiduciary responsibility'.[22] Trust becomes an issue when an institution does not meet these basic preconditions. And when it becomes an issue, trust is not cultivated by working on the 'other' but rather by the people in the institution working on themselves to create the above-mentioned preconditions of trust.

In the area of science and technology, trust came to the fore at the time of public opposition to nuclear power. The public, it was argued, misperceive the risks, hence communication from trusted experts about the 'actual' risks would serve to allay public anxieties. Despite repeated efforts, there was little evidence that such risk communication reduced the gap between expert risk assessment and public perceptions. And as shown in our questions about optimism/pessimism for new technologies reported earlier in this chapter, nuclear power retains its negative image.

The failure of risk communication was attributed, amongst other things, to a 'crisis of confidence': a breakdown of public trust in those involved in the management and regulation of the civil nuclear programme. The same arguments, misperception of risks and lack of trust, have been used to account for public opposition to biotechnology. This is an extended form of the 'deficit model' of the public in the sense that the public are in deficit both with respect to knowledge of the real risks (sound science) and in their trust of those doing sound science. However, a closer look at this line of argument suggests that it is not without problems. While it is the case that the public perceive risks in certain technologies, this should not necessarily be taken as a sign of mistrust. People recognise the risks of air transport, but having confidence in the system, they mostly continue to fly around the world. Equally, our respondents perceive some, albeit small, risks in medical biotechnologies. But they are prepared to discount such risks, because there are perceived benefits and they trust the medical profession. The trust–risk perception–support equation is clearly complex; we will look at aspects of it later in this section.

There are both conceptual and methodological reasons for avoiding survey questions that ask directly about trust. To ask about trust directly is to question its very basis, to sow the seeds of doubt. A question such as 'Do you trust the government?' may evoke the perception that something could be wrong. The very posing of the question destroys the familiarity which is characterised by the absence of risk perception. In the case of trust (which is principally associated with the perception of a risky future), it asks explicitly for something which is normally part of the taken for granted and forces the respondent to think about the different levels of and reasons for trust. In this sense a direct question may measure a general image of an institution, an image more to do with risk perception itself than with trust which is (as mistrust) a *reaction following* the risk perception. Finally, for some respondents the direct question may evoke socially desirable answers (which are then more like clichés than typical for the respondents' own behaviour; for example, people will often say they do not trust the media when, in terms of actions, the media is a major source of information).

Trust in actors representing biotechnology

In the light of these conceptual and methodological issues, we developed an indirect question as an indicator of trust. Respondents were asked: 'Now I'm going to ask you about some people and groups involved in the various applications of modern biotechnology and genetic engineering. Do you suppose they are doing a good job for society or not doing a good job for society?' The judgement of an actor group as 'doing a good job for society' is likely to be based on a view that the actor is both competent and behaves in a socially responsible way. Thus, we propose that 'doing a good job' constitutes a proxy measure of trust as it avoids the problems outlined above with direct questioning. If we subtract the percentage of respondents who say 'doing a good job' for those saying 'doing a bad job' we have an estimate of the relative levels of trust in different actors.

Table 10, based on those who offered a positive or negative response, shows surprisingly high levels of trust in most of the actors involved in biotechnology. The majority of Europeans with a view trust all the actors with the exception of industry. In contrast to the findings of other surveys which have led to speculations about the 'crisis of confidence' in institutions of contemporary society, with respect to biotechnology, albeit with only cross-sectional data for 1999, a rather different picture emerges. This is clearly a result of the different form of the question. The newspapers are an interesting case in point. With the current question, those thinking the newspapers are doing a good job outnumber those thinking newspapers are doing a bad job by four to one. By contrast, in answer to the following question: 'Who would you trust to tell the truth about biotechnology?', only 21 per cent of respondents selected 'television and newspapers'. But, as expected, where we have data from the indirect and direct measures of trust for the same actor groups, the rank ordering of actors is more or less similar. The two measures are clearly associated, thus for the medical profession, 60 per cent of those who consider doctors to be doing a good job for society also selected them as likely to tell the truth about biotechnology, whereas only 29 per cent of those who said 'not doing a good job' said they trusted them to tell the truth. A similar pattern exists for other actor groups used in both question sets.

Table 10. European confidence in biotechnology actors (%)

	Doing a good job (%)	Not doing a good job (%)	Trust surplus/ deficit (%)
Medical doctors keeping an eye on the health implications of biotechnology	88	12	76
Consumer organisations checking products of biotechnology	88	12	76
The newspapers reporting on biotechnology	81	19	62
Ethics committees advising on the moral aspects of biotechnology	79	21	58
Environmental groups campaigning about biotechnology	78	22	56
Shops making sure our food is safe	74	26	48
Farmers deciding which crops to grow	72	28	44
Our government in making regulations on biotechnology	68	32	36
The churches offering viewpoints on biotechnology	53	47	6
Industry developing new products with biotechnology	45	55	−10

The direct question falls short on two grounds. As we have argued above, asking about trust in an actor is conceptually and methodologically flawed. But, beyond this, people may not see the function of the newspapers as 'truth-telling'. Their role may be seen as raising critical issues in the public domain, challenging industry and government and forcing a debate. If they achieve this then they may be seen as doing a good job; whether they tell the truth or not is incidental. The same logic may hold for perceptions of government. While 68 per cent see the government as doing a good job, in the question asking about 'trust to tell the truth' the percentage drops to 19 per cent. Perhaps the public have reason to doubt the veracity of politicians, but apparently this does not dent the confidence of the majority that the politicians are doing a good job when it comes to biotechnology.

In Table 10 it can be seen that 'industry' is the only actor included in the question set that has an overall trust deficit. Looking at the 17 European countries we find a substantial trust surplus for industry in the Netherlands, Portugal, Finland and Switzerland, and a substantial trust deficit in Denmark, Greece, Italy, France, Ireland, Norway and Sweden. We might expect that such differences in the level of trust in industry would be related to attitudes to biotechnology and this is partially confirmed. We assumed that asking respondents if they think their government is doing a good job on biotechnology or not, would lead people to consider their confidence in the regulation of biotechnology. Of course few will know much about the regulatory arrangements, so for many such a judgement will be based on a more general assessment of the competence and trustworthiness of government, formed on the basis of other areas of regulatory activity. Across the European countries levels of trust in government range from 34 per cent in the UK to 88 per cent in the Netherlands. While the low percentage figure for Britain is likely to reflect the longer term impacts of the BSE crisis, an agricultural fiasco that is often mentioned as a lesson for the future of GM foods, it may also reflect systemic differences in European political systems. Across Europe there are a variety of democratic systems, some oriented towards consensus building and consociationalism, for example the Netherlands, Finland, Denmark and Germany, while others are organised along the lines of conflicting/adversarial political parties for example the UK, Ireland, Greece and Italy. Consensus-building democracies, often associated with coalition governments, are likely to lead to greater levels of trust, as more of the electorate will identify with at least one section of the coalition. In this sense, measures of trust may reflect the wider political context as well as specific assessments of particular areas of governance.

An index of confidence in the food chain: the production, distribution and regulation of GM foods

A composite measure of trust was constructed from the questions asking whether various actors were 'doing a good job' for society. A latent class analysis[23] indicated that a three-class model fitted the responses across all ten items. One class was associated with a tendency to trust all actors and a second with a tendency to express no opinion. The third was defined by a tendency to distrust government, industry and shops in respect of their involvement with biotechnology. This makes intuitive sense as it is these three actor groups that are (or could be) responsible for the production, regulation and distribution of GM food. Given that we are interested in people's trust in particular actors and not in generalised or 'existential' trust, we use these negative responses to form our composite indicator of trust in biotechnology actors. This avoids the possible conflating of trust in particular actors with a psychological tendency to trust people in general. The resulting summated scale of negative responses runs from 1 to 4 and, for clarity of presentation, is reversed so that a high score indicates high trust.

Figure 6 plots the index of confidence in the food chain against the mean level of dread risks for 'green biotechnologies' (GM crops and foods). The correlation between these two indicators (at the country level, $N = 17$) is 0.5 and, as can be observed from the scatter plot, the trend is very clear. In the Netherlands, Portugal, Finland and Switzerland we see high trust and low dread risks. At the opposite extreme Norway, France, Sweden and Denmark show low support and high dread risks. It is important to note that this is an ecological correlation, based on aggregate country-level data. As such this ecological correlation cannot be interpreted as the relation between the two variables at the level of individuals. Hence, in countries where there is greater trust in the food chain, the central tendency of the public is to perceive less dread risk in food biotechnologies. Furthermore a similar plot of trust and support for GM foods shows a very similar pattern. Hence we have strong evidence for a linkage between trust, risk perception and support for GM foods. Although the literature points in the direction of trust leading to lower risk perception and greater

Figure 6. Trust and 'dread risk' of GM food and crops

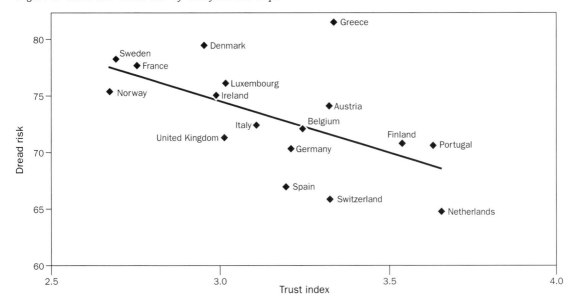

levels of support, our data do not allow us to make such causal inferences without a further modelling exercise. This is presented in the next section.

Modelling personal characteristics and attitudes to biotechnology

In this chapter we have examined a range of factors associated with Europeans' perceptions of biotechnological applications. In this final section, we test a model that includes the simultaneous effects of all of these possible influences on people's overall attitudes towards biotechnology. Path modelling, using the Amos 4 software package, is employed as the most suitable technique for this purpose. For this analysis we take attitudes towards 'green biotechnologies' as our dependent variable.

The variables in the model

A latent construct, 'support', is used as the main dependent variable in the model. This was developed as follows. First, three combined scores (for GM foods and crops) were created, one for usefulness, one for moral acceptability and one for encouragement. A confirmatory factor analysis showed that each of these indicators had a standardised factor loading of between 0.70 and 0.85 on the single factor of support.

The predictors or independent variables in the model are described in earlier sections of this chapter and comprise: *trust,* the index of trust

drawing on three questions asking whether government, industry and shops were 'doing a good job' for society in the context of biotechnology; *technology optimism,* a summated scale made up of the number of 'will improve our way of life' responses to the six technologies; *dread risk,* the index of risk perception; *engage,* the index of engagement with biotechnology, and finally, sociodemographics characteristics *gender, level of education* and *age,* introduced as dummy variables.

The model

The hypothesised model tested is presented in Figure 7. Four key variables, *trust, technological optimism, dread risk* and *engagement* are entered simultaneously as predictors of *support* (correlations between these variables are modelled but not shown). Sociodemographic characteristics are mediated by these more proximal variables. The model performs well based on an RMSEA of 0.02, CFI = 1, meaning that the correlations implied by the model closely approximate the observed values. As in all modelling exercises other models could account for the observed relationships equally well, but this model is theoretically well grounded and cannot be rejected given the data.

The model explains 35 per cent of the variance in *support.* Holding all other predictors constant, the four variables *trust, technological optimism, dread risk* and *engagement* each has a significant and independent effect on the level of *support.* With the

Figure 7. Modelling support for 'green biotechnologists' in Europe

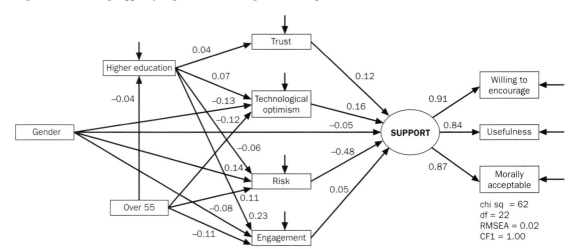

exception of *dread risk,* the effect sizes are modest. This is not unexpected as *dread risk* refers directly to 'green biotechnologies', while the other three predictors are less specific in nature. The socio-demographic characteristics are all mediated through the four variables above. This means that for example, those with higher education are more likely to be amongst the engaged public of biotechnology, to be optimistic about new technologies, to have greater trust and to perceive lower dread risk. In this sense education is not directly linked to support but cultivates a particular set of attitudes that lead to greater support. On gender we find that women are equally as likely as men to trust, but to be less optimistic about technology, to perceive more risk and to be less engaged. This pattern is replicated for people over 55 years. For gender there is also a direct path to support. This means that factors outside the scope of our model are implicated in the greater support by men and lower support by women.

Country differences

The model described above is based on all the respondents across the 17 European countries. Introducing *country* as a dummy variable we can assess whether the model adequately accounts for different levels of support in the different countries and if so we can look at the relative size of effects of *trust, dread risk, engagement* and *technological optimism* for each country. In all but three countries (Finland, Spain and Italy) we find no additional direct effects of country on support. This means that for the majority of countries there is nothing

unique that is not captured by the four key variables. In this sense, although we are dealing with different cultures and national identities, such differences as exist are expressed through the key variables. Paralleling the findings of the qualitative research elsewhere in this volume,[24] our analysis provides some evidence that Europeans represent biotechnology in shared terms, such as trust, risk, etc. But there is variation in the level of trust and risk perception both between countries as a whole and for individuals across countries. That is to say, holding *trust, technological optimism, dread risk* and *engagement* constant, there are no differences between most of the European countries in terms of levels of support compared to the European mean. There appear to be three exceptions to this: Finland, Italy and Spain. For these countries, as with gender, there is a direct effect to support that is not accounted for by the model. Given that the model is based on individual characteristics and attitudes, such direct country effects are probably to be found at a higher level of aggregation – something to do with 'culture', the catch-all category for which we have no explanation.

Of the remaining countries, those which have no additional direct effects on support, the United Kingdom is closest to the European average position on support. Hence we use the UK as the reference country against which the other countries are judged in relative terms. This comparison with the UK shows three groupings of countries. The relatively more supportive are Finland, Italy, Spain, Netherlands and Switzerland; relatively less supportive are Austria, Luxembourg, Sweden, France, Norway, Greece and Denmark; and the remainder – Germany,

Belgium, Ireland and Portugal – are similar to the UK. Note this is not dissimilar to the ranking of countries outlined earlier in this chapter, but here we are using a more inclusive definition of support based on the three judgements of usefulness, moral acceptability and encouragement. Regarding country differences we find that while technological optimism is relatively lower in Germany, Austria and Greece this is offset by relatively higher trust, leading to similar levels of support.

Trust appears to play a more significant role in support in Finland, Switzerland, Portugal and the Netherlands, but it is not a relative lack of trust that is implicated in lower levels of support in other countries. Rather, lower support is associated with higher dread risk in Sweden, France, Norway, Greece and Denmark.

Traditional 'blue' and modern 'green' world views

This section explores the opponents of biotechnology, going beyond traditional sociodemographics to understand what lies behind critical perspectives on biotechnology. Using cluster analysis we find that the opponents of biotechnology or 'pessimists' comprise two distinct groups. Firstly there is a traditional or value conservative group of 'blue' critics and secondly, a modern group of 'green' sceptics.[25]

A comparison of the 'blue' and 'green' groups shows that the 'blue' traditionalist group tends to be older, less educated, less concerned about the risk, less knowledgeable, inclined towards the right of the political spectrum, more religious, materialist rather than postmaterialist in outlook and living in rural rather than urban settings. Table 11 shows percentages of blue and green critics across Europe. In some countries the analysis did not identify the blue and green clusters and these are shown in the table.

The 'traditional' and 'modern' sceptics share the assumption that modern biotechnology will make our way of life worse. The shared assumption is, however, backed up by different arguments and conclusions. The 'blue' argument has no external references. It is closed in and around its own values. Its warrants question the technological intervention in nature as such. Its modality is 'in the "nature" of things'. Without rebuttals only a change in values would lead to a different conclusion. The 'green' argument on the other hand refers to (perceived) uncertainty and risk as its principal warrant. The backing evaluates

uncertainty against knowledge and risks against benefits. Its modality is conditioned: 'at the present stage' of technology and knowledge. The rebuttal makes it possible to reach another conclusion: with increased and certain knowledge and/or less (perception of) risk, the argument might transform into or lead to the same conclusion as the optimists.

The concerns behind these arguments are as different as the social groups expressing them are distinct. The 'blue' argument is backed by moral (or religious) values, the 'green' by uncertainty and risk. The 'blue' critique is 'Faustian'. The whole enterprise of biotechnology is perceived as a modern covenant with Mephisto. Even in the form of a technical success modern biotechnology pawns the soul. Insight into the workings of nature is problematic as such. The 'green' scepticism is more 'Frankensteinian'. Insufficient knowledge of the consequences, not the insight itself, is problematic. The danger is the possibility of the technology going its own uncontrolled way, and thus turning into a monster or demon. Experiments with life might unforeseen and unintentionally take the power from its creator.

Among the European countries there is marked variation in the size and characteristics of the traditional and modern groups. A closer look at the

Table 11. 'Traditional blue' and 'modern green' opposition to biotechnology.[a]

	1996 (%)		1999 (%)	
	Blue	*Green*	*Blue*	*Green*
Belgium	7	9	–[b]	–[b]
Denmark	12	18	19	19
Germany	9	14	8	11
Greece	8	11	15	23
Italy	9	7	14	13
Spain	6	4	6	6
France	4	10	14	12
Ireland	7	9	13	13
Luxembourg	11	10	12	10
Netherlands	8	15	9	12
Portugal	5	3	4	4
UK	10	14	–[b]	–[b]
Finland	–[b]	–[b]	12	14
Sweden	9	9	6	11
Austria	–[b]	–[b]	14	17
Norway	14	14	17	19
Switzerland	14	17	–[c]	–[c]

a The variable constructions used for the cluster analyses in 1996 and 1999 are slightly different

b The cluster analysis gave no meaningful solution.

c It was not possible to perform a cluster analysis on the Swiss data in 1999.

results of the cluster analyses for 1996 and 1999 is complicated by the fact that not all variables used in the analyses in 1999 were identical with those used in 1996 due to changes in the survey. However, it is possible to make some general observations.

In 1996, there was a relatively greater number of 'green' opponents in the countries in northern Europe and a relatively greater number of 'blue' opponents in the southern Catholic countries. This is likely to reflect cultural differences between the north and the south. In 1999, however, there has been a relative increase of the size of the 'blue' group in several countries such as Denmark, Germany, France and the Netherlands. In Sweden and Greece, on the other hand, the 'green' group has increased relatively in size. All in all, the difference in the distribution between 'blue' and 'green' in the south and the north is less pronounced in 1999 than it was in 1996. These changes in the structure of the segmentation may indicate the turbulence caused by the years of controversy about modern biotechnology. Thus, some of the most significant changes in the segmentation pattern have occurred in those countries where there have been the biggest increases in the number of opponents, such as Greece, France and Denmark. In these countries there seems to have been a mobilisation of new groups of opponents. As a consequence the structure of the resistance to biotechnology in Europe has become more complex.

Austria and Finland did not fit the model in 1996. These two countries may both be considered to be extreme cases. For Finland biotechnology was introduced during a period of rapid modernisation. The lack of a blue–green segmentation pattern is probably a reflection of a more general optimism about technological innovation. By contrast, in Austria biotechnology arrived late in the day and then the debate was highly critical, so critical that it was political correct to be opposed. That both countries have the blue–green segmentation by 1999 suggests that the debate became normalised in the period 1996–99, albeit in opposite directions. The UK and Belgium do not fit the model in 1999. Here the turbulence caused by food scandals and in the case of the UK, the fierce debate following the Pusztai case[26] is likely to have mobilised resistance that follows logics outside the 'blue' and 'green' arguments.

It appears that in the watershed years resistance by the 'blues' has taken on a greater social sharedness and that they have come to trust other oppositional actors to a greater extent than in 1996. Yet their general level of awareness of biotechnology and their engagement in the issues is still at a lower level than the 'greens'. Perhaps these follow from the general characteristics of the 'blues': lower levels of education and higher age. That they are less positive towards public consultation is likely to be a reflection of a more materialistic values and right-wing political views. Economic and political values still stand in the way of the grand coalition of the opponents.

Conclusions

Review of the findings

Our analysis and interpretation of the Eurobarometer survey shows a complex pattern of public perceptions across Europe and within the different European countries. As was found in the 1996 Eurobarometer survey the European public are not technophobic. While they are optimistic about technologies in general, the longer term trend of declining optimism in biotechnology has continued. Some countries are more optimistic than others. Thus Spain, Switzerland, Portugal and the Netherlands are amongst the most optimistic while Denmark, Norway and Greece are the most pessimistic.

Yet Europeans are not anti-biotechnology. The medical or 'red' biotechnologies are widely supported as they were in 1996. What has changed is the attitudes to the agricultural or 'green' applications of biotechnology. In all countries except Finland and Spain, the weight of opinion is against GM foods, but GM crops are viewed slightly more favourably. In general, those applications of biotechnology that are seen to bring benefits tend to be supported, even if they carry some risks. The influence of moral issues on attitudes to biotechnology, so apparent in 1996, is still strong. It is evidenced in the differing judgements of cloning of animals and the cloning of human cells and tissues. Both are seen, to varying degrees, as useful and risky. However, where the cloning of human cells is viewed as morally acceptable, the cloning of animals is not. And, just as we found in 1996, moral considerations act as a veto against certain applications of biotechnology. Ethical considerations are not epiphenomenal, for the European public this is likely to be a continuing source of concern over applications of biotechnology.

We find evidence for an engaged public of biotechnology, who are more active, aware and knowledgeable about the topic. Typically they are male, younger and better educated. Across all countries and for all applications of biotechnology the engaged public are more supportive. They judge the applications to be more useful and more morally acceptable. However, in the perception of risks the engaged public come to the same view as the unengaged. In this regard scientific assurances that biotechnology is without risk will carry little credibility.

In the 1996 Eurobarometer research we found that 'risk to society' appeared to play only a modest role in the determination of support for particular applications of biotechnology. New questions in the 1999 survey about particular dangers resulting from food biotechnologies show that perception of so-called 'dread risks' is strongly related to support. Interestingly, even amongst the supporters of the 'green' biotechnologies, concern about dread risks is widespread.

Medical doctors, consumer organisations and newspapers are seen across Europe as groups that are doing a good job for society over the issue of biotechnology. While 'government' lags behind these three, it still is seen by 68 per cent of Europeans to be doing a good job. Of ten actor groups included in the survey, industry was the only one for which the majority of Europeans thought they were 'doing a bad job'. In those countries where there is trust in the food chain – industry, government and shops – we find higher support and lower perceptions of dread risks for GM foods.

A multivariate analysis explored the relative importance of engagement, trust, dread risks and technological optimism in the formation of overall support for the 'green biotechnologies'. All four factors are implicated in support, with dread risk the strongest and engagement the weakest.

People who are pessimistic about biotechnology divide into two distinct groupings. The 'traditional blues' base their opposition on moral arguments, while the 'modern greens' focus on the risks and present uncertainties. The 'greens' are more prevalent in northern Europe, as are the 'blues' in southern Europe.

Implications

Finally, we comment on three issues that have a bearing on the fate of biotechnology in Europe. What seems clear from the Eurobarometer of 1999 is that applications of biotechnology in the agrifood area are amongst the most problematic. GM foods and to a lesser extent GM crops are not supported in the great majority of countries and the extent of opposition has increased since 1996. How can we account for this? First, the perceived absence of consumer benefits of GM foods would not in itself lead to opposition, but the prevalence of 'dread risks' of GM foods and, in some countries, a lack of trust in the food chain, are the conditions for anxieties and opposition. Added to this, the absence of GM labelling probably accentuated any perceived risk in the public mind. It is a pity that in our design of the Eurobarometer survey we did not include questions on trust in scientists. This is an actor group whose role in matters of risk has been very visible. From the scientific community the public have been exposed to contradictory views on the safety of GM foods. In this context the BSE crisis has had a lasting impact. Reassurances of no possible risks were proved to be wrong. Some of the public may simply find it difficult to believe statements of the same tenor in relation to GM foods. And at the end of the day why would anyone take any risks with GM foods for no benefit? BSE and GM foods have called scientific expertise into question.

The second issue raised by the survey is why the engaged public of biotechnology are more likely to see benefits and more likely to support applications of biotechnology. Is this merely a reformulation of the science literacy model: that knowledge leads to support of science? In some respects it is but perhaps the real issue is in the interpretation and normative implications that can and should be drawn from the empirical regularity observed across numerous studies of this kind: that there is an association between knowledge and support for science and technology. One interpretation, and we consider it simplistic, is based on a presumed causal relation between the antecedent (scientific knowledge) and the consequent (support for science). The generally small but positive correlations are taken to corroborate this causal model, leading to the normative implication that the public should be educated in matters scientific because science is 'a good thing' and people ought to support it. We would argue that the explanation of the empirical regularity is more problematic than this and that it is unlikely to be revealed in the snapshot provided by a social survey. Consider the role of formal education. Higher education, greater knowledge of biology and genetics, and an interest in talking about the subject typifies the engaged public of biotechnology, and this public is, on the whole, more favourable towards biotechnology. But there is more to scientific education than knowing about scientific 'facts'. A scientific education generally presupposes that science is highly valued, and therefore engagement in a topic like biotechnology is at one and the same time an expression of a set of values and of knowledge. Taking the empirical finding out of its context and concluding that with a little more scientific education the public would support biotechnology is naïve and unrealistic, as it fails to acknowledge the values that lie behind interest in the subject.

Some people will bring a different set of values to their interest in science, values which lead them to a critical view. Our evidence would suggest that such people are, at present, the minority, as the overall pattern is that engagement is associated with greater support. In this sense, engagement is one of the manifestations of particular value orientations which may vary in direction – supportive or critical – and over time.

That there is an association between higher trust and the perception of lower dread risks and a greater willingness to support food biotechnologies probably comes as no surprise. The search for trust has become a panacea in the minds of many institutions that experience difficulties with their constituents. It is an issue that goes beyond biotechnology and it is often said that there is a crisis of confidence in institutions in Western societies. While trust may be an issue, the implicit analysis, as often as not, points to the public as the problem. It is the public that do not have enough trust and to whom appropriate messages must be transmitted by credible communicators.

But trust cannot be demanded, it has to be earned. Those who seek to be trusted must work on themselves to build the preconditions for the other to regard them as trustworthy. The preconditions, or foundations of trust, include compatibility of values, competence and a record of successful risk management and public accountability. If scientists frame an issue in such a way as to exclude or to deny the relevance of the public's moral qualms, conflicts in values become apparent. Food scares challenge the perceived competence of science and the regulatory systems to identify and manage risks. And when people think that a risky technology is being forced upon them regardless, they wonder whether this serves the public interest.

In this sense it will take far more than the use of credible scientific communicators to reassure sections of the European public and to build trust in modern biotechnology.

European and national publics

This chapter has drawn on statistical analyses of the European public as a whole and separately of the publics in the European countries included in the Eurobarometer survey. It is apparent that many of the same issues are implicated in the formation of public perceptions of biotechnology across Europe, for example, levels of optimism in technology, the extent of trust in the food chain, the perception of risk and the degree of engagement in biotechnology. Across most of Europe there is widespread support for medical applications of biotechnology. But it is also very clear that there is no single European position on biotechnology as evidenced by differing public and political responses to agrifood applications of biotechnology. Here, if anything, it may be concluded that the European publics have become more polarised. In Spain, the Netherlands and Finland there is the highest level of support for GM crops and foods, while in Austria, Denmark, France and Greece the publics are opposed. Illustrating the association between public perceptions and public policy, in the former three countries the environment ministers argued for moving away from the 1999 moratorium on the commercial planting of GM crops, while in the latter group of countries the ministers supported the moratorium. From this we draw two conclusions. First, that public perceptions of biotechnology do matter, and, second, that in different countries and at different times (since we assume that public attitudes change) particular applications of biotechnology will raise public concerns, while others will not. If this is accepted, then the development of multilevel regulatory arrangements at both European and national levels will need great sensitivity.

Notes and references

1 Biotechnology and the European Public Concerted Action Group, 'Europe ambivalent on biotechnology', *Nature*, 387 (1997), pp845–7.

2 Gaskell, G, Bauer, M W and Durant, J, 'The representation of biotechnology: policy, media, public perception', in Durant, J, Bauer M W and Gaskell, G (eds), *Biotechnology in the Public Sphere: A European Source Book* (London: Science Museum, 1988), pp3–14.

3 The Eurobarometer on Biotechnology (52.1) was conducted during November 1999. The survey con-

ducted in each EU country used a multistage random-sampling procedure and provided a statistically representative sample of national residents aged 15 and over. The total sample within the EU was 16,082 respondents (weighted to 1000 per EU country, except Luxembourg represented by 600 respondents).

4   Gaskell, G, Einsiedel, E and Priest, S *et al.*, this volume, pp96–115.

5   Wagner *et al.*, 'Nature in disorder: the troubled public on biotechnology', this volume, pp80–95

6   Fischoff, B, Slovic, P, Lichtenstein, S, Read, S and Combs, B, 'How safe is safe enough? A psychometric study of attitudes towards technological risks and benefits', *Policy Sciences*, 9 (1978), pp127–52.

7   Burt, C, 'The factorial analysis of qualitative data', *British Journal of Psychology*, 3 (1950), pp166–85.

8   Converse, P E , 'The nature of belief systems in mass publics', in Apter, D E (ed.), *Ideology and Discontent* (New York: Free Press, 1964), pp206–61.

9   Greenacre, M and Blasius, J (eds), *Correspondence Analysis in the Social Sciences: Recent Developments and Applications* (London: Academic Press, 1994).

10 Durant, J, Evans, G and Thomas, P, 'The public understanding of science', *Nature*, 340 (1989), pp11–14; Evans, G and Durant, J, 'The relationship between knowledge and attitudes in the public understanding of science in Britain', *Public Understanding of Science*, 4 (1995), pp57–74; Miller, J, *The Role of Public Attitudes in the Policy Process* (New York: Pergamon Press, 1983); Miller, J, 'Scientific literacy: a conceptual and empirical review', *Daedalus*, 11 (1983), pp29–48.

11 See, for example, EU–US Consultative Forum on Biotechnology, *Final Report* (Brussels: European Commission, 2000).

12 Bodmer, W, *The Public Understanding of Science* (London: Royal Society, 1985).

13 INRA, *Eurobarometer 46.1, Les Europeens et la Biotechnologie Moderne. Draft* (1997).

14 Wynne, B, 'Knowledges in context', *Science, Technology and Human Values*, 16 (1991), pp111–21.

15 Converse, P E (see note 8).

16 Tajfel, H, 'Social stereotypes and social groups', in Tajfel, H (ed.), *Human Groups and Social Categories: Studies in Social Psychology* (Cambridge: Cambridge University Press, 1981).

17 See, for example, Fischoff *et al.* (note 6); Slovic, P, 'Perceptions of risk', *Science*, 236 (1987), pp280–85.

18 Hu, L and Bentler, P M, 'Cutoff criteria for fit indices in covariance structure analysis: conventional criteria versus new alternatives', *Structural Equation Modeling*, 6 (1999), pp1–55.

19 Not shown in the path diagram are three residual correlations that were estimated. One, e2 – e1, is described above. The other two are e5 – e8 and e6 – e9. We believe that these correlations result from the identical question format for these pairs of items about risk and encouragement.

20 Wagner, W, *et al.* (see note 5).

21 Luhmann, N, *Trust and Power* (Chichester: Wiley, 1979).

22 Barber, B, *The Logic and Limits of Trust* (New Brunswick, NJ: Rutgers University Press, 1983).

23 McCutcheon, A C, *Latent Class Analysis* (Beverley Hills: Sage Publications, 1987).

24 Wagner, W, *et al.* (see note 5).

25 For a detailed description of the analysis and the results, see Nielsen, T H, 'Behind the color code of "no"', *Nature Biotechnology*, 15 (1997), pp1320–21; Nielsen, T H, Jelsoe, E and Olsson, S, 'Traditional "blue" critique and modern "green" scepticism. On the complexity of scepticism towards modern biotechnology', in Bauer, M and Gaskell, G (eds), *Biotechnology: The Making of a Global Controversy* (Cambridge: Cambridge University Press, in press).

26 Dr Arpad Pusztai found that some rats fed on GM potatoes developed alarming side-effects, including irregular organs and immune-system damage. He claimed in a television documentary that the public were being used as 'guinea pigs' for GM food safety. His employers, Rowett Research, immediately suspended him and debate has raged ever since over the validity of his research findings.

Address for correspondence

George Gaskell, Department of Social Psychology, London School of Economics, Houghton St, London WC2A 2AE, UK. E-mail g.gaskell@lse.ac.uk

Nature in disorder: the troubled public of biotechnology

Wolfgang Wagner, Nicole Kronberger, George Gaskell, Agnes Allansdottir, Nick Allum, Suzanne de Cheveigné, Urs Dahinden, Carmen Diego, Lorenzo Montali, Arne Thing Mortensen, Uwe Pfenning, Timo Rusanen and Nina Seger

Researching public concerns

The European public: between hope and worry

The 1996 Eurobarometer survey on biotechnology indicated that public perceptions of modern biotechnology vary with respect to areas of application.[1] In general, medical and pharmaceutical applications were strongly supported, agrifood applications received at best a mixed response, and transgenic animal applications were widely opposed.

When we statistically investigated these data as well as those from the 1999 Eurobarometer survey[2] some interesting and puzzling findings emerged. While people's opinions were, in part, based on judgements regarding the 'usefulness' of the different applications, unexpectedly, perceptions of risk and safety did not appear to significantly influence levels of public support. More surprising, however, was that the most important predictor of support was whether the application was considered to be 'morally acceptable' or not.[3] Another issue was that, in respect of biotechnology's regulation, respondents from all European countries said they had more confidence in international organisations than in national institutions. These findings demanded further exploration and led to the research reported in this chapter.

Surveys, such as the Eurobarometer on biotechnology from which the above findings originated, are well indicated – to use a medical analogy – for certain research questions, for example: 'What is the distribution of opinions on an issue across a population?' However, such surveys are poorly indicated for other questions. They do not reveal what lies behind expressed opinions or which representations or currents of opinion people draw upon in making judgements on specific issues. For example, the Eurobarometer survey does not tell us what people understand by 'moral acceptability' and 'risk' as general constructs in relation to particular applications of biotechnology. Because these terms were provided by the survey itself, important questions remain about the nature of the underlying concerns to which they give voice. The phrase 'morally acceptable' may have quite different connotations when applied, for example, to GM foods and crops, as compared to transgenic animals. In addition, the phrase 'morally acceptable', even with careful translation, may have different connotations in different countries. Above all, in surveys people express their opinion by choosing the most plausible among the alternatives, which is not equivalent to being convinced of the chosen alternative. Moreover, everyday thinking is more complex, ambivalent and sometimes even contradictory.[4]

It is not only the public who frame biotechnological issues in a moral discourse. Currently, there is a great deal of interest in professional bioethics, which offers a 'top-down' (rational and deductive) approach to the clarification of the moral issues raised by applications of the technology. This is undoubtedly useful, but it runs the risk of neglecting public sentiment. The approach used in the current research was 'bottom-up'; empirical and inductive. Its objective was to understand the nature of the public concerns by exploring and adding phenomenological detail to the statistical insights gained from the 1996 Eurobarometer survey.

To explore the representations underlying public perceptions of biotechnology, a series of focus-group interviews was conducted in the following countries: Austria, Denmark, Finland, France, Germany, United Kingdom, Italy, Portugal, Sweden and Switzerland. In order to attempt the ambitious task of drawing comparative conclusions across a number of European countries, key aspects of the research – for example, the content of the moderator's topic guide, the selection of interviewees, the analysis process and the final interpretation – were a collective enterprise involving all the primary researchers in a number of meetings and two workshops. (See the methodological note below for details of the procedure.)

Focus-group discourse and representations of biotechnology

Focus-group research, while increasingly popular, is a problematic method for social scientific inquiry. There are the individual participants who contribute their opinions to the discussion, but who also react to the opinions of others and in so doing may modify their own. Consequently, the 'whole' of a focus-group talk cannot be conceptualised as merely *the sum* of individual contributions, although it does *consist* of individual contributions. The whole attains a collective quality, which transcends individual opinion and it is on this level that our interpretation focuses. Social representations theory provides a suitable starting point as a theoretical frame.[5]

The discourse-total of a focus group or even of a series of focus groups in a culturally more-or-less homogeneous sample reveals the content and structure of one or more shared discourses. A discourse reflects the way in which people re-construct and represent their local world by means of communication. One can imagine a focus group's communication as a process of symbolic 'coping', through which the group of individuals, by way of their interaction, try to come to terms with a disputed issue. The totality of any such shared discourse that becomes visible in this process is not the product of any particular individual. It is therefore not adequate to equate these discourses with the participants' opinions, arguments or attitudes. An individual does not need to share a representation in each and every detail in order to engage in the conversation of the group. Even if a person maintains an opinion that opposes or challenges a certain representation, he or she is an integral part of the collective endeavour of symbolic coping with an issue.[6]

In this sense, the following analysis takes a broader view than that of individual beliefs. Even when a particular phrase or sentence drawn for one group participant is used to illustrate a specific point, it is because the quote captures an essential part of the representational system which is typical for a shared discourse as a whole.

Although a single focus group does not capture the entire richness of representations circulating in a population's discourse, a series of such groups or interviews does in fact go some considerable way towards achieving this. The number of necessary groups is ascertained by the criterion of saturation applied to the material produced by the groups. Saturation is achieved when an additional group does not add any more *relevant* detail to the existing material. Although the saturation criterion might not have been reached in all countries, we will refer to our sample of focus groups as representing the general public in terms of the discovered discourse and representational patterns.

From the analysis of the Eurobarometer survey it was clear that some European countries are more enthusiastic about biotechnology than others. Hence, in the analysis of the group discussions we set out to explore whether different countries could be characterised by different patterns of represen-tations and concerns. In the event the similarities across countries were much more evident than the differences. Particular representations often drew upon different examples relevant to the local context, but at the core we found what can be described as a set of overlapping and common ideas that we assume to underlie public attitudes.

The chapter proceeds from a discussion of the relationship between scientific developments, public sentiments and everyday reasoning to the public's ambivalent impression of scientific and techno-logical progress and their implied threats. Medicine is identified as the realm of application where real progress is most clearly seen. Then the popular understanding of the notion of risk is presented which is based on two parallel but diverging representations of nature and life: nature seen as an animistic or spiritual force or, quasi-scientifically, as a complex and therefore uncontrollable process. Subsequently, the public's ideas about food are discussed, thereby surpassing the technocratic notion of food as a commodity. Finally, people's views about societal implications such as trust, participation in democratic processes and regulatory activities are presented. A methodological note presents the details of method.

Science: challenges to common-sense orthodoxy

Before describing what we have called the shared concerns about biotechnology, it is appropriate to typify two common forms of argumentation in the public sphere which are offered to justify a position for or against a biotechnological application. These forms of argumentation set the context both for our own findings and for some of the broader debates in contemporary society in relation to technology.

The first type of argumentation can be referred to as *religious and/or metaphysical*. Here the duties and obligations of the individual are defined by principles, the validity of which is based on superhuman or extrahuman powers. Life is God's creation and with that creation come moral absolutes and religious sanctions. God may be replaced by nature, an expression with more modern connotations but denoting an entity with a similar status as bearer of sacred values that commands our respect and obedience. Belief takes priority over scientific reasoning and beliefs together with values have their origins outside of the individual, for example in God, tradition and nature, which must all be venerated.

The second type of argumentation draws inspiration from the rise of *scientific culture and utilitarianism*. Scientific culture has its roots in the Enlightenment project according to which knowledge and reason are seen as the foundations of human happiness. Utilitarianism is an offspring of this very project. Utilitarianism anchors all value in sentient beings, in the feelings of pleasure, pain and related emotions. Along with the growing confidence through the nineteenth century that science and technology could bring solutions to most human problems, utilitarianism became a dominant ethical principle. Moral action was defined as that which provided the 'greatest good for the greatest number'. With the power of reason, humans could develop rational rules for the organisation of society. Science and scientific reasoning and the knowledge of means and ends, became the paradigm of reason, including moral reason. With ends judged on a utilitarian basis, particularly in the Anglo-Saxon world, it was proposed that a universal morality could be established on the basis of 'sound scientific argument'.

There is a long history of challenges and counter challenges between these metaphysical and scientific/utilitarian forms of argumentation. Think of Darwin *vs* Wilberforce on the ascent of man. However, towards the end of the nineteenth century, science had become the dominant cultural force, and religious and metaphysical arguments were clearly on the defensive to a point where being 'educated', 'modern', 'progressive' and 'enlightened' was almost equal to being convinced of 'the scientific world view'. Religious or metaphysical positions still had strong advocates, but in many countries they have been on retreat throughout the twentieth century, at least until the later decades.

In contemporary debates on the vexed issue of biotechnology, these old and well-known confrontations are still alive. On one hand, we find the dominant voice of 'sound science', of the 'objective' assessment of risk and the presumption of functional equivalence between GM and non-GM products.

Here science is given the unique position of both evidence and judge on matters of technology and risk; other forms of evidence are mere irrationality.

On the other hand, there are those who view biotechnology as a unique threat to both humankind and nature. A threat that symbolises the modern-day version of the horrors which beset those who first ate from the tree of knowledge. 'Playing God', 'trespassing nature's boundaries', 'committing hubris' are some of the warnings from some opponents to this instance of 'scientific progress'.

However, the hegemony of science as the highest form of truth is now meeting challenges on a number of fronts. While many still argue for a return to traditional ethics in the belief that the modern era has fallen far short of its promise to establish moral principles by reasoned argument, others in the postmodern camp argue for a relativism of science: it is but one form of truth and others are equally valid. In addition, one should not forget the question regarding the intellectual and moral integrity of scientists – industrial science is as much about profit as truth seeking. Last but not least, there are the challenges from within modern science itself. Scientific models gave safe predictions in the past, but for example the theories of complexity and chaos are now well-known scientific reasons for doubts about the possibility of predictions. In this vein, notions like the 'precautionary principle', or the likelihood of 'unknown' and even 'unknowable risks', as well as ethical and moral dimensions of science and technology are common arguments in the political discussion about biotechnology.

Interestingly, our conversations with the European public regarding biotechnology found evidence of all these arguments, from the scientific to its various challengers. Particularly in the context of medical biotechnology, technological progress is seen as a means of improving human welfare. Second, and a dominant argument among the opponents, is the necessity of venerating nature and God's handiwork. The third argument deals with moral relativism and questions the integrity of experts, whether scientists or ethicists. The fourth form is not always articulated in a sophisticated way, but it views nature as a complex system and as a result, prediction and control as beyond human capabilities.

Europeans, as we will describe in this chapter, appear to be ambivalent about technology and its impact on society. Technology is neither unambiguously good nor bad, in the shades of grey there are other forms of truth which are legitimate and persuasive. In their own terms, our interviewees are addressing, without too much confidence, one of the fundamental cleavages in today's modern society.

Biotechnology's advance: a 'runaway train'?

For the public, the development of biotechnology is probably more ambiguous and contested than any other contemporary technological development. It appears as a development that escapes the broader public's understanding and control. For most of the groups, biotechnology 'happens' without their active participation in its process. The image of a 'runaway train' captures the idea of this technology as an unstoppable and steady advance to an unknown destination; fuelled by industrial science, without control signals along the tracks, leading to the silent diffusion of genetic applications into everyday life. The public is a group of mere bystanders who cannot participate in the decision-making, consumers who cannot react to this technological innovation by informed choices, politicians who at best struggle to adapt regulation to the present state and handle it with restrictions when the train has already passed the station, and ethicists who attempt to set morally defined boundaries. The technological imperative promoted by industry seems to be over-whelmingly strong. This view is captured particularly well in the following excerpt from Austria:

> Person A: *I think one should not get into it at all* [i.e. not do genetic engineering].
>
> Person B: *That's no longer possible.*
>
> Person C: *No. I think so as well.*
>
> Person B: *Dear A, the train has departed! It is already on the tracks, at 180 km per hour!*
>
> Person A: *I'm only saying –*
>
> Person B: *You cannot stop it anymore! If you stand in its way, you will simply be run over* (laughter).

This complex issue comprises several dimensions. The lack of knowledge and information, develop-ment progressing too fast, and the thorny issue of trust and regulation, are all issues which will be dealt with later in this chapter. These issues make people feel quite helpless in their effort to cope and to come to terms with this technology.

First, biotechnology is rightly seen as unfinished business. If 'scientists have not finished their research', if 'they cannot say anything about the consequences' and if it is 'an unfinished new technology' (German), how are the general public supposed to know about these issues? The lack of scientists' in-depth understanding of their new products gives the impression of uncertainty: 'I'm afraid that at the moment there is nobody, who really knows the effects of all that; neither a scientist nor anybody else' (Austrian).

Second, the more this technology progresses, the greater the knowledge gap between science and the public: 'All the information they give us will never be sufficient,' because 'progress is too fast to allow projections for the future' (French). Effects are seen to be long term and therefore any information and knowledge gained today does not reflect any potential future consequences. While the effects of today's inventions are coming to be known, new and completely different products and their associated technological knowledge may come on to the market which invalidate today's projections. The public's lack of knowledge and information and the increasing number of new applications make people relate to older technologies. The increasing degree of progress in biotechnology is associated with greater lack of knowledge.

The perception of an accelerating technological progress is often accompanied by a nostalgia for the 'good old days', when technology had not yet invaded our lives and when food and life in general were completely 'natural', meaning pure and healthy. However, it is often acknowledged that the past cannot be brought back. An appeal to traditional values and a romanticism of a life in tune with nature frequently go hand in hand with the fatalism that unwillingly accepts modern technology as being unavoidable.

Most focus groups have, however, tried to come to terms with technological reality. They not only feel that there are reasons to withdraw from an increasingly complex world of science and technology, but clearly see that similar challenges have occurred in the past and that progress is a dilemma in itself. A considerable number of focus groups see parallels in past developments which became normalised after having been in the marketplace for a long enough time. Biotechno-logical applications 'will be everyday issues for our children', even if we 'consider them to be a nightmare today' (Finnish), but for this to happen society will need to develop coping strategies.

Other focus groups developed the idea that the improvement of human destiny has necessary costs: 'there is risk in everything we do, in progress and in any course of life…. I mean we've got cars, we've got accidents' (Italian). Progress in itself brings uncertainty, and we cannot avoid paying the appropriate price for our standards of living. Technology in itself is neutral and its consequences depend on how it is used or misused in the absence of sufficient knowledge. It is not clear who should shoulder the burden of proof because future effects are difficult to know in principle. It is a matter of choosing whether or not to accept the potentially adverse effects: 'You can never forbid the development of knowledge, even if we don't agree about everything. Knowledge has its own value' (Swedish).

The comfort provided by this reasoning, however, never lasted very long in the focus-group discussions, because 'every invention is dangerous, it is the use made of it but here it is the intrinsic dangerousness that stems from lack of knowledge. We simply do not know, and nobody knows' (Italian). As a result, the argument takes a distinctive political turn towards the issues of control and regulation, issues which are analysed later in this chapter.

Medical biotechnology as a paradigm of progress

Medical applications feature prominently in the array of biotechnology applications. These applications probably assemble more diverse subapplications than the number of crop and food applications found nowadays. Europeans have an impression of this diversity, although they appreciate that they do not fully understand all the aspects that characterise the field of medical research. Their evaluations of medical applications differ, as we found in the Eurobarometer survey. For example, genetic testing and production of medicines through GM bacteria is considered far more positive than producing xenotransplants. People all over Europe are concerned with the violation of human and animal dignity, the identity of organisms as separate species and the sanctity of living beings, as well as safety issues. These concerns have also been voiced about other biotechnological applications. Some aspects of medicine, however, warrant separate consideration.

Three aspects of the popular image of medicine set it apart from other applications. The first aspect is that 'medicine' is the prototypical example when thinking of science in general.[7] This means that medicine represents an anchor where it is *the* typical example of scientific activity, and illustrates medicine's proximity to people's lives. Medical treatment and its underlying research is probably the closest conscious encounter that an average person will have with science and its applications.

As a result, it is also thought to be better understood than other more remote fields of scientific activity. Many medical advances, even if they are produced by genetic engineering, are considered as progress and perceived as an example of positive science.

The second aspect is that medical diagnosis and treatment are experienced personally and vicariously through the media, but far less frequently than food and eating. Furthermore, while eating is normal, illness and disease are always experienced as deviations from the norm. Therefore, people on the street legitimately consider themselves to be experts in the domain of food preparation and consumption, but need to resort to the widely trusted expertise of physicians in the medical domain. At the same time, while people can envisage alternatives to GM food and crops, such as natural breeds of crops and local foods, when confronted by disease most people see no alternative than to turn to doctors and their welcome advice on what to do.

The third distinct characteristic of the medical field is its promise of relief from unpleasant conditions, even if it is an infrequent experience. Innovative, and for that matter, better medical treatment, does have a high potential to extend human wellbeing and life expectancy. Better medical treatment means emergency relief in the short term. By contrast GM foods offer no apparent benefits, beyond promises of help to the developing world, of which many Europeans are rather sceptical.

Perhaps more clearly than with other applications, in the medical field the groups weigh utility against social and moral costs. For example, if xenotransplants promise to make the stealing of Peruvian street-children's kidneys unprofitable, for example, then these transplants are welcomed. But not always. Concerns about transgenic animals lead some to discuss alternatives to xenotransplantation. 'Would it be necessary if organ donation were to be better organised?', some people wonder.

The goal of helping humans lead decent lives without suffering is worth taking some risks: 'In medicine, when it is about "repairing" humans by producing GM medicine, which would not be available otherwise, then I do have a superordinate goal. That is, I have an enormous problem which is the ill human being, whom I can hopefully cure. In this situation it is justified to take some risk' (Austrian).

Present-day resistance to biotechnology in the medical realm is therefore often seen as ephemeral: people in the past also resisted innovations which are today as self-evident as trains and syringes. As time passes, the 'new medicine' will be accepted as well and the real and the long-term benefits will only become visible in the long run.

It is when it comes to creating new life – that is using the idea of cloning animals for medical research or to help a couple have children – that people express their gravest reservations. On one hand, it is a fact that procreation is a natural activity, as is eating and drinking, and therefore should not be replaced by artificial means, especially if it involves cloning: 'The human reproduction process cannot be substituted by cloning. Instead, childless couples must cope with being childless' (Swedish). Given natural means to procreate, the new artificial methods are perceived to be superfluous and unnecessary on one hand, and at the same time socially and morally unacceptable on the other. What will parenthood look like or what will be the identity of such children in the future? On the other hand, the creation of life, whether human or other, is an act of God or nature. Man should not interfere in these realms. Some interviewees modify their reservation with political or democratic concerns such as: Who will decide which life to create and for which use? Are these creatures going to be 'robotic soldiers', 'little Einsteins' or 'designer babies'? The groups are afraid of a new eugenics movement based on these very genetic methods.

Put together, medical applications that involve genetically engineered bacteria or even cloned human cells are not covered by the above concerns. These things are not clearly identified as living beings and are therefore not part of the naturally structured 'pyramid' of visible life.

Risk, hazards and delayed effects

The ambivalence about progress, imagined as a 'runaway train', is to a large extent based on the perceived lack of expert knowledge of long-term consequences and risks. It is well known that risks which are not undertaken voluntarily, whose consequences are uncertain and which may occur a long way in the future are of far greater concern to people compared to more familiar and voluntary risks.[8] GM food and other biotechnological applications are seen to be in the former category, often described by the label 'dread'. However, the term 'risk' figures infrequently in the public's vocabulary – and even less so in its probabilistic interpretation. Instead, concerns are often voiced in words such as 'hazard', 'danger' and 'uncertainty'.

One of the most popular themes across all our groups is the idea of danger lurking in the future

caused by what we do today. There is something inherently disturbing about this uncertainty. Further, uncertainty about the future opens up a legitimised space for discussions about a range of hypothetical or contingent concerns such as environmental, social and political risks, and especially the delayed health effects: 'Well I am worried… it's the unknown, and we've mentioned cancer, the side-effects; it's things that we don't know about' (British).

There are two possible reasons why the idea of unspecified, delayed effects is such an appealing argument in discussions on biotechnology. First, it often appears that invoking an uncertain future is a comfortable way to voice non-specific concerns. Worries that are not well articulated are projected into the future. It seems to be more socially acceptable to say that you are worried about something that will happen some time in the future when you cannot explain your fear and when you are unable to put it in scientific terms. This is particularly true for many focus-group discussions about GM food.

Second, when people feel that they are incapable of evaluating the likelihood or severity of assumed dangers, they turn to experts and government in order to make the relevant judgements and to decide on the appropriate course of action to protect the public. However, many respondents believe that there have been too many examples of misplaced trust in the past to happily accept scientific reassurances pertaining to GM food and other biotechnological applications. In the UK, for example, the BSE crisis is frequently cited as a reason for fearing the introduction of a new type of food. The delayed effects of Creutzfeldt-Jakob disease on victims have been widely publicised by the mass media, and seem to be a part of the collective consciousness of the British public. It is this fact that most often provides a starting point for British thoughts about GM food: 'How would you feel if, like with BSE, five, ten, fifteen years down the line they're crippled in the hospital, lying there, horrible death' (British). The widespread awareness of BSE throughout Europe, with its images of distressing illness, clearly contributes to the feelings of unease about GM food. Another frequent anchor for discussing biotechnology and its applications is the 1986 Chernobyl accident: 'Nuclear energy was not presented as dangerous either, and now there is a place where you won't be able to live for the next 450 or 500 years without suffering' (Austrian). Whether referring to BSE, to nuclear energy or to other science and technology experiences, a lack of responsibility of those in charge is always pointed out, resulting in undesirable long-term effects: scientists being naively overconfident in their – often preliminary – findings, politicians withholding information and industry following commercial interests.

Nature's dignity and life's complexity

Nature's revenge

Whenever the focus groups refer to dangers or hazards, expressions like 'tampering', 'meddling', 'fiddling' and 'interfering' with 'nature, evolution and creation' dominate the discussions. This vocabulary expresses a strong distrust in the works of scientists and attributes a will to both nature and the life processes emphasising the moral implications. The groups demonstrated that the public debate on biotechnology is in fact deeply influenced by polarised views of nature.[9] Discussions about delayed effects, for example, frequently tend to employ an animistic twist: 'There is no need for violence against nature, nature should be respected…. Man tickles nature, tickle today and tickle tomorrow, at some point nature will rebel' (Italian). In this view, 'messing around with nature' will inevitably bring negative consequences where the forms are unpredictable at the present moment. However, there are different assumptions about whether future effects can be known in advance or not. According to the above presented delayed-effects model, predictions about nature are possible, but because new technologies are applied before sufficient knowledge about long-term effects is available, the whole process becomes problematic. Other aspects pertaining to 'nature's taking revenge' are based on the belief that future effects are in principle indeed unpredictable or that nature may be attributed intentionality. As a result, the argument takes two forms: a spiritual form and a non-spiritual form.

The spiritual form. This is the more traditional form where interfering with life and nature – two terms which are often used interchangeably – contradicts our obligation to venerate nature and life, and in particular human life. Here, nature is seen as a superior force.

The non-spiritual form. Two variants represent a non-spiritual form of the argument. An apparent scientific form is based on the elementary understanding of recent scientific insights such as chaos theory, complex systems and equilibrium theory. Here, nature is established as a complex system, life as being highly dynamic, self-regulating and continuously changing. The second form of the non-spiritual view of nature is a more mechanistic model, where nature is seen in a utilitarian way, subjected to the needs of humans. Both models assume a mutual dependency between humans and nature where it is implied that there is a need to protect nature for humankind's benefit.[10]

Finally, it must be noted that the subject of bio-technological research and application is often set apart from other parts of nature. The manipulation of life is incomparable to interfering with other inanimate materials.

Nature as a spiritual force

People arguing within the spiritual frame often express strong concerns about the idea of interfering with nature or God's creation. 'Whether you call it God or nature, I don't think that humans can do it better' (Austrian). Although expressions such as 'playing God' or 'tampering with God's creation' are frequently used in most of the groups, they rarely have religious connotations. Rather, the argument expresses an inexplicable moral sentiment or gut reaction against human hubris. In the absence of other ways of expressing moral values, religious arguments may become an important reference point. The explicit reference to religious ideas is more frequent in some Catholic countries, such as Italy, while in other countries, such as in the UK or France, such frames in fact are rare.

According to this view, nature or God are powers which deserve our respect and veneration. Everything in nature as well as in God's creation has an intended purpose; there is nothing arbitrary. There are clear limits which ought to be respected and things with which we ought not to meddle. Sometimes, nature's or God's plans may not be intelligible, since pain and suffering exist. This may be hard to accept, but we need to keep in mind that problems we try to fight may in fact have a higher purpose. Therefore, one should accept nature's way, in both good and bad times. Humans should try to live in harmony with nature, since this natural and divine order will turn out to be the best in the end, although at first sight, biotechnology promises to make life easier. According to the natural order of things, experiments are not sensible and are impudent attempts to play God which will be punished by nature taking revenge. By daring to play God we should keep in mind that he who sows the wind, reaps the storm.

People referring to the 'biotechnology is against nature' argument, feel obliged to accept and respect an existing natural (or divine) order where life in particular is viewed to be most venerable and where all forms of life must be respected. Therefore, human life is sacred and the creation of life is a natural process. Natural procreation signifies the existence of something new and unique, also known as the 'wonder of life'. Biotechnology means tampering with life's fundamentals by enabling humans to create and determine life themselves. There is still remarkable controversy over whether it is more acceptable to manipulate plants and animals as compared to humans, and at least in some countries there are frequent debates on animal rights.

With cloning, it is not so much the technique which evokes strong opposition. Cloning some human cells for medical purposes may be perfectly acceptable, but the idea of creating whole living beings which could live side by side with naturally born humans is utterly unacceptable. It is interference with natural procreation. Contrary to being unique, the outcome is a reproduction of something that already exists: it is a copy lacking any form of individuality. Similarly, genetic engineering makes it possible to determine the course of a life in such a way that destiny is no longer transcendental, but in fact designed – in a God-like manner – by human actors. Most often expressed in a cynical way, it is suspected that it will be possible to produce 'little geniuses', 'supermodels', or whatever will be considered desirable.

It is interesting to note that genetic testing, one of the most supported applications of biotechnology in the Eurobarometer survey, is discussed more ambivalently in the focus groups. In addition to the misuse of genetic information, focus groups strongly reject the possibility of deselecting 'unworthy' life at the embryonic stage. There is a strong feeling of unease because it is not up to humans to decide who should live and who not. Such discussions repeatedly end up in topics like abortion or euthanasia. If humans were able to determine human life, 'designer babies' and 'humans made to measure' which can be manufactured by a life-producing industry would result. According to this view, the human 'products' (such as 'babies chosen from a catalogue', 'human fighting machines' or 'living spare-parts depots') would then be produced for specific purposes, and then followed by commercialisation. This is considered to be an improper instrumentalisation of man, signifying a threat to human dignity and to universal human rights. Eugenics and visions of the ideal race embodied in Hitler's Aryan project serve as anchors for this viewpoint.

However, the spiritual framing of nature does not exclusively result in a clear rejection of biotechnology. Frequently, the technology is perceived in a thoroughly ambivalent way. One source of ambivalence is, for example, people's awareness that a strict prohibition of such interference would extend to many modern-day customs and practices. Furthermore, help in the form of more thorough medical intervention would be denied. The moral obligation not to interfere and the promises of modern biotechnology pose dilemmas which are hard to solve: 'I'm torn between the devil and the deep blue sea' (British). Biotechnology is presented as the old temptation where to eat from the tree of knowledge is signified as a 'devil's bargain': the strong fascination for the forbidden knowledge goes hand-in-hand with the focus groups' convictions that there will be a high price to pay.

Nature and life as complex systems

The second and, so to speak, more scientific frame, is based on popular versions of system complexity and chaotic behaviour. The argument is often not presented in a very sophisticated way, but instead refers to general statements about the systemic interrelatedness of living nature: 'Yes, because interrupting nature with one thing will affect something else, it's a knock-on effect, something that isn't always obvious straightaway' (British).

According to this argument, nature is such a highly complex system that we cannot possibly anticipate the outcomes of our interventions. Humans probably are not aware of nature's interrelated processes. Biotechnology is more critical compared to other technologies because it interferes with living nature in a mechanical way while nature itself does not follow mechanical rules. Instead, it is characterised by self-regulated and continuous change and, when left to itself, to a certain extent it is predictable. However, if we attempt to control nature, we will destroy its delicate equilibrium. Changes introduced in living beings through genetic engineering are so immediate that they evade the eternal and slow-working mechanisms which characterise natural evolution and adaptation. Effects may not only be invisible and delayed, but even occur in completely different domains from those intended. In addition, uncontrollable chain reactions may be triggered: 'When you have set in motion a certain mechanism that you don't know how to control, how can you turn back? When you have developed bacteria and you still don't have the tools, how can you block such situations because they are against nature?' (Italian). In most cases, such ideas are related to the irreversible domino effect of things spiralling out of control due to living nature's self-procreating character: 'The problem is with every other gadget, however dangerous, someone says to stop constructing it. This is not like that; these multiply by themselves' (Italian). Any artefacts in the genome will be passed on to future generations and there is no possible way to reverse it.

Unintended and irreversible effects are not expected in only environmental contexts and bacteria, but also in medical applications such as xenotransplantation or cloning, even though the dangers remain unspecified most of the time. According to this viewpoint, biotechnology is a powerful genie to be summoned – who knows if we will be able to force its undesired consequences back into the bottle?

Food: commodity or symbol?

In any survey, GM crops and particularly GM food are the most rejected biotechnological applications. What leads to the public resistance to GM products? One line of argument is that the introduction of GM foods occurred at a time of significant value changes in Europe and that genetic modification became a focal point for concerns emerging from other issues. Large segments of the European public always respected the symbolism of food in their daily life and rediscovered the role of food in healthy lifestyles over the most recent few decades. This came about owing to a complex variety of issues. These included a number of prominent health scares about food safety (salmonella in eggs and chicken, BSE in beef, and dioxins in chickens and pork), unease about the industrialisation of food production and the concerns about animal rights, food surpluses and imports from distant parts of the globe, the globalisation of the food chains in the hands of a small number of supermarkets, the emergence of global restaurant fast-food chains, and the disappearance of some traditional food such as *trippa* and some kinds of *pecorino* in Italy or unpasteurised cheese in France due to EU regulation. Greater prosperity was also a factor as people could afford to think of supporting higher standards of animal welfare and to purchase the more expensive organic and local foods.

Ironically, with increasing European integration and standardisation, large segments of the European public discovered local produce, organic or biological farming and 'slow food' as opposed to 'fast food'. This was the case in countries with the tradition of an elaborate food culture such as France and Italy, as well as in countries with a strong industrialised agricultural sector such as Germany or with an organic agricultural sector such as Austria. This tendency leads to tensions and conflicts when food is viewed purely from the perspective of safety and economics. Increasingly the public bring value orientations to decisions about food beyond its biological and nutritional characteristics. Some do not want to eat food with additives or extra doses of hormones, others resist the idea of a globalised menu of fast food where the origins of ingredients are not well documented or that is interpreted as a sign of US domination. The irradiation of food was widely rejected in Europe and the USA as this technique carried connotations of nuclear irradiation. The complaint brought up by one of our focus-group participants even merges two of these enigmatic issues by stating, 'I think that we all eat genetically radiated foodstuff all the time' (Austrian).

Linked to this issue is labelling and consumer choice. Many focus groups ponder the strong sense that they are being deprived of information about the composition of their foodstuffs by increasingly powerful supermarket chains and politicians being lobbied by the industry. There have been campaigns, and in some countries legislation, over battery hens, caged veal calves and deep-litter pigs. This resistance aligns with an increasingly more ecologically minded European public who are concerned about foods that threaten particular species such as dolphins and whales, and bring ethical considerations to food consumption.

Food's ubiquitous symbolism and meanings were rediscovered, or at least given greater emphasis, in the focus groups. Since food and eating are as old as human society it is hardly surprising that they are deeply cultural. What we are or are not prepared to eat, the ways in which food is prepared, with whom we eat it, its role in ceremonies, etc., affirm, in different groups, markers of ethnicity, social status and ideological, religious and national identity. For example, in the West the majority of people would not welcome the idea of eating dog or whale meat; in some Eastern countries the eating of pork and beef would lead to similar revulsion. Because cultures are heterogeneous and food is central to culture, people care about what they eat and what their food tastes like. A better taste that is promised by some proponents in the GM food industry is a non-issue because a 'better' taste would also be a taste that is different from Europeans' present variety of dishes.

Taste is not negotiable exactly because local foods and their tastes grew out of a long tradition of cooking that cannot be bettered by industrial means: 'Making food more durable is good, but changing the taste is not so good' (Portuguese). Therefore, despite a generalised distrust, Italian focus groups, for example, express trust in their politicians' capacities to regulate GM-food issues because they share the same values when it comes to food and tradition.

Many Europeans suspect that the so-called 'new food' is being tailored only to the needs of mass production, industry and ever longer transport routes, and they arrive at the conclusion that: 'We all start from an experience that is of food, that until now has not given us any disturbance. Why go and change the taste of food or make the tomato more nutritious? We don't need it' (Italian). The 'natural' and 'grandma's' style of preparing food becomes a shorthand for identity, for sensing oneself as belonging to a cultural group, a feeling that goes far beyond any consideration of nutritional value, WTO trading rules, or practicalities in industrial food production.

The discussion accompanying the reception of GM food has sharply increased people's awareness of their local cultural identities. GM technologies are seen as anti-cultural. At a time of an abundance of food in the West they are seen as unnecessary, perceived to be a product of the industrialisation of the food chain led by global companies with the USA in the vanguard. Those pressing the claims for GM technologies on the criterion of sound science and rejecting the demand for labelling merely reinforce the suspicion of the public that they are guinea pigs in a massive experiment. It appears to many in Europe that they are personally expected to bear unnecessary risks, and that they are socially expected to accept a further challenge to local cultures.

The resistance to GM foods is one element of a wider value change that has been triggered by the very introduction of GM food products into culturally aware countries. It is a manifestation of a rejection of the industrialisation and globalisation of food production, a rediscovery of the significance of food to healthy lifestyles and of its social and cultural meanings. Increasingly, sections of the public are showing a willingness to pay more for

traditional products and, of course, many supermarkets are catering to such enthusiasms.

Lack of information and lagging regulation

What was previously regulated by forms of custom, tradition and values[11] is replaced by rational decision-making in modern society, or so it is thought. In this way the future becomes less transparent and more probabilistic, particularly if the topic of decision is as complex as biotechnology. The very idea of risk is bound to the aspiration to calculate, to control and to decide about the future. Therefore, uncertainty and ambiguity are distinctive characteristics of future-oriented decision-making such as the regulatory measures taken by national governments. This is clearly recognised by our focus groups.

At this point, it should be clear that concerns about trust, responsibility and regulation cannot be separated from the topics reported earlier in this chapter. What is being presented here is a set of conclusions which our focus groups extract from different vantage points, such as fears regarding the rapid technological development and the future dangers, as well as from the nature and life models regarding biotechnology.

Regulation, responsibility and trust

What is strongly felt and expressed by the groups is the need to regulate biotechnology. There were a number of reasons brought forward to justify this position: the perceived non-existence of regulation, inappropriate existing regulation, moral issues, and the need to regulate product labelling in order to enable consumers to make informed choices. In addition, an important argument was the existence of unknown risks that require special caution as mentioned in a previous section.

The demand for regulation applies to both industry and scientists, and requires effective control bodies. However, the groups recognised that there are inherent difficulties or obstacles to effective regulation. A first obstacle is the speed of scientific and technological development which hinders proactive moves. In contrast, it seems that regulation is able to manage present and past development but in a reactive way. A second obstacle was identified as the need for international coordination and harmonisation which results in compromise solutions. A third obstacle was seen in the relative powerlessness of democratic institutions compared to multinational companies.

Because biotechnology is seen as containing unknown dangers, manifested only at some point in the future, people turn to experts and governments to make the relevant judgements and to decide on the appropriate course of action to protect the public. In other words, in this case uncertainty leads to an ambivalent form of trust – trust of those in whom the public needs to trust. But for many it appears that 'too many things have gone wrong in the past, all the things that we've eaten and taken and then suddenly they've come up with something that's got a problem, and you've thought to yourself well I thought that was tested, that's why I took this pill' (British). Hence, there are too many examples of misplaced trust in the past to enable happy acceptance of scientific reassurance about GM food and other applications of biotechnology.

This feeling is even expressed as a 'gut reaction', a feeling of unease, which seems to indicate that, on the one hand, for some people the idea that scientific knowledge is contingent and provisional may also be a familiar and well-understood one. On the other hand, at issue may also be the trustworthiness of scientists and politicians to reveal the dark side of the new developments that might point to potential problems,[12] such as in the history of the British BSE crisis.

Although the focus groups did not develop a very clear idea about which specific body should be in charge, they had a clear view on the standards – such as competence, independence and trust-worthiness – that a regulatory institution ought to meet. On these closely related criteria many of the key actors in the biotechnology debate were viewed to fall short.

The biotechnology industry, with its understand-able pursuit of profit, was seen as neither independent nor trustworthy. More ambivalence was attributed to public science, represented by universities. Sometimes, science was associated more with basic research, and sometimes more with economic and political interests due to its financial dependence. Similarly, government institutions were judged to occupy a middle position, where they are neither totally dependent on nor independent of industry. The media was seen as dependent on industry and politics, and also on 'headline hunting'. As a result, the information provided by the media was also perceived as problematic. Only consumer or environmental organisations received high levels of trust arising from their perceived independence. At the same time however, they were frequently perceived to be a voice of opposition which lacks real power and sometimes even competence to be influential.

An important obstacle for trusting institutions was the lack of transparency in biotechnology policy. People felt as though they were being 'kept in the dark and fed on shit' (British). Industry's resistance to labelling GM food was judged as a conspiracy indicator because 'it's already here, but we don't get any information, we don't know what we are eating and how it might affect the next generation' (Swedish). This lack of trust was closely linked to the issue of power. Against big industry, for example, 'People can't do anything about it.... Whenever they say, "Now we have started cloning" or "We now produce maize," then it will be done. It's definite and we can't do anything about it' (Swiss).

Another frequent obstacle to trust was that most of the key actors were seen as having too much of a financial interest in the technology. 'Who could resist the temptation of making money? Not scientists, not politicians, not writers nor Greens, some of them are surely corrupt' (French). For the focus groups, this assumption of strong economic interest reduced the credibility of any other motivation to engage in biotechnology. 'You know very well that [transgenic] corn is not for the developing world, it is for making money' (French).

The focus groups were at the same time aware of their dependency on experts since the topic's complexity requires expert knowledge and specialists. People want to trust, but the trustworthiness of scientists is viewed ambivalently. In general, however, many focus groups believe that biotechnology cannot be regulated on a national basis since it is an object of international business where it develops and it changes at high speed. It is associated more closely with commercial interests, meaning the profit of the involved enterprises, than with a motivation to improve people's welfare. This is not a far cry from assuming conspiracy in any informational and regulatory activity, especially on the national level.[13]

In this scenario, consumers have no basis for free choice, they cannot rely on state regulations and, above all, they feel like guinea pigs in a global experiment which might get out of hand if their fears are not taken seriously by the experts. Because of this, any institution which needs to regulate biotechnological issues should be interdisciplinary and international. Such a body is imagined to be less biased, more competent and to have global influence. However, at the same time, such an international body is also perceived to be a double-edged sword, since it could threaten national identities.

Democratic participation and consumer rights

The recent debates on risks, however, point to the necessity of discourses transcending the simple information pertaining to potential hazards. This form of communication requires a more direct input from experts, stakeholders and members of the public. In this sense, many focus groups expressed a strong desire for wider coverage and more in-depth public discussion: 'They obviously must talk to the people. They are going to have to do a bit more hard work on it to present it to the public' (British). Such a discussion could allow each group to voice their interests and values and at the same time reach a common understanding regarding the problem and the potential solutions. In this sense, participation is not only a normative democratic goal, but it is also a requirement of rational decision-making where uncertainty evaluation is part of the management effort. Therefore, public debates must have democratic consequences, such as referenda. 'There should be a referendum on whether people in Finland support any GM food. People should vote for or against that' (Finnish). This view was widely shared by most focus groups.

Debates and enlightenment are also necessary for consumers to be able to exercise their right to informed choice. This right is not exercised at present because of the lack of credible information, and perceived lack of information leads to the rejection of any suspicious product. Some focus groups were 'afraid that something is declared as biotechnology and [the people] don't understand it. [They] need more information' (Swiss). However, if given the choice between GM and non-GM products, most focus groups agreed that people would vote for non-GM food, resulting in a reduction of GM sales. This is often assumed to be the real reason behind industry's resistance to label GM products. Hence, the crucial point is the consumer's right and ability to reject GM food.

In contrast, consumer choice in the medical realm was considered to have different implications: individual choice from the available medical offerings was accepted by many focus groups. 'It's true that if someone has the choice between dying and having a heart that was put in a pig [*sic*] and it has to be transplanted, if he chooses to take that heart, why should it be immoral?' (French). In contrast to food, focus groups were ambivalent towards strict regulatory measures in medicine. The problem is depicted as one of a minority of people suffering from specific diseases and the majority of healthy people being sceptical towards biotechnology. Having a general ban on biotechnology was considered to be unacceptable.

Conclusions: culture, discontentment and politics

We set out to investigate the basic concerns of the European public regarding biotechnology, traces of which appeared in the two Eurobarometer surveys conducted in 1996 and 1999. With the use of focus groups, an impression of how local discourse unfolds in a partly controlled setting was achieved. While the actual results of focus-group discussions varied both in content quantity and quality, of course, it was surprising to see how much the ten European countries have in common. When it comes to the basic questions pertaining to nature and life, or fear of global technology and economic developments, the European public implicitly demonstrate shared cultural roots. These roots transcend national boundaries, language barriers and north–south contrasts.

Even though these countries do have much in common, it must not be forgotten that local variations do exist. Divergence exists with respect to local foundations which relate to specific European or national subcultures and experience. Such anchors are, for example, the frequent references to BSE in the British focus groups, the 'Belgian Blue' (a non-GM breed of cattle with unnatural body features yielding more meat) in the Swedish groups, and other local metaphors for science or agriculture 'gone mad'. But these are located on a quite superficial level well above the substratum of Greco-Roman and Judeo-Christian undercurrents, which shapes the majority of European mentalities.

Summarising the string of quite often impressively sophisticated arguments and their cultural bases in the focus groups results in the following: in all mentioned countries, biotechnology is introduced to the field of an existing culture. This culture is constituted by a series of representations and associated beliefs, attitudes as well as affective and emotional underpinnings. The relevant representations in the present context are ideas and images regarding the workings of nature and life, as well as their general cultural significance and the interdependent stability of a multitude of other representational systems. Put together, the widely shared representational systems and practices determine the feeling of cultural 'belongingness' and, hence, identity. Economic and technological innovations are always being introduced to this field and their ability to be understood depends heavily upon the cultural symbolic system. In the course of history the interpretative repertoire is, of course, steadily enriched by innovations and their symbolic fields, where the technologies that became common good are now familiar.

All biotechnological applications, whether agricultural or medical, are thrown together into the cultural field. When discussing medical applications, the discourse of the focus groups tended toward the notions of progress in medicine to heal untreatable diseases, the concerns of the new technology rushing on like a 'runaway train' where the public does not have any chance to catch up in order to understand or to have influence, and lesser concerns about safety and unknowable delayed effects. The mention of agricultural and food applications triggered concerns about ecology and other future hazards (the explicitly cultural frame: 'nature hitting back'), the 'runaway train', and also a rejection of 'novel food' based on cultural identity.

Concerns about whom to trust, whom to entrust with regulation and how to participate as citizens and consumers in this development were triggered by all realms of discourse: progress in medicine, the lack of knowledge due to rapid developments, the idea of delayed hazards, and the threat to identity through novel food. Finally, the ideas of biotechnological development being a runaway train and having delayed effects stimulated each other mutually.

Among the four discursive realms – delayed effects, 'runaway train', medicine as progress, and trust together with regulation – a difference in the degree to which cultural images determine the groups' discussions appears. The high degree of moral rejection pertaining to certain biotechnological applications, which we observed in the two Eurobarometer surveys, is primarily owing to the image of 'nature as a spiritual force'. This image carries powerful sacred connotations that are valid not only for the expressly religious, but also for the more secular public. Hence, the icon stands for our deeply ingrained heritage of moral reasoning vis-à-vis life in general. No other image is as strong as this one in our focus groups, notwithstanding the 'nature and life as a complex system' model. This last-mentioned form of justifying one's arguments can be seen as being derived from the former image. It is derivative in the sense of being informed by the popularised versions of recent

scientific discoveries such as chaos and attractor theory, systems theory, etc. The basic notion of nature being a complex system and therefore unpredictable in the long run reminds us of the traditional image of humans' limited knowledge. Both are part of the European cultural heritage.

Another striking feature of the groups is the way in which discussions on the subject of biotechnology were associated with a variety of other more-or-less related topic areas. Although biotechnology is not well understood, and perhaps even because of this, other issues that might be termed contemporary discontentments of society came into focus in the groups. These included more general discussions about the industrialisation of agriculture, trust in the political process and in politicians, the pressures of globalisation on culture, the natural environment and transnational institutions. On these, the groups talked as citizens and often as citizens with real concerns about present and future prospects for society. In this sense those applications of biotechnology that are disapproved of have become emblematic: merely another case of things going wrong and the contemporary ills of society.

As we have reported, our groups represent medical biotechnology in terms of the value of alleviating disease and the amelioration of human suffering. But at the same time the representations of food biotechnology, cloning and more general issues around the speed of development and the regulation of biotechnology reflect some deep-seated concerns that cannot be dismissed as merely ephemeral anxieties. It is notable that these concerns are widely held across our groups and are voiced by even those who are inclined to express support for biotechnology. It has been said that the public must come to terms with biotechnology, our findings point to the need for biotechnology and its proponents to come to terms with the public.

The public's concerns will not be alleviated by reassurances that all aspects of the technology are safe. On one hand, there is the relative absence of trustworthy experts. The conditions for trust need to be rebuilt with independent experts who are seen to be able to regulate effectively and proactively. On the other hand, the public's concerns extend beyond the narrow criteria of health and safety. Cloning is a case in point. This is represented as a fundamental challenge and threat to the moral and natural order – as almost a *sui generis* danger to the very fabric of society.

Yet, at the same time the public are not anti-science. Although many admit with some regret that they are poorly informed, they appreciate the role of scientific research in the systematic testing of new developments. The perception that some applications of biotechnology are going ahead before such research has been completed is evidence of confidence in science as a system of knowledge acquisition.

We have also seen the paradox of information. In itself, the strategy of science communication in the sense of public relations is not the answer to public concerns, yet without information or when information is perceived to be withheld, trust is the victim.

The findings from our inquiry into the concerns of the European public point to the need for a dual commitment on the part of the key actor groups involved in modern biotechnology: one commitment to transparency in science and technology, in regulatory debates and in regulation, and another to openness to hear and to accommodate the public's concerns. Such a dual commitment would be evidence of institutional learning, another precondition for both trust and the knowledge that biotechnology is in safe hands.

Methodological note

This chapter is based on a number of focus groups[14] which were conducted in Austria, Denmark, Finland, France, Germany, the United Kingdom, Italy, Portugal, Sweden and Switzerland. In each country, a minimum of four focus groups included, on average, 5–8 discussants per group. The focus-group participants were not selected to be statistically representative of the public of any country. The aim was rather to collect the significant currents of

Table 1. Number, dates, locations and criteria of composition of focus groups

Country	Number of groups (total number of participants)	Dates	Locations	Criteria for group composition
Austria	8 (54)	July 1999, November 1999 through January 2000	Vienna, Innsbruck, Linz	Age, education, region, interest in biotechnology (participants having visited an exhibition on genetic engineering), mothers of small children, interest in economy.
Denmark	6 (42)	September 1999 through April 2000	Copenhagen, Aars, Naestved, Aalborg, Kolding	Education levels, social engagement and political interests.
Finland	5 (17)	January, February 2000	Kuopio	Age, education levels.
France	4 (26)	June, November 1999	Paris	Education levels.
Germany	5 (42)	September 1999, March 2000	Jena, Stuttgart	Education levels, family status.
Italy	6 (36)	September through December 1999	Naples, Milan, Verona, Rome, Torino, Bari	Area of residence, level of education, humanistic vs scientific education, religious orientation, political orientation, profession.
Portugal	4 (23)	July, November 1999	Lisbon	Education levels, family status.
Sweden	4 (20)	September 1999, January 2000	Östersund	Age, education levels.
Switzerland	4 (29)	August through November 1999	Zürich	All groups mixed by sex, age, education and attitudes towards biotechnology.
United Kingdom	4 (26)	July, December 1999	London	Age, children in household, education, newspaper readership.

opinion in a particular country and to chose people who were likely to articulate the range of such currents of opinion. In most countries, previous research had shown age, gender and level of education as being associated with characteristically different opinions on biotechnology, and these, therefore, were used as selection criteria. In addition, the researchers in different countries used local knowledge to specify additional criteria aimed at maximising the range of currents of opinion (Table 1). Participants were recruited by commercial companies or by the researchers themselves. Participants were paid an incentive at the end of the discussion.

The content of the moderator's topic guide drew results from the Eurobarometer, from relevant literature as well as from pilot interviews. As expected, these pilot interviews showed that few people have readily available and detailed arguments to explain what lies behind their opinions, and in particular that moral concerns are often embedded in tacit knowledge. To elucidate the underlying 'representations', a variety of indirect questioning techniques were designed, for example, free associations to keywords and card-sorting tasks based on different applications of modern biotechnology. These proved to be useful stimuli, acting as catalysts for discussions within the focus groups. Further, moderators were encouraged to focus on these issues in order to enable comparative analyses, but to feel free to explore context-specific topics and arguments.

Group discussions were audiotaped and/or videotaped and subsequently transcribed verbatim. The transcripts were analysed using one of the computer programs ATLAS/ti or NUD*IST and following a common coding frame.

The coding frame was developed by the team of closely cooperating researchers. The frame involved a series of hierarchical structures for each of ten principal codes, such as trust, risk, moral, regulation, information, etc. For each principal code (e.g. trust), the next level captured the related emergent themes (e.g. existential trust, reasons for distrust). Next, all text units under each theme were identified and finally a small number of exemplary quotations were selected. Having completed this text 'decomposition', any significant commonalties across the ten principal codes were identified. Each country team then wrote a narrative account of the broader currents of opinion for each principal code, and noted any common elements across codes.

The final task, and the one that is reported in this chapter, involved comparing and contrasting the results of the analyses of the different European countries. This was the work of a two-day workshop in which, having analysed and interpreted the national data, the group set out to explore whether, in general, countries had unique concerns, or whether there were some concerns common across a number of countries. In this event we found a number of rather similar representations or currents of opinion about the issue of biotechnology across all the countries. However, these were often rooted or illustrated in the context of particular national events or experiences. The result was a collection of typical models regarding biotechnology concerns, related to different issues circulating in European countries.

Notes and references

1 Gaskell, G and Eurobarometer Research Team, 'Europe ambivalent on biotechnology', *Nature*, 387 (1997), pp845–7.

2 Gaskell, G, Allum, N, Bauer, M, Durant, J, Allansdottir, A, Bonfadelli, H, Boy, D, de Cheveigné, S, Fjaestad, B, Gutteling, J M, Hampel, J, Jelsoe, E, Correia Jesuino, J, Kohring, M, Kronberger, N, Midden, C, Nielsen, T H, Przestalski, A, Rusanen T, Sakellaris, G, Torgersen, H, Twardowski, T and Wagner, W, 'Biotechnology and the European public', *Nature Biotechnology*, 18 (2000), pp935–8; and this volume.

3 Gaskell, G, Bauer, M W and Durant, J, 'Public perceptions of biotechnology in 1996: Eurobarometer 46.1', in Durant, J, Bauer, M W and Gaskell, G (eds), *Biotechnology in the Public Sphere: A European Source Book* (London: Science Museum, 1998), pp189–214.

4 Billig, M, Condor, S, Edwards, D, Gane, M, Middleton, D and Radley, A, *Ideological Dilemmas* (London: Sage, 1988).

5 Bauer, M and Gaskell, G, 'Towards a paradigm for research on social representations', *Journal for the Theory of Social Behaviour*, 29 (1999), pp163–86; Moscovici, S, 'Notes towards a description of social representations,' *European Journal of Social Psychology*, 18 (1988), pp211–50; Wagner, W, Duveen, G, Farr, R, Jovchelovitch, S, Lorenzi-Cioldi, F, Marková, I and Rose, D, 'Theory and method of social representations', *Asian Journal of Social Psychology*,

2 (1999), pp95–125; Gaskell, G, 'Individual and group interviewing', in Bauer, M W and Gaskell, G (eds), *Qualitative Researching with Text, Image and Sound* (London: Sage, 2000).

6 Wagner, W, 'Social representations and beyond – brute facts, symbolic coping and domesticated worlds', *Culture and Psychology*, 4 (1998), pp297–329; Wagner, W and Kronberger, N, 'Killer tomatoes! Collective symbolic coping with biotechnology', in Deaux, K and Philogene, G (eds), *Representations of the Social* (Oxford: Blackwell, 2001).

7 Bauer, M, 'The medicalisation of science news – from the rocket–scalpel to the gene–meteorite complex', *Social Science Information*, 37 (1998), pp731–51; Durant, J, Evans, G and Thomas, G P, 'Public understanding of science in Britain: the role of medicine in the popular representation of science', *Public Understanding of Science*, 4 (1992), pp57–74.

8 Slovic, P, 'Perception of risk', *Science*, 236 (1987), pp280–5.

9 Douglas, M, *Risk and Blame. Essays in Cultural Theory* (London: Routledge, 1992); Descola, P, 'Constructing natures: symbolic ecology and social practice', in Descola, P and Pálsson, G (eds), *Nature and Society. Anthropological Perspectives* (London: Routledge, 1996), pp82–102.

10 Descola, M (see note 9).

11 Weber, M, *The Protestant Ethic and the Spirit of Capitalism*, translated from German by Parsons, T (New York: Scribner, 1958).

12 Wynne, B, 'Misunderstood misunderstandings: social identities and public uptake of science', in Irwin, A and Wynne, B (eds), *Misunderstanding Science. The Public Reconstruction of Science and Technology* (Cambridge: Cambridge University Press, 1996).

13 Compare Wynne, B (see note 12).

14 Krueger, R A, *Focus Groups. A Practical Guide for Applied Research*, 2nd edn (Thousand Oaks: Sage, 1994); Morgan, D L and Krueger, R A, *The Focus Group Kit*, vols 1–6 (Thousand Oaks: Sage, 1998).

Address for correspondence

Professor Wolfgang Wagner, Kepler Universität Linz, Institut fuer Pädagogik und Psychologie, Altenbergerstrasse 69, A-4040 Linz, Austria. E-mail w.wagner@jk.uni-linz.ac.at

Troubled waters: the Atlantic divide on biotechnology policy

George Gaskell, Edna Einsiedel, Susanna Priest, Toby Ten Eyck, Nick Allum and Helge Torgersen

Introduction

On both sides of the Atlantic biotechnology has long been promoted by governments as a strategic technology of the twenty-first century. Yet the contrast between the fortunes of biotechnology in North America and Europe is striking. Ernst & Young show that the European medical or 'red' biotechnology sector is dwarfed in comparison to the USA.[1] In terms of market capitalisation, revenues, R&D and the number of employees, Ernst & Young report a widening Atlantic gap. For the 'green' or agricultural sector of biotechnology, the picture is even more stark. Many different varieties of GM crops have been extensively introduced in North America, while in Europe, from 1999 on-wards, no permissions for the commercial planting of GM crops have been issued, field trials have been disrupted by protest groups and the 90/220/EC directive has been rewritten incorporating a variety of new and more stringent conditions.

This transatlantic divide has been the focus of widespread speculation in newspapers, academic journals, and national and international bodies, and has led to policy and trade conflicts. In 2000, then US President Clinton and European President Prodi launched an initiative to attempt to resolve the conflict. The EU–US Biotechnology Consultative Forum was established to 'consider the full range of issues of concern in biotechnology in the United States and the European Union'. The Forum made 22 recommendations which it hoped would have a positive impact in the short to medium term. However, it is not clear whether the new US administration will retain an interest in the Forum's work.

In this chapter our objective is to explore why biotechnology has made easy headway in the North America, while in much of Europe it has been the subject of political and public controversy.

Our procedure follows the example of a political scientist, Robert Putnam.[2] We identify a number of 'frequently cited explanations' for the transatlantic biotechnology divide which we have encountered in the literature, at conferences and in the media.

These we subject to critical scrutiny. Our analysis has been informed by three sources of data that are available to us. First, we can compare public perceptions in the USA, Canada and Europe (for simplicity we will refer to these as regions) using the Eurobarometer survey; second, we have comparative time-series analyses of the elite media coverage in the three regions; third, we have details of key policy-making in the three regions; and finally, we draw on our expert knowledge from social science and from years of engagement in research on biotechnology in the public sphere.

The frequently cited explanations are in three overlapping categories reflecting our conception of the public sphere, as outlined in the introduction to this volume: those explanations concerned with differences in policy regimes and regulation, those with the role of the media and finally those that focus on public perceptions. While we assume that these foci are not autonomous, but impact upon each other in complex ways, we will pragmatically consider the three categories of explanations separately.

Although we judge that our comparative data sets go beyond those that have been available to most researchers who have addressed the issue, we must sound a note of caution. Policy and regulation, media coverage and public perceptions reflect and constitute a specific cultural context. Some characteristics of the three regions, which may be very relevant to the explanation of the transatlantic biotechnology divide, are not captured in our data. Hence, hypotheses derived from such explanations remain untestable for the present. In other words, while we may be able to reject some of the frequently cited explanations that are currently in circulation, we have modest aspirations regarding the identification of the cause or causes of the transatlantic divide. Now we turn to frequently cited explanations, in the three categories of policy and regulation, media coverage and public perceptions (summarised in Table 1).

Table 1. Summary of frequently cited explanations for the transatlantic divide

Policy and regulation

- R&D policies have been more favourable to biotechnology in North America than in Europe.

- North American regulatory climate has had a favourable impact on the development of biotechnology.

- Transparency is greater in North America and fosters confidence in biotechnology.

- North American strategy on risk and uncertainty has been more conducive to the development of biotechnology.

- Contrasting structures and roles of the agricultural sector on either side of the Atlantic shaped responses to biotechnology.

Media

- Tabloid sensationalism fomented European opposition.

- A 'spiral of silence' condition made dissent less visible in North America in comparison to Europe.

- The European press framed biotechnology less favourably.

Public perceptions

- Europeans are technophobic.

- Europeans oppose all genetic manipulation.

- Europeans are irrational about risks.

- BSE turned the European public against green biotechnologies.

- North Americans trust their food chain more than Europeans.

Other explanations

- Images of the environment.

- Food, culture and identity.

- The role of interest groups.

Policy and regulation

R&D policies

It has been suggested that North American agencies are better geared up to support R&D in biotechnology than their equivalents in Europe. Governments in both Canada and the USA have played key roles in developing the research base for biotechnology. In the USA, the National Institutes of Health (NIH) have been substantial funders of biomedical research since the 1970s. The US Department of Agriculture (USDA) has also played a major role in the support of agricultural biotechnology research, particularly to the land grant institutions. The continuing role of the Department of Energy and NIH in supporting research into the human genome accounts, to some extent, for success in mapping the human genome earlier than expected. Support from these agencies for the Human Genome Project increased 14-fold to about US $400 million (about UK £270 million) from 1988 to 2001.[3] Since the early 1980s, the Canadian government has played a key role in supporting the establishment of collaborative research networks between industry, government and universities. Genomics research recently received a boost with the provision by the federal government of US $200 million (UK £137 million) for a four-year national programme.

Several organisational issues contributed to biotechnology R&D flourishing more rapidly in the USA than in Europe. These include the high level of integration among key actors including universities, industry, and related institutions such as hospitals. This early collaboration among diverse actors led to closer connections between basic research efforts and clinical applications, in turn promoting the growth of small firms and attracting venture capital. These networks of actors developed into active regional clusters, promoting rapid progress from research to commercialisation.[4] On the policy side, the Bayh-Dole Act passed by the US Congress encouraged universities to collaborate with commercial concerns to promote patenting and the utilisation of inventions arising from federal funding.

In Europe, on the other hand, the emphasis on scientific specialisations, the individualistic roles played by elite research institutes, and the lack of collaboration among actors from different sectors contributed to a slower pace of research and development.[5] The consequences of these organisational differences are telling: expenditures on R&D are about one-third of the US figure and the number of patent applications granted is far smaller, albeit that the conditions for the granting of a patent in Europe are generally more stringent. In 1998, 147,000 patents were granted in the USA and 36,718 by the European Patent Office.[6] In 1998, total equity financing in the EU was about US $900 million (UK £615 million) while in the USA it was about US $4.5 billion (UK £3 billion).[7] In terms of number of employees in 1998, the USA had 140,000 in the biotechnology sector; in contrast, the EU and Canada had 46,000 and

10,000 respectively.[8] While the European Commission was engaged in creating uniform and supportive conditions to boost the development of biotechnology, implementation was slower and faced more challenges. The European biotechnology sector still suffers from structural inadequacies including 'insufficient collaboration between academia and industry, lack of coordination of research across member states, shared access to resources and infrastructure, and inadequate venture capital'.[9] It is clear that the USA enjoyed a first-mover advantage in biotechnology R&D. And the speed with which biotechnology was developed in North America was enhanced by unique organisational and structural arrangements and policy initiatives which, in turn, led to faster commercialisation efforts. We cannot reject the frequently cited explanation that R&D policies have been more favourable to biotechnology in North America than in Europe.

North America's regulatory climate is more favourable to biotechnology

The introduction of biotechnology proceeded much more gradually in North America than in Europe, allowing both public opinion and regulatory procedures to adjust over a longer period of time. With the discovery by American scientists that genes could be introduced from one species to another, the scientific community went through a period of reflection and debate in the famous Asilomar meetings in the early 1970s. This led to the first guidelines developed by the NIH in 1975, designed to provide strict containment procedures for experiments using recombinant methods. In part these guidelines were adopted to pre-empt government regulation that might have interfered with academic freedom.[10] These guidelines have been modified over the years but are still in place and were among the first efforts to regulate biotechnology. British scientists, also at Asilomar, helped to influence the development of similar guidelines in the UK.

Experience with the first federally sanctioned field test of a genetically engineered microorganism occurred in 1987. This was the field test of ice-minus bacteria on strawberries, conducted after five years of regulatory review.[11] Local public attention to this event was high with the media providing extensive coverage. Citizens in Monterey, California were opposed to the test site and legal action was mounted by Jeremy Rifkin's Foundation on Economic Trends, and Californians for Responsible Toxics Management. Environmental groups sabotaged some of the early field trials and local

media coverage highlighted a range of risks. However, the court rejected petitions to halt the trials and the EPA introduced an assessment strategy that helped to calm fears.[12] In general, these events did not arouse much attention in the national media. The rBST commercialisation controversy in the 1980s was a further significant event in the evolution of biotechnology in the USA. From the sheer volume of studies on the issue, it is perhaps the most intensively examined case from a policy, scientific, and public point of view.

In essence, the controversy centred on issues that were also being raised in Europe: risks for human health, animal welfare issues, impacts on small farms, and effects on the domestic dairy industry.[13] However, consumer concerns were attenuated in part by scientific assessments suggesting no negative impacts on human health, credible third parties such as the American Cancer Society echoing these findings, a voluntary labelling system allowing consumer choice, and the post-approval monitoring programme that was carried out. The proximity of Canada to the USA and the ubiquity of US media gave Canadians direct exposure to these various controversies and their associated issues. Canadians went through a milder debate over rBST. In general, the American experiences provided lessons for Canada. In a replay of assessments of rBST elsewhere, Canadian expert committees convened to assess the impacts of this hormone found no adverse impacts on human health but concluded that there were deleterious effects on animal health.[14] Because quotas were still in place for the dairy industry, concerns about animal welfare were also a convenient reason for rejecting rBST use in Canada.

During this entire period from the 1980s through the early 1990s, there was regulatory attention to biotechnology as a potentially risky issue, participation was high among key stakeholders and the debates were very much in the public arena (in the media, the courts, through public documentation). As noted by Krimsky and Wrubel:[15]

> It is fair to say that the level of pre-market public scrutiny of some of the first products of agricultural biotechnology has been unprecedented.... The policy issues in agricultural biotechnology have been exceptionally well articulated in diverse media sources. In part, this may be due to the fact that at no time in modern history has a society had so many 'watchdog' groups made up primarily of nonprofit advocacy organizations dedicated to promoting an idea, a way of life, or simply democratic participation in technological decisions.

The Krimsky and Wrubel description holds true for the 1980s, a period in which there were conflicts among the FDA, the USDA and the US Environmental Protection Agency (EPA) about institutional responsibilities and competencies regarding the regulation of biotechnology in general, and agricultural biotechnology in particular. Since the middle of the 1990s there has been a trend towards decreasing interest in environmental issues and a stronger emphasis on free trade and competitive-ness in general, which was much more pronounced in the USA and Canada than in most European countries.

Europe also saw a number of controversies over biotechnology, but these varied by country. For example, in Denmark and Germany, debate in the mid-1980s was lively around the 'contained use' of GMOs for the production of insulin and the human growth hormone. In the Netherlands, where the first 'deliberate releases' were approved in 1988, protesters destroyed experimental crops. While both North America and Europe saw localised protests, perhaps the significant difference was the locus of regulation. The European countries, developed their own regulations and ways to deal with biotechnology, which then had to be harmonised on a EU level. National idiosyncrasies were exported to the EU, while lobbying activities from all sides made use of intra- and international conflicts, as well as of those among EU institutions such as the different Directorates General, the European parliament and the European Council. In contrast to the multilevel system in Europe, US policy developed in a more homogeneous way in a more-or-less single-level system. Like the conflicts between different Directorates General in the European Commission there were tensions between the FDA, the USDA and the EPA. But in the USA these were ironed out by a governmental decision under the impetus of competitiveness. With Europe's more complex multilevel system, this was not a feasible option.

A further difference is the content of regulation, which pertains less to the substantial criteria for risk assessment rather than to the necessity to undergo such an assessment. In the USA, all transgenic organisms are regulated under existing legislation and there is a presumption that regulatory oversight is unnecessary unless there is a reason to anticipate a risk. Products have only to be investi-gated if they lack 'substantial equivalence' defined in terms of a change in nutritional components or allegenicity. By contrast, in the EU transgenic organisms are regarded as novel on account of the process of genetic manipulation. As such new regulatory mechanisms were set up and access to permission for market placement, especially for products, is demanding, although in principle there is a 'fast track' procedure as well. So in comparison, while the scientific criteria for an assessment are not that different between Europe and the USA, the way the criteria are applied differs greatly. Overall, we cannot reject the hypothesis that the North American regulatory climate has had a favourable impact on the development of biotechnology.

Transparency cultivates public confidence in innovation

It has been suggested that the transparent style of policy-making in North America facilitates techno-logical innovation by fostering public confidence.

Transparency in how government decisions are made is an important feature of trust in institutions. In the USA, regulatory decisions by government institutions are often subject to legal challenge. This forces them to have persuasive arguments available, if possible in quantified and scientific terms, to support their positions. Federal agencies are mandated to announce regulatory intent in the *Federal Register* and public comments are solicited prior to final drafting of legislation.[16] For field tests of transgenic plants expressing plant pesticides, for instance, the developer is required to consult with the EPA on data requirements and at the same time, the EPA notifies the public and invites comment in the *Federal Register*. Before commercial distribution of a genetically engineered crop, public notification is also required and comment solicited.[17]

This tradition of openness is supported by legal frameworks such as 'sunshine laws' which require public bodies to hold their meetings in public, and 'freedom of information' legislation which allows individuals or organisations to access additional administrative files. In Canada, transparency is also required for rule-making, and publication in *Canada Gazette* is the primary mechanism for public notification. Legislation on access to information, although more recent, parallels the Freedom of Information Law in the USA. However, government agencies have some way to go in terms of openness, with institutional decisions governing approval of new biotechnology products still not as open as in the USA and opportunities for public input considered minimal or non-existent. A comparative assessment of public accountability and transparency on biotechnology regulation puts the USA and Australia as the most open.[18] Furthermore, a complex array of sanctions encourages food producers, manufacturers and retailers to ensure product safety. This complex of criminal and civil sanctions including tort and contractual tools can be used by government or private parties (individuals, public-interest organisations) to make producers, manufacturers and retailers liable for problematic products. The onus on these players creates significant incentives to ensure products brought to market are safe. All in all, the North American regulatory system has many transparent elements which may be a factor in public confidence in innovation.

Yet, when we look at the European countries we find that some of those countries with the most open regulatory style have experienced considerable public protest over GM developments. For example, Denmark has a history of repeated public controversies, and the Netherlands has had its share of public protest. In these countries transparency in times of controversy temporarily increased public protest. Hence it is too simplistic to assume a direct link between regulatory openness and lack of public protest. However, the lack of openness may have contributed to exacerbating protests in Britain and France that were already going on. Conversely, regulatory 'openness' was in place when the ice-minus case was debated in the USA without preventing public protests. And, for a long time, those European countries with the most opaque regulatory practices (generally in southern Europe) have had the lowest level of protest. Overall it may be concluded that mere transparency may be necessary to deal with contested issues once conflict has broken out, but it is not sufficient to prevent the rise of public protest, or that lack of transparency generates the conditions for public disquiet.

Additionally, transparency can be (mis)used to conceal facts behind a facade of seemingly transparent rules simply by debating and deciding issues behind closed doors. This is what the Danish NGOs accused their government of doing. The revolving-door syndrome in the US administration where industry officials and academics end up in regulatory positions and vice versa – a system at odds with the claim that regulation is at an arm's length from industry – might be as prone to such practice as is any of the European governments' or EU institutions' allegedly opaque regulatory habits.

Transparency not only allows opponents to have their say, but it also implies clear administrative responsibilities and procedures, and this is of great advantage to those who seek permissions to implement the technology. This is equally true of the practice of using the courts to rule on aspects of new technologies in the USA. This tends to limit the range of legitimate arguments to those of natural science and economics. This essentially conservative framing of issues acts in favour of the innovator.[19]

In conclusion, while we can reject the simple association between transparency and public confidence in biotechnology, transparency as implemented in the USA may act in support of innovation for reasons unconnected with public confidence.

Risk and uncertainty regimes

One explanation for the transatlantic divide is neatly captured by MacKenzie who comments that:

> The US has adopted an optimistic mindset and approaches the evaluation of new products and technologies by questioning 'why not?', whereas the European approach is more pessimistic, involves trying to predict the unknown, and questioning 'why?'.[20]

Although this is something of an overgeneralisation, the expression of these mindsets in the area of biotechnology is seen in differing regulatory concepts (product vs process), frameworks (existing regulatory mechanisms vs new technology-specific approaches), and location of decision-making authorities (institutional vs political). If there is anything that characterises the differing stances of North America and Europe, it is symbolised by the differing interpretations of the precautionary principle and science-based risk assessment. It would be inaccurate to assert that regulation in North America is not precautionary at times,[21] or that Europe does not engage in science-based risk assessment, however, interpretations, practices and the stringency of regulatory oversight vary.

There are two examples where differences in technological optimism (or entrepreneurialism) has been visible. First is in the number of field trials. The database of OECD member countries shows that 71 per cent of field trials have been conducted in the USA with 9 per cent in Canada. Only two European countries are above 2 per cent: France at 5.3 and Italy at 2.4 per cent.[22] The number for the USA may be even higher since many trials do not need the permission that would be required in the EU. The second arena is in the granting of intellectual property protections to developers. The USA was the first country to grant patent rights for GMOs (in 1980 for GM bacteria for bioremediation), was the first to grant patents to higher life forms, and its patent system is considered most open to inventors. The general philosophy, articulated early on by the courts, was that anything, except for a human being itself, is patentable without reservation,[23] a philosophy that has been under criticism from NGOs and international agencies.

In the USA, while efforts have been directed towards promoting the development of biotechnology, relatively little attention has been given to examining potential negative environmental and health impacts. For example, the FDA is considered to be six years behind in its promise to develop standards to address the possibility of allergens or toxins in GM foods while the USDA has been spending less than US $2 million a year (less than 4 per cent) of its research budget on risk assessment.[24] The EPA, historically associated with greater regulatory scrutiny, has been increasingly sidelined. Recent contingencies have forced a reassessment and some minor changes to North American policy-makers and producers. To strengthen scrutiny of genetically engineered food, the FDA has now made it mandatory that it be notified by manufacturers of plant-derived GM foods and animal feeds at least 120 days before these products are marketed (a procedure which was previously voluntary). Canada implemented a process for developing a voluntary labelling standard in 2000 and the FDA recently also developed its own draft standard (now at the consultation stage). Previously, regulators in both countries had insisted that labelling standards for GM foods were not necessary or even counter-productive suggesting a non-existing risk; this move was clearly in response to more vocal calls for labelling. More funding has recently been allocated to examining safety and environmental issues in the USA. The Starlink episode (where a bioengineered variety of corn not approved for human consumption had been found in taco shells) has resulted in more controversy, product recalls, and a major FDA and EPA investigation. Finally, export-dependent market pressures in both Canada and the USA, stemming from European rejection of GM crops, have pushed a number of agricultural producers to introduce identity-preservation systems to segregate GM from non-GM crops.

There are two aspects to the differing philosophies described here. The first has to do with science and risk and the second with uncertainty. In the North American case, the promotion of the use of 'sound science' has been heard repeatedly. The underlying message is that decisions not based on science are 'political'. Implicit in this argumentation is that values can be separated from facts: there is one single truth accessible through scientific investigation, and that all scientists would come to the same conclusion if they used sound science. There is little or no room for values in making these decisions, since the terms of reference or the underlying framing of the problem at stake, is identical to that of already known problems. There is also a strong faith in the ability to manage risk, either by technical means or through compensation. In Europe, although both regulators and industry would endorse the virtues of the 'sound science' approach, there are indications of changing interpretations of the relations between science and policy.[25]

In the case of uncertainty due to a lack of robust scientific knowledge, North American policy-makers have often suggested that it should not be used as an excuse for withholding permission to go ahead with a new technology, as the benefits usually outweigh the (uncertain) risks. By contrast, European policy-makers, pressed by consumer concerns, have taken a different approach. This is highlighted in the struggle around the precautionary principle which the EU has adopted as a guiding rule for dealing with uncertainty. Its emphasis is the opposite of the US approach. In the case of a possible severe risk, uncertainty shall not be used as an excuse not to take measures to prevent the risk from materialising, even if its existence cannot (yet) be scientifically demonstrated. The European Commission has tried to substantiate the principle in a recent publication emphasising its role as an instrument only for dealing with scientifically asserted uncertainty.[26] However, a whole range of questions remains to be answered, for example what counts for a severe risk, who has the competence to claim it, and how much evidence is sufficient to invoke the principle? The principle found its way into several international treaties (such as the Cartagena Protocol on Biodiversity), and is at the base of the EU regulation for transgenic organisms. The USA and Canada have fought its adoption describing it as 'unscientific legal nonsense' and alleged that the EU's motivation is to open up loopholes for arbitrary trade restrictions.[27]

At the base of the 'sound science' vs 'precautionary principle' dispute is a different approach both to uncertainty and to concerns that cannot be framed in a (natural) scientific way. As already mentioned, the latter is not considered to have any legitimate relevance in the case of biotechnology by the US side.[28] The European perspective differs by assuming that it is not possible to separate science from value judgements, for example in questions of the acceptance or non-acceptance of a risk. Science informs the decision-maker but is not the sole arbiter, as decisions are acknowledged to have to take into account the broader context and may have wider implications. As scientific advice may also be 'biased', it is necessary to listen to those who are not scientific experts but who are knowledgeable on other grounds. Therefore, the regulatory process must be open to a wider range of stakeholders, who may bring other concerns and relevant arguments.[29]

In the context of biotechnology, the North American approach to risk and uncertainty is more risk tolerant than it is in Europe. Without making a claim for wider cultural differences in risk attitudes (for which there is plenty of contrary evidence, for example pesticides and food additives), we cannot reject the explanation that the North American strategy has been more conducive to the development of biotechnology.

Domestic policies, international trade and globalisation

Canada and the USA are each other's largest trading partners although the EU comes second to Canada in trade volume with the USA. The establishment of the North American Free Trade Agreement (NAFTA) pushed the North American countries towards greater harmonisation on a number of fronts. Concerned about the effect of NAFTA, the EU proposed a Transatlantic Free Trade Agreement in 1994. While this was not achieved, an agreement to maintain informal links was reached through the New Transatlantic Agenda.[30] The current agreement, the Transatlantic Economic Partnership, reflected the shortcomings of attempts to foster better trade relations in that these agreements did not include the most contentious areas of agriculture, audiovisual services, and culture.[31]

The continuing failure to resolve contentious issues of agricultural trade policy resulted in Europe and North America relying on the WTO's dispute resolution process. The WTO became the arena for testing the limits of trade policies, and 'turned EU–US disputes into tests of trade rules and access to new markets in developed and undeveloped countries around the globe'.[32] The European ban on hormone-treated beef is a case in point. The EU refused to abide by the WTO ruling that the EU ban against hormone-treated beef was a violation of international trade rules since no scientific evidence existed that these hormones posed a risk to human health. This resulted in US sanctions against EU products. This, in combination with longstanding international disputes over rBST and GM commodity crops, linked biotechnology to the broader movement against globalisation.

The agricultural contexts in both North America and Europe provide an interesting backdrop to policy preferences and public reactions. In the USA and Canada, more space implies larger farms, lower unit costs and more competitive price structures. As a consequence, agricultural surpluses have grown and there is greater dependence on bulk commodity exports.[33] This puts even greater emphasis on the already entrenched philosophy of ensuring that trade barriers are reduced if not eliminated. Another consequence is that North American consumers expect low food prices. Canadians, for instance, spend under 10 per cent of their disposable income on food and beverages compared with from 8 to 26 per cent spent in most industrialised countries.[34] In Europe, the smaller land areas available mean smaller farms and higher unit costs, encouraging emphasis on high value-added products as opposed to bulk production.[35] The need to ensure the viability of the farming sector has led to a complex system of subsidies through the Common Agricultural Policy (CAP) which continues to consume much of the EU's budget. This has also contributed to higher food prices for European consumers.

The 13-year European experience with the ban on rBST is instructive for what it tells about the different rationales brought to bear on the GM food issue.[36] What is telling are the various rationales used by the EU in support of a moratorium followed by an outright ban. At different points, issues of public health, animal welfare, consumer anxieties, and concerns about domestic production and international trade were relevant. It is likely the case that these various rationales, applied to GM food in general, all are deemed to be legitimate political issues for Europeans, but not in the USA.

Fundamentally, the USA and Canada are committed to increasing the export of their agricultural surpluses, while Europe tries to adapt agricultural production to domestic consumption in order to cut back subsidies as they would not be able to export surpluses at competitive prices. Underlying this reasoning is that EU countries (with the exception of Sweden) do not want to shed large parts of their agricultural sector for societal and political reasons, which would be a consequence of accepting unrestricted terms of trade favouring the industrialised agricultural systems of North America. This is not only economically motivated in a strict sense; rather, it stems from a political choice to keep a sector that is less productive than its transcontinental counterpart. This is in striking contrast to the textile, steel and coal sectors, for example, where such support was not deemed politically necessary. The rapid sacrificing of small-scale agriculture is considered socially unsustainable, even if existing policy appears economically unsustainable in the light of many new members waiting for access to the EU. In return for substantial subsidies, it seems that European governments aim to keep the countryside populated, to keep rural life intact, to retain the form of landscape that exists, and even to serve its inhabitants' desire for myths about and emotional links to rural life, the protection of nature even if it is cultivated and, by implication, the preconditions for trust in food quality. Such arguments are both socially relevant and politically legitimate in Europe but they would hardly convince a WTO dispute panel, following the rationale of economic performance as the main global common denominator.

We cannot reject the idea that contrasting structures and roles of the agricultural sector on either side of the Atlantic have played a part in shaping responses to biotechnology.

Media explanations

The media in context

The extensive literature on the relationship between mass-media content and public opinion encompasses theories of agenda-setting[37] and agenda-building,[38] the spiral of silence,[39] the press's role in legitimising or delegitimising various points of view,[40] and various, often speculative, theories of framing and information processing, as well as a number of theories specific to news about technological risk. The latter includes theories that argue that the news media amplify risks (that is, that they 'blow them out of proportion') as well as theories that argue, conversely, that the media understate risks and/or overstate the degree to which 'responsible authorities' have risks under control.[41] Analysis of the data collected in this project for their contribution to supporting or eliminating some of these theories will continue for many years.

Tabloid sensationalism in Europe

Generally speaking, the USA and Canada do not have a national press. Although there are a few

nationally recognised newspapers, notably the *New York Times* and the *Washington Post* in the USA, the *Globe and Mail* and *National Post* in Canada – used as the basis of the media data presented elsewhere in this book – these are not actually read widely on a daily basis beyond the East Coast cities. However, their influence among the elite class, including policy-makers, is generally acknowledged; it is just of a different nature than the influence of leading papers in various European countries. With the exception of *USA Today* which carries news stories in a shorter format for a working-class audience, tabloids distributed nationally are not taken seriously as vehicles for providing the public with news. North America also does not have the exact equivalent of the European tabloid press which has been cited by the American press as a factor in cultivating fears among European consumers over biotechnology issues. The *New York Times*, for example, has published numerous articles in which European (often British) tabloids are accused of sabotaging a new, wonderful technology. One report mentioned that it was the British tabloids which had labelled GM foods as Frankenfoods,[42] while another reported:

> . . . a trip to London has become a distinctly Kafkaesque experience. Pick up a tabloid newspaper, flick on a television talk show, study the graffiti on street walls and you are greeted by a constant refrain: 'GM is evil.' [43]

To some extent, this attitude may reflect US misunderstanding of the nature, functions and readership of the tabloids. But it may also reflect 'third-person-effect' assumptions about the influence of sensationalistic news accounts on others – that Europeans are more likely to be affected by these portrayals. This theory, attributed to Davison,[44] proposes that people may be predisposed to overestimate the effects of media on persons other than themselves. Since our study did not directly investigate the tabloids, we do not have strong empirical evidence for rejecting this popular idea. However, we must question explanations which rest on widely discredited theories of strong, direct and uniform media effects on news consumers.

Press structures: objectivity, opinion and diversity

An important difference between the press systems in North America and much of Europe may be more significant. The dominant US news paradigm relies on objectivity as the paramount ethical standard for journalistic work. News reports are supposed to be 'balanced' – that is, to provide opposing points of view for disputed interpretations or left/right political positions. This system is challenged in cases such as the cloning controversy, in which scientific and ethics experts were sometimes juxtaposed as though representing competing rather than complementary perspectives,[45] or the global-warming debate, in which journalists' attempt to 'balance' pro- and anti-global-warming perspectives seems to have contributed to a great deal of public confusion despite the existence of a stable and widespread consensus among scientists on this issue. The news media are 'not supposed to' provide opinion or commentary, outside of the confines of the 'editorial' or 'op-ed' (opinion-editorial) section that may or may not be read or heeded by most subscribers. The reasons for this are complex and largely economic, related to US media's dependence on advertising revenue and a general pattern of economic concentration increasingly characteristic of the US press.[46]

In much of Europe, on the other hand, journalists are expected to have opinions and to write from a point of view. The European press is much more political in tone than that in the USA. The newspaper reader is generally aware of the political orientation of a particular paper. Some may read more than one source of news to get a full range of views, others may read only the newspaper that is consistent with his or her own political views. In any event, while readers on both sides of the Atlantic expect the news media, including the print press, to call their attention to looming issues of importance and striking events of the day, and while the press on both continents is likely to be especially dependent on scientific experts and policy-makers for news of events in highly technical areas such as biotechnology, the news media in the USA are expected to print 'the truth' – and this applies especially to the two elite papers included in this study – while the news media in Europe are also expected to provide 'opinions'. While some argue that this contrast is diminishing, with some European newspapers leaning more towards the US style of 'objectivity', the basic difference remains.

This difference in the interpretation of the role of news media goes a long way toward explaining why commentators in the USA find the European media too 'sensational'. Related to differing news logics is the extent of competition between media outlets in Europe in contrast to North America. Most North America towns are served by a single newspaper, whereas in Europe a range of national

and local papers compete for audience share. Such competition pushes newspapers to provide more sensational approaches to news.

But it also suggests one potentially important reason why the food biotechnology controversy became an open public debate in Europe before it became one in North America, a reason that does not depend on the degree of statistical difference in opinion poll results. It is possible that the range of discourse was broader and more elaborated in the European press than in North America contributing to a US 'spiral of silence' in which only pro-biotechnology opinions were legitimised and the existence of opposition or resistance – present in the USA as in Europe, though not necessarily to the same degree – was rendered less visible. This spiral could be exacerbated by media dependence on expert voices for this scientifically complex set of issues.

The idea that only certain voices are heard within the mass media, and that North American media tend to be even more selective in terms of minority voices, is only partially supported by the evidence gathered here. What is supported is that special-interest groups are present in less than 10 per cent of all articles for both North America and Europe within both time periods, and that business and science interests are well-represented. This is proof that some of the factors are in place for a spiral of silence to occur in both regions. What is not supported is the contention that this is more the case in North America than Europe.

In both regions and in both time periods, science and business voices are the most frequently cited actors, with political figures coming third. No other single actor group reaches 10 per cent. Table 2 shows the percentage of mentions of the three actor categories and the combined percentage of other actors in the three regions. Two comparisons are of relevance. As judged by the 'other actor' percentages the European press are not as dominated by independent science, business and politics to the same extent as either the USA or Canada. Secondly, of the three major actors in the press, 'independent science' is the most prominent in Europe, while in Canada and to a lesser extent the USA 'business' is the dominant actor.

In this way biotechnology is cultivated as a business in the North American press, while in Europe it is about science and a wider range of other actors. However, it is important to note that this comparison of groups represented in leading papers does not tell the whole story. The domination of US news by the Associated Press wire service means

Table 2. Main actors mentioned in biotechnology press coverage, 1993–96 and 1997–99

Actors in news (%)	Europe		Canada		USA	
	1993–96	1997–99	1993–96	1997–99	1993–96	1997–99
Independent science	51	42	29	25	28	25
Business	15	18	52	48	36	30
Political	14	14	6	12	20	22
Other actors	19	27	12	15	17	23

that local and regional papers often report exactly the same national and international stories in almost exactly the same way throughout the country. We do not believe this to be the case, at least to the same degree, in much of Europe. But to test this hypothesis would mean a much larger and yet more complex study of news heterogeneity within a number of countries. Further, spiral-of-silence phenomena (in which less-prominent opinions are *more rarely* voiced due to fear of being ostracised by a group) may result from subtle issues of implied legitimacy or acceptability of various points of view, not just their statistical prominence in news accounts or popular perceptions of opinion distributions.

Our data cannot rule out the spiral-of-silence condition whereby dissent was less visible and perhaps less legitimised in public discourse in North America in comparison to Europe: some media data are consistent with this interpretation.

Framing biotechnology: progress vs caution

One explanation for differences in public perceptions between North America and Europe is that the European press cover wider issues and are more critical. The homogeneity vs heterogeneity of available news stories can be assessed using the concept of framing. While often defined differently (or not at all) by various media commentators, the number and distribution of frames generated and maintained in the mass media offer a proxy of the availability of elaborated discourse within the circulation area. An examination of the frames taken from the content analyses conducted in the various regions shows that there is some evidence for this explanation. While the 'progress' frame was used frequently in all three regions in both time periods, the USA is the only region in which the percentage increased over time (from 50 to 63 per cent). Canada was relatively stable at around 36 per cent. Although Europe experienced a significant decrease between the two time periods (from 51 to 39 per cent), progress still is by far and away the dominant frame in European press coverage.

In addition to the progress frame, the economic prospect frame was very prominent in both Canada and the USA, though much more so in Canada between 1997 and 1999. In the USA, this framing actually decreased between the two time periods, from 27 per cent of the articles between 1993 and 1996 to 13 per cent between 1997 and 1999. These are the only two frames that account for at least 10 per cent of the coverage in North America. In Europe, on the other hand, both the ethical and public accountability frames reach over 10 per cent. These frames tend to be more complex and take into account a number of issues, such as regulation, religion and science. The higher frequency of these frames within the press would allow readers more access to these complex viewpoints.

Again, a valid comparison of discourse range and complexity would have to take into account local and regional papers and probably other news media, such as broadcast media, web sites, internet messages, and a range of popular-culture products. Overall, definitive statements about cause and effect are not unambiguously supported by our data. But our evidence suggests that the different media traditions characteristic of North America and Europe contributed to the more rapid escalation of debate in Europe. We find a more elaborated range of press coverage in Europe than North America, and less prominence to business actors and to the framing of biotechnology in terms of progress and economic prospect.

The publics

Now we turn to frequently cited explanations concerning the publics, using as our data Eurobarometer and comparable North American surveys.

'Europeans are technophobic'

To what extent are European attitudes to biotechnology a reflection of broader technophobia? Theorists of the industrial society[47] argued that the mass prosperity and welfare-state provision of the post Second World War decades undermined the dominant values of economies directed towards production and growth. Inglehart has charted the emergence of post-materialist values as societies outgrow their incessant need for material possessions and look to quality of life, environmental protection and civil liberties to provide a more meaningful existence.

Could such disengagement from the materialist worldview and the resulting decline in optimism about the results of technological advancement account for the sceptical reception of biotechnology in Europe? In the surveys, respondents were asked the following question about seven technologies: 'Do you think it will improve our way of life in the next 20 years, it will have no effect, or it will make things worse?' Here we look at the responses to three of the technologies: the internet, genetic engineering and nuclear power (Figure 1).

Looking at the results for the internet, it is evident that Europeans are certainly not Luddite technophobes. If anything, taking into account both the percentages saying the internet will 'improve our way of life' and those who say it will 'make things worse', the Europeans are more optimistic than Americans or Canadians. We also asked about computers and the results follow a not dissimilar pattern. By contrast views about civil nuclear energy are mixed in all three regions. While the Americans are the most optimistic, they are still lukewarm, at less than 50 per cent.

Turning to genetic engineering, we find that the Americans are the most optimistic: 10 per cent more optimistic than the Canadians and 13 per cent more than the Europeans. But what is perhaps

equally interesting and rather surprising is the substantial and similar minority in all three cases who consider that genetic engineering will 'make things worse'. The received wisdom that North Americans have greeted genetic engineering with the same enthusiasm as the life sciences industry, with our survey showing 35–40 per cent pessimistic, is clearly erroneous. However, it is certainly the case that Americans and Canadians appear considerably more likely to be optimistic about biotechnology than Europeans.

To investigate our putative explanation more explicitly, a more detailed analysis is required. The suggestion is that Europeans have a less optimistic view about new technologies than Americans and Canadians and it is this that explains the less optimistic beliefs that Europeans have about biotechnology. Translating this suggestion into some testable hypotheses is relatively straightforward. We take an overall measure of optimism about the six technologies other than biotechnology to be an indicator of a respondent's generalised attitude towards new technologies. If our explanation is correct, we should see a correlation between people's general attitude to technologies and their optimism about biotechnology. Furthermore, Americans and Canadians should, on average, score more highly on this generalised attitude than Europeans. Differences in optimism about biotechnology between regions should disappear or be reduced when we hold technology optimism constant, showing that at least some of the difference in biotechnology optimism between regions is mediated by technology optimism.

Figure 1. Optimism and pessimism for three technologies: genetic engineering, nuclear power and internet in the USA, Canada and Europe

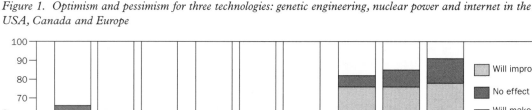

A summated scale of 'will improve' responses to the six technologies other than genetic engineering was computed and used in the analyses that follow.

Turning to our first hypothesis we find that technology optimism (TECHOPT) is indeed correlated with optimism about biotechnology (BIOPT). The two are moderately and positively correlated (0.39). People who are optimistic about technology in general are more likely to be positive about biotechnology. Our second hypothesis concerns the relative levels of technology optimism across the three regions. The mean scores on TECHOPT are as follows: Europe 3.7, Canada 4.1, and America 4.2. The mean scores for America and Canada are not significantly different from each other. The hypothesis that there is greater general optimism about technology in North America cannot be rejected.

In order to test our third hypothesis, that differing levels of generalised technology optimism can explain the differences in optimism about biotechnology between North America and Europe, we conducted a series of nested logistic regression models. In these models, BIOPT was used as the dependent variable. Independent variables used in addition to TECHOPT were for region (Europe and Canada, using America as the reference category) and controls for age and education (two dummy variables indicating university graduate and being aged over 55 years).

Our results show that, firstly, when age and education are controlled, there is no difference in Canadian and American respondents as to the likelihood of expressing optimism about biotechnology. By contrast, the odds of a European being optimistic about biotechnology are about 50 per cent less than that of an American or Canadian. Secondly, again taking age and education into account, technology optimism is associated with a higher probability of being optimistic about biotechnology. For each one-point increase in respondents' scores on TECHOPT, the odds of being optimistic about biotechnology increase by about 40 per cent. At the same time, taking account of this, the difference in relative probability of optimism about biotechnology between Europeans and North Americans is reduced. This tells us that at least some of the difference between the North America and Europe in the probability of being optimistic about biotechnology is due to Europeans being less optimistic about technology in general. Finally, a third regression model shows that the effect of technology optimism on biotechnology optimism is greater in Europe than it

is in America. In other words, in Europe, people's overall attitude to technology is a stronger predictor than it is in America of how optimistic people are about biotechnology.

Overall, then, we have reasonable evidence to suggest that the generally more positive beliefs of North Americans about the promise of new technology in general play a significant part leading them to view biotechnology more favourably than Europeans do. While this does not account for all the difference, it is without doubt a factor. We consider some other possibilities in the sections that follow.

'Europeans oppose all genetic manipulation'

It is sometimes argued that Europeans are opposed to all modern biotechnology on the grounds that it is unnecessary, ethically dubious or carries unacceptable risks. We know that some Europeans tend to be pessimistic about the contribution biotechnology will make to life, but how does this translate into attitudes towards different applications of biotechnology? Respondents were asked whether they thought each of four biotechnologies was useful, risky, morally acceptable and to be encouraged. The four technologies were described to respondents as follows:

- Genetic testing: using genetic tests to detect inheritable diseases such as cystic fibrosis.

- Medicines: introducing human genes into bacteria to produce medicines or vaccines, for example to produce insulin for diabetics.

- GM crops: taking genes from plant species and transferring them into crop plants to increase resistance to insect pests.

- GM food: using modern biotechnology in the production of foods, for example to make them higher in protein, keep longer or change the taste.

Prior to this question respondents were asked whether they had heard about each of the applications before, providing a filter to exclude those people who are probably responding with non-attitudes. Figure 2 shows the mean levels of support (encouragement) for the applications. The scale runs from 1 (most opposed) to 4 (most supportive), with 2.5 as the midpoint.

There are a number of interesting features captured in the figure. First, across the four applications Americans are always the most supportive, followed by the Canadians, and the Europeans are the least supportive. Second, the

Figure 2. Support for four applications of biotechnology

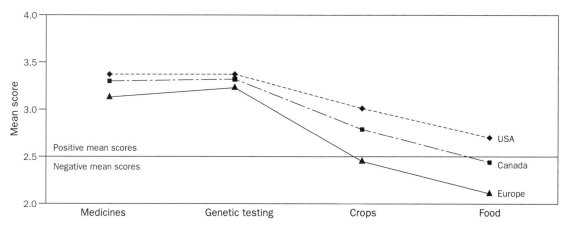

'red' biotechnologies (medicines and genetic testing) are viewed much more positively than the 'green' biotechnologies (GM foods and crops) in all three regions. Third, the transatlantic biotechnology divide appears to be limited to the 'green' biotechnologies. It is notable that in contrast to the 'red' biotechnologies, for which attitudes are rather similar, attitudes towards 'green' biotechnologies are markedly different across the three regions. And finally GM foods are not only the least supported of the four applications but on average are viewed negatively in both Canada and in Europe. These results suggest that talking in terms of a transatlantic divide on biotechnology, that is across all applications of modern biotechnology, is an oversimplification at least as far as public perceptions are concerned. Europeans are supportive of the 'red' biotechnologies as are the Canadians and the Americans. While Europeans are clearly opposed to GM foods, so are the Canadians albeit to a lesser extent.

'Europeans are irrational about risks'

It has been suggested that the Europeans are simply more 'irrational' than North Americans as evidenced by the reliance on 'non-scientific' thinking to settle what is essentially a scientific issue. Bradbury[48] and Priest[49] have argued that there are two competing explanations for how people interpret technological risks. One posits a 'correct' scientific or 'rational' standard of risk against which actual perceptions may be quantitatively compared. In the alternative view, the 'accuracy' of risk perceptions is not the issue, rather, different understandings of risk are attributed to differing value orientations. It seems

likely that differences in how foods are valued in North America and Europe, consistent with a values-based interpretation of technological risk, provide a more sound explanation. In cost–benefit analyses, risk (as potential for cost) and benefit are combined to suggest an 'optimal' course of action. Perhaps the charge of irrationality might be interpreted as the refusal or inability to weigh up both risks and benefits.

From the surveys we have a number of indicators of risk perceptions. All of them show that Europeans do indeed have higher risk perceptions than Canadians or Americans. For example, asked whether GM foods are 'risky for society', 60 per cent of Europeans agreed compared with 58 per cent of Canadians and 49 per cent of Americans.

The approach of Slovic and colleagues[50] leads us to consider alternative measures of risk perception. The judged magnitude of risks of a technology have been demonstrated to vary systematically according to differences in various 'qualitative attributes' perceived to be associated with these technological hazards. Those hazards that are familiar, voluntary, non-catastrophic and naturally occurring are generally viewed as less risky. DNA technology was identified in the 1980s as having similar 'dread risk' qualities to nuclear power.[51] To assess the extent of dread risks we asked respondents if they agreed or not with the following statements:

- 'Even if it has benefits, GM foods are fundamentally unnatural'

- 'If anything went wrong with GM foods it would be a global catastrophe'

The extent of agreement to the first question was for Europe 69 per cent, Canada 59 per cent and in the USA 49 per cent. For the second question the comparable scores are 57 per cent, 54 per cent, and 40 per cent. On three measures of risk attitudes it is clear, then, that more risk is perceived in Europe than in Canada or the USA. But, just as importantly, these results also show that it would be quite wrong to talk about an absence of risk perception in either the USA or Canada.

Beliefs about risks should not necessarily be taken as indicating entirely negative attitudes towards any given application of biotechnology. We know that people perceive risks with medical applications, but these risks are deemed acceptable, presumably because of the expected benefits. Asked whether 'the risks of GM foods are acceptable' some 21 per cent of Europeans agree, compared with 28 per cent in Canada and 39 per cent in the USA. These differences in risk acceptability may well be the result of differential assessments of the benefits of GM foods. This hypothesis can be tested using another survey item. Asked whether GM foods 'would bring benefits to a lot of people', 28 per cent of Europeans agree, while in Canada it is 55 per cent and in the USA 65 per cent. Here the 'transatlantic divide' comes into sharp relief. Americans and Canadians are much more favourably disposed to the idea that GM food may bring benefits – an idea that finds very little favour across the Atlantic.

Is it possible, as seems plausible, that the differences we noted in risk acceptance between the regions can be at least partially explained by the large differences in beliefs about benefits? Of those Americans that agree that GM food is risky for society and that it will bring benefits, 58 per cent say that the risks are acceptable. The comparable figures for Canada and Europe are 42 per cent and 50 per cent respectively. These differences in risk acceptance compared to those observed earlier, where we did not control for risk perception and benefits, are much attenuated. Moreover, a logistic regression with risk acceptability as the dependent variable suggests that the difference in the probability of considering the risks acceptable, holding benefit and risk perception constant, is not significantly different from America in either Canada or Europe.

We have evidence, therefore, that, in all regions, people assess the acceptability of risks from GM food, at least in part, according to a quite rational calculus of risks vs benefits. The charge of an irrational European public seems unwise if it is intended to mean that Europeans have an unrealistic longing for a risk-free world. In Europe,

as in America and Canada, benefits are taken into account when evaluating the risks. It is because of the greater benefits that North Americans believe might result from the introduction of GM food, whatever particular level of risk they perceive, that they are, on the whole, more willing to accept the risks such as they may be. The question, of course, remains as to what lies behind this rather widespread belief in America that GM food might prove to be beneficial.

'BSE turned the European public against green biotechnologies'

The crisis over bovine spongiform encephalitis (BSE) and the recognition in 1996 that the consumption of infected meat was implicated in a rise in cases of Creutzfeld Jakob disease (CJD) was the culmination of a number of food scares in Europe. Many have argued that the failure of the European regulatory systems to protect human health had immediate and dire consequences on public attitudes to the introduction of GM foods. While there can be little doubt about the severity of the fallout from the BSE crisis, was it the sole trigger event that turned Europeans against GM foods? There is evidence that the public were wary of genetic technologies as early as 1979. Cantley writes that 'public and political opinion was learning to see gene technology, genetic engineering, biotechnology and so on as a single, vague and disquieting phenomenon'.[52] In a survey in 1979, respondents in nine European countries were asked about genetic research. Some 33 per cent said it was 'worthwhile', but 35 per cent said it was an 'unacceptable risk'. Another question asked about synthetic food (the GM-food label was yet to be coined). Here 23 per cent said it was 'worthwhile' against 49 per cent saying it was an 'unacceptable risk'. In 1991 the first of the series of Eurobarometer surveys on biotechnology was conducted. Asked whether such research (biotechnology/genetic engineering) on food is worthwhile and should be encouraged a majority (58 per cent) agreed, but some 32 per cent disagreed.

In summary, survey evidence from the 1970s to the early 1990s, predating the BSE crisis, shows a sizeable percentage of the European public having reservations about biotechnology as applied to foods. While the BSE/CJD crisis may well have acted to amplify existing negative attitudes, it cannot be seen as the single origin of such attitudes.

'North Americans trust their food chain more than Europeans'

One of the food retailers in the UK advertises its products with the slogan 'food you can trust'. This suggests that the conditions for familiarity, typified by the absence of risk perception have broken down.

A composite measure of social trust was constructed using some of the questions asking whether various biotechnology actors were 'doing a good job' for society.[53] A latent-class analysis[54] indicated that a tendency to distrust government, industry and shops formed a related category. This makes intuitive sense as it is these three actor groups that are (or could be) responsible for the production, regulation and distribution of GM food. The resulting summated scale of negative responses runs from 0 to 3 and, for clarity of presentation, is reversed so that a high score indicates high trust. The mean scores are as follows: Europe = 2.2, Canada = 1.8 and the USA = 2.0. With Europe scoring highest on this index, we have some evidence to reject the hypothesis that general overall levels of trust in institutions relevant to food biotechnology explain observed regional differences in responses. However, further analyses at the national level are in progress to determine how complex and subtle patterns of trust and distrust may explain attitudes to particular applications of biotechnology.

Other speculative explanations

Finally, we briefly consider three further issues that are outside our empirical investigation but which appear to be plausible factors in the biotechnology divide.

'The industry's marketing strategy was misguided'

One interpretation of public opinion, while outside our empirical enquiries, merits some comment. It is well established that if social change is forced on an unwilling group there is a tendency for the group to exhibit a counterforce, resistance to change. And added to this, if the change is perceived to bring risks to the group, then since people have no choice in the matter, the risks will be seen as involuntary, and will loom large in people's minds. People are willing to tolerate voluntary risks that are far greater than involuntary risks. As Starr commented 'we are loath to let others do unto us what we happily do to ourselves'.[55]

Freedom of choice has a bearing on European responses to biotechnology. Consider the contrasting receptions in Britain of Zeneca's tomato puree and sold in the supermarkets in 1996, and the events that led to the boycott of GM foods by the leading food retailers in 1999 for fear of a consumer backlash. Zeneca's tomato puree sold well and there was no public debate or consumer opposition. Significantly it was clearly labelled as a product of modern biotechnology. But, by the following year the situation had started to change. European regulators were unprepared for the first shipments of Monsanto's GM soya, which would enter the food chain unlabelled. The ensuing debate, orchestrated by NGOs, created fertile ground for people to become sensitised to possible risks of GM foods. People felt they were forced to take an involuntary risk and by the time the supermarkets responded to public anxieties and announced that GM products would be withdrawn from the shelves, many members of the public assumed that they had been eating GM foods for years. Pushing unlabelled GM products into the market was a high-risk strategy. In the 1996 Eurobarometer, 75 per cent of Europeans disagreed with the statement 'it is not worth putting labels on genetically modified foods' and the decision to ignore this cannot have helped to smooth the introduction of such products. Interestingly, in 2000 more than 80 per cent of Americans thought that 'the FDA should require labelling on all fruits, vegetables and foods that have been genetically altered', but when asked 'as far as you know, are there any foods produced through biotechnology in the supermarket now?', only 36 per cent said 'yes'. A Canadian survey shows rather similar findings. Some 87 per cent say that GMOs should be labelled, 46 per cent think that the majority of the foods they buy contain GMOs, and 48 per cent think that the presence of GMOs in food to be very or somewhat dangerous to human health.[56] As the realisation of penetration of GM products dawns on North Americans how will they react: with easy indifference or with anxiety? Time will tell.

With products that had benefits for 'big business' but not for the consumer, the absence of labelling was not well advised. The counterforce of resistance may have made suggestions of possible risks to human health more plausible. Forced exposure to an involuntary risk without any tangible benefits cultivated suspicion of US multinationals in general and to the demonisation of Monsanto in particular. As was said at the time, Monsanto's charm offensive in Europe (a major public-relations campaign to counter opposition to GM foods) offended many and charmed very few.

Images of the environment

Europeans, particularly in the northern countries, are more inclined than North Americans to link environmental protection with farms and farming. Environmentalism is an established aspect of political agendas leading, at least some Europeans, to increasingly expect agriculture to nurture and protect the environment. Lacking the great wilderness areas of North America, which are a focus for a great deal of environmental conservation, Europeans tend to see farming and the environment as coterminus: a country walk or a summer picnic take people along established pathways through farms. Such experiences and views, supported by the advertising of products as 'straight from the farm', have cultivated a myth of European farming as a rural idyll. Europeans have been shocked to find, as part of some recent food scares, that farming is more or less an industrial enterprise. In North America we suspect that such myths and concerns are less prevalent.

Food, culture and identity

US popular culture was once captured in the icons of baseball, hotdogs and apple pie, displaced in recent times by the quintessential American meal of hamburgers and french fries. The fast-food culture supports the impression that US food is both homogeneous and mundane. But some unique dishes and more encompassing cuisines exist in parts of the USA. Shortridge and Shortridge[57] describe various foods throughout the USA, including Cincinnati chili, Michigan pasties, and Maine lobsters. Southern Louisiana has become famous for its Cajun and Creole cuisines,[58] and some ethnic and racial foods have been successfully integrated into mainstream US consumer culture.[59] In addition, there is a heterogeneous food counterculture characterised by organic food, local production, and limited processing.[60] This movement, as well as others with connections to local foods, may emerge as a critical mass to question the legitimacy of GM foods and food crops. However, the USA is the acknowledged inventor of the 'TV dinner' and of the 'fast food' restaurant now franchised around the world.

In many European countries and regions, local culinary specialities including wines and beers are a defining attribute of identity. Culinary traditions are not merely a collection of ingredients but constitute part of the social fabric. Indeed, discussions about food ethics are almost as old as European civilisation itself. Zwart argues that the pre-modern concern with ethical issues of consumption has been extended in recent times to concerns about production.[61] Thus organic food is now available, at a price, in most supermarkets and the treatment of farm animals, chickens, calves for veal and the transportation of animals are current concerns. While fast food is popular in Europe, mobilisation against what some see as the Americanisation of food has become a platform of the antiglobalisation campaigns.

While our data do not provide direct indication of food-related cultural and value differences between North America and Europe, we find it difficult to ignore them in comparing reactions to food biotechnology. Food clearly retains some of its symbolic value in North American and European culture. But while in the USA it no longer plays the role in daily life as it did for previous generations, in Europe it seems as if there is a revival in the food culture and traditions.

The role of interest groups

Some have argued that 'Green activism' was instrumental in turning the European public against biotechnology. Since the 1970s European politics has become more open to and influenced by single issue movements such as environmentalism. Today a number of European parliaments have ministers from green parties. From 1996 Greenpeace and Friends of the Earth campaigned against agricultural biotechnology, a topic that had not been prominent before.

In the following years vigorous campaigns were launched in many European countries. The term NGO became synonymous with organised opposition, protests and disruption of field trials, prominently covered by the media. They campaigned on environmental and health risks, broader political issues such as the vertical integration of food chain and multinationals, and moral issues such as the exploitation of life for commercial ends. The campaigns, more-or-less sychronised across Europe, turned biotechnology into a political issue.

We would argue that while the NGOs were successful in mobilising support amongst a European public that held them in high regard, they were not the instigators of European concerns about agricultural biotechnology. The Eurobarometer surveys show that as early as 1991 there were widespread concerns of the same type as in 1999. The NGOs capitalised on existing, if vaguely articulated, opposition. Over the years this was amplified and transformed into a considerable political moment.

In North America campaigns against biotechnology in general and agricultural biotechnologies in particular occurred at various times in the 1980s and 1990s but seldom reached national attention. We would argue that in North America, unlike Europe, there was less organised opposition, until the problems in Europe migrated across the Atlantic. Since then, NGOs have been successful in persuading some large food companies to withdraw GM ingredients from baby food. While we would reject the idea that NGO action sparked European opposition to biotechnology, there is little doubt that their campaigns both articulated and amplified public concerns.

Conclusion: single or multiple causes?

The relative fortunes of the biotechnology industries differ across the Atlantic and there has been much speculation about the extent to which the difference can be attributed to a more facilitating public sphere of North America, in contrast to the constraining public sphere of Europe. Our objective in this chapter was to subject a number of frequently cited explanations for the transatlantic divide of biotechnology to critical scrutiny. Our intention was to eliminate some of these frequently cited explanations on the basis of evidence drawn from our project's database of policy, media coverage and public opinion, and to arrive at a listing of the more plausible explanations, that is, those which we could not reject. The 16 frequently cited explanations fall into four categories. Those that attribute the transatlantic divide to differences in the policy and regulatory climates, those which attribute the divide to differences in media coverage, those which focus on the publics and finally some other explanations which we feel are worthy of consideration, but about which we have little direct evidence.

We are able to reject some of the explanations. For example, there is little evidence to support the hypothesis that transparent policy development leads to a tolerant public attitude to new technology, or that the European media has concentrated exclusively on possible downsides of biotechnology, or that the European public are wholesale antitechnology and as such opposed to all forms of biotechnology, or that the BSE crisis

was the sole origin of European hostility to agricultural biotechnologies. But perhaps what is more striking is the number of frequently cited explanations across the three broad categories that we cannot reject. Many appear to contain more than a grain of truth.

North America by comparison to Europe had a head start in developing biotechnology. It had established institutional networks and infrastructures for research and for the exploitation of research into applications. With the help of the courts it came to regard biotechnology as 'ordinary' and to encourage the patenting of new discoveries. There is a culture that favours innovation and has confidence that emerging problems can be solved. Agricultural biotechnology offered a way to cut unit costs, increase productivity and support export markets and solve the problem of declining farm incomes. By contrast, Europe started later with less-developed support networks. Biotechnology was taken to be novel and requiring new legislation. Different countries established their own regulatory frameworks and then confronted the challenge of multilevel policy formation within the emerging European political system. Concerns about the longer term effects of GMOs for the environment and human health (not unrelated to BSE and other scandals) led, in part, to the adoption of the precautionary principle. With the reform of the CAP and a reduction of farm subsidies on the agenda as well as social and political pressures to retain the farming sector, GM crops were not a welcome development.

With respect to the media, there are important transatlantic differences that might be a part of more-or-less constraining public spheres. While rejecting simple causal models that would seek to explain public perceptions as the direct result of media content, the American and European media differ in important ways. In North America journalists aim to write, and the public expect to read, the 'truth'. In Europe, newspapers are more opinionated, often with an explicit political slant. The North American press somewhat mainstreamed the industry perspective; relatively more coverage is given to industry sources and to progress stories. In Europe there is much more diversity of reporting, a wider range of actors cited and issues covered. There is more competition among the press in Europe, an encouragement to take a different tack on a story and sometimes to sensationalism.

With respect to the publics, the Europeans are somewhat less enthusiastic about the contribution of technology to everyday life than are North Americans. But in both Canada and in the USA there is, as in Europe, a substantial minority who are pessimistic about biotechnology. And while on average Europeans are opposed to 'green' biotechnologies there is solid support for the 'red' biotechnologies. Lying behind the transatlantic differences in public perceptions are relatively more confident beliefs in the benefits of agribiotechnology in North America, but relatively stronger concerns about the risks and uncertainties associated with genetic modification in Europe.

Finally, although we have no direct evidence, we believe that other issues such as the industry's marketing strategy in the 1990s, and the relative importance of environment and food related values cannot be ignored.

This situation of multiple plausible causes often confronts the historian, and here we can take note of what Boyce terms the 'fallacies in interpreting data'.[62] One is the reductive fallacy; identifying and privileging a single element in the proffered explanation for no compelling reason, other than perhaps it makes a better story to talk about a single causal agent or event, rather than accepting the complexity of the situation.

We are inclined to conclude that there is no one cause of the transatlantic divide. Rather we must assume that the developing science and technology of biotechnology triggered a complex interplay of mutually interrelated aspects of the public spheres in North America and Europe, and in combination with different economic, legal and financial systems contributed to different trajectories for the technology itself, its regulation, media coverage and public reception. The trajectory of the technology and its representation in the public sphere will continue to evolve. If this conclusion to our assessment of the frequently cited explanations is valid, then we must caution against the identification of single causes, however attractive it may be for rhetorical and other purposes.

We hope this result, while it might be less definitive in terms of identifying a single cause than some might have hoped, will be useful for those seeking to comprehend other technological controversies in the future, as well as for those seeking further insight into the current controversies over the wise use of biotechnology. Sociocultural systems and technological systems interact in enormously complex ways. Understanding these interactions requires attention to a number of factors that are most clearly visible on the institutional or societal level, rather than the individual level. Regulatory climate, not just specific regulations; media systems, not just specific messages; and social values, not just individual opinions, all clearly contribute to observed outcomes. It is not at all the case that North America will always be more receptive to new technology than Europe: in the recent case of embryo stem-cell research, for example, the USA has acted relatively swiftly to limit and control activities to which some Europeans have not so far raised very much of an objection. But it will always be the case that these multiple social factors (regulation, communication and culture) must all be taken into account in trying to explain the dynamics of technology adoption – or rejection.

Notes and references

1 Ernst & Young, 'Integration', *8th Annual European Life Sciences Report* (London: Ernst & Young, 2001).

2 Putnam, R D, *Bowling Alone: The Collapse and Revival of American Community* (New York: Simon and Schuster, 2000).

3 US Department of Energy, *US Human Genome Project* <http://www.ornl.gov/hgmis/> (2001).

4 Owen-Smith, J, Riccaboni, M, Pammolli, F and Powell, W, 'A comparison of US and European university-industry relations in the life sciences', *Management Science* (in press).

5 Owen-Smith, J *et al.* (see note 4).

6 World Intellectual Property Organisation <www.wipo.org/ipstats/en/>.

7 Ernst & Young, 'Communicating value', *European Life Sciences 99, Sixth Annual Report* (London: Ernst & Young, 1999); Ernst & Young, *Biotech '99: Bridging the Gap, Thirteenth Biotechnology Industry Annual Report* (London: Ernst & Young, 2000).

8 White, K, 'Economic profile of the biotechnology sector', Paper prepared for Canadian Biotechnology Advisory Committee (2000).

9 Galloux, J-C, Prat Gaumont, H and Stevers, E, 'Europe', in Durant, J, Bauer, M W and Gaskell G (eds), *Biotechnology in the Public Sphere: A European Source Book* (London: Science Museum, 1998), pp177–85.

10 Fredrickson, D S, *The Recombinant DNA Controversy:*

A Memoir (Washington, DC: American Society for Microbiology Press, 2001).

11 Krimsky, S and Wrubel, R, *Agricultural Biotechnology and the Environment: Science, Policy and Social Issues* (Urbana, IL: University of Illionois Press, 1996).

12 Krimsky, S and Wrubel, R (see note 11).

13 Collier, R, 'The regulation of rBST in the US', *AgBioForum*, 3 (2000), pp156–63.

14 Canadian Veterinary Association, 'Expert Panel on Human Safety of rBST', Report to Health Canada (Ottawa, 1998); Royal Society of Physicians and Surgeons, 'Expert Panel on Human Safety of rBST', Report to Health Canada (Ottawa, 1999).

15 Krimsky, S and Wrubel, R (see note 11).

16 MacKenzie, D, 'International comparisons of regulatory frameworks for food products of biotechnology', Paper prepared for Canadian Biotechnology Advisory Committee (2000).

17 MacKenzie, D (see note 16).

18 MacKenzie, D (see note 16).

19 Jasanoff, S, 'Ordering life: law and normalization of biotechnology', *Politeia*, 62 (2001), pp34–50.

20 MacKenzie, D (see note 16).

21 US Food and Drug Administration and US Department of Agriculture, *A US Government Submission to the Committee on General Principles of the Codex Alimentarius Commission for the Committee's April 10–14, 2000 Meeting* (2000).

22 OECD, *Summary of Data from OECD's Database of Field Trials* <http://www.olis.oecd.org/biotrack.nsf > (2001).

23 Diamond v. Chakrabarty (447 U.S. 303, 1980).

24 Eaglesham, A, 'Changing the nature of nature: corporate, legal and ethical fundamentals', in Eaglesham, A, Brown, W F and Hardy, RWF (eds), *The Biobased Economy of the 21st Century: Agriculture Expanding into Health, Energy, Chemicals, and Materials, NABC Report 12* (New York: National Agricultural Biotechnology Council, 2000).

25 European Commission, *Communication from the Commission on the Precautionary Principle*, COM (2000)1.

26 European Commission (see note 25).

27 Josling, T, 'International institutions, world trade rules, and GMOs', in Nelson, G C (ed.), *GMOs in Agriculture: Economics and Politics* (London: Academic Press, 2001).

28 Thompson, P, 'Bioethics issues in a biobased economy', in Eaglesham, A, Brown, W F and Hardy, RWF (eds), *The Biobased Economy of the 21st Century: Agriculture Expanding into Health, Energy, Chemicals, and Materials, NABC Report 12* (New York: National Agricultural Biotechnology Council, 2000).

29 European Commission, '1b, Democratising expertise and establishing a scientific reference systems', in *European Governance: a White Paper* (Brussels: European Commission, 2001).

30 Bach, J, 'US–EU trade issues', *Foreign Policy*, 4 (1999).

31 Bach, J (see note 30).

32 Bach, J (see note 30).

33 Fischler, F, 'EU and US farm policies: where do they differ and where do they converge?', Presentation to the Congressional Economic Leadership Institute, Washington DC, 17 May 2001.

34 Agriculture and Agri-food Canada, Agriculture and agri-food online <http://www.agr.ca/> (2000).

35 Fischler, F (see note 33).

36 Brinckman, D, 'The regulation of rBST: the European case', *AgBioForum*, 3 (2000).

37 McCombs, M and Shaw, D L, 'The agenda-setting function of the mass media', *Public Opinion Quarterly*, 36 (1972), pp176–87.

38 Lang, G E and Lang, K, *The Battle for Public Opinion: The President, the Press, and the Polls during Watergate* (New York: Columbia University Press, 1983).

39 Noelle-Neumann, E, *The Spiral of Silence: Public Opinion – Our Social Skin*, 2nd edn (Chicago: University of Chicago Press, 1993).

40 Hallin, D, *The Uncensored War* (Berkeley: University of California Press, 1989); Herman, E and Chomsky, N, *Manufacturing Consent: The Political Economy of the Mass Media* (New York: Pantheon, 1988).

41 Freudenburg W R, Coleman C L and Gonzales J H C, 'Media coverage of hazard events – analyzing the assumptions', *Risk Analysis*, 16 (1996), pp31–42.

42 Petersen, M, 'Monsanto campaign tries to gain support for gene-altered food', *New York Times* (8 December 1999).

43 *New York Times* (7 June 1999).

44 Davison, W P, 'The third person effect in communication', *Public Opinion Quarterly*, 47 (1983), pp1–15.

45 Priest, S H, *A Grain of Truth: The Media, the Public, and Biotechnology* (Oxford: Rowman and Littlefield, 2001).

46 Bagdikian, B, *The Media Monopoly* (Boston: Beacon Press, 1992).

47 Strumpel, B, 'Macroeconomic processes and societal psychology', in Himmelweit, H and Gaskell, G (eds) *Societal Psychology* (London: Sage, 1990).

48 Bradbury, J A, 'The policy implications of differing concepts of risk', *Science, Technology & Human Values*, 14 (1989), pp380–99.

49 Priest, S H (see note 45); Hornig, S, 'Reading risk: public response to print media accounts of technology risk', *Public Understanding of Science*, 2 (1993), pp95–109.

50 Fischoff, B, Slovic, P, Lichtenstein, S, Read, S and Combs, B, 'How safe is safe enough? A psycho-metric study of attitudes towards technological risks and benefits', *Policy Sciences*, 9 (1978), pp127–52.

51 Slovic, P, 'Perceptions of risk', *Science*, 236 (1987), pp280–5.

52 Cantley, M, 'The regulation of modern biotechnology: a historical and European perspective', in Brauer, D (ed.), *Biotechnology, vol. 12* (New York: VCH, 1995), pp505–681.

53 Gaskell, G, Allum, N and Wagner, W *et al.*, this volume, pp53–79.

54 McCutcheon, A C, *Latent Class Analysis* (Beverly Hills: Sage Publications, 1987).

55 Starr, C, 'Social benefit versus technological risk', *Science*, 165 (1969), pp1232–8.

56 Leger Marketing, *How Canadians Perceive Genetically Modified Organisms* (Montreal: Canadian Press/Leger Marketing, 2001).

57 Shortridge, B G and Shortridge, J R (eds), *The Taste of American Place: A Reader on Regional and Ethnic Foods* (Lanham, MD: Rowman and Littlefield, 1998).

58 Ten Eyck, T A, 'Managing food: Cajun cuisine in economic and cultural terms', *Rural Sociology*, 66 (2001).

59 Witt, D, *Black Hunger* (New York: Oxford University Press, 1999); Bell, D and Valentine, G, *Consuming Geographies* (New York: Routledge, 1997).

60 Belasco, W J, *Appetite for Change* (New York: Cornell University Press, 1993). This proposition was formally assessed using Baron and Kenny's procedure for testing mediation effects: Baron, R M and Kenny, D A, 'The moderator-mediator variable distinction in social psychological research: conceptual, strategic and statistical considerations', *Journal of Personality and Social Psychology*, 51 (1986), pp1173–82.

61 Zwart, H, 'A short history of food ethics', *Journal of Agricultural and Environmental Ethics*, 12 (2000), pp113–26.

62 Boyce, R W D, 'Fallacies in interpreting historical and social data', in Bauer, M W and Gaskell, G (eds), *Qualitative Researching with Text, Image and Sound: A Practical Handbook* (London: Sage, 2000), pp318–35.

Address for correspondence

George Gaskell, Department of Social Psychology, London School of Economics, Houghton St, London WC2A 2AE, UK. E-mail g.gaskell@lse.ac.uk

Biotechnology, technoscience and the public sphere

George Gaskell, Helge Torgersen, Nick Allum and Martin W Bauer

Introduction

The research reported in this book explores the reception of modern biotechnology in the public spheres of Europe and North America, with an emphasis on the years from 1996 to 2000. The public sphere – the intersection between regulatory activities and public opinion – is a vital part of the symbolic environment in which biotechnology has developed. It has been an environment of continuing conflicts, contested claims and controversy.

Much of the European public has become increasingly ambivalent, supporting health-related applications of biotechnology, while opposing the development of GM foods. The media's interest in biotechnology has increased and coverage, while still generally positive, has embraced issues such as ethics and public accountability. The natural-science paradigm and scientific expertise has been challenged with the institutionalisation of ethics and questions about the treatment of uncertainty. Governments have faced the competing pressures of economic competitiveness and the need to formulate a politically sustainable regulatory framework. In addition, European institutions and the governments of EU member states have faced the challenge of multilevel policy-making. All in all, the picture that biotechnology in the public sphere paints has become increasingly complex, and the question arises how the different parts of the public sphere relate to each other. In this chapter, we will explore some aspects of the relation between public opinion and policy, constituting the public sphere of biotechnology.

A major determinant for this relation is the perceived role of science in society. Since the meetings in Asilomar in the early 1970s, biotechnology's capacity for generating controversy around the globe appears to be undiminished. In mid-2001 the issue under the spotlight is stem-cell cloning. In the USA, President George Bush, supported by the religious right, ruled out federal funding for all but limited embryonic stem-cell research. His advisor on bioethics, Leon Kass, argues in favour of the 'wisdom of repugnance', an instinctive reaction against such things as human cloning. He says 'in an age in which everything is held to be permissible so long as it is freely done, repugnance may be the only voice left that speaks up to defend the central core of our humanity'.[1] On the other side of the Atlantic, while the UK quickly modified legislation on embryonic research, France and Germany called on the United Nations to develop an international convention to outlaw the cloning of human beings for the purposes of reproduction. Such a law was needed, said the foreign ministers, to 'enshrine the unacceptable nature and violation of human dignity' implied by cloning. By 2001 biotechnology had thus become an issue of global governance.

The scientific ethos

Are the past and continuing controversies over biotechnology a signal of a breakdown in the implicit contract between science and society? In the 1940s Merton discussed the potential threats to the autonomy of pure science posed by social pressures from totalitarian states.[2] He argued that, having liberated itself from theology, science should not become the handmaiden of the economy or the state. To do so leads to science that is acceptable only in so far as it meets the criteria of these extra-scientific institutions, and in doing so the ethos of the scientific enterprise is threatened. He also recognised the importance of technological developments on the public's view of science. In the past antiscientific sentiment had been held in check by the success of science in improving human welfare through technological applications. However, when technological applications meet with disapproval, it is science itself that is held responsible.

Merton characterised the 'ethos of science', the institutional norms and values that lie behind the scientific enterprise. These are universalism, the assessment of claims and warrants on the basis of pre-established universal criteria; communism, the common ownership of goods – science as public knowledge; disinterestedness, exemplified in the accountability of scientists to their peers through the process of review by fellow experts; and organised scepticism, the iconoclastic questioning of the 'taken for granteds of society' through systematic and detached enquiry.

This is an idealist statement of the scientific ethos, and indeed it was criticised as such. But it may still have some contemporary relevance. First, it may well be that this depiction of science and of the scientist informs the popular imagination and provides the basis on which public trust in the institution of science is grounded. From films and documentaries, books and newspapers the image of the scientist is the specialist working in the (university) laboratory with single-minded determination to crack the puzzle of the Big Bang or a little-understood human disease, either for the pursuit of knowledge as an end in itself, or for the common good. Such an image establishes the preconditions for trust in science which, like many other institutions in society, concern assumptions about shared values, expertise, accountability and social responsibility. Second, it is a characterisation of science that is structurally far removed from the technoscience of modern biotechnology. The Ernst & Young report on European Life Sciences 2001 presents an account of the 'defining events' of the previous year.[3] These are categorised under the headings of finance and markets, deals (mergers and acquisitions), products and technology and public policy. Of 17 defining events the only scientific reference is to the unveiling of the human genome, and that was the product of an uneasy alliance between the so-called gene entrepreneur Craig Venter and the publicly funded Human Genome Project. Of course the general public do not necessarily read the Ernst & Young report and the mass media give considerable coverage to new discoveries and scientific developments, but, as evidenced in the analysis of media coverage, 'business' is one of the three main actors featured in press stories, reinforcing the perception that this is not an activity that fits the public's representation of trusted science. There is undoubtedly expertise reflected in discoveries at the frontiers of imagination. But the other preconditions of trust are absent. The evident commercialisation and industrialisation of biotechnology, with the pursuit of private knowledge, patents and profits, hardly meets Merton's criteria of universalism, communism, disinterestedness and scepticism, or the public's expectations about the values, accountability and social responsibility of science. Biotechnology has become a technoscience, a commercial enterprise accountable to financial markets and to shareholders. In this context the findings of the Eurobarometer survey asking whether ten actor groups were 'doing a good or a bad job for society' is telling. 'Industry' was the only one for which a majority of Europeans who answered the question said 'a bad job'.

Public concerns about technoscience

While it is inevitable for the realisation of the potential of modern biotechnology that the pendulum has swung away from pure science to technoscience, this, we argue, has contributed to public concerns outlined in the previous two chapters.[4] But it is important to put these concerns into perspective. When questions are posed and issues discussed in the rather formal context of a survey interview, or the less formal setting of a focus group, most people are prepared to express opinions on a range of issues. Yet, it must be said that biotechnology is not a major concern for the majority of the European public. Around 50 per cent of Europeans said that before the survey interview in autumn 1999, they had never talked about biotechnology before, and only 5 per cent said they had talked about the subject frequently. The 'engaged public' of biotechnology is relatively small, even after the extensive media coverage of the 'watershed years' 1996–97. Interestingly, as reported in the chapter on public perceptions,[5] the 'engaged public', those with greater awareness, knowledge of biology and behavioural involvement in biotechnology issues, on average hold more favourable attitudes to applications of biotechnology. However, biotechnology has made some impact on the wider public. Of the seven applications included in the survey, a majority of people had heard of five of them before and when invited to discuss these and other issues, only a minority opted for the 'don't know' response or declined to participate in a discussion.

What is striking, judging from the survey and qualitative research, is the relative similarity in the dominant themes and discourses about biotechnology, and in the structure of attitudes and opinions, albeit that some people are more favourable to biotechnology and others more critical. The medical applications directed towards life saving, the betterment of health and the identification and, by implication, the curing of inherited diseases are welcomed. These applications of biotechnology are seen as exemplars of progress and to be in the hands of a widely trusted medical profession. But other applications and aspects of the technology, its development and regulation, are troubling. With the exception of medical applications, people talk about biotechnology in a number of interrelated currents of concern. Captured in the metaphor of a runaway train, biotechnology appears to have no braking mechanisms, it is powered by an alliance of industrial science and government for whom the destination is profits, it progresses at increasing speed with no regard for the warning signals of public opinion, and its eventual destination is unknown and possibly unknowable. With all this speed how can scientists know what is going to happen next, or what will happen to future generations?

This leads to a second current of concern, expressed in the survey in terms of 'dread risks' and, in the group discussions, as the possibility of delayed effects. Given a general presumption that experts do not understand the longer term effects of genetic modification, people ask whether we will reap a bitter harvest in years to come. Such worries are anchored in past problems, for example thalidomide, HIV-contaminated blood and BSE. Can people have trust in scientific and governmental reassurances that GM foods have no conceivable risk? Many think not because in the context of the runaway train scenario, common sense points to not trusting such statements.

Effective regulation is a further current of concern. External and not self regulation is seen as an imperative, but where, people ask, are the effective regulatory bodies, given that the drivers of the runaway train are government and industrial science? Even if legitimate regulators existed how can they exercise proactive control over such a fast-moving technology? Given that this is a technology for which national boundaries are irrelevant, echoes of the 'risk society',[6] where are the international bodies with the power to impose controls?

Finally, and perhaps at the root of the above concerns, it is the paradigm of the biotechnology project that leads to unease and at times something close to Kass's concept of repugnance. The idea of intentionally moulding or manipulating what are taken to be the fundamental building blocks of nature or human identity is simply alien. Even amongst those survey respondents who expressed overall support for applications of biotechnology, a majority think that GM foods and cloning animals threaten the natural order and that there would be a global catastrophe if things went wrong. The objections are both spiritual (so-called 'blue' or conservative resistance) and secular (so-called 'green' or modern resistance),[7] but come together

in the conclusion that biotechnology will, it is thought, inevitably lead to dire consequences. The hubris of science will be met with its nemesis, either because we have an obligation to venerate nature and human dignity, or because those who meddle with elements of a complex system can never know what the overall effects will be. These issues 'trouble' a public who appreciate the contribution of technology to everyday life, understand that life without risk is not an option and recognise the role of scientific testing of innovations.

To dismiss their troubles over biotechnology as merely irrational would be highly irrational itself. First, it would ignore some concerns about the scientific ethos of the technoscience of biotechnology. The preconditions for trust in scientific statements from 'technoscience' have yet to be established. Second, it would disregard deep-seated values which are at the core of European civil society. While people's understandings of nature and of human dignity are seldom articulated with the precision of a philosopher, they are an important component of the collective representations – the 'taken for granteds' of life – that define people's ideas of their culture and identity, and the ways they think and talk about the rights and wrongs of new challenges posed by applications of biotechnology. These values came into consideration, in part, because two of the first products of the new technology became, through metaphor and symbolism, to be associated with basic human concerns. Dolly the sheep, linked to human reproduction and to eugenics, and Monsanto's Roundup Ready Soya (and other GM crops) raised the questions about food purity and contamination. Uninvited, but so challenging they could not be ignored, these innovations entered national public spheres variously characterised by a *political context* of the relations between the political elite and the public and by typical modes of regulation; a *cultural context* reflected in collective representations, myths, literature and popular culture; a *technological context*, the recent history of past successes and problems with technologies; and a context of *current public opinion* as reflected in debates over economic growth, concerns over globalisation, European integration, the future of farming, global warming, etc.

Into these national environments, biotechnology became an element in a variety of debates and a platform for mobilising a variety of different groups. Because national publics give more or less attention to particular issues at different times, and when issues emerge into the limelight they take on local colour, we observe a range of different reactions to the challenge of biotechnology.

Characterising the public spheres

To simplify the analysis of these complex national environments and to do so in a way that affords the possibility for cross-national comparisons, our research conceives of the public sphere in terms of the intersection between, on one hand, policy and regulation and, on the other, public opinion, captured in the media and public conversations. Both can only be approximately described, and there is room for different interpretations, however, we can arrive at some tentative conclusions from a pragmatic analysis.

We take policy to be the sum of political intentions, the generation and setting of measures and the actors' communication about this in a particular field.[8] It can be investigated by analysing interpretations, decisions and measures of policy-makers, be they politicians, regulators or those, in a wider perspective, involved in decision-taking. Public opinion is a summary term for a complex arrangement of structured and less structured expressions of short- and long-term views within the general public (itself a highly aggregated construct). It is represented in the mass media, i.e. formal communication approachable through media analysis, and in conversations, i.e. informal communication captured in surveys and interviews. Since public opinion can be conceptualised into two separate arenas, our model of the public sphere is a triangle of mediation between policy, the media and public perceptions.

The comparative chapters in the second part of this book present an analysis and interpretation of each of the three arenas of the public sphere. Here we explore the extent to which the arenas of the public spheres of Europe and North America are in or out of 'alignment', that is the extent to which policy and public opinion, roughly, converge on either a 'pro' or 'anti' stance towards biotechnology. This is a pragmatic approximation in order to describe a certain congruence between, on one hand, political measures taken and, on the other hand, opinions communicated in the mass media and the thrust of public views as emerging from focus-group work or surveys.

The voting behaviour of some national representatives at the European Commission's committee of national experts on applications for marketing transgenic plants, and public perceptions in the same countries as measured in the Eurobarometer surveys for 1996 and 1999 show indications of such alignment (Table 1).

In all four countries the 'official opinion' and public perceptions are aligned. From 1996 to 1999 there is no change in the Netherlands (pro) and in Austria (anti). France and the UK show movement towards a more anti stance in both the 'official position' and in public perceptions.

In using the term alignment we are aware that this significantly, and perhaps simplisticly, reduces the actual complexity of the relation between public opinion and policy. At the same time, we are at pains to avoid the suggestion of any normative connotations. Value judgements about the virtues or otherwise of alignment and non-alignment will depend on the context and time, and whose perspective is privileged. For example, it seems

Table 1. Alignment of 'official opinion' and public perceptions

a Official opinion on product applications 1996 vs 1999 (estimation based on known votes)

Favourable (pro) ⟵					⟶ *Restrictive(anti)*
	France 96				France 99
UK 96			UK 99		
					Austria 96 and 99
Netherlands 96 and 99					

b Public perceptions of GM foods 1996/99 (source: Eurobarometer 46.1 and 52.1)

Percentage of public opposed to GM foods					
20	30	40	50	60	70
		France 96			France 99
	UK 96		UK 99		
					Austria 96 and 99
Netherlands 96	Netherlands 99				

likely that civil nuclear power in the USSR pre-Chernobyl developed in the context of a supportive party elite. By contrast, heart transplantation and IVF were greeted with considerable expert and public disquiet in their early years. In the case of biotechnology, value judgements may be ambivalent. For example, when policy, media and public opinion are aligned with a pro or facilitating 'attitude' this may constitute an optimal commercial environment for some, while being a highly risky and unethical position for others. Situations of non-alignment are likely to be indicative of public controversy and possibly conflict over aspects of the technology.

A further consideration is that, while it might be expected that alignment would be reached at some time in the future, we make no predictions for the short term. Jasper models the life cycle of technological controversies over civil nuclear power in the USA, France and Sweden and proposes three distinct phases.[9] In the pre-political phase there is minimal public controversy and a general acceptance of expert opinion. Then comes the political phase when doubts raised by experts are aired in the media and this is accompanied by the mobilisation of activists on both sides of the controversy. And finally, comes the post-political phase characterised by declining controversy and media interest as some form of accommodation is reached on the technology. The issue is resolved by one or more of the following: government action, media and public boredom or an understanding between the opposing activists. Writing in the late 1980s Jasper notes the contrasting outcomes in the three countries. French opinion became increasingly pro-nuclear, American increasing anti and Swedish somewhere in between. But the post-political phase is not necessarily the end of controversy. While the Chernobyl disaster in 1986 had little impact on France or the USA, it reignited the controversy in Sweden.

This model of the life history of a controversy would suggest that over the longer term we might expect to see the three arenas of the public sphere moving towards alignment, to the eventual 'normalisation' of biotechnology when it is no longer political and merely taken for granted. This could be in an affirmative way, like the personal computer or, for the most part, the mobile phone; it can also be in a rejecting fashion, as with nuclear power in many European countries today. But we must be cautious in drawing too close a parallel between civil nuclear power and other 'single' technologies, and biotechnology which embraces distinct applications in many domains including the medical, pharmaceutical, agrifood, animal, and the environmental. Different domains of application of biotechnology, and different applications within any one domain may have unique life cycles of controversy.

To this extent, making longer term predictions about biotechnology as such reaching the post-political phase would be just too simplistic. Looking at specific applications there are examples of all three phases. While in the 1980s there were heated debates (Phase 2: political) over 'contained use' in the production of enzymes, hormones and pharmaceuticals, the issue was closed by legislation in the early 1990s (Phase 3: post-political). In this context the proposed use of GM bacteria for bio-remediation almost went politically unnoticed (Phase 1: pre-political). But, as the 1990s progressed, 'deliberate release' into the environment took over as the focus of intense controversy (Phase 2: political).

At present it would appear that many applications of biotechnology other than contained use can be appropriately characterised in most countries as in the 'political phase'. New research and applications of biotechnology continue apace. Such developments are throwing up new opportunities, challenges and ethical issues, generating increasing levels of media coverage and leading to the mobilisation of pro and anti groups on a variety of topics. In such a period of rapid technological change the public sphere is dynamic and unpredictable. As the political phase evolves we may expect that at different times and in different environments (countries), the direction of influence and feedback between policy and public opinion will vary. Theorists of the policy process and of the media outline different examples of such relations. Hood and colleagues find evidence for two risk regimes in an analysis of a state's response to health-related hazards: 'client politics' where the level of regulation is related to the power of interest groups, and by contrast 'responsive government' where policy developments reflect public opinion.[10] Hall's analysis suggests that the liberal market economics of Thatcherism was a revolutionary shift in the policy paradigm and, by implication, outside any form of influence from public opinion.[11] Hence, there is evidence for both policy and public opinion taking the lead under different conditions. The influence of the media on public perceptions has a long and somewhat unproductive history in terms of unequivocal findings. Mazur argues for strong effects: increased media coverage of a controversy leads to declining public support.[12]

Other models making weaker claims for media effects, for example 'agenda setting' appear to be more plausible but are not easy to test empirically.[13]

Given that variants of applications of biotechnology may be in different phases of the life cycle of controversy, and that, at a particular time, the public sphere may be in or out of alignment, in our exploration of the dynamics of the public sphere we keep an open mind as to the balance of influence between policy and public opinion.

Alignment of policy, media and public perceptions

Table 2 brings together the results of the analyses of policy, media coverage and public perceptions

for applications of biotechnology in the 'red' (GM medicines and genetic testing) and 'green' (GM foods and crops) domains. For each domain, policy, media and public perceptions are characterised on a dimension from relatively facilitative to relatively constraining. For policy and media coverage the categorisation of countries is based on the analyses presented elsewhere in this book.[14] For public perceptions we have calculated average scores for encouragement for the 'red' and 'green' applications separately using the Eurobarometer survey.

Green biotechnologies

There are two notable features in Table 2: firstly, the extent of alignment within the countries and

Table 2. National public spheres from relatively facilitative to relatively constraining

a 'Green' biotechnologies

	Facilitative		*Constraining*	
Policy	**Germany,**[a] **Finland, Netherlands, Canada, USA,** Switzerland	Portugal	*Austria,*[b] *France, Sweden, UK, Greece, Denmark,* Italy	
Media coverage of 'green' issues	**Germany, Canada, USA,** Italy	Finland, Netherlands, *France*[c]	*Austria, Sweden, UK, Denmark, Greece,* Switzerland, Portugal	
Public preceptions of 'green' biotechnologies	**Finland, Netherlands, Canada, USA,** Italy, Portugal	Germany, UK	*Austria, Greece, Sweden, Denmark, France,* Switzerland	

a Bold text indicates facilitative alignment.
b Neither bold nor italic indicates non-alignment.
c Italic indicates constraining alignment.

b 'Red' biotechnologies

	Facilitative		*Constraining*	
Policy	**UK,**[a] **Italy, France, Greece, Sweden, Finland, Netherlands, Canada, USA, Portugal Switzerland,** Denmark[b]	**Austria, Germany**		
Media coverage of 'red' issues	**Germany, Canada, USA, Italy, Portugal**	**Switzerland, Finland, Netherlands, Austria, UK, Greece, Sweden, France**	Denmark	
Public perception of 'red' biotechnologies (all countries have positive mean scores)	**Germany, Finland, Netherlands, Portugal, Canada, USA, France, Greece, Italy, Sweden, Switzerland,** Denmark	**Austria, UK**		

a Bold text indicates facilitative alignment.
b Denmark is the only non-aligned country.

secondly, the bifurcation of countries between 'pro' and 'anti' alignment. In bold, and on the left-hand side of the table, are the countries which have relatively more facilitative public spheres. Their position on policy, media coverage and public perceptions is relatively more 'pro' than the remaining countries. In this group of countries we find Germany, Finland, the Netherlands, Canada and the USA. In bold italics, and to the right-hand side of the table, are the countries in which the public sphere comes together in a relatively more oppositional stance. Here we find Austria, Denmark, France, Greece, Sweden and the UK.

In three countries, Switzerland, Portugal and Italy, we observe non-alignment. Italy's relatively constraining policy stance, reflected in its continued support for the de facto moratorium on the commercial planting of GM crops, is due, in part, to the influence of a minister of the environment from the Green Party. This policy stance contrasts with media coverage and public perceptions that are relatively favourable for 'green' biotechnologies. In Switzerland, notable for probably the most significant and sustained public debate over biotechnology leading up to the referendum in 1999, while policy is relatively facilitative, public opinion is relatively constraining. Notwithstanding the 'pro' vote there are clearly residual tensions between policies consistent with the economic importance of the life sciences industry and public opposition to GM crops and foods, in line with the position of the widely respected farming sector.

In Portugal the government was initially supportive, but in 1999 followed other EU countries in suspending authorisations of GMO releases. While the public is still amongst the most positive in Europe, since 1996 there has been a marked increase in opposition, a shift that parallels the media coverage which, while low key, is typified by concerns over risks.

What might account for the bifurcation of the public spheres with respect to the 'green' biotechnologies? Why is it that the public spheres are supportive in Finland, Germany, the Netherlands, Canada and the USA, but opposed in Austria, Denmark, France, Greece, Norway, Sweden and the UK? Looking back to 1996 we note that many countries have not changed their position. But there are some notable shifts. At that time, while the German public was relatively negative towards biotechnology, the media had a relatively positive tone and government policies were moving towards the deregulation of constraints on biotechnology. In the period 1997–99 public perceptions moved

towards greater support, possibly following the lead of government policy and media coverage. Contrast this with Greece, where in 1996 public perceptions were amongst the most supportive of biotechnology in Europe. By 1999 the Greek public opinion had swung from positive to negative, leading the government to become the early campaigner for the de facto moratorium.

In different countries and at different times it appears that government actions and public opinion have been instrumental in changing the tone of the public sphere. As a very broad generalisation it might be argued that France, Germany, the Netherlands, Norway and Sweden are countries where, on balance, government action led the way; by contrast and again, on balance, it might be argued that public opinion was more influential in Austria, Denmark, Greece and the UK. This brings us back to Italy, Switzerland and Portugal. In 1999 the Italian policy is more constraining than public opinion, while the reverse is the case in Switzerland. It is difficult to predict whether or not these public spheres will remain non-aligned or whether there will be an evolution to alignment, and who or what will lead.

In contrast to the established debates over biotechnology in Italy and Switzerland, in Portugal the debate has hardly started. It might be argued that the arenas of the public sphere are moving towards constraint, albeit at different speeds. However, it is also possible that events in other European countries, particularly responses to the revisions of the directive 90/220 EC, will have a decisive efect on the trajectory of the public sphere in Portugal.

Currently, there is only inconclusive evidence of the emergence of a post-political phase in terms of Jasper's phases of technological controversies. While one characteristic of such a post-political phase is alignment of policy and public opinion, another one is declining media interest. The media intensity index[15] shows that in no countries is there a decline in media intensity from the period 1992–96 to 1997–99. However, it may be that those countries with relatively lower rates of increase in media coverage are approaching the transition towards the post-political Phase 3. If these countries show a parallel tendency towards alignment this would be a further indication of approaching normalisation.

Taking the case of 'green' biotechnologies, of those aligned in a facilitative direction the Netherlands, together with Canada and the USA, show below-average growth in media coverage. However in Finland and Germany where there is the same pattern of alignment, media coverage shows well-above-average growth. A constraining alignment and low media growth is seen in Denmark, Greece, Sweden and the UK, but the same alignment is associated with high media growth in France and Austria. Overall there are more countries where policy and public opinion are aligned, which also show relatively lower media growth than high media growth. Without the stimulus of external events we might expect that countries in former group would increasingly incline towards normalisation and to declining political controversy.

However, the absence of external events seems unlikely. For example, in response to concerns raised by various European member states, the directive 90/220 EC on deliberate release and the placing on the market of GMOs has been revised to include more stringent provisions for risk assessment, monitoring and labelling, as well as for public participation and a wider range of expert advice. These new policies are explicitly intended, and likely, to have an impact on public opinion. But, as has been seen in the past, the effects of such seemingly responsive measures have been unpredictable. They can either defuse current controversies, or, by officially acknowledging the risks, lead to the amplification of risk perceptions amongst the public.[16] Across the Atlantic, developments are similarly unpredictable. In both the USA and Canada there is overwhelming support for the labelling of GM foods, amongst a public that is largely unaware of the extent to which biotechnology has entered the food chain. Will North American publics accept the technical fait accompli or will European anxieties migrate across the Atlantic, and how will the regulators respond?

Red biotechnologies

In terms of the 'red' biotechnologies, both the European and North American public spheres are overwhelmingly in alignment and in a facilitative stance. In Germany and Austria some constraints stem from past controversies over the uses of genetic testing, which have become topical once again as this application extends into genetic databanks and is more powerful in its predictive capacity. In the national media there is greater caution in Denmark and to a lesser extent in Austria, Greece, Sweden, Switzerland and the UK. However, the 'benefits' of the 'red' biotechnologies also feature prominently in press coverage. The publics, while often acknowledging the possibility of risks, feel that these are outweighed by the benefits, and hence there is overall support. In terms of Jasper's model it might be argued that many applications within 'red' biotechnology, such as the development and production of drugs and vaccines, have moved to a transitional state between the political (Phase 2) and post political (Phase 3) stages of the life cycle of technological controversies.

Whether this direction of change will be sustained towards 'normality' or be disrupted by new issues and returned to a political Phase 2 is open to question. Developments in the uses of genetic testing and other applications of biotechnology in the medical domain are increasingly the focus of controversy. To the ethical dilemmas raised by research on human embryos and the judicial status of the embryo, will be added the opportunity of genetic tests to predict, and act upon, future risk, beyond existing disability. As has been evidenced in the USA, these issues have mobilised groups who in the past have had little interest in biotechnology. As a precondition for controversy, in Europe a wide variety of regulatory arrangements exist, with some countries having virtually no restrictions and others calling for forms of prohibition. While the survey data suggest that the 'red' biotechnologies have been, by and large, insulated from the controversy over and increasing public opposition to GM foods and crops, these new developments in the fields of diagnostics, cloning and genetic testing may ignite public opinion, with attention eventually shifting from agrifood to medical and diagnostic biotechnologies.

In conclusion, we can say that there is indeed a relation between public opinion and policy as established in our research, but it is far from linear and there is no simple conclusion to be drawn. While for most of 'red' biotechnology, and in most countries, there seems to be alignment in a facilitative stance, the picture is more inconsistent for 'green' biotechnology. Most 'green' applications are still in Phase 2, and while some 'red' applications are moving towards Phase 3, foreseeable controversies may shake this alignment and bring red biotechnology back to Phase 2. Conflict over biotechnology will, in all probability, stay with us.

Democracy, ethics and sound science

In a commentary on the linkage between public perceptions, as evidenced by the 1999 Eurobarometer, and national policies, *Nature Biotechnology* observed that public opinion and country support for the continuation or removal of the de facto moratorium on commercial GM crop planting in Europe was strikingly aligned.[17] The editorial went on to suggest that idealists would interpret the alignment in terms of the power of democracy while cynics would attribute it to the influence of politicians on the public. The present analysis adds the third arena, that of media coverage, to the public sphere. And it is notable that in the greater majority of countries, policy, media and public perceptions are singing in unison.

This opens up issues concerning the effects of policy-making on public opinion and, of course the reverse, the effects of public opinion on policy-making. And it raises questions about the legitimate mechanisms within democratic societies to resolve the type of conflicts that have arisen over biotechnology. The traditional view is that legitimacy rests with parliaments to come to a decision between competing claims. On issues of science and technology where parliamentarians are seldom specialists, they rely on scientists to guide their deliberations. But with governments having the dual roles of promoting and regulating the technology, and many scientists working in technically applied rather than pure or fundamental science, conflicts of interest may be seen, at least by some, to exist.

The entrance into the debates of now widely respected extra-parliamentary voices, such as environmental and consumer organisations, suggests that some dimensions of biotechnology were ignored by the traditional political arenas. This is hardly a novel development in the history of democracies, but in the context of science, as for other vested interests in past times, such an external challenge to its established authority has not been greeted with enthusiasm. The challenge comprised two related issues: the authority of science to adjudicate on matters of risk and the role of extra-scientific and extra-parliamentary agents in deliberations about the regulation of a new technology. In essence the issue is how should the democratic process operate in relation to a modern science that is part of the economic and political system and whose impacts become the focus of public controversy.

Scientific and other conceptions of risk

The natural science paradigm specifies methods for dealing with the known and quantifiable; that which is not amenable to measurement is not considered within the purview of science. Hence the development of ethics can be understood as a way of assimilating, or at least being seen to take seriously, anxieties raised in the public sphere. The institutionalisation of ethics has led to some notable constraints on certain developments of biotechnology, mostly related to embryo experimentation and cloning. However, there are some unintended consequences of the professionalisation of ethics.

Ethics emerges as a forum in which to categorise public concerns that are judged to be of a non-scientific nature. While science is considered to be value free, objective, rational and the domain of experts trained in the scientific method and techniques of risk assessment, ethics is seen as emotional, value laden and outside the purview of the scientific enterprise. Ethics is thus regarded as the domain of another group of experts who are often as remote from the public as are scientists. With this division of labour, ethics implicitly insulates or protects scientific activities and regulation based on 'sound science' from the concerns expressed in the public domain. The framing of risks associated with developments in biotechnology solely in terms of those that are recognised and familiar to contemporary science has been challenged on a number of grounds. The definition of what constitutes a risk is not value free and the assessment of risks presupposes certain tractable and often debatable assumptions. And beyond this how can risks, operationalised in terms of the probability of adverse consequences, be attributed to the unknown? In other words, what is the relation between risk and uncertainty?

For the public, the idea of reducing the potential dangers of biotechnology to known risks, those that can be quantified, is an alien approach. Risk may be a useful analytic category in the esoteric life world of experts, but it is not part of the life world of ordinary people, who are more inclined to take what is called a contextural perspective. There are risks and uncertainties inherent in doing things that upset socially and culturally defined ways of acting, and to do such things is often described as immoral. In this way the distinction between risks and ethics is meaningless, the two concepts are intermingled and judged on an all-or-none criterion rather than through the lens of probabilities.[18]

There are different types of uncertainty related to a new technology,[19] and the failure to take appropriate action raises moral concerns in the public mind. First, there are those uncertainties that could be reduced in principle by further empirical research; not to complete such research before implementing the technology would be seen as immoral. Second, there are those uncertainties that are not reducible in principle; here, to deny the extent of the uncertainty or to claim that more research is in the pipeline would be seen to be immoral. Finally, there are those uncertainties which some experts claim are unknowable; to dismiss these out of hand as fantasy and to proceed with the application of the technology would again be morally unacceptable. Those who sweep uncertainties under the table are unlikely to have formulated a risk-management strategy, also adding to the perception of indecent and immoral haste in the implementation of the technology.

While the public know about the possibility of side-effects from medicines and assume that these are the subject of scientific monitoring, when talking about the development of biotechnology, they entertain two other types of concerns or hazards. The first flow from the novel procedures used in biotechnology. These are widely perceived to be a threat to the natural order and to have unknown, perhaps unknowable, consequences in the years to come. These we might call 'moral hazards', in so far as to promote the technology today in the light of such possibilities, and without plans to conduct the necessary safety research, appears to the public to be immoral. The second type of concern relates to the role of science and technology in society. These concerns go beyond biotechnology, but it seems as if biotechnology has brought them to the fore. People worry about where technology will lead to, they wonder who is in charge, whether or not scientists are independent of or accountable to the biotechnology industry, who should decide on the future shape of society and who will speak up for the interests of the ordinary person. These concerns might be called 'democratic hazards'. If science stays insulated from a consideration of these moral and democratic hazards and is seen to reject their validity, public distrust will be the outcome.

Preconditions for a pluralistic debate

In response to the evident public concerns the report of the EU–US Biotechnology Consultative Forum Report argues that 'transparency in decision taking, inclusive and meaningful participation [act] as the foundations of confidence in public institutions'.[20] This sentiment was echoed by Mr Philippe Busquin, the EU Commissioner for Research, in 2001 with a call for a pluralist debate to agree rules on biotechnology with the European Community. These comments perhaps reflect a growing realisation that the opaque and implicit mechanisms for democratic involvement in science and technology have been less than successful. This raises the question as to how the views and values of the public can be brought into the process of decision-taking. Since it is hardly practical to run modern societies on the basis of referendums on the wide range of contentious policy options across the many domains of policy-making, perhaps the issue is how to build public confidence in the regulatory process. While it is not within our expertise to define the mechanisms for national and international governance to achieve this end, the following considerations are intended as an agenda for discussion.

In Shaw's play *Pygmalion*, when Professor Henry Higgins opined that women 'listening very nicely and going off and do precisely what they want', he captured the essence of what many people believe to be the status of public consultation on matters of science and technology: a smokescreen behind which scientists and governments carry on as before. In trying to open up the process of decision-taking beyond the election, pressure group or survey, a number of experimental forms of participation have been tried out, such as consensus conferences, public meetings and deliberative democracy. Essentially these are mechanisms for hearing the voice of (some) of the public. But having heard the voice the next question is how that voice is embraced within policy deliberations.

To help to clarify the outcomes of any exercise in listening to the public voice, consider the following types of dialogue between A (the decision taker) and B (the embodiment of the public voice who is influenced by A's decisions but has little power). In the extreme case, there is the non-dialogue, **1** A ignores B and decides independently. We then move to two types of dialogue which lead to the same outcome as the non-dialogue. **2** A acknowledges B, but since A thinks B is ignorant and uninformed, A ignores B: the *technocratic style*. Or, **3** A acknowledges that B is ignorant and tries to inform B while deciding autonomously: the *public-relations approach*. In type **4** we see the emergence of a form of real dialogue. Here, A listens to B but does so in terms of A's definition of the problem and its possible solutions. B's view is heard only in so far as B talks in terms of A's definition: the *sound-science approach*. In all these forms of (non-)dialogue, B will not feel committed to its outcome because their voice has not been heard. In type **5** we see what might constitute a genuine attempt at *public consultation*. A has a 'position' but tries to understand B's viewpoint on the issue. A is willing to learn from B and to accommodate to B, i.e. A is prepared to modify his/her position, and B understands this is part of the social contract. A takes the decision and in a public record makes the criteria explicit and, if B's position is rejected, explains the reasons for the rejection. Even in such a case, B feels committed to the outcome.

In the sense of type 5, *meaningful consultation* implies being heard and being taken seriously and, if a viewpoint is not accepted, hearing why. It implies a commitment of time and patience on the part of the decision-taker to listen to a range of viewpoints, preparedness to accommodate the views of others and public accountability through publicly recording the basis on which the decision was made and the reasons for rejecting certain positions. And when consultation is so structured, it provides an incentive for B, the public, to engage in the democratic process. It might be argued that if this type of consultation is implemented a number of consequences would follow.

First, it would lead to the emergence of visible institutional structures and mechanisms that could be the focus of trust. Such visible structures would address public concerns over what we have termed 'democratic' hazards. Although most Europeans believe that biotechnology must be regulated, with the exception of pharmaceuticals, few have any idea who is, or should be, responsible for such regulation. Second, public concerns, which go beyond 'objective scientific risks' are likely to be addressed and not ignored. As we have argued, the sidelining of public concerns about 'moral' hazards is an obstacle to public confidence. Third, it would encourage transparency and full disclosure with the provision of information on potential risks, accompanied by a stated risk-management strategy. And finally, it would necessarily acknowledge the import of national diversity in responses to new technologies. The European public is not homogeneous, different cultures are almost defined by differing values and national imperatives, and these inform the hopes and fears that people bring to the representation of applications of biotechnology.

In the debate on biotechnology we see the public represented in two guises. As an economic consumer who buys in the marketplace, with concerns focusing on the price, availability and safety of goods, and as a citizen who debates in the public sphere, votes in elections and has concerns extending across a wide range of social, political and other issues facing contemporary society. As biotechnology has emerged as the subject of scrutiny so has the public as citizen been increasingly in evidence and the pre-eminent concerns been those of the citizen rather than the consumer. The trajectory of the development of biotechnology in its many forms and applications is likely to be greatly influenced by the extent to which the process of policy-making and the content of regulation accommodate to the citizen of the twenty-first century.

Notes and references

1 Kass, L R, 'Why we should ban human cloning now: preventing a brave new world', *New Republic Online* (21 May 2001).

2 Merton, R K, *Social Theory and Social Structure* (Glencoe, IL: The Free Press, 1949).

3 Ernst & Young, 'Integration', *Eighth Annual European Life Sciences Report* (London: Ernst & Young, 2001).

4 Gaskell, G, Allum, N and Wagner, W *et al.*, this volume, pp53–79; Wagner, W, Kronberger, N and Gaskell, G, *et al.*, this volume, pp80–95.

5 Gaskell, G, Allum, N and Wagner, W *et al.* (see note 4).

6 Beck, U, *Risk Society: Towards a New Modernity* (London: Sage, 1992).

7 See Gaskell, G, Allum, N and Wagner, W *et al.* (note 4).

8 Heclo, H H, 'Policy analysis', *British Journal of Political Science*, 2 (1972), pp83–108.

9 Jasper, J M, 'The political life cycle of technological controversies', Social Forces 67, 357–77 (1988).

10 Hood, C, Rothstein, H, Spackman, M, Rees, J and Baldwin, R, 'Explaining risk regulation regimes: exloring the "minimal feasible response" hypothesis', *Health, Risk and Society*, 1 (1999), pp151–66.

11 Hall, P A, 'Policy paradigms, social learning and the state. The case of economic policy making in Britain', *Comparative Politics* (1993), pp275–96.

12 Leahy, P and Mazur, A, 'The rise and fall of public opposition in specific social movements', *Social Studies of Science*, 10 (1980), pp259–84; Mazur, A, 'Media coverage and public opinion on scientific controversies', *Journal of Communication*, 31 (1981), pp106–15.

13 McCombs, M and Shaw, D L, 'The agenda-setting function of the mass media', *Public Opinion Quarterly*, 36 (1972), pp176–87.

14 Grabner, P, Hampel, J, Lindsey, N and Torgersen, H, this volume, pp15–34; Bauer, M W, Kohring, M, Allansdottir, A and Gutteling, J, this volume, pp35–52.

15 Figure 2 in Bauer, M W, Kohring, M, Allansdottir, A and Gutteling, J (see note 14), p39.

16 Renn, O, 'Risk communication and the social amplification of risk', in Kasperson, R E and Stallen, P J M (eds), *Communicating Risks to the Public: International Perspectives* (Dordrecht: Kluwer Academic Publishers, 1991), pp287–324.

17 'Reasons to be cheerful', *Nature Biotechnology*, 18 (2000), p905.

18 Thompson, P, 'The ethics of truth-telling and the problem of risk', *Science and Engineering Ethics*, 5 (1999), pp489–510.

19 Funtowicz, R O and Ravetz, J R, 'Three types of risk assessment and the emergence of post-normal science', in Krimsky, S and Golding, D, *Social Theories of Risk* (Westport: Praeger, 1992), pp251–73.

20 EU–US Consultative Forum on Biotechnology, *Final Report* (Brussels: European Commission, 2000).

Address for correspondence

George Gaskell, Department of Social Psychology, London School of Economics, Houghton St, London WC2A 2AE, UK. E-mail g.gaskell@lse.ac.uk

Part III
National profiles

Austria: narrowing the gap with Europe

Helge Torgersen, Caroline Egger, Petra Grabner, Nicole Kronberger, Franz Seifert, Patrizia Weger and Wolfgang Wagner

Austrian policy development: forerunner or freewheeler?

Pre-1996

In the mid-1980s, biotechnology together with in-vitro fertilisation, started to become the subject of debate. While the scientific community denied the need for a specific law, the (not very prominent) pharmaceutical industry feared that the lack of a stable regulatory framework might lead to a loss in competitiveness. At the same time, Austria was beginning to come into line with EU regulations. In 1992, the Austrian parliament held an expert commission of inquiry on 'technology assessment of genetic engineering'. Its findings were critical, particularly of the release of GMOs. Although the fostering of a broader public discussion was one of the explicit aims of the commission, this was not sought. Even when the Ministry of Health presented a draft law, without waiting for the parliament's recommendations, there was little public reaction.

The law, enforced in 1995, regulates the contained use, release and marketing of GMOs, genetic testing and gene therapy. Among the several principles mentioned, the 'ethical principle' refers to human applications only. The law also makes provision for the avoidance of products that are 'socially unsustainable'. Apart from this, the law follows the EU directives closely. However, the official stance of the environment agency on GMO releases exceeded the European mainstream. It objected to any possible negative environmental outcome of agricultural practice.[1] This position was later backed up by several studies and contributed to what after 1998 became the 'restrictive' EU position. Neither this 'green' approach nor the parliament's attempts to anticipate – and thus pro-actively mitigate – predictable conflicts, nor the attempt to avoid them via legal regulation, proved successful.

Mobilisation forerunner

A formidable public mobilisation took place from early 1996 onwards. This lasted for almost three years and made its mark on official policy (Table 1). It preceded similar developments in other European countries. Before 1996, environmental NGOs had taken up GMO releases as a major issue. At the same time, the Ministry of Health expected to receive the first release proposals. In response, the Ministry of Health funded a public research institute, which proposed a GMO release in order to undertake biosafety research. The first public hearing, mandated by Austrian law, demonstrated the difficulty the Ministry faced in handling such a new area of research. Public opposition increased when a proposal for herbicide-resistant maize was submitted; not least because genetically modified crops were seen as a threat to Austria's many organic farmers. Two ministers publicly opposed the proposal and the company withdrew. The third proposal, initially less controversial, provoked a scandal when the company released the plants before permission was granted. This event was widely covered in the media. The Minister announced a moratorium and, although it was immediately lifted by the Chancellor, the country has not yet seen any releases. This domestic Austrian public mobilisation set the scene for the conflicts that followed.

As in many other European countries, a new debate arose late in 1996 on the pending importation of GM crops, such as maize and soya, which was permitted under EU law. Building on arguments already established, the NGOs launched several successful offensives. Their aim was to make it clear that they would not approve of any GM product being imported into Austria, despite EU regulations. This added a European dimension at a point when the Austrians' initial enthusiasm for the EU was cooling. Furthermore, it resulted in two contradictory policy initiatives: one for banning and one for labelling GMOs.

Spurred by domestic pressure, the government banned the import of GM maize in 1996. This was

Table 1. *Key policy events in Austria, 1996–99*

Date	Trigger	Event	Outcome
May 1996	Illegal release.	After first release applications had caused massive NGO and tabloid press outrage; public rejection of agricultural biotechnology.	Start of GMO debate; agriculture becomes paramount; Volksbegehren launched in autumn and conducted in April 1997.
Autumn 1996	Soya imports.	Labelling debate fuelled; retail chains react. NGOs and opposition demand import ban; activists occupy Minister's office; disagreements on draft Food Law within government.	Decrees on strict labelling of food, animal feed, seeds; European dimension added; government under pressure from two sides.
December 1996	EU market approval for GM maize.	Massive protests; debates on labelling and banning intensified; retailers start to remove products from shelves. Opinion polls show support for Volksbegehren demands.	Import ban on GM maize (February 1997); new release application withdrawn; decree on labelling anticipating novel food directive.
February 1997	Dolly the sheep.	Short-lived flaring of discussion on gene analysis and ethics.	None.
April 1997	Registration period for Volksbegehren.	Peak of NGO and tabloid press campaign during the weeks leading up to Volksbegehren.	1.23 million signatures; NGO–government summit.
November 1997	Patenting directive.	Disagreement between coalition parties; protests from opposition and NGOs.	Blockade of negotiations of Special Advisory Board.
April 1998	Attempts to solve high-profile crimes.	Media initiate relatively intense reporting on DNA analysis.	Polarisation of debate becomes obvious.
April 1998	Exhibition on genetic engineering.	Following Swiss example, attempt to rationalise debate.	Debate calms down, policy starts shifting.
May 1998	Patenting directive.	New but moderate protests.	Most of Austrian MEPs vote in favour.
May, August 1998	Several studies.	Debate on Austria's loss of competitiveness.	Medical biotechnology officially backed.
1999		Regions (Carinthia, Salzburg) plan to establish genetic-engineering-free areas by law.	Laws not yet amended.
December 1999	New release application.	Meeting of NGOs with government.	Austrian Cabinet approves of experiment (April 2000); debate quietens further.

clearly an affront to the EU approval system for GM products. Initially Italy and Luxembourg joined the Austrian position. Since competent authorities in other countries considered the Austrian scientific reasoning to be flawed, the expectation was that Austria would be forced to withdraw its ban. However, due to a lack of decision-making within EU institutions, the ban remained, as did subsequent bans.

The large numbers of products containing soya served to highlight the problems inherent in GM food labelling. Critics of biotechnology considered that a negative labelling system would be more effective. This would indicate that products were 'genetic-engineering free'. However, in the press and official documents, this was referred to as 'positive' labelling, implying that non-GM products were superior to GM ones. In 1997, in an unprecedented move, NGOs joined forces with three big retail chains in a working group on genetic-engineering-free food. The aim was to establish a pragmatic definition that would provide a threshold for contamination in order to enable the establishment of a non-GM market, an attempt that later failed. Interestingly, it was an array of environmental NGOs that engaged in activities that in other countries would have been considered the task of consumer organisations. As there are no powerful such organisations in Austria, environmental NGOs could successfully take up consumer arguments. This may explain why, in the Eurobarometer survey, environmental organisations appear to be considered slightly more credible than consumer NGOs.

The debate on labelling defined the consumer as a major anti-GM-food actor, and retailers began to fear a loss of consumer confidence. In April 1998, the Ministry's Commission on Food decreed a strict process-based definition, ostensibly in order to protect the food industry's reputation. This almost eliminated the opportunity for a non-GM label.

After the 'illegal' release attempt in 1996, protesters exploited the political momentum to alter regulation. They launched the most important public event so far: a Volksbegehren (people's initiative).[2] Its aim was to ban GM food, the release of GMOs, and patents on genes. In spring 1997, after an emotional tabloid-supported campaign, the Volksbegehren came to be the second most successful of its kind ever. With approximately 21 per cent of the electorate subscribing, it was the most successful initiative carried by NGOs, but not officially backed by a political party. This marked the climax of the Austrian conflict on biotechnology. At the same time press coverage was steadily increasing.

The success of the Volksbegehren put the Austrian government under pressure from two fronts. On one hand the EU demanded compliance and industry and the research community simultaneously warned that Austria would fall behind technologically. On the other hand, NGOs supporting the Volksbegehren reproached the government for following EU regulations against the people's will.[3] As a reaction to the federal government's perceived immobility, some Länder (provinces) considered declaring 'gene-technology-free areas'. The Green Party for example, incorporated abstention from agricultural biotechnology into their general concept of regional economy, building upon terms like 'identity'. Although attempts to ban agricultural biotechnology at the Länder level mostly failed, by the year 2000, ten municipalities had officially declared themselves to be 'free of genetic engineering'.

Over the next three years, several release proposals were submitted, but NGO activists retaliated with public protests. This convinced the applicants that their attempts were futile, and official policy made it clear that governmental approval was not forthcoming.

In a revision of the law in 1998, the government met some of the critics' concerns. The method of appointment to the Scientific Advisory Commission, which had hitherto kept a low profile, was amended.

The public's right to be heard during the release application process was expanded. Provision was made for liability following a 'polluter pays' principle. Remarkably, these issues had not been on the Volksbegehren's agenda. Researchers and industry were highly critical, claiming that Austria would be the least attractive state within the EU for business and investment in biotechnology. For the first time, the embarrassed Scientific Advisory Committee demanded a voice in the debate.

The scientific community had remained largely silent. Following the success of the Volksbegehren, scientists became aware that they were losing credibility amongst lay people. They needed a way to introduce, according to the scientists, a more balanced view into the public discussion. Earlier, the Swiss had devised an exhibition on biotechnology, in conjunction with NGOs and other critical groups. This exhibition was adapted and shown in several Austrian cities during 1998 and 1999. As a first step towards normalisation, it sparked some debate but no particular critique, and media coverage became less adversarial. This may have been due to the exhibition's emphasis on basic research and medical applications. While for most people agricultural biotechnology and especially GM food was 'out', medical applications of biotechnology including genetic testing had remained remarkably uncontested even during the most intense debates. The Austrian Gene Law prohibits the use of data from genetic tests, and insurance companies did not urge a revision. Hence, the insurance issue, that had attracted considerable attention in other countries, such as the USA, was not debated publicly in Austria.

Medical and basic research applications met hardly any criticism with the exception of transgenic animals and cloning. The advent of Dolly the sheep in 1997 triggered intense press coverage, but only for a short time. In the Volksbegehren campaign, transgenic animals were addressed either as research objects or in an agricultural context. The animal rights point of view was to the fore, while the issue of xenotransplantation, being rather complicated and directly related to medical benefits, was never topical. The selective predominance of the food issue was again highlighted when Austrian MEPs voted in favour of the patent directive – contrary to the promises given after the Volksbegehren. Even then no storm of protest arose: it was almost a non-issue.

In 1998 press coverage of successful convictions of murderers due to forensic DNA profiling contributed to the acceptance and normalisation of genetic testing. Hardly any protest or activism reached the headlines, and interest turned to uncontested medical applications. There were several positive television and press reports on projects for gene therapy at research institutions, forecasting a boom for Austria. Ethical aspects were routinely and seemingly sufficiently dealt with by medical boards in the same way as other experimental medical projects. By contrast, agricultural biotechnology and GM food were mostly considered unacceptable, without any further debate.

Caught between the de-escalation of the debate and the persistent rejection of agricultural biotechnology, in 1999 the government attempted another transgenic plant release, this time an apricot tree. In early 2000 the new right-wing Council of Ministers decided to go ahead with the release. In response to opposition and calls by NGOs, a 'gene summit' was held in spring 2000 to discuss the way forward. This ended without any tangible result. The issue seemed to have settled down and the positions were clear, not least because of developments at EU level. NGOs took up other issues and addressed agricultural biotechnology more consistently, but in a more low-key manner. During early 2000, with a new right-wing government in place, Austria engaged in other issues, resulting in only sporadic media interest in biotechnology. The 'duck and cover' strategy of industry and government finally seemed to have paid off.

EU relations

Ironically developments abroad contributed to the Austrian domestic normalisation. Driven by the policy shift in major European countries like France, the UK and even Germany, the EU adopted policy positions much closer to what had always been the Austrian stance. For example, the UK, in contrast to Austria, had been opposing any link between environmental risk and food risk assessment. When in 1996 the UK representative on the Article 21 Committee rejected antibiotic-resistant markers in food, this marked a major transition and antibiotic markers became an issue under directive 90/220 at the EU level.

Austria's ban on GM maize and the failure by EU institutions to come to a conclusion highlighted a constitutional deficit in the EU decision-making process. This contributed to the realisation that the framework for EU decision-making needed revising.[4] Various amendments, bringing EU decision-making closer to the Austrian position,

were proposed in 1998 and adopted in 2000. These included time limits for marketing approvals and mandatory monitoring. In addition, the Austrian request to include additives into the labelling directive was taken up by the EU.

At the same time, pressure from the EU on the Austrian government diminished. Over time, the Austrian stance became less isolated. Between 1998 and 2000, several countries banned previously approved GM products as well. Restrictive demands from France often exceeded the Austrian position, rendering it relatively mainstream. In 1999 the EU Commission issued a de facto moratorium until the directive 90/220 was revised, giving retrospective legitimacy to the Austrian decisions to ban the import of some GM crops. Early in 2000, when the EU adopted the precautionary principle as a general rule in biotechnology decision-making, this corroborated the Austrian position even more since Austria had always cited the principle in defending contested decisions. Taken together, we can say that, by the end of the decade, Austria had re-entered Europe while Europe had implicitly accepted some of the Austrian positions.

Media coverage

As a continuation of our longitudinal media analysis from 1973 to 1996,[5] we scanned the weekly newsmagazine *Profil* and the daily newspaper *Die Presse* for articles on biotechnology and related topics. These are both opinion leaders and represent different poles of the Austrian left–right spectrum. During the mid-1990s, they both started to provide articles online, which could be retrieved for our update, after we sampled the articles by index. However, we have to take into account that, even according to a prima facie view, coverage differed considerably between the quality and the tabloid press. Especially over the years of controversy, the tabloid with the highest circulation spoke out against agricultural biotechnology. Hence, the picture presented is but a small window of the overall Austrian press coverage. It includes only quality media that are considered to be comparatively positive *vis-à-vis* biotechnology.

Since 1975, the intensity of media coverage of biotechnology has developed almost exponentially (Figure 1). Starting from a low intensity in 1994, there was a significant rise in media reporting that peaked in 1998 and decreased in 1999 to around 70 per cent. In the late 1990s, media reporting on biotechnology reached a level comparable to those of other European countries.

Figure 1. Intensity of media reporting on biotechnology in the Austrian press

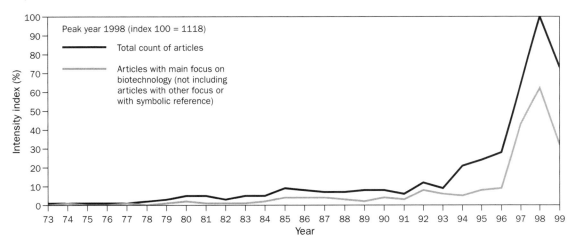

When media reporting on biotechnology began, topics were covered mainly in the science section of the daily newspapers. During 1997, biotechnology acquired a major political dimension as more articles were published, side by side with political news, in local, national and international sections. In 1998 and 1999, this trend was mostly reversed. Hence, the genuinely political debate on biotechnology seems to have taken place before 1998, in contrast to other European countries.

Certainly the Volksbegehren on biotechnology in April 1997 was the main trigger for intensified reporting. But already the illegal field release of GM potatoes in spring 1996 had prepared the ground by providing the media with good headlines. From then on, there was a steady stream of issues: the discussions on importing GM soya and maize in autumn 1996, the political debates about labelling GM food and, last but not least, the demands of the Volksbegehren. The tabloid press in particular served as spokespeople for the NGOs' demands and played a major part in the mobilisation of supporters for the Volksbegehren, preceding similar developments, for example, in Britain. Thus, the Austrian population was, at an early stage, confronted with a variety of biotechno-logical issues at a broad level. The interest continued and increased over the next year or so, only to decline in 1999.

For our description, the years from 1995 to 1999 can be divided into two phases connected by a 'hinge year' (1997), with distinct patterns of topics, content and intensity (Table 2).

Phase 1, 1995–96: political dimensions. During this phase the issue of biotechnology started to gain

importance in political debates. Right from the beginning it provided controversies. Over time, the number of political actors matched the number of actors from science. While enthusiastic reporting on breakthroughs in medicine and on possibilities of applying biotechnological knowledge prevailed, serious concerns and dilemmas referring to ethical principles, boundaries and acceptable vs unacceptable risks appeared. The most prominent issues at the beginning of this phase were related to research options in genetics and to inheritance and genetic determination. Eventually, experiments with GM crop plants, European policy towards GM products in general and the first imports of GM maize and soya resulted in a massive clamour by environmental NGOs and by 'the public' for labelling and far-reaching regulations. Within these years, interest groups became prominent in public and political debates.

The 'hinge year', 1997: the public's claim. With respect to events, procedures and debates related to biotechnology, 1997 was indeed a very 'moving' year for Austria. Major political events such as the government's ban, in February, of the import of GM maize in opposition to EU approval, resulted in significant shifts in the media discourse as coverage increased significantly. Most obvious was the dominance of the 'public accountability' frame and the decrease of the still-relevant 'progress' and 'ethics' frames (Figure 2).

Growing quests for public participation, the call for public involvement and, most of all, demands for openness of procedures, reflect the changes in framing from 1997 onwards. Indeed, the public participated in the debate as it finally came to

Table 2. Austrian media profile, 1992–99 (threshold for categories: 5 per cent and above)

Phase	1992–96		Hinge 1997		1998–99	
Frequency (%)[a]	33		22		45	
Frame (%)	**Progress**[b]	40	**Accountability**	48	**Progress**	41
	Ethical	29	Progress	29	Accountability	23
	Nature/nurture	10	Ethical	6	Nature/nurture	14
	Accountability	8	Economic	6	Ethical	8
	Runaway	6	Pandora's box	5		
Theme (%)	**Regulation**	18	**Public opinion**	23	**Genetic research**	21
	Genetic identity	15	Regulation	20	Agrifood	15
	Genetic research	12	Agrifood	10	Medicine	10
	Medicine	12	Medicine	10	Public opinion	14
	Agrifood	10	Genetic research	9	Regulation	14
	Public opinion	10	Cloning	5	Genetic identity	11
	Moral	8	Economics	5		
			Moral	5		
Actor (%)	**Independent science**	32	**Business**	25	**Independent science**	34
	Politics	30	Politics	24	Business	24
	Business	8	Independent science	22	Politics	18
	Media	6	Media	15	Media	13
	EU	6	Interest groups	8	EU	6
	Interest groups	6				
Benefit/risk (%)	**Benefit only**	47	**Benefit only**	33	**Benefit only**	57
	Neither	28	Neither	29	Both	16
	Risk only	17	Both	24	Risk only	16
	Both	9	Risk only	15	Neither	11
Location (%)	**Austria**	31	**Austria**	48	**Austria**	33
	USA	12	USA	12	USA	16
	Europe	7	World	5	UK	6
	World	6				

a Percentage of corpus (which includes only those articles which focus on biotechnology) in the period; total *n* = 358.
b Bold indicates highest frequency within phase.

Figure 2. Frames in the media coverage on biotechnology in Austria

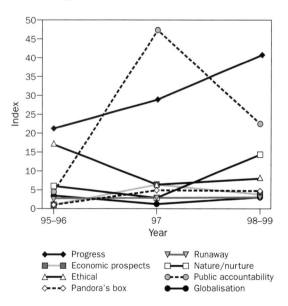

support the Volksbegehren. Understandably, during this year NGOs had their highest appearance as actors in the Austrian media.

While the quality press had focused previously on scientific progress in biotechnology, they now discussed responsibilities, contested decisions and further regulation. The trend during the first phase to increasingly cover food debates in general, and labelling in particular, continued and intensified. As food issues were much to the fore in the public mind, NGOs succeeded in mobilising even more support in order to establish a definition and a control system for a 'genetic-engineering-free' label. Several political debates were going on in parallel and the visibility of politicians in the disputes remained high.

The advent of Dolly the sheep in 1997 was a highly salient issue for a very short period of time. While coverage turned out to be very transient, it was the cloning of humans that received far more attention than animal cloning proper. During this time, the UK as the location of events reached its highest percentage ever.

It is important to note that the majority of articles in quality newspapers still emphasised the benefits of biotechnology, although the mentioning of risks increased considerably and thus the general tone of reporting grew more negative. Interestingly, and in contrast to other countries, the moral framing of biotechnology issues decreased enormously at the beginning of 1997. The emphasis was on public accountability rather than on more individual moral issues.

Phase 2, 1998–99: the return of science. After the considerable media attention in 1996 and 1997, the frames changed again. Although media coverage peaked in 1998, this was not due to major contro-versies reported. Food remained a prominent issue and reporting covered mainly GM product labelling, but political actors appeared less frequently.

In contrast, around 40 per cent of the articles on biotechnology again celebrated new develop-ments and breakthroughs. The formerly dominating public-accountability frame decreased, whereas genetic and medical issues regained importance. Especially in 1999, genetic fingerprinting and iden-tification of criminals became a major topic. By the end of 1999, the media focused on the Human Genome Project and the competition between different research teams. Scientists were even more frequently mentioned than in Phase 1. In many articles, scientific experts gave their opinions on the possibilities and risks of medical biotechnology. Since articles increasingly displayed the beneficial aspects of medical biotechnology, the overall tone of reporting in the quality press became positive. From time to time, though, there were still reminders that benefits go hand-in-hand with risks.

Coverage of some topics remained more or less stable over time. Medicine and basic research, for example, always appeared in the narratives of progress. Other topics had had their ups and downs; for instance regulation was covered in ethical debates and claims for openness of procedures, as well as in an economic context. At the turn of the century, however, the quality press portrayed biotechnology mostly positively.

Public perceptions

Resistance to biotechnology and many of its appli-cations has been rather high in Austria in com-parison to other European countries ever since the technology slowly became a topic of public debate

in the first half of the 1990s.[6] This tendency has not changed during the last few years. However, Austrian and European positions have generally drawn closer to each other mainly due to increasingly critical views in many other European countries, and a more differentiated view in Austria.

General attitudes towards biotechnology

Figure 3 contrasts technological optimism for biotechnology, nuclear energy and other modern technologies (amalgamating solar energy, computers and information technology, telecommunications, new materials and substances, and space exploration), both for Austria and for Europe. Respondents are considered optimistic if they expect a technology to improve the way of life and pessimistic if they think that it will make life worse.

In Europe, on average, the number of optimistic respondents towards modern technologies remained unchanged from 1996 to 1999, but the number of optimists concerning biotechnology has decreased. In Austria, in contrast, there are more optimists with regard to technology in general and to biotechnology in particular in 1999 than in 1996. General technological optimism has nearly reached the European average, but biotechnology still remains a controversial topic in Austria. Although the number of optimistic respondents has increased, Austria remains one of the most critical

Figure 3. Technological optimism in Austria and the EU, by year (nuclear energy data assessed in 1999 only)

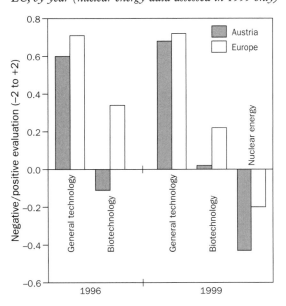

countries with respect to technology in general, to biotechnology and especially to nuclear energy.

Biotechnology and nuclear energy are topics of high salience for the Austrian public, both technologies being subjects of a successful Volksbegehren. In 1978 a slight majority of Austrians voted in a referendum against the use of nuclear power in Austria, even though this would result in a completed nuclear power plant never being used. In focus-group interviews with Austrian citizens the debate on nuclear energy still serves as a major reference point for judging modern technologies such as biotechnology and genetic engineering. In the light of the Chernobyl accident in 1986, over the years many perceived the Austrian anti-nuclear stance as being warranted. The example of nuclear technology is frequently used to justify being critical about biotechnology: 'In Austria there is no nuclear power plant, and equally there should not be any genetic manipulation.'

Austria, together with Denmark and Germany, is one of the countries in which awareness, both in 1996 and 1999, about biotechnology was highest in comparison to other European countries. Respondents who said they had ever discussed biotechnology were classified as being highly aware, while those stating that they have never talked about it were considered to have low awareness. The intensification of the Austrian debate on biotechnology at a political level in 1996–97, plus a sharp increase in media coverage, resulted in the Austrian public's sensitisation to the topic which has remained salient ever since. Figure 4 shows the relationship between awareness and evaluation of biotechnology. Unsurprisingly, awareness has an effect on opinion: highly aware respondents express either optimistic or pessimistic views about biotechnology more often and resort to 'don't know' responses less often. This polarisation is more pronounced in women than in men.

The comparatively high awareness about biotechnology in Austria in general does not go along with a higher level of biological knowledge on the issue. Although the level of textbook knowledge in Austria has increased more than in Europe between 1996 and 1999 (1996: 2.74; 1999: 3.18 on a five-point knowledge scale), Austria still is at the lower end of the European countries, jointly with Portugal, Spain, Italy, Ireland and Germany. In 1999 Austria more or less reached the European average for 1996.

Asked whether the statement 'ordinary tomatoes do not contain genes while genetically modified tomatoes do' is true or false, in 1999, 44 per cent of Austrian respondents gave the correct answer; this is more than the European average (38 per cent). In 1996 only 34 per cent of the Austrian respondents found it plausible that naturally grown tomatoes contain genes. That is, the belief of natural tomatoes being 'gene-free' significantly decreased from 1996 to 1999. Considering that Austrians show rather low knowledge, this is surprising. It may be explained by the fact that slogans like 'for a gene-free Austria' were frequently heard in the Austrian debate on the topic, and there were frequent references made to the erroneousness of this belief in the media due, not

Figure 4. Relative frequency of optimists ('biotechnology will improve quality of life'), indifferent respondents ('will not have an effect'), pessimists ('will make things worse') and 'don't knows', by awareness of biotechnology

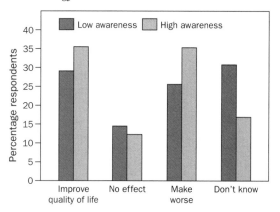

Figure 5. Relative frequency of optimists ('biotechnology will improve quality of life'), indifferent respondents ('will not have an effect'), pessimists ('will make things worse') and 'don't knows' by basic textbook knowledge of biotechnology in Austria

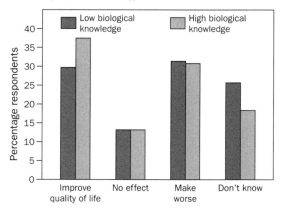

least, because of our group's earlier study. However, it must be noted that still more than half of Austrians and nearly two-thirds of Europeans either find this statement plausible or do not know what to answer. This not only indicates an inadequate understanding of what a gene is, but also shows that lay people frequently approach the topic from a consumer's perspective. They perceive GM products as just one of the many foodstuffs produced with the use of pesticides, chemicals, hormones or other substances: 'Of course it is more healthy to do it normally and in a natural way than adding something or injecting something into it.'[7]

Figure 5 shows the effect of knowledge upon optimistic and pessimistic attitudes towards biotechnology. More highly knowledgeable respondents (between 5 and 7 correct answers out of 10 on our questionnaire) are more decided in their opinion. They less often 'don't know' what effects biotechnology will have on their lives than less knowledgeable respondents (0 to 4 correct answers). But in contrast to 1996, in 1999 we do not find a polarisation effect, i.e. the tendency for high-knowledge respondents to express a more pronounced – either optimistic or pessimistic – opinion. Instead, in 1999 in Austria, better biological knowledge seems to be associated with a more optimistic view of biotechnology.

There is a significant effect of the consumption of quality vs tabloid newspapers on attitudes towards biotechnology. Readers of the Austrian tabloid press are less aware of the topic. In this group there are more respondents who are undecided about what effects to expect.

Furthermore, readers of tabloid papers tend to hold a more pessimistic view as compared to readers of the quality papers. This is not surprising, though, because one of the leading tabloid Austrian papers, *Kronenzeitung*, strongly supported the anti-biotechnology debate preceding the Volksbegehren in 1997, and it still does so. Readers of the quality press on the other hand tend to express a more pronounced and, in general, more optimistic opinion of biotechnology.

Attitudes towards specific applications of biotechnology

It is notable that regarding public perceptions, biotechnology is no longer perceived as an homogeneous field, but as a summary term referring to a variety of different applications that are often divergently evaluated. When asked what comes to mind when thinking of biotechnology, a typical answer in interviews is: 'I mean, genetic engineering, there are so many different domains. You have food, and the health domain, then even procreation. Maybe there is something else, I don't know. And these are completely different things.'

Figure 6 gives an overview of average Austrian attitudes concerning seven different applications of biotechnology. Respondents were asked whether they thought that each of the applications was useful, risky, and morally acceptable and whether it should be encouraged. The figure shows that for all applications mentioned in the survey, the attitude towards encouraging a specific application is strongly determined by its perceived usefulness and

Figure 6. Average evaluation of usefulness, risk, moral acceptability and willingness to encourage biotechnology applications in Austria

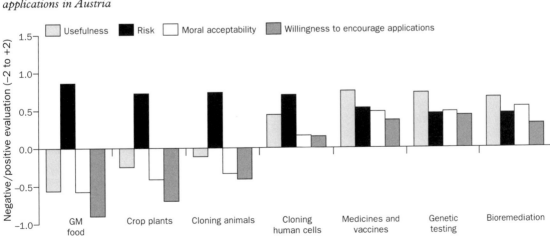

by its moral acceptability (average usefulness = 0.47; moral acceptability = 0.42 in multiple regression). Perceived risk on the other hand is a poor predictor of support for an application, there is virtually no application that is not seen to be risky.

Considering specific applications, Austrians, like most Europeans, tend to draw a clear distinction between medical applications on the one hand, and food and agricultural applications on the other hand: 'I've got positive and negative impressions [about genetic engineering]. I think it's positive concerning medicine, negative concerning food.' Medical applications, like the production of pharmaceuticals and vaccines or genetic testing, are, on average, encouraged significantly more strongly than food applications.

In Austria, the low acceptance of GM food and agricultural applications remained stable from 1996 to 1999, with 43 per cent of respondents in the survey opposing the use of modern biotechnology in the production of food, and 36 per cent rejecting the manipulation of crop plants to make them more resistant to pests. In other European countries the average attitude towards GM food approached the Austrian stance by becoming more critical. Accordingly, in 1999 all over Europe only 21 per cent of respondents say that they would buy GM fruits if they tasted better. In 1996, 27 per cent were willing to do so. In spite of already being sceptical of GM food in 1996, the Austrians became even more so in 1999 (1996: 17 per cent; 1999: 13 per cent willing to buy GM fruits).

The four perceptions (usefulness, risk, moral acceptability and encouragement) can be interpreted to reflect a certain kind of logic in the respondents' thinking. People who think that an application is useful, not risky, morally acceptable and should be encouraged are straightforward 'supporters'. Those who think that an application is useful, however risky, but morally acceptable and should be encouraged are 'risk-tolerant supporters'. Those who think that an application is not useful, risky, morally unacceptable and therefore should not be encouraged are clear 'opponents'. A total of 59 per cent of Austrian respondents in 1996 and 69 per cent in 1999 resorted to one of these logics averaged over all applications. Table 3 gives the percentage of each of these logics for Austria and Europe in 1996 and 1999. It is clear that the frequency distribution of logics for crop and food applications has scarcely changed from 1996 to 1999 and is heavily dominated by straightforward opposition. For medical applications, genetic testing and medicine production, however, there is

a sharp increase in the number of risk-tolerant supporters somewhat at the expense of straightforward supporters. For these medical applications Austrians and respondents from the overall EU show a close similarity. In 1999 the two cloning applications mentioned in the survey were opposed by a higher percentage of respondents than the application of bioremediation (the use of living organisms to degrade environmental contaminants). These three fields of application were not assessed in the 1996 survey and can therefore not be compared over time.

Overall, medical applications are evaluated more positively in comparison to GM food and crops and Austrian attitudes became more differentiated in 1999. There are fewer unconditional supporters, but more risk-tolerant supporters in 1999 than there were in Austria in 1996. More Austrians seem to have become aware of the potential usefulness as well as of the risks involved in certain biotechnological applications, that is in 1999 they evaluated the diverse applications by taking trade-offs and conditionalities into account.

Taken together, Austrians show a rather 'European' way of responding to affective and moral concerns. However, compared to other Europeans, they are significantly more sceptical in their assessment of utilities, risks and the role of democratic decision-making in the field of biotechnology.

In focus-group discussions, two main reasons for the distinct evaluation of medical and food applications were heard: usefulness and free choice. Concerning usefulness, in the domain of medicine, biotechnology is perceived to be a welcome solution to hitherto unresolved problems, and to provide a highly useful improvement in quality of life. When it comes to food, Austrian respondents usually are proud of the traditionally high quality of food found in the country: they endorse organic farming and feel they have higher food safety standards than other countries. Good food quality is perceived to be part of the national identity; there is no need to use biotechnology in this domain. It is interesting to note that reference to traditional forms of food production and to responsibilities for the region also form part of the discourse on political initiatives, mainly at a community level, against GMO releases. Such arguments have been brought forward in defending several municipalities' declarations to be 'free of genetic engineering' and have even had a role at county level in policy making to defend regional identity.

A second aspect is the importance of free choice for the consumer. With medicine, the argument

Table 3. Relative frequencies of evaluation logics for seven biotechnological applications in Austria and Europe, in 1996 and 1999

	1996		1999		Austria[a]	
	Austria (%)	Europe (%)	Austria (%)	Europe (%)	1996	1999
Crops						
Supporters	11.2	33.1	12.0	22.7	20.0	19.5
Risk-tolerant supporters	10.4	25.3	13.2	22.3	18.6	21.4
Opponents	34.4	15.1	36.4	22.7	61.4	59.1
'Decided'	–	–	–	–	41.1	49.5
Food						
Supporters	9.1	20.7	8.9	14.3	16.6	14.4
Risk-tolerant supporters	8.1	20.3	9.5	16.4	14.6	15.4
Opponents	38.0	25.8	43.3	34.3	68.9	70.1
'Decided'	–	–	–	–	39.9	49.0
Cloning animals						
Supporters	–	–	12.1	15.8	–	–
Risk-tolerant supporters	–	–	20.0	22.0	–	–
Opponents	–	–	36.4	15.8	–	–
'Decided'	–	–	–	–	–	–
Cloning human cells						
Supporters	–	–	15.3	22.2	–	–
Risk-tolerant supporters	–	–	31.1	35.6	–	–
Opponents	–	–	34.2	28.7	–	–
'Decided'	–	–	–	–	–	–
Medicines						
Supporters	27.3	39.0	21.4	30.5	44.1	31.4
Risk-tolerant supporters	21.1	34.9	31.2	35.9	34.1	45.8
Opponents	13.4	7.0	15.5	9.8	21.7	22.7
'Decided'	–	–	–	–	44.4	52.3
Genetic testing						
Supporters	28.1	45.7	23.1	41.0	43.5	33.4
Risk-tolerant supporters	19.7	31.1	30.6	32.5	30.5	44.2
Opponents	16.8	5.4	15.5	6.7	25.9	22.3
'Decided'	–	–	–	–	47.7	53.1
Bioremediation						
Supporters	–	–	23.8	31.2	–	–
Risk-tolerant supporters	–	–	30.8	33.8	–	–
Opponents	–	–	15.7	11.1	–	–
'Decided'	–	–	–	–	–	–

a Normalised percentages reflecting the percentage of those respondents in each category who provided a full set of
   answers, the 'decided' respondents. That is, they are percentages normalised to 100% relative to the frequency of
   'decided' respondents. Therefore these percentages do not reflect the true frequency of respondents in each category
   and country sample and cannot be used to compare changes between 1996 and 1999, but only to compare relative
   patterns between countries.

goes, it is the individual that is concerned, who is in a state of crisis and who can decide whether to have treatment or not. Food, on the other hand, is more proximal to everyday life. With food, free choice is perceived to be endangered, since the spread of GM plants will render it impossible to know whether a food product contains GM ingredients or not. Consequently, people fear that

all consumers will be affected and that the spread of GM food across the supermarket shelves will occur without their consent.

Cloning is a highly controversial topic in Austria. On one hand, there is a widespread association with Frankenstein's monster and other horror scenarios, mainly connected to the idea of cloning entire humans. Within the context of medicine, on the other hand, cloning is frequently judged to be an acceptable and highly useful technique. Similar to other medical applications, there are many risk-tolerant supporters. Figure 3 shows that the application 'Cloning human cells or tissues to replace a patient's diseased cells' is endorsed more often than the application 'Cloning animals such as sheep to get milk which can be used to make medicines and vaccines'. This might be surprising because in the first case, it is humans who are concerned while in the second, it is animals. Impressions from group discussions indicate that objections to cloning do not address the technique of cloning itself, but mainly refer to the idea of producing entire living beings. Cells and tissues, even of human origin, are more abstract entities, distant from autonomous beings. Cloning animals, like Dolly the sheep, is perceived as yet another step on the slippery slope towards the morally unacceptable, horrific scenario of cloning whole humans.

Trust and regulation

In general, Austrian respondents are comparatively critical towards most groups and institutions involved in modern biotechnology when asked whether these actors are doing a good job for society. Concerning the question about who is trusted to tell the truth about modern biotech-nology, both in Europe and in Austria the medical profession is mentioned most frequently (53 per cent for Europe vs 51 per cent for Austria). Other institutions perceived to be trustworthy sources of information are consumer organisations (Europe 52, Austria 49 per cent), environmental organisations (Europe 45, Austria 53 per cent), universities (Europe 31, Austria 29 per cent) and animal welfare organisations (Europe 25, Austria 31 per cent). Industry is frequently perceived to be biased, there is very little trust that a particular industry would tell the truth (Europe 4.5, Austria 4.0 per cent). Concerning political actors, throughout Europe political parties are not trusted (Europe 3.1, Austria 4.2 per cent) and only moderate trust is extended to national governments (Europe 17, Austria 18 per cent). In contrast to Europeans, on average in Austria there is less trust in media reports (Europe 21, Austria 14 per cent) and in information provided by international institutions (Europe 16, Austria 13 per cent).

Respondents classified as pessimistic about the future effects of biotechnology show more confidence in those NGOs critical of biotechnology

such as environmental organisations (pessimists 62, optimists 56 per cent), but less confidence in the medical profession than do optimists (pessimists 44, optimists 54 per cent). Similarly, they trust more in national than in international institutions (national institutions 18, international institutions 10 per cent), while optimists show a similar degree of trust for both national (17 per cent) and international institutions (18 per cent).

Respondents unacquainted with the topic or having little biological textbook knowledge, in general show more distrust in many of the actors involved. More knowledgeable respondents tend to doubt the medical profession (49 vs 52 per cent) and the media (10 vs 16 per cent) to tell the truth about biotechnology. Fewer readers of the Austrian tabloid press tend to express trust in universities (27 vs 52 per cent), in national (17 vs 26 per cent) and in international institutions (11 vs 27 per cent), but more tabloid readers trust in the medical profession (50 vs 44 per cent) and in farmers' associations (16 vs 10 per cent) than readers of quality newspapers.

In the focus-group interviews, people said that they felt ignorant and uninformed about regulation, actors and their role in the Austrian debate on biotechnology. Most respondents were unaware of any laws, regulations or actors in the field; they repeatedly asked for clarification on whether GM products can be sold in Austria and whether these must be labelled or not. Concerning the question whom to trust, two aspects are discernible: on one hand, actors are trusted if they are perceived to have good motives, and on the other hand, they appear trustworthy if they are perceived to be competent. The medical profession, for example, represented by the prototype of the family doctor, is perceived to be highly trustworthy in the sense that it shares interests with the general public. Participants doubted, however, that doctors really are up-to-date concerning the developments of modern biotechnology and were even more dubious about their ability to have a decisive role in public debate. The main function of environmental groups is seen as pointing out problems and in controlling industry and politics. Their role in creating awareness on the topic is considered to be very important, although their opinions are not always shared. Austrian politicians and the Austrian government are repeatedly criticised because of their reluctance to take action. They are perceived as being torn between the interests of industry, other countries and the public.

Conclusions

Despite the Austrian government's attempts to scale down the public debate, there is considerable public support for a rather restrictive 'Austrian way'. In comparison to other countries, Austrian policy-making is perceived to be critical and therefore in line with the consumers' interests. Hence, the Austrian 'precautionary blockade' of agricultural biotechnology may find its counterpart in a still-sceptical public, while the endorsement of medical biotechnology enjoys broad backing among an increasingly ageing population. This split in policy can be traced back to the early 1990s. Despite the relatively small presence of the medical biotechnology industry in Austria, there had always been support for products that were deemed useful. For agricultural biotechnology it is, however, a chicken-and-egg question whether official caution and avoidance behaviour preceded or followed on from public rejection.

With its restrictive position, Austria had a difficult stance within the EU prior to 1998. When other countries became more restrictive, with hindsight Austria appeared to have been a forerunner within the EU. In fact, there was a heavy public mobilisation against GM crop plants almost a year before the issue became salient in other European countries. The reason for this being that Austria was a latecomer with respect to plant biotechnology: there had been no experimental releases before 1996. When the country finally entered the debate on releases, agricultural products of biotechnology were already at hand or their advent foreseeable. The release discussion immediately turned into a debate on agricultural trajectories followed quickly by the issue of risks from eating GM food. With the emergence of GM food products, it was easy to establish a link between GMOs and their risk/safety assessment and past food scandals where such assessments, retrospectively, had failed to deliver accurate answers. This rendered the issue more relevant for the general public and, consequently, attractive for environmental NGOs which soon adopted the language of consumer protection. Most significantly, it became highly salient for the media. Hence, environmental and food issues pertaining to GMOs became linked in an unprecedented way.

After 1997, public opinion and European mainstream biotechnology politics on agricultural applications seemed to follow a path that was more similar than before to the 'Austrian way'. However, rather than as a genuine forerunner, it is more appropriate to see Austria as a freewheeler when it comes to developments beyond its influence. It was not the stringency of the Austrian position that brought a shift in the EU policy but the aftermath of the BSE and other food controversies in countries as diverse as the UK and France, Denmark and Greece. If ever Austria had been a forerunner in Europe, then maybe it was in establishing such a link.

Acknowledgements

This work was funded by grants from the Austrian Federal Ministry of Education, Science and Culture (GZ 650.275/1-III/2a/99 to Helge Torgersen and GZ 650.274/1-III/2a/99 to Wolfgang Wagner), and by the European Commission ('European Debates on Biotechnology (EUDEB) Concerted Action', BIO4-98-0488 and 'Life Science in the European Society: Towards the 21st Century (LSES)', QLG7-CT-1999-00286).

Notes and references

1 Torgersen, H and Seifert, F, 'Precautionary blockage of agricultural biotechnology', *Journal of Risk Research*, 3 (2000), pp209–17.

2 A Volksbegehren (people's initiative) allows a Bill to be put before parliament on condition that it is supported by at least 100,000 voters. Supporters have to sign the initiative in the presence of the authorities. Parliament is then obliged to deal with the proposal; there is no legal requirement beyond this. Before the initiative on biotechnology, 14 Volksbegehren succeeded in raising the requisite number of signatures, and three of them led to pertinent laws.

3 Grabner, P and Torgersen, H, 'Österreichs Gentechnikpolitik – Technikkritische Vorreiterrolle oder Modernisierungsverweigerung?', *Österreichische Zeitschrift für Politikwissenschaft*, 1 (1998), pp5–27.

4 Levidow, L, Carr, S and Wield, D, 'Genetically modified crops in the European Union: regulatory

conflicts as precautionary opportunities', *Journal of Risk Research*, 3 (2000), pp189–208; Wagner, W and Kronberger, N, 'Killer tomatoes! Collective symbolic coping with biotechnology', in Deaux, K and Philogene, G (eds), *Representations of the Social* (Oxford: Blackwell, 2001).

5 Wagner, W, Torgersen, H, Seifert, F, Grabner, P and Lehner, S, 'Austria', in Durant, J, Gaskell, G and Bauer, M (eds), *Biotechnology in the Public Sphere: A European Sourcebook* (London: Science Museum, 1998).

6 Wagner *et al.* (see note 5).

7 Wagner, W and Kronberger, N (see note 4).

Address for correspondence

Helge Torgersen, Institute of Technology Assessment, Austrian Academy of Sciences, Strohgasse 45, A-1030 Vienna, Austria. E-mail: torg@oeaw.ac.at

Canada on the gene trail

Edna F Einsiedel and Jennifer E Medlock

Introduction

Canadian writers reflecting on the country's historical experience have invariably focused on technology, equating the historical narrative with a discourse on technology.[1] Starting with case studies on the fur trade to staples, commodities, transportation, and on to modern communication technologies, the intertwining of Canadian geographic realities and technology has been a common thread.[2] While biotechnology history in this country is still being written, this context is an important backdrop to understanding the trajectory of this technology's development in this North American state.

In this chapter, we will explore the ways biotechnology has been framed in the policy, media and public perception arenas and, like the others in this volume, will provide a way of both particularising the narrative while at the same time locating it within the international context.

Public policy

The dominant role the state has always played in Canadian life is one of the attributes distinguishing Canada from its more market-oriented neighbour to the south. Not surprisingly, technological initiatives have often taken place under the guidance and support of government. Its geography and much smaller market base – one-tenth that of the USA – required a more proactive role in the economy. Not surprisingly, with the recognition of the scope and potential impacts of the scientific discoveries around molecular biology and recombinant technologies in the 1970s, the federal government was the key actor in setting up a framework for the development of this technology.

The policy story can be described in two acts: the first is the build-up phase and the second is the commercialisation phase. As we will see, in the second act, the play is disrupted by its audiences. Key events are summarised in Table 1.

Phase 1, 1995–98: the build-up. The Canadian government identified biotechnology as a strategic technology in 1980 and announced a National Biotechnology Strategy in 1983. This initial development plan was designed to foster the development of the biotechnology scientific and industrial base.[3] Its focus was on promoting biotechnology research in a few targeted areas including agriculture, forestry, aquaculture, mining and pharmaceuticals. Additionally, with the realisation that a stronger effort could be promoted by better integration of university, industry and government research and development activities, a funding programme to enhance such collaborations between the three sectors was initiated.

To fund the strategy, Canadian $11 million (about UK £5 million) was allocated in 1983.[4] To facilitate effective transfer of technology to industry, the Industrial Research Assistance Program (IRAP) provided companies with financial support to access technologies developed in universities and federal and provincial research organisations.[5] Four Network Centres of Excellence devoted to biotechnology were also funded in the academic sector.

The strategy was overseen by an Interdepartmental Committee on Biotechnology and a National Biotechnology Advisory Committee, with the latter consisting of representatives from the private sector, academia and government. The mandate of this Advisory Committee was to provide advice to the Minister of Science on the progress of the National Biotechnology Strategy and to identify specific issues and policy requirements for the development of biotechnology.

Along with policy support and facilitation of the development of the industrial base, the need for a regulatory framework was also growing. Following multistakeholder consultations in 1988, a regulatory approach was developed which emphasised risk assessment *on the basis of novel traits*. That is, 'plants which possess characteristics or traits sufficiently different from the same or similar species' would trigger an assessment of risk. Thus, products would be examined on a case-by-case basis, which is more commonly referred to as the product approach to regulation, in contrast to a

Table 1. Key policy events in Canada, 1985–99

Date	Trigger	Events	Outcomes
June 1985	Harvard University applies for a patent for the 'oncomouse', a GM mouse predisposed to cancer.	The Patent Office of Canada rejects Harvard's application for a patent for the oncomouse in 1995. There was an appeal to the Federal Court which was rejected in April 1998. Unlike the USA or Europe, no patents of either plants or animals had been allowed in Canada up until this time.	3 August 2000: The Federal Court of Appeal overturns lower court ruling and orders the patent to be issued.
March 1988	Health Canada receives the first industry application to sell rBST in Canada.	After more than 10 years of studying rBST (and considerable public pressure), two panels are convened, one on human health and the second on animal welfare. The former concluded rBST was safe for humans, the latter concluded rBST posed unacceptable risks to animal health.	Health Canada announces a ban on the sale of rBST in January 1999.
February 1997	Cloning of Dolly the sheep in 1997; cloning of triplet goats by Nexia Biotechnologies of Montreal in April 1999.	The Royal Commission on New Reproductive Technologies initially recommends legislation to prohibit the use of human embryos in cloning in 1993. Legislation is tabled in 1996, but dies on the table in 1997 when a federal election is called. The first cloning of livestock in Canada in 1999 leads to renewed calls for cloning legislation.	The federal government is expected to introduce a new round of legislation in 2000, but an early federal election is called in November.
August 1998	Monsanto launches a lawsuit against Saskatchewan farmer Percy Schmeiser. Monsanto Canada Inc. vs P Schmeiser, Docket T-1593-98 <www.fct-cf.gc.ca/bulletins/T1593-98/>.	Monsanto claims that Schmeiser planted the company's patented GM canola seeds in 1998 without having signed a technology protection agreement. Schmeiser denies the accusation, claiming that the Roundup-resistant canola seeds had been dispersed by wind or passing trucks. Schmeiser files a countersuit.	The case is heard in a Saskatoon courtroom in June of 2000, and in March 2001, the court rules in favour of Monsanto.
August 1998	The federal government releases the Canadian Biotechnology Strategy.	This new strategy replaces the outdated 1983 National Biotechnology Strategy, and recommends the formation of an independent expert advisory body on biotechnology issues.	The Canadian Biotechnology Advisory Committee is formed in September of 1999.
February 1999	Breakdown of Biosafety Protocol talks in Cartagena, Columbia. The UN-sponsored Protocol is meant to act as a framework for regulating trade in LMOs.	The Miami Group, headed by Canada, blocks agreement on the Protocol in Cartagena by refusing to negotiate on their positions.	Agreement on the Biosafety Protocol is eventually reached in Montreal in January 2000. In the final version, the precautionary principle was included in the preamble but the Protocol could not override WTO rules.

Table 1. Key events in Canada (continued)

Date	Trigger	Events	Outcomes
Summer 1999	The GM food debate hits Canada in summer 1999.	The government responds to public and media concerns about the labelling of GM foods by forming the Voluntary Labelling Standards Committee in September 1999. It maintains that mandatory labelling is not necessary because GM foods do not pose a significant health or safety risk.	The Committee will develop national standards for voluntary labelling of products by industry.
Summer 1999	Continuing GM food debate.	The Canadian government requests that the Royal Society of Canada create the Expert Panel on the Future of Food Biotechnology.	In February 2000, the Panel is formed and will produce a report on risks and benefits of GM foods.
November 1999	Representatives of 135 nations gather in Seattle to hammer out an agenda for the next round of WTO negotiations.	Biotechnology issues loom large at the summit. Canada, along with the USA and others, wants international trade in GM foods on the agenda, but the European Commission refuses to deal with biotechnology exclusively in terms of trade, arguing that health and safety concerns must be dealt with first. Further disagreements arise over intellectual property and patenting rights surrounding GMOs.	The meetings collapse as negotiators are unable to reach consensus on an agenda for new talks.
November 1999	NGOs pressure food companies to drop use of GM ingredients.	Greenpeace and Friends of the Earth spearhead campaign and are joined by two Canadian organisations, Council of Canadians and the David Suzuki Foundation. Questions are raised about the safety of GM foods.	In December 1999, McCain Foods (based in New Brunswick) announces that it will no longer accept GM potatoes from Canadian farmers.

process-based approach. This risk-assessment approach would come into play by virtue of the introduction of novel traits from any means (for example, from artificial mutagenesis or selective breeding), not just from recombinant DNA methods.

One implication of this regulatory approach was that products of modern biotechnology, by and large, would not be singled out as being substantially different from their conventionally derived counterparts solely on account of the process by which they were developed. They could consequently be managed through existing legislation and institutional structures. Thus, seven ministries share responsibilities in biotechnology regulation: Agriculture, Health, Environment, Fisheries, Mining, Industry, and Foreign Affairs and Trade. For products of food biotechnology, the Food and Drugs Act was the regulatory reference, supplemented by the Novel Foods Regulations in 1999.[6] This product approach is, of course,

markedly different from the European one, which tends to be process orientated.

From the late 1970s to the late 1980s, a flurry of biotechnology companies went public in the USA, and Canadian companies got caught up in similar commercialisation development efforts.[7] It was a heady time for biotechnology companies, and media stories focused on venture capitalist optimism as various companies started offering their shares in the stock markets. Research efforts resulted in some important discoveries from Canadian laboratories including the identification of the Duchenne muscular dystrophy gene in 1986 and the cystic fibrosis gene in 1989.

Biotechnology efforts were also focused on agriculture, considered the most important of the industries arising out of the country's biological resources. In the most recent comprehensive census in 1996, the agrifood industry was worth over Canadian $70 billion (about UK £32 million), or 8.8 per cent of Canada's GDP. At the same time, adverse climate, soil and other geographic conditions prevent profitable agriculture in much of the country. Despite being the world's second largest country, only 7 per cent of the area is arable. Finally, Canadian agriculture is highly dependent on world markets, with 70 per cent of the country's total agricultural production being exported.[8] All these suggest that value-added or new crops play a very important role in Canada's efforts to address domestic as well as international agricultural needs.[9]

In the agricultural biotechnology sector, canola was the first crop to undergo transgenic development. The quintessential Canadian agricultural success story, canola (a derivation from 'Canadian oleic oil') was invented in Saskatchewan in the 1970s when scientists turned rape-seed (which produces an inedible oil used primarily as an industrial lubricant) into canola. This was not just an edible oil, but one with an attractive lipid profile for consumers, with its lower saturated fat than other cooking oils. The first field tests of genetically engineered canola began in 1988 and the product was subsequently launched on the market in 1995.

By 1999, 43 products had received approval and 4300 field trials had been approved in Canada[10] in contrast to 1485 in Europe by the same year. This was an explosive rate second only to the USA, and a sign of the rapid proliferation of agricultural biotechnology that was not constrained by controversy or resistance. Products receiving approval included canola, potatoes, maize, flax, soyabeans, tobacco, tomatoes and wheat. Primary genetically modified traits included herbicide resistance, resistance to insect pests, viruses and funguses, stress tolerance and nutritional changes.

In 1998, a new national biotechnology strategy was unveiled, this time in anticipation of the commercialisation challenges and the socio-ethical questions a number of applications were already raising. A Canadian Biotechnology Strategy was announced in 1998 with a new advisory committee. This new strategy was focused on further facilitating commercialisation. Not surprisingly, consideration of socio-ethical concerns, a missing element in the first policy strategy, was now an important pillar of this second strategy.[11]

Unlike the regulatory picture in the USA, which was shaped in part by political activism and public controversy,[12] the regulatory process in Canada was shaped through multistakeholder consultations and little controversy. The exception was recombinant bovine somatotropin (rBST). In early 1999, about ten years after Monsanto had first applied for product approval, the Minister of Health made the decision to reject this application, a contrast to its legal use south of the border. Unlike their counterparts in the USA, dairy farmers in Canada were operating within a quota system for milk production. This meant in part that the supply of milk was controlled to meet demand, and competition for increasing production volumes was not a significant factor.[13]

The rBST topic was the only biotechnology issue of some prominence in the media in the preceding two years. The controversy revolved around regulatory conflicts within Health Canada and public accusations made by some government scientists about being pressured to approve rBST when they did not feel all safety questions had been addressed. Senate hearings on the issue served to further hold up the spotlight on rBST as did a media event staged with Jeremy Rifkin, well-known North American biotechnology critic, pouring milk from a bucket on to the front steps of parliament. In this context, Health Canada commissioned two panels to examine the rBST issue: a human health panel and an animal welfare panel. The former concluded that milk from rBST-treated cows was safe for human consumption,[14] while the animal welfare committee concluded that rBST had deleterious effects on animal health.[15] It was on the basis of the latter that the Health Minister decided to reject rBST use in Canada, an interesting indication that factors other than human health considerations were also pushing policy decisions in particular directions.

On the medical side, the growth in biotechnology companies was even more significant, with about close to half of the companies engaged in therapeutics and diagnostics, in comparison to a quarter in agrifood biotechnology.[16] In general, growth in the medicine and health sector has proceeded with some mostly positive attention from the media and very little public discussion.

Phase 2, 1999: conflict and controversy. The summer of 1999 was the period when the GM food debate hit the broadcast media and news pages. The general public pressure created by greater media attention and greater NGO activity provided the impetus to create the Voluntary Labelling Standards Committee to develop standards for the labelling of GM food products. The Committee's work is ongoing but its appointment was a significant departure from the earlier government position. This previous position was also based on voluntary labelling (i.e. labelling only for toxicity or allergenicity) with the exception that a common standard was not in place. Thus, for companies interested in labelling their products as 'GMO-free' or for those who would consider putting a label for the consumer that the product had been genetically modified, the standards that were to be devised would ensure that the labels would be 'truthful and not misleading'.

In the face of pressure from the NGOs, only Seagram (a large distillery) and McCain Foods succumbed, with the latter announcing it would no longer use GM potatoes. The chairman's words significantly summed up the position of those in the industry who would similarly stop using GM ingredients in the USA: 'GM material is very good science but at the moment, very bad public relations.'[17]

Talks on the BioSafety Protocol became another arena for staging the GM fight. This UN protocol was meant to provide the framework for trade in LMOs. Countries that are signatories agree to create and abide by a framework designed to minimise potential risks posed by the trade or the accidental release of agricultural and food products that have been genetically modified. The 1999 discussions in Cartagena stalled between the big producers and Europe and a number of developing countries. The USA was not a signatory at Rio so was not an official participant, but its influence was much felt among the producer countries led by Canada. This group (called the Miami Group) was intent on promoting three positions: that the Protocol would not override WTO trade rules; that the precautionary principle would not be used in decision-making; and that processed foods would be exempt from the Protocol. The talks continued in Montreal where agreement was finally reached that WTO rules would prevail over trade in LMOs, the position supported by Canada, USA, Australia, Argentina, Uruguay and Chile. However, the precautionary principle was included in the preamble, allowing Europe and its developing country allies also to claim victory.

On the domestic stage, another battle was being played out in a prairie courtroom between Monsanto and Saskatchewan farmer Percy Schmeiser, this one billed as the David vs Goliath story. Monsanto accused Schmeiser of growing the company's Roundup Ready canola seeds without signing a technology protection agreement. Schmeiser, on the other hand, claimed the GM seeds cross-pollinated with his own crops, by seeds blown from passing trucks, carried by bees, or the wind, and that he did not knowingly plant them. The case has assumed

symbolic and substantive importance as it represents another arena for the competing claims of benign vs high-risk environmental impacts of GM crops. A ruling delivered in 2001 upheld Monsanto's right to enforce its technology protection agreements with farmers.

On another front in the intellectual property arena, a legal dispute also developed around the Harvard oncomouse, a mouse genetically engineered for use in cancer studies. Unlike the USA and European countries, Canada had not allowed patenting of higher life forms prior to August 2000. The Harvard oncomouse patent case reached all the way to the Federal Court of Appeal, where the patent office was ordered to issue the patent, rescinding the patent office's earlier rejection of the Harvard application.

In looking at the policy landscape in Canada, the federal government was a key political actor as it developed and implemented a national innovation policy on biotechnology. In the first two decades, this process proceeded with little public attention but with significant impacts on the context for biotechnology research. It fostered conditions for industry growth by promoting research and development, supporting innovation networks between the public, private and university sectors, and the further development of human resources in these research areas.

The influence of government is also evident in the arena of regulations and standards setting. Regulatory frameworks are, of course, important in setting environmental and product safety standards and the move toward a risk-assessment framework based on a product approach was significant in this respect. Both the innovation policy and regulatory approach were key pillars in the policy approach to biotechnology, with both these policies having significant roles in building the country's biotechnology infrastructure. It was evident that the country could no longer rely on its natural resource base; biotechnology was a means to provide 'value-added' dimensions to these natural resource-based sectors including forestry, fisheries and mining. The siren call of membership in the post-industrial knowledge-based economy was a key motivator, as was global economic competitiveness.

The policy process is never predictable, however. There are, what economists like to call, 'externalities' which further influence and shape the policy process. Activities by NGOs, consumer responses, international events, all contribute to moving the policy process in particular directions and one important arena where these actions are played out is the mass media. It is this arena which we examine next.

Media coverage

The *Globe and Mail* was the only national paper in circulation during the entire duration of our media study (from 1995 to 1999 inclusive) and it was our primary story source. The *Globe* is an opinion-leading publication, geared towards an affluent, highly educated audience, and has an average daily readership of 990,000 (1999 figure). We also did a frequency count of stories on biotechnology that were broadcast in the same time frame on the public and private national networks, the CBC and CTV.

The year 1999 was a watershed in terms of media coverage in Canada – the point at which biotechnology events were given significantly more attention than in the previous three years. A look at television coverage of both the national public and private networks shows the total number of stories climbing dramatically in 1999 (Figure 1). Newspaper articles in the national paper published in 1999 account for more than one-third of our sample (104 out of 299), while the previous four years average out at approximately 16 per cent each (Figure 2). Accordingly, we split our data in relation to this change in intensity, labelling stories from 1995–98 as 'Phase 1', and those from 1999 as 'Phase 2', with a noticeable increase in the frequency of stories between 1998 and 1999.

Overall, biotechnology was cast in a positive light by the *Globe and Mail* (Figure 3). Throughout our period of study, stories were framed predominantly by the ideas of progress and economic prospects (78 per cent of all articles fell into one of these two frames). Progress stories describe scientific discoveries and breakthroughs, such as the Human Genome Project and its predicted revolutionary impacts on medical science, new gene discoveries (e.g. the breast-cancer genes BRCA1 and 2, the genetic link to Alzheimer's disease), and GM crop innovations (e.g. the Bt gene added for insect resistance, or GM food promoted as a solution to world hunger). The economic prospect frame encompasses articles about mergers within the biotechnology sector, movements of stock prices and regulatory approval of drugs.

About seven in ten of the articles presented a more positive than negative valuation of biotechnology. When benefits and risks mentioned within stories were tallied, there were almost twice as many benefits as there were risks (453 benefits were mentioned vs 260 risks). While a rosy picture

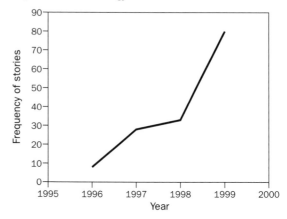

Figure 1. Biotechnology on Canadian television

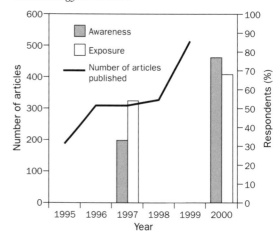

Figure 2. Media coverage, exposure and awareness of biotechnology in Canada

Figure 3. Absolute valuation of articles

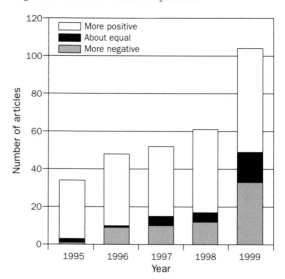

of biotechnology in the *Globe and Mail* emerged early on, a comparison across Phase 1 (1995–98) and Phase 2 (1999) revealed the predominantly enthusiastic view as beginning to fade.

Phase 1 vs Phase 2: from optimism to concern

The year 1999 (Phase 2) marked the beginning of a more critical look at biotechnology and its effects, with stories discussing only the risks and not the benefits of biotechnology appearing more than three times more often than in Phase 1. A break-down of Phase 1 articles showed no 'risk-only' stories in 1995, while in 1996 through 1998, there were only 5–6 per cent. In 1999, that figure jumped to 15 per cent, and was accompanied by a greater appearance of articles with attention to both risks and benefits. These increases came, of course, at the expense of benefit-only coverage, which decreased from 44 per cent in Phase 1 to 28 per cent in Phase 2.

Along with a more pronounced risk discourse, the overall evaluation of biotechnology was less optimistic in Phase 2 than in Phase 1. Although in both time frames the number of stories judged as having a positive view of biotechnology far outweighed the number seen as negative, the overall percentages of negative valuation stories doubled, from 16 per cent in Phase 1 to 32 per cent in Phase 2. Also, the number of neutral stories more than doubled between Phase 1 and Phase 2 (to 15 from 7 per cent). Overall, then, while coverage of biotechnology remained generally positive, there was a clear trend towards increasingly critical coverage in 1999.

As mentioned above, articles were framed largely in terms of technological progress and economic potential throughout the entire study. Phase 2, however, is characterised by the emergence of three other frames: ethics, 'Pandora's box', and globalisation (which discussed biotechnology in an international context). The first two characterised stories packaged as socio-ethical dilemmas or as raising grim possibilities of unpredictable and mostly negative consequences. Most of the articles falling within the frame of globalisation had to do with the European GM food debate and the consequences this might have for Canadian agriculture. Also within this global frame were stories about international organisations (the WTO) or treaties (the Biosafety Protocol).

GM food

Of all themes (see Table 2), the largest change between Phase 1 and Phase 2 occurred in the agrifood (GM food and crops) category (10 per cent of the Phase 1 stories, 27 per cent of the Phase 2 stories). Attention to GM food and crops also increased as Phase 2 progressed, with three times as many stories written in the second half of 1999 than in the first. Before the GM food controversy crossed the Atlantic, during the pre-1999 era, stories with a GM food theme were consistently about the growth hormone rBST, and the drawn-out process of regulatory approval in Canada.

The majority of newspaper coverage of GM food in 1999 occurred in the context of events and opinions coming from Europe. The strong opposition of the European public was described in some stories as a barrier to Canadian economic growth in the biotechnology sector. The federal government and its regulatory agencies such as Agriculture Canada and the Candian Food Inspection Agency were portrayed as pro-GM foods and were consistently described as battling the EU's calls for tougher trade rules on GM products (for example, during the Biosafety Protocol discussions). Some stories noted European public concern and wondered when that concern would manifest itself in Canada. On the other hand, one story in particular noted that 'the issue has stirred about as much passion among Canadians as the arrival of Groundhog Day'.[18]

Not coincidentally, the rise in concerns reflected in the media were voiced by environmental advocacy groups which included Greenpeace, the Council of Canadians, Friends of the Earth, and the Canadian Environmental Law Association. These environmental groups questioned the adequacy of Canada's regulatory system and demanded that GM foods be labelled. In response, the government's consistent position was to try to reassure the public that GM foods 'are stringently tested and are completely safe'[19] and 'just as safe as conventional varieties'.[20]

Other 1999 GM food coverage described mergers between biotechnology companies, fluctuations in stock market prices, as well as GM food being the solution to the problem of world hunger.

Other themes

Three other themes dominated our study: medicine, economic prospects and regulation. More stories fell under the medical than any other theme in both phases. These stories basically run the whole gamut of medical applications of biotechnology, from drug approvals to 'gene of the week' stories, the Human Genome Project,

Table 2. Canadian media profile, 1995–1999 (threshold for categories: 5 per cent and above)

Phase	1. 1995–98		2. 1999	
Frequencyª (%)	65		35	
Frame (%)	**Economicᵇ**	46	**Progress**	39
	Progress	35	Economic	34
	Ethical	9	Public accountability	8
	Public accountability	5	Pandora's box	8
			Ethical	7
			Globalisation	6
Theme (%)	**Medical**	35	**Medical**	25
	Economic	20	Agrifood	27
	Regulation	13	Economic	18
	Agrifoodᶜ	10	Regulation	12
	Generic research	7	Moral	7
	Cloning	6	Public opinion	5
Actor (%)	**Business**	48	**Business**	47
	Independent science	27	Independent science	19
	Politics	10	Politics	14
	Interest groups	5	Other	7
			Media/public	6
Benefit/risk (%)	**Both**	47	**Both**	56
	Benefit	44	Benefit	28
	Risk	5	Risk	15
	Neither	4	Neither	1
Location (%)	**Canada**	46	**Canada**	41
	USA	34	USA	34
	Europe	14	Europe	16
Risk actor (%)	**Business**	52	**Business**	47
	Independent science	33	Politics	23
	Politics		Independent science	19
			Media/public	8
Benefit actor (%)	**Business**	56	**Business**	52
	Independent science	37	Independent science	33
	Politics	5	Politics	11

a Percentage of corpus in the period: $n = 299$.
b Bold indicates highest frequency within phase.
c 'Agrifood' includes the labelling theme.

xenotransplantation and gene therapy. Notable about the medical biotechnology stories in general is that they tended to be portrayed in more positive terms, with less attention to risks. Stories with a regulation theme centred around the rBST approval process and delays in adoption of new reproductive technology legislation.

Actors

Media coverage in Canada centred on industry actors and scientists, with these two groups dominating both phases of the study. Business actors

were dominant, accounting for close to half of all actors in Phases 1 and 2 (48 per cent and 47 per cent respectively). This group includes producers, distributors, farmers, and scientists in private laboratories. Independent science actors (27 per cent in Phase 1 and 19 per cent in Phase 2) include university scientists and those working in hospitals, at public research institutions or within scientific organisations. Political actors (primarily government actors) also played a role, and were most commonly involved in stories about GM food and related labelling issues. They had a stronger presence in Phase 2, representing 14 per cent of all actors, as opposed to 10 per cent in Phase 1, as they became more involved in labelling policy discussions and responded more frequently to a rise in consumer concern about GM food. On the whole, political actors were consistently portrayed in a negative light during the period of the study, being twice as likely to be seen as responsible for risks rather than benefits to society (such as allowing GM crops to be planted without adequately ensuring safety).

Negative coverage of the Canadian government continued into the year 2000. A media analysis conducted for the Voluntary Labelling Standards Committee focusing on the first quarter of 2000 portrayed the Canadian government, as head of the Miami Group, as inflexible and ready to scuttle a trade treaty on GM food at the Biodiversity Conference in Montreal. That is, until the final hours of talks when an agreement was finally reached.

The changing distribution of actors between Phases 1 and 2 shows biotechnology becoming more of a mainstream issue. Voices from the media and public categories became more prevalent (4 to 6 per cent). The majority of actors in the media category included columnists holding forth on the issue of GM food, while actors in the public category included average consumers. Many of the 'other' actors in this study were patients involved in medical biotechnology studies, or patients who could potentially be helped by new research breakthroughs (Jesse Gelsinger – an American patient who died from a failed gene therapy, or women with a history of breast cancer in their family).

In terms of story location, not surprisingly, Canada was the dominant location of events in our media study in both phases, followed closely by the USA. Overall, Canada accounted for 44 per cent of the articles and the USA about a third.

Public perceptions

In 1997, our national survey of Canadians on various aspects of biotechnology showed that the topic was a bare register in the consciousness of most Canadians. When prompted about a range of applications, the public was cautiously accepting of and optimistic about biotechnology, particularly when contrasted with Europeans. The year 1999 proved to be significant when non-government groups, particularly Greenpeace, shifted their sights across the Atlantic and focused initially on Canada. The spotlight on food biotechnology was given a boost in the pages of the national media. In this

section, we will explore how public perceptions shifted between the two survey time points (Table 3).

Top-of-mind images about biotechnology were explored through the open-ended question, 'What comes to mind when you think about biotechnology in a broad sense, that is, including genetic engineering?' While only a third of participants in 1997 ventured a response, three years later over three-quarters (77 per cent) gave a comment, an evaluative reaction or some associational concept. Positive associations included phrases such as 'a technological improvement', 'curing diseases' or 'eliminating birth defects'. Negative associations were typically statements or admonitions such as 'I disagree with cloning' or 'humans shouldn't be tampering with nature'. About six in ten mentioned associations without any indication of whether they felt one way or another, mentioning terms or phrases such as 'DNA', 'genetically engineered foods' or 'gene therapy'.

A shift in attentiveness also occurred during this period. Two-thirds recalled seeing something in the media in 2000, up from 54 per cent three years earlier. However, this did not necessarily result in increased discussion. About the same number said they had never discussed biotechnology with anyone (44 per cent). About the same number discussed the subject infrequently (slightly under half) and fewer than one in ten admitted to discussing the subject 'frequently'.

Evaluations of biotechnology applications

The most striking finding from the surveys done in 1997 and 2000 was the perceptible shift between these two time points towards lower overall acceptance of biotechnology applications. This is evident in a shift in the intensity of valuation as well as the direction of such valuation. People were less likely to say they 'definitely agreed' about the utility of an application than to say they 'agreed'. In addition, while risk perceptions remained the same, respondents in the more recent survey were less likely than in 1997 to view the applications as being 'useful' or 'morally acceptable'. The upshot of this is that for most of the applications, far fewer people 'definitely agreed' that the applications should be encouraged.

On the whole, while about half to three-quarters were still prepared to encourage the various applications, the drop in support is notable. Those willing to encourage modification of crop plants for pest resistance fell from 77 to 61 per cent, the most notable change. There was also an 11 per cent drop

Table 3. Perceptions of specific applications 1997–2000

Applications	Attitude	Useful		Risky		Morally acceptable		Should be encouraged	
		1997	2000	1997	2000	1997	2000	1997	2000
Using biotechnology in the production of food and drinks.	*Definitely agree*	29	22	21	24	29	18	17	17
	Agree	38	35	34	34	41	37	33	32
Inserting genes from one plant species into a crop plant to make it more resistant to pests.	*Definitely agree*	49	30	11	18	39	24	40	224
	Agree	33	42	27	31	40	31	36	37
Introducing human genes into bacteria to produce medicines and vaccines.	*Definitely agree*	59	44	9	11	44	29	50	33
	Agree	31	39	26	31	41	46	35	43
Introducing human genes into animals to produce organs for human transplants, such as into pigs for human heart transplants.	*Definitely agree*	29	24	28	27	18	15	22	19
	Agree	37	40	35	37	33	32	33	33
Using genetic testing to detect diseases we might have inherited from our parents, such as cystic fibrosis.	*Definitely agree*	44	52	17	9	28	36	35	41
	Agree	38	37	29	23	44	43	39	39
Cloning animals such as sheep whose milk can be used to make drugs and vaccines.	*Definitely agree*		21		25		15		16
	Agree		36		35		31		29

in support (from 60 to 49 per cent) among those who would encourage using biotechnology for food and drinks. Genetic testing appears to be the exception, with more respondents in 2000 supporting its utility and moral acceptability than in 1997, and fewer perceiving risks.

Another indicator of this increasing uncertainty about support for biotechnology is the drop in the numbers of people willing to support more applications. In 1997, about seven in ten supported at least four applications; in 2000, a lower majority of 56 per cent indicated support for four to six applications. Those who were likely to support more applications were younger Canadians, those with more education, men, those who did not consider themselves religious, and those from the Atlantic provinces. It should be noted that one of the applications used in 1997 ('developing genetically modified animals for medical studies, e.g. a mouse that develops cancer') was dropped in favour of an application question on cloning ('cloning animals such as sheep whose milk can be used for the production of drugs and vaccines'). The cloning application is admittedly more controversial and may account for the drop in numbers willing to support at least four applications. When both these non-

comparable items are taken out of the comparison pool, the mean number of applications supported in 1997 is 3.54 in comparison to the mean number of 3.16 in 2000. The difference between these means is statistically significant ($t = 6.01$, $P < 0.01$), suggesting that the drop in support across the five comparable food and medical applications is a substantive one.

The pattern of greater acceptance of medical over food applications found in numerous studies also held true for the Canadian public, with the exception of xenotransplantation – a medical application which remains controversial. While a significant shift in attitudes occurred between 1997 and 2000, with this positive predisposition noticeably tempered, on the whole, attitudes remained relatively more positive than those in Europe

Perceptions of GM food

Uncertainty about GM foods increased during this study's time frame, a finding which incorporated uncertainties about its benefits and risks, lack of confidence in the regulatory system, and views about the use of biotechnological vs traditional means of modification. While over half were found to agree that GM foods would 'bring benefits to a lot of people', over eight in ten also agreed that 'current regulations are not sufficient to protect the public from risks', and close to six in ten expected the worst – that a global disaster would be the outcome for anything going wrong (Figure 4). In terms of the strength of these attitudes, it was apparent that those who saw GM foods as having negative impacts felt more strongly about their views than those who saw benefits and fewer risks. While around a third 'strongly agreed' that GM food was 'against nature', that a global disaster would ensue if anything went wrong, and that only traditional breeding methods ought to be used, far fewer registered as strong feelings on the benefit side.

Conclusions

The challenge for most governments concerning biotechnology is 'to make it happen'.[21] However, making biotechnology happen – building a policy agenda and implementing it – is hardly straight-forward, as many governments have discovered. Different visions of the shape and direction of various applications are promoted, as is the vision of making the technology *not* happen. The media often provide the conduit for the social amplification of these contending visions. Publics play a variety of roles in a spectrum that ranges from passive bystander to active participant.

Figure 4. Attitudes to GM food

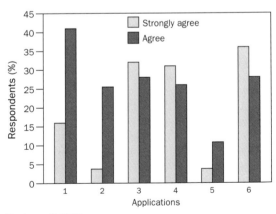

Key to applications.
1. GM food will bring benefits to a lot of people.
2. The risks from GM food are acceptable.
3. Even if GM food has benefits, it is fundamentally against nature.
4. If anything went wrong with GM food, it would be a global disaster.
5. Curent regulations are sufficient to protect people from any risks linked to GM food.
6. Only traditional breeding methods shoul dbe used rather than changing the characteristics of plants and animals through modern biotechnology.

When we started off with the role of the state in the innovation and diffusion of technology, the Canadian story had the state playing a central role in the development of biotechnology as a strategic technology. The government's initial role as promoter and innovator was critical in the development of an industrial capacity, particularly in the pharmaceutical and medical sectors. The development of its role as controller and regulator proceeded more slowly in processes that were both active and reactive.

A key decision early on was that of treating products of biotechnology as essentially no different from traditional products. This theme was a consistent one in government responses to safety questions as reflected in media coverage. For example, in talking about Roundup Ready soya-beans, a government spokesperson was quoted as saying, 'There is no safety risk and no change in nutritional composition.' This framework put Canada squarely in the camp of the dominant actor internationally in biotechnology – the USA – in terms of how biotechnology was to be regulated and managed. The challenge for most regulatory systems is posed by consumer questions about, if not resistance to, applications, particularly in the area of food and crops. If risk is seen to be manage-able for these products, perceptions of risk and the other values consumers bring to their assessment of technology are the less predictable factors.

The media's coverage of food and agricultural applications showed a definite shift from its typically positive coverage of biotechnology over the years. Because consumers had hardly any experience with these products, much of their experience would have been vicariously through the media. Thus, while we have no evidence of a direct link between media coverage and public perceptions, there are clues in the data provided above that Canadian publics may have been responding to information through the media at the same time that the media were covering the issues with echoes of their audience interests in mind. The din from across the Atlantic was heard by Canadian publics through their media, transported to local shores by issue entrepreneurs of the environmental movement.

While policy-makers have had to respond in a variety of ways to what they saw as some increasing discomfort and concern among Canadians, all in all, the reception of biotechnology in this country (relative to Europeans), while remaining cautiously optimistic, is beginning to show signs of concern . Whether this will continue to be the case is the big question.

This may be the appropriate time to pick up where we left off in our opening remark about Canadian identity and technology. What we see here is a country that has been optimistic about technology generally and has similarly been initially optimistic about biotechnology. Increasing information has brought about an unease, a pattern not so dissimilar from what happened in Europe with more 'knowledgeable' countries. Relatively speaking, however, Canadians remain somewhere between the pessimism of Europeans and the more optimistic Americans. While officially casting its lot with a biotechnology future, Canadian enthusiasms may be dampened by considerations emerging in many post-industrial countries – a search beyond simple economic benefits to a mindfulness about a broader range of concerns around technological issues.

Notes and references

1 Kroker, A, *Technology and the Canadian Mind* (Montreal: New World Perspectives, 1984); Grant, G, *Technology and Empire: Perspectives on North America* (Toronto: House of Anansi, 1969); Innes, H, *Essays in Canadian Economic History* (Toronto: University of Toronto Press, 1956); Innes, H, *The Fur Trade in Canada* (New Haven: Yale University Press, 1930); Innes, H, *A History of the Canadian Pacific Railway* (Toronto: University of Toronto Press, 1971); McLuhan, M, *Understanding Media: the Extensions of Man* (Toronto: McGraw-Hill, 1964).

2 Kroker, A (see note 1).

3 Task Force on Biotechnology, *Biotechnology: A Development Plan for Canada*, Report to Minister of State for Science and Technology (Ottawa, 1981).

4 Ministry of State for Science and Technology, *Federal Expenditures for Biotechnology, 1981–1986* (Ottawa, October 1986).

5 Ernst and Young, *Evaluation Study of the National Biotechnology Strategy* (Ottawa, 17 October 1991).

6 Health Canada, *Guidelines for the Safety Assessment of Novel Foods*, vols I and II (Food Directorate, Health Protection Branch, Health Canada, September 1994).

7 KPMG, 'Improving Canadian biotechnology regulation', Report prepared for the National Biotechnology Advisory Committee (Ottawa, March 1995).

8 Small, E, 'New crops for Canadian agriculture', in Janick, J (ed.), *Perspectives on New Crops and New Uses* (Alexandria, Va.: ASHS Press, 1999), pp15–52.

9 Small, E (see note 8).

10 Canadian Food Inspection Agency, *Summary of Confined Field Trials* <www.cfia-cia.agr.ca/english/plaveg/pbo/triesse.shtml> (2001).

11 Canadian Biotechnology Advisory Committee, 'Workplan for biotechnology review unveiled', press release (Ottawa, 21 February 2000).

12 See, for example, Krimsky, S and Wrubel, R, *Agricultural Biotechnology and the Environment* (Urbana, Il: University of Illinois Press, 1996).

13 Powell, D and Leiss, W, *Mad Cows and Mother's Milk* (Montreal: McGill-Queens University Press, 1997).

14 Royal College of Physicians and Surgeons, Expert Panel on Human Safety of rBST, *Report to Health Canada* (Ottawa, January 1999).

15 Canadian Veterinary Medical Association, Expert Panel on rBST, *Report to Health Canada* (Ottawa, November 1998).

16 BioteCanada, *Canadian Biotechnology '98: Success from Excellence* (Ottawa, 1999).

17 Powell, D, 'Hot potato', *National Post* (4 December 1999): A4.

18 Dale, S, 'Mind and matter: a plea for labelling biotech foods', *Globe and Mail* (10 January 1998): D5. 'Groundhog Day' is the symbolic reference to the groundhog rodent coming out of hibernation to forecast either the arrival of spring or continuing weeks of winter. This is basically a yearly media non-event.

19 Scoffield, H, 'Honey, there's a gene in my soup', *Globe and Mail* (21 August 1999): D5.

20 Scoffield, H, 'Canola looks to genetics for its future', *Globe and Mail* (23 August 1999): B3.

21 Jasanoff, S, 'Product, process, or programme: three cultures and the regulation of biotechnology', in Bauer, M (ed.), *Resistance to New Technology: Nuclear Power, Information Technology and Biotechnology* (Cambridge: Cambridge University Press, 1995).

Address for correspondence

Professor Edna Einsiedel, Graduate Program in Communication Studies, Faculty of Communication and Culture, University of Calgary, 2500 University Drive, NW, Calgary, Alberta, Canada T2N 1N4. E-mail einsiede@acs.ucalgary.ca

Denmark: the revival of national controversy over biotechnology

Erling Jelsøe, Jesper Lassen, Arne Thing Mortensen and Mercy Wambui Kamara

Introduction

Development of biotechnology in Denmark prior to 1996 can be divided roughly into three different periods. The earliest period, until the beginning of the 1980s, was characterised by very little public debate and no formal regulation – in fact, almost silence. In about 1980 some debate took place about reproductive and human gene technology. This was triggered by the first trials of IVF treatment at the national hospital in Copenhagen and a Danish Member of Parliament proposing limits to human gene technology to the European Council. The big surge in public attention to biotechnology occurred in 1983–84, when plans for the first industrial applications of modern biotechnology became known. This was the beginning of the second period, which was characterised by a high level of controversy, especially initially. There was a lot of activity at the political level, intense public debate and high media coverage. This period lasted until 1990–91. At the political level, the most significant result of the debate and controversy was the Danish Act on Environment and Gene Technology in 1986. The Act was perceived by Danish industry to be very restrictive towards biotechnology.

As a reaction to the very critical debate, parliament decided to initiate information campaigns and broad public debate. Amongst these activities was the first Danish consensus conference on gene technology in agriculture and industry. This took place in 1987, organised by the then newly established Danish Board of Technology. Thus, in the second half of the period, policy activities had a consensus-seeking element and a participatory approach became part of the development. The high level of controversy and debate was a learning process both for politicians and other actors on the public scene. The debate about biotechnology was not the only contentious issue, controversies about other new technologies were also experienced during the 1970s – most significantly nuclear energy. The nuclear power issue was eventually settled by a parliamentary decision in 1985 which

removed nuclear power from Danish energy policy.[1]

The food and the pharmaceutical industries are major economical sectors in Denmark. In the second half of the 1980s another biotechnological application was subject to debate and regulatory activity: Roundup-resistant sugar beet developed by Maribo Frø, which was the first example of an agricultural application of biotechnology.

Towards the end of the second period the EU directives on deliberate release and contained use were implemented, causing some public debate but no major change in the Danish biotechnological policy.

Policy activities dealing with human biotechnology ran parallel to the debate and policy on agriculture and industry. The most important political event in this field was the establishment of the Danish Council of Ethics in 1987, which had a central role in debate on and assessment of biotechnology for humans.

The third period took place in the first half of the 1990s. It was characterised by a relatively low level of debate compared with the preceding period, an indication that the consensus-seeking policy might have been successful. Danish biotechnological companies, in particular Novo Nordisk, publicly stated that they were satisfied with the restrictive rules in the legislation because it had helped to ensure public acceptance of biotechnology. The consensus, however, if there was one, was confined to the contained use and production of medicines and enzymes. The Eurobarometer survey of 1993 (as in 1996 and 1999) showed that there was a differentiated pattern of attitudes towards biotechnology regarding food and medicines[2] but this differentiation did not attract much attention when the results of the survey were published.

The first half of the 1990s was characterised by quite a lot of policy activity but only limited interaction with the public sphere. Some of the parliamentary decisions in this period (such as the decision in 1994 that all GM food should be labelled) increased in importance when the controversies about GM foods became an issue in

1996 and thereafter. Increasingly, the policy activities in this period were related to EU regulation, which was also the case with the decision about labelling in 1994.

Danish biotechnology policy 1996–2000

Reopening the issue

After five years of relative quiet, biotechnology emerged as a social and political issue in 1996. The events triggering the reopening of biotechnology policy as a focus of intense public attention were the planned marketing of GM soyabeans produced in the USA and, to some extent, GM maize. The soya issues emerged in the political arena during 1995–96, when Monsanto applied for approval of Roundup Ready soya in the EU. Soya was thus the first GM food product to be marketed to Danish consumers and became a test case for the GM food project. Furthermore, it was a test of the parliamentary decision of 1994 which stated that it was Danish policy to demand labelling of food products containing GMOs or products produced with the help of GMOs. The Danish government decided in March 1996 to object to Monsanto's application and, despite latent controversy, soya did not became a prominent political issue until the autumn. The specific trigger for the reopening of the biotechnology issue was media reporting of ships containing GM soya approaching Denmark in October 1996.[3]

In the Danish parliament, the soya issue was looked at from two perspectives: controversies over labelling requirements and reconciliation of GMOs with the principles of organic farming. The labelling question was brought to a temporary halt by a guideline from the Minister of Health requiring food products based on GM soyabeans to be labelled, but not additives such as lecithin from soya. The organic question was a prominent issue, since organic farming was moving from niche production towards an accepted part of Danish agriculture in the mid-1990s. This question was settled by a parliamentary decision stating that organic products must not be contaminated by GMOs at any stage in the production chain.

Just as calm was restored after the soya issue, the announcement of the successful cloning of Dolly the sheep in March 1997 reopened the more fundamental questions about the biotechnological project. On the political scene, the Dolly issue was temporarily settled by a parliamentary decision in June 1997 stating that the government should strive

for the establishment of an international regulation banning human cloning and laying down rules for animal cloning. The issue continued to pop up as a minor theme throughout the period but it did not lead to new regulatory initiatives.

GM foods, including GM crops, remained a prominent topic on the Danish biotechnology policy agenda throughout the period. In 1999, a consensus conference on GM foods arranged by the Board of Technology, resulted in a document which, although critical, did not reject biotechnology altogether. Although the conference did not bring about any direct political outcomes, it helped to keep the issue on the agenda. In November 1998, the critical voices in the Danish public, and indeed the British moratorium on GM plants, resulted in an agreement between the Confederation of Danish Industries, the Danish Agricultural Council and the seed producers. These agro-industrial and industrial actors agreed to impose a one-year moratorium on the growing of commercial plants and the marketing of GM seeds in Denmark. As part of the agreement, the right to hold field trials of GM plants was maintained. Another part of the agreement was to make a codex for the use of GM crops in Danish agriculture.

The voluntary agreement between the Danish actors was followed up by an agreement between Denmark, Italy, France, Greece and Luxembourg in 1999 to block new applications of deliberate release. The result was a de facto moratorium on approvals of deliberate releases, not only in Denmark but in the entire EU. This agreement was announced to be in effect until the planned revision of the directive on deliberate releases which would ensure a revised legal framework for regulating GM plants in the EU. Shortly after this agreement, the environmental NGO, NOAH (Friends of the Earth Denmark), demanded that Denmark withdraw a recommendation for a pending application for GM beet. The Ministry refused to do so but asked the seed producer, Trifolium, to withdraw their application: a proposal they turned down.

Although GM food was the dominant issue throughout the period, other issues also made their way to the political arena. In June 1999 it became known that medical doctors at the municipal hospital in Aarhus had treated patients suffering from liver cancer with live GM influenza virus. The leading scientist broke the rules laid down by the Scientific Ethical Committee when treating patients not participating in planned trials and, furthermore, illegally charged large sums of money for the treatment of some of the patients.

In early 2000, the issue of intellectual property rights made its way to the political arena. Just before the final reading of an Act passing the EU directive on patenting of biotechnological inventions, it was discovered that the directive could have far-reaching consequences for medical research as well as for developing countries. The uproar caused a postponement of the final reading in parliament, and the Danish Ethical Council was asked to make a statement. The Council arranged a hearing and produced a rather critical statement. The Act, however, was passed without important changes shortly thereafter. Key policy changes are summarised in Table 1.

The political arena

Apart from the formal political outcomes of the soya and Dolly issues, there were changes in the biopolitical arena. As mentioned above, these two

Table 1. Key policy events in Denmark, 1996–2000

Date	Trigger	Event	Outcome
October 1996– February 1997	GM soya is shipped from USA to Europe, arriving 11 December 1996.	First GM product on the Danish market. First example of radical resistance in Denmark (blockade). Parliamentary debate on labelling (4 December 1996).	Instruction by the Danish Food Agency on labelling of foods derived from GM soya. Significant increase in public awareness of GM foods.
March–May 1997	Dolly the sheep.	Public debate and media coverage. Hearing on cloning arranged by the Board of Technology (9 April) and Parliamentary debate on cloning (May). Statement on cloning by the Danish Council of Ethics.	Parliamentary decision stating that the government should work to ensure international regulation banning human cloning and regulating animal cloning.
May 1997	Debate about cloning.	Formation of BIOSAM, a joint committee of representatives from other public bodies.	Cooperation on ethical issues related to cloning and biotechnology on mammals.
May 1998	Public debate and resistance to GM foods. Austrian petition on GMOs.	Members of 19 Danish NGOs present 77,416 signatures against GM foods to the Minister of the Environment.	The Minister recognises the public resistance but makes no promises of action.
November 1998	Resistance to GMOs among Danish consumers; British moratorium.	One-year voluntary moratorium. Agreement between Minister of Environment, and organisations from industry and agriculture to stop commercial growing of GM plants or marketing of GM seeds in Denmark in 1999.	De facto moratorium on commercial growing of GM plants or marketing of GM seeds in Denmark. There is no halt to field trials with GM plants, however.
March 1999	Public debate on GMOs, etc.	Consensus conference on GM foods.	Final document on GM foods. No measurable political impact.
March 1999 – June 2000	Continued debate about cloning. Activities related to this are initiated by BIOSAM.	The Danish Council of Ethics arranges meetings in March and November 1999 and issues booklets on cloning and ethics. Discussion paper in June 2000 by the Council of Ethics and the Council for Animal Ethics on cloning.	In light of the continued development and improvement of cloning techniques it is the intention to make a statement about cloning.
June– September 1999	Trials with gene therapy at the municipal hospital in Aarhus using GM influenza virus for treatment of liver cancer.	Leading scientist breaks the rules set by the science ethical committee and illegally treats patients who did not take part in the trials and of whom some paid large sums of money for treatment.	The trials are abandoned by the hospital, the scientist resigns and eventually the science ethical committee lays a criminal charge against him.
June 1999	French proposal on blockade of applications for deliberate releases in the EU.	Agreement between Denmark, France, Luxembourg, Italy and Greece to block new applications for deliberate releases in the EU until the revision of 90/220/EEC ensures a revised legal framework.	De facto moratorium of approvals for deliberate release in the EU.

Table 1 (continued). Key policy events in Denmark, 1996–2000

Date	Trigger	Event	Outcome
July–September 1999	Agreement between five countries in the EU about de facto moratorium of approvals for deliberate releases.	The Minister of the Environment is called by the Danish NGO NOAH to withdraw Denmark's recommendation to approve GM beet. The Minister refuses but asks the seed producer Trifolium to withdraw the application. The company refuses.	Public focus on a political dilemma for both government and industry.
July 1999	News of an increasing number of field trials with GM plants in Denmark	Activists destroy GM crops on two different sites in Denmark.	First case of destruction of GM crops in Denmark.
June 1999–April 2000	Report from BioTik, June 1999.	The BioTik working group recommends regulation based on ethical considerations. The Minister of Trade and Industry reports to Parliament followed by a debate in March and April 2000.	Parliamentary decision stating that the government should work to ensure international regulation of biotechnology based on ethical criteria such as usefulness, integrity, justice and participation.
February 2000	Agreement by the Minister of the Environment for a one-year moratorium in Denmark in 1999.	The Danish Agricultural Council publishes a codex for GMOs in Danish agriculture as part of the agreement. The codex is criticised by NGOs.	Continued debate about the future of GMOs in Danish agriculture.
October 1999–May 2000	Implementation of EU directive 98/44 on patenting of biotechnological inventions in Danish legislation.	Third reading of the Bill in parliament is postponed. The Council of Ethics is asked to make a statement. It arranges a hearing and makes a rather critical statement. Finally the act is passed without important changes.	Implementation of the directive after public debate and media coverage.

events revived the debate on biotechnology as a social issue in Denmark. There were, however, also qualitative changes in the political debate on biotechnology compared to the debates in the 1980s. First of all, contained use (industrial biotechnology) which formed the major issues of the 1980s, seemed to have been taken off the political agenda by all actors during this period. Instead, focus was primarily on GM foods accompanied by issues like cloning and intellectual property rights.

Another change at the policy level was the tendency to move the political debate towards ethics, thus changing the dominant risk frame from the 1980s. Strenuous (and successful) efforts were made, e.g. in parliamentary debates, to restrict the soya issue to the well-known risk frame, and thus to political management within the existing regulatory framework.

During this period the political process slowly adjusted to the arguments raised by the public and addressed the moral and ethical dimensions of gene technology. At first this development was seen as a broadening of the political debate – to a large extent as a result of the cloning issue, where one of the concrete results of the parliamentary debate was a decision to form a committee addressing ethical

issues in relation to biotechnology. In May 1997 BIOSAM was established as a joint committee with representatives from the Danish Council of Ethics, the Board of Technology and the Central Scientific Ethical Committee, the Danish Council of Animal Ethics and the Danish Inspection Committee for Research Animals. Since 1997, BIOSAM and its members had actively taken up ethical issues in relation to biotechnology, arranging hearings and conferences for instance on xenotransplantation (1999) and cloning (1997, 1999).

In this line, bringing ethical questions into the political process was also brought about in 1997 by BioTik – a working group appointed by the Minister of Trade and Industry to ensure a more balanced debate about modern biotechnology. Bioethics was one of the issues to which BioTik paid particular attention, and one of the outcomes of the working group was a report recommending regulation based on ethical principles.[4] This report was followed by an account from the Minister of Trade and Industry in 1999 to parliament and a debate on this issue. The result was a parliamentary decision stating that the government should try to ensure international regulation of biotechnology was brought about, based on criteria suggested by the BioTik working group. Thus, criteria like usefulness, integrity, justice and participation became part of the official Danish biotechnology policy, along with risk. Despite this demonstration of the importance of ethics, Danish regulation was not radically changed from its risk-based foundation.

Other actors also took up the new ethical framing of biotechnology. Prominent members of the Social Democrats for instance published a discussion paper, stressing the importance of many of the values found in the BioTik report.[5] Another example was a codex for the use of GMOs in Danish agriculture, issued by the Danish Agricultural Council as a part of the agreement on a national moratorium in 1998.[6] The codex included an acknowledgement of ethical considerations regarding manipulated animals. Plants, by contrast, should be assessed only in terms of risk.

Changes in organised resistance

Another consequence of the events in 1996–97 was a change in the organised resistance against gene technology.[7] General mobilisation amongst existing NGOs opposing gene technology took place. Since Greenpeace International made gene technology a key issue in 1996, Greenpeace Denmark became one of the most active players on the national arena, but organisations with a lower profile during the first half of the 1990s took up the issue again. Among these was especially NOAH, who, after being the most important NGO in the 1980s, totally disappeared around 1991, but now re-entered the scene. Apart from spawning minor NGOs like Oplysning om Genteknologi (Information about Gene Technology) and Org imod Gensplejsning (Organisation against Genetic Manipulation), the soya controversy also provided a platform for the newly established NGO, Danmarks Aktive Forbrugere (DAF, Active Consumers in Denmark). After a long tradition of organised resistance to biotechnology, mainly based on dissemination of information and 'playing by the rules' in terms of inputs to the political process, the entrance of DAF marked a departure in a slightly more direct and radical direction. The new radical resistance was seen for the first time when DAF, Greenpeace and other organisations tried to blockade the unloading of GM soyabeans. Later on, in 1999, other organisations organised direct actions such as trampling GM crops.

One noteworthy development was an indication of a more formal collaboration between different NGOs and even between NGOs and other actors like retailers. For instance, the Consumers Association entered into an alliance with the Co-op movement to disseminate information about biotechnology. More significant was, however, an initiative to collect signatures against GM foods – a collaboration between 19 Danish NGOs opposed to GM foods, based on a similar action in Austria. More than 75,000 signatures were gathered and presented to the Ministry of Environment and Energy, who recognised the public resistance but did not promise concrete action.

Despite the revival of NGO attention to biotechnology in the late 1990s, their direct impact on Danish biopolicy was marginal. Many of the critical NGOs used their right to respond to biotechnological issues submitted to hearings, but they were never successful in changing decisions. The major success of the critical NGOs was perhaps more indirectly through maintaining biotechnology as a prominent issue in the public eye, and by taking up single issues and forcing the policy system to respond to each case.

Media coverage

During the 1990s, debates about biotechnology in the Danish media underwent a change. In the period 1987–91 there were intensive general discussions about the new perspectives opened up by recombinant DNA technology: scenarios for its possible applications in the near and distant future, ethical problems in transgressing boundaries for human intervention in life processes, democratic control with decisions that may not affect only individuals but populations or humankind as a whole. In this period, the Danish public went through a great educational process and concepts like 'gene', 'DNA', 'gene splicing', 'cloning', etc., became everyday language for the informed public. Images from the world of science fiction – like Frankenstein's monster – gave way to more realistic ideas about biotechnological possibilities and risks. One might say that early in the 1990s modern biotechnology was accepted as a fact. Its application could be disputed but not its actual existence. Figure 1 shows the intensity of media coverage over time.

After this intensive phase, media coverage of biotechnology was more sporadic during the 1990s until queries about specific applications raised all the issues again. The debates were now provoked by real applications – not just future possibilities – and they came back with an intensity and force that was surprising for observers who may have mistaken the relative calm for public acceptance.

Figure 1. Intensity of articles on biotechnology in the Danish press

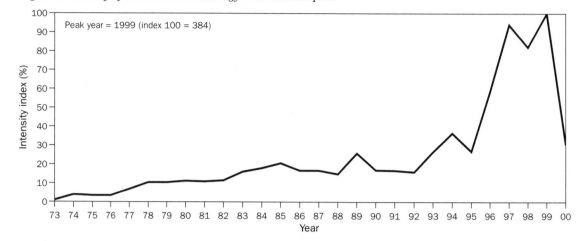

That this was a mistake could have been deduced from survey data – amongst others, the Eurobarometer data for 1993 and 1996 – which consistently showed a high proportion of scepticism combined with high knowledge in the Danish public. However, media coverage of GM soya and maize in food or of the first well-documented example of somatic cloning (to mention but two examples) in the mid- and late 1990s was unexpectedly intense and critical.

In our description of Danish media coverage of biotechnology in the period 1972–96,[8] we selected two national newspapers, *Politiken* and *Information*, as representative of the opinion-leading Danish press in the period. We still consider this choice to be well founded although *Information* is a relatively small newspaper and its stance is more critical than several other national newspapers in some respects. Nevertheless, its position as opinion leader is well established and very strong. For this and for comparative reasons we have based the description of the media coverage in the period 1997–2000 on the same newspapers (Table 2).

Between 1997 and 2000, 'new biotechnology' was not a single-topic public debate as was the case in the 1980s. The debates consisted of several defined topics rather than 'questions about applications of new biotechnology'. Each topic was identified and followed up separately. Instead of *one* story the coverage could be regarded as *several* stories each of which had its own storyline, framing, themes, actors and driving conflicts of values and interests. The stories were, of course, intertwined with arbitrary points separating them. Bearing in mind this reservation we found that the media coverage of new biotechnology from the mid-1990s could be summarised by three stories:

- the story of genetically modified food,
- the story of medical applications of gene technology, and
- the story of biotechnology and money.

Each story is told with background, frame and salient events in which the actors and the conflicts become recognisable characters. Thus, in the story of medical applications of gene technology, the cloning of Dolly the sheep was an event. It raised a media storm between February and March 1997, and has since then been used as a reference point for serious as well as less-than-serious media events (like the Dr Dick Seed project).[9] In the story of GM food, pivotal events were related to questions about regulation, and in the story about biotechnology and money, the main negative reference point was Monsanto's effort to secure dominant market positions for its patented products.

The story of genetically modified food

Between 1997 and 2000, the Danish media extensively featured biotechnology issues. Articles on food biotechnology represented the highest number of articles featured followed by articles on GMO release. Significant political and scientific events were also frequently reported and commented on. The influence of the EU on the Danish national policies was extensively sketched out following the events that paved the way for the January 1997 Novel Foods Regulation and the proceedings of the respective negotiations. Autumn 1998 through to spring 1999 witnessed intensive coverage of the follow-up to Dr Arpad Pusztai's claim that GM

Table 2. Danish media profile, 1987–2000

Phase	1. 1987–96		2. 1997–2000	
Frequency (%)[a]	37		63	
Frame (%)	**Ethics**[b]	**24**	**Accountablity**	**45**
	Progress	23	Ethics	22
	Economic	19	Progress	12
	Accountability	13	Economic	9
	Nature/nurture	6	Pandora's box	8
Theme (%)	**Plant breeding**	**17**	**GM Foods**	**12**
	Microorganisms	11	GMO release	10
	Reproduction	9	Legal regulation	9
	Animal breeding	8	Ethics	8
	DNA research	6	Public opinion/policy	6
	Ethics	5	Plant breeding	5
Actor (%)	**Universities**	**23**	**Industry**	**19**
	Media	12	EU, EC, EP	14
	Industry	10	Gov. research institute	8
	Government	9	Public opinion	7
	Ethical communication	7	Government	7
			Private laboratories	5
Benefit/risk (%)	**Both**	**41**	**Risk only**	**61**
	Benefit only	28	Both	21
	Risk only	25	Benefit only	16
	Neither	6	Neither	2
Location (%)	**Denmark**	**62**	**Denmark**	**47**
	USA	17	USA	11
	UK	2	UK	8

a Percentage of corpus (which includes only those articles which focus on biotechnology) in the period; *n* = 503.
b Bold indicates highest frequency within phase.

potatoes affect human and animal health. Dr Pusztai was suspended from his position, the formal reason given was that he had presented his findings to the media before they had been published in a peer-reviewed journal. Initially, Dr Pusztai was presented as a distinguished scientist who became a victim of his whistleblowing research which challenged vested powerful interests. It was claimed that his boss and colleagues had been working closely with the biotechnology industries and had treated Dr Pusztai badly. As the issue gained momentum his research claim became secondary and other scientific claims against Dr Pusztai's work were reported, and with this the media interest in the Pusztai case slowly withered. However, because of this case and the May 1999 events of the monarch butterfly,[10] there was extensive coverage of the risks posed by food and agricultural biotechnology to consumers, the environment, biodiversity, and human and animal health. It was hypothesised that this risk was not only very high but that it was already present.

Similarly, the row in Britain over GM foods (winter and spring 1998–99) turned into a Danish media frenzy. Public attacks on GM crops and the boycott of GM products by British supermarket chains were reported, although mostly as acts of bravery by the public or environmental and consumer organisations ('David vs Goliath'). Danish supermarkets were portrayed as watching the UK scenario closely with it only being a question of time before Danish shoppers followed suit.

With the events surrounding the EU deliberations of the Commission Regulation (EC) No. 49/2000 of 10 January 2000 on new rules for GM food labelling, the EU was portrayed as a hindrance to democracy, considering only industrial and international competitiveness at the expense of consumer and public interests. It was also portrayed as an obstacle to the Danish consensus and more precautionary policies promoted at home. Throughout, ethical, moral and public accountability underpinnings were high-lighted as absent from industrial policy and as desirable in future national and EU discussions and evaluative criteria.

Whereas biotechnology industries were presented as the key actors responsible for the perceived risks and benefits of biotechnology, national and EU governments were portrayed as puppets in the hands of the biotechnology industries. And whilst environmental organisations were portrayed as the spokespeople for the public, the public was painted as the victim, who may, in the end, never influence the GM food trajectory. All in all, throughout this period, there was the demand that the biotechnology industries stop introducing new foods or crops into the marketplace for moral and democratic reasons. This was partly due to the perceived risk presented by food and agricultural biotechnology, partly due to the perceived lack of benefit to the general public and also due to an increased public ambivalence. For the same reasons, both the national governments and the EU were urged to regulate this area of public policy more rigorously.

Although the media highlighted health and environmental risks, moral and ethical considerations stood out as the guiding criteria for evaluation. It was often argued that it was immoral or ethically wrong to introduce or release GM food and crops against the will of the general public. The very negative nature of food and agriculture biotechnology was not portrayed as a result of the perceived risks to human health. Indeed, it was argued that, although other unhealthy food products already existed on the market, this was no excuse for the industry or government to introduce additional unhealthy products. At issue was that it is ethically or morally wrong to knowingly produce food or crops that might pose risks to humans, animals, ecology or environment in the face of an ambivalent public attitude.

The story of medical applications of gene technology

Medical biotechnology issues received considerable attention in the Danish media during this period albeit less so than food and agricultural biotechnology. Attention was paid particularly to DNA research, the human genome, cloning, gene therapy and, to a lesser extent, xenotransplantation, diagnostics and genetic screening. This was probably due to the fact that there were significant discoveries in these areas during this period, in addition to the events surrounding Dolly the sheep (during the early period of 1997), followed by Polly the GM lamb with a human gene inserted, and the announcement of the mapping of the human genome in February 2001.

Throughout, DNA research was portrayed as beneficial to society and, while human genome and gene therapy were portrayed as both positive and negative, medical diagnostics, genetic screening and animal cloning were, on the whole, portrayed negatively. Generally, risks related to DNA research other than those regarding research issues were seen as minimal. Whereas xenotransplantation and gene therapy were portrayed as posing health and moral risks, human and animal cloning were argued to pose moral and ethical risks.

Medical biotechnology was generally sketched out in the frame of progress. Ethical concerns only emerged later. For example, DNA research, human genome and gene therapy were initially presented as scientific breakthroughs critical for society, and only then were negative consequences to society considered. Public accountability and ethical concerns were also raised. The same could be said about cloning. With the advent of Dolly and Polly, cloning was framed in terms of progress and as a scientific breakthrough. However, in later articles and media, the consequences and meaning of this development to society and humankind in general were framed in terms of ethics and public accountability.

As with GM food, economic interests and international competitiveness are deemed to be the main driving force for the biotechnology industries and for the national government. However, referring to the potential benefits to research and to medicine, it is, all in all, painted as a desirable development, which, if not misused, might benefit society by solving health problems such as cancer. This is why the risks are portrayed as both morally and otherwise acceptable. The media has cautiously encouraged both national government and the EU to regulate this area for the purposes of ethical and public accountability. In general, however, medical biotechnology has enjoyed a relatively positive evaluation and therewith support.

The story of biotechnology and money

Economic aspects of biotechnology were important in the media coverage of biotechnology in this period with the 'goldrush' prospects of biotechnology markets as a driving force for governments and large companies as well as for individuals. Consumers, the public, and moral and ethical values were the victims. There were significant differences in the way the economy was presented in the GM food and in the medical context. In the food context, gene technology was seen as being driven by international companies, the American ones being the worst: powerful, unscrupulous and operating in close contact with the US government. Of Danish companies only one, Danisco, was widely known and although it was pursuing the same goal and had a problematic public image, it was relatively harmless compared to the big US 'rascal', Monsanto. Key events in the story about the biotechnological goldrush in the food markets were assaults on democratic and ecological values (like the soya or the monarch butterfly case) or on innocent victims in developing countries. In the medical context, gene technology was also driven by big companies but their motives for high profits were generally explained by high research costs and so, in the end, by the beneficial nature of their enterprise. The image of NovoNordisk was generally very positive, although a lot of positive attention was also paid to pioneers (individual researchers, new R&D companies) who might succeed in combining scientific progress with economic profit. At the same time, medical biotechnology was seen as an area where quick profits could be made by bluff, or by immoral or rogue researchers. In general, researchers were suspected of being economically motivated or dependent, and their scientific integrity was explicitly commented on in many articles.

Patenting is one of the issues that demonstrates the main characters and conflicts of the economic story. Here again, the dubious role of the Americans was seen in the way they patented ideas without having contributed anything of genuine scientific or intellectual value and with the sole purpose of profiting from their use. In America patenting is seen as a cynical means of making money out of knowledge, be it the knowledge belonging to traditional cultures, knowledge acquired by well-known techniques without new intellectual contributions (like the patenting of human genes), or whatever. In Europe, however, patents are still regarded as serving their purpose of protecting genuine intellectual property and thereby making research economically possible. The gene patent directive, passed by the EU in May 1998 and followed up by revisions of Danish patent law between October 1999 and March 2000, received media coverage from this perspective (for example, being criticised as unclear) as well as from the ethical perspective (for example, being criticised for allowing patents on life).

Here are a few key events of this story. According to the media, biotechnology food and agricultural products offer real economic prospects for biotechnology companies such as Monsanto and Novartis while not benefiting the general public or consumers. For example, Monsanto's Roundup Ready soyabean was seen as profitable for Monsanto, as was Bt maize for Novartis. Many articles on Monsanto's Roundup Ready soyabean mentioned not only that Monsanto had a patent for the soyabeans but also that it had a patent on the chemical, Roundup, to which these crops were resistant. Another reference case was Monsanto's terminator technology, which controls the germination of seeds produced by GM plants. Monsanto was portrayed as the 'bad guy' who was out to control the agricultural production chain from the farm to the market due to its patent on the terminator technology. The terminator technology was seen as posing economic benefits (to Monsanto), while posing dire economic risks to poor farmers in developing countries who could not save seeds to replant from their own farms, making them dependent on big biotechnology companies. There was some discussion about the possibility of this technology helping developing countries. However, the main picture informed more about economic risks than benefits to those who cannot afford to buy Monsanto's patented products. Against this background, the media attention to Monsanto's economic problems in September 1999 was generally framed as a victory for European consumers and other victims of the market strategy of this company, rather than as negative news.

Summary

The period 1997 to 2000 witnessed intense media coverage of biotechnology issues such as on the creation of Dolly the sheep, the penetration of the first generation of GM food products in the marketplace and the new rules on labelling and patents.

Generally, the Danish media were very negative towards modern biotechnology, more so in the case of food and agricultural biotechnology than in the case of medical biotechnology. Biotechnology was presented as an economic project that will only benefit biotechnology companies while posing risks to the environment, consumers, ecology, and animal and human health.

Public accountability and ethical considerations were critical throughout this period. Although public accountability and ethical frameworks became the main evaluative criteria for modern biotechnology, some developments, such as the advent of Dolly the sheep, the mapping of the human genome and gene therapy, were seen as progressive.

Public perceptions

Eurobarometer surveys

The revival of the public debate and controversy in Denmark from 1996 onwards is also reflected in survey results. According to the Eurobarometer surveys of 1996 and 1999, optimism regarding bio-technology and genetic engineering fell from 45 per cent in 1996 to 37 per cent in 1999 and pessimism increased from 30 to 38 per cent. The number of pessimists thus exceeded that of the optimists for the first time. The degree of pessimism in Denmark in 1999 was the second highest in Europe being only a little lower than in Greece with 39 per cent. Optimism, on the other hand, was not much lower than the European average of 40 per cent.

The difference between attitudes to *biotechnology* as opposed to *genetic engineering* was very marked in Denmark. A little more than 50 per cent of respondents were negative about genetic engineering, whereas only 25 per cent were negative when asked about their expectations of biotechnology. There is a particularly strong relationship between gender and attitude. Some 47 per cent of all women were negative about biotechnology and genetic engineering, whereas for men this figure was only 30 per cent. Thus, women account for almost the entire rise in pessimism between 1996 and 1999.

The difference in ranking of pessimism and optimism towards biotechnology and genetic engineering compared to other European countries can be accounted for by a low percentage of 'don't know' answers. This is probably an indication of a high degree of public awareness of biotechnology and genetic engineering. Public awareness was also indicated by the number of applications of modern biotechnology that the respondents said they had heard of. The survey showed that public awareness was high, in fact the highest in Europe. In addition, more people in Denmark said they had talked about biotechnology either frequently or occasionally than in any other European country.

At the same time, Denmark is in the group of countries, together with Sweden and the Nether-lands, that had the largest number of correct answers to the knowledge questions about relevant biology. There was no clear relationship between knowledge and attitude. As in 1993 and 1996, the most significant tendency in this respect was that of a

falling number of 'don't know' responses to the question about expectations of biotechnology and genetic engineering with increasing numbers of correct answers. On the trend knowledge scale (i.e. the knowledge questions that were asked in 1993, 1996 and 1999) there has been an increase in the number of correct answers throughout the whole period from 1993 to 1999.

Perceptions of risk and ethics

In the 1999 Eurobarometer survey, the pattern of response to the questions concerning applications of modern biotechnology in Denmark largely followed the general pattern of positive responses to medical applications and more negative responses to food and crops. Similar patterns were found for 1993 and 1996 both in Denmark and the rest of Europe. This differentiation of attitudes was more pronounced in Denmark than in Europe as a whole. While attitudes towards medical applications were slightly more positive in Denmark than the European average, attitudes to applications on food and crops were considerably more negative. This is similar to the findings of 1996 but the Danes' attitudes towards GM crop plants became more negative, which probably reflects the extensive debate about GM soya and maize as well as the beet developed by two Danish companies. Characteristically, perceptions of utility were higher than average in Europe for all applications except for food which was significantly lower.

The change towards a more negative attitude towards GM crop plants was the most significant amongst the changes regarding attitudes to those applications that were also included in the 1996 survey. However, the attitude towards GM crop plants was nevertheless less negative than that that to food. With respect to the willingness to encourage the three applications that were new in the 1999 Eurobarometer survey (cloning of animals ('the Dolly question'), cloning of human cells or tissues, and use of GM bacteria to clean up oil slicks or dangerous chemicals), Denmark ranked in the middle. Attitudes towards these applications were slightly more positive than the European average. The Danish average regarding willingness to encourage cloning of animals was slightly below zero – expressing a slightly negative attitude.

Willingness to encourage various applications in Denmark is shown in Table 3. The ranking of applications is roughly the same as for the mean scores on Figure 2. Bioremediation received slightly less support than the cloning of human cells. It also

Table 3. Willingness to encourage applications of modern biotechnology in Denmark, Eurobarometer 1999 (% of whole sample)

	GM food	GM crops	Medicines	Genetic testing	Human cell cloning	Animal cloning	Bioremed- iation
Agree and strongly agree (%)	28	39	64	66	55	37	53
Disagree and strongly disagree (%)	57	46	16	17	24	38	21
Opinion holders ('decided')(%)	84	86	80	83	79	75	74

Figure 2. Average evaluation of usefulness, risk, moral acceptability and willingness to encourage biotechnology applications in Denmark

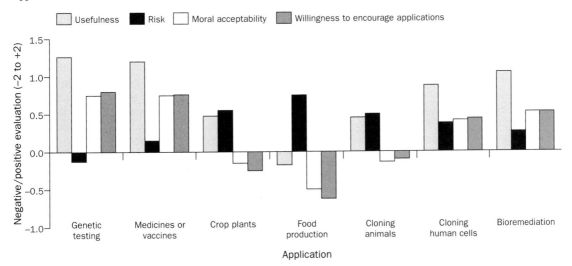

received fewer opponents though. Almost two-thirds supported genetic testing whereas only about a quarter supported GM foods. The percentage of respondents who had an opinion ('decided') was generally high but higher for GM food and crops than for the other applications, which is probably due to the high level of public attention to and debate about these two applications.

In Table 4 the baseline represents those respondents who expressed an opinion on all four attitudinal dimensions. We included only those respondents who had firm opinions because it was

Table 4. The distribution of logics amongst the 'decided public', Eurobarometers 1996 and 1999 (total decided public = 100%)

	GM food		GM crops		Medicines		Genetic testing	
	1996	1999	1996	1999	1996	1999	1996	1999
Supporter (%)	22	14	34	28	58	43	61	55
Risk-tolerant supporter (%)	21	21	35	31	35	47	30	36
Opponent (%)	57	64	32	42	7	10	9	9
'Decided' (%)[a]	51	49	56	49	72	57	65	61

a Proportion of 'decided' as percentage of the whole sample of respondents.

the most reliable way to make time-series comparisons with 1996 owing to the changes in the wording of the question between the two surveys (for details about the change in question format and the problems arising from it see Gaskell *et al.*)[11]. There was a decrease in the number of 'decided' for all four applications but this was small for food. By contrast, there was a marked decrease in the case of medicine. If the change in question format influenced the answers, then this influence appears to be smallest for food, which was the subject of most coverage and public debate since 1996. On the other hand, the number of respondents who expressed an opinion on all four attitudinal dimensions was higher for medical applications than for food and crops, despite the fact that the number of 'decided' was highest on encouragement for food and crops (Table 3). This means that more respondents expressed an opinion on whether they were willing to encourage GM food and crops even if they responded with 'don't know' to one or more of the questions about usefulness, risk and moral acceptability than was the case for medicine and genetic testing. That is to say, more people appeared to express an opinion about GM food and crops no matter whether they felt uncertain or ambivalent about some of the attitudinal dimensions mentioned in the questionnaire.

Risk perception was high in Denmark on most applications. However, as in 1996 when the design of the survey for the first time made it possible to analyse for predictors of 'willingness to encourage' various applications of modern biotechnology, risk was not the most important predictor. For all applications, moral acceptability was by far the most important predictor compared to risk perception. Multiple regression analysis showed that the predictive value of risk perception was low for all applications, highest for crop plants ($\beta = -0.12$) and lowest for food and cloning of animals and human cells or tissues ($\beta = -0.07$ for food, -0.07 for the cloning of human cells and tissues, and -0.06 for the cloning of animals). By contrast, the predictive value of moral acceptability was high ($\beta = 0.55$ for crop plants, 0.41 for food, and 0.65 for cloning of animals).

The differentiation of attitudes to applications on food and crops compared to medical applications was also clearly expressed in the focus-group interviews we held. A common argument against GM food was that it is only for the economic benefit of the food industry. As one interviewee said, 'All this about changing the taste [of the foods] is purely economic thinking, I can't see any reason for it at all.' Even though the majority of the people interviewed supported medical applications, there were also frequent indications of ambivalence. Thus the same interviewee said: 'For instance, insulin can already be made, you know, I don't know, what it is made of but I think it is some human glands... and a thing like organ transplantation and the like – I am not so sure if I got heart disease, that I would have a new one.'

The emphasis on ethics was also made very clear by some of the interviewees: 'I also think that seeking knowledge about gene manipulation is a bit strange, because to me, at any rate, it is an ethical, moral, question.... Therefore I don't think I need more knowledge about the technology itself and the damage. I would prefer to discuss and gain knowledge about the moral and ethical issues, since I have already decided that I don't like it.'

Answers to the battery of items in the Eurobarometer 1999 survey specifically designed to measure attitudes to various aspects of risk and ethics basically followed the same pattern as in Europe as a whole. On average, the answers were somewhat more negative regarding both risk perception and ethical arguments. 'Don't know' responses as well as 'neither–nor' answers were at a lower level than in the rest of Europe. This means that on most items both positive and negative attitudes showed higher frequencies. The item 'Cloning of animals/GM food is so complex that public consultation is a waste of time' showed especially interesting answers. In 1999, Denmark ranked near the top regarding support for public consultation together with the Netherlands, France and Sweden. By contrast, in 1996, Danish answers to the similar question showed surprisingly low support for public consultation. This change is probably due to a different translation into Danish of the question in 1999.

The strongest agreement with risk and ethics items were to those stating that cloning of animals/GM food was 'fundamentally unnatural' or 'threatened the natural order'. This was similar to the rest of Europe. It gives support to the conclusion that ethical arguments acted as a veto. However, the 'strong-risk' arguments pointing to risks as unavoidable and catastrophic had high support too, and, at the same time, they were well correlated with the ethical arguments that referred to biotechnologies as unnatural. Conversely, the items containing statements about risks being avoidable or mentioning utility arguments were poorly correlated with these stronger arguments.

Widespread ambivalence even amongst people who are supportive of biotechnology was characteristic in Denmark. Thus, in Denmark, as in the rest of Europe, there is a large majority of people who support GM foods or cloning of animals, for instance, but who nonetheless agree with the statements about biotechnology being unnatural.

Trust

The trust expressed by the respondents in Denmark also followed the general pattern in Europe, i.e. a high level of trust in NGOs with consumer organisations ranking highest and very low levels of trust in industry and political parties. The medical profession, who also have a high level of trust in Europe, on average 53 per cent, was at a somewhat lower level in Denmark (43 per cent). This may be due to a critical debate in Denmark about the health sector or to the aforementioned major gene-therapy scandal in a Danish hospital. National government bodies in Denmark were trusted more than in Europe on average (26 vs 15 per cent) but the level was still not very high.

The fact that 81 per cent of the Danish respondents said they did not feel sufficiently informed about biotechnology can also be seen as an expression of this lack of trust in industry and politicians. Interestingly in this connection, trust in the media also seemed to be low (14 per cent).

Similar viewpoints were expressed in our focus-group interviews. One of the interviewees tried to summarise a discussion by saying, 'Who is then deciding? It is those who have the biggest purse, who can convince the politicians, that things are as they say, isn't it? Greenpeace followed by NOAH try to pull in the opposite direction, but then again, it is a question of the money – who has the most money to convince them [politicians] that they are right?' And yet, many interviewees were convinced about the importance of the NGOs, also as sources of information. One person said, '[The grassroots movements are] important in this issue as they have been – or are – in so many other issues.... It is difficult for the politicians to become informed, it is certainly also difficult for the rest of us.... So therefore I think it is quite important to have such grass-roots movements.'

The last statement points to the fact that when people say they do not feel sufficiently informed it may also be an expression of a genuine feeling that there is so much knowledge and information that they do not have, or that the information is uncertain or insufficient to enable an informed opinion. Furthermore, there is much that the government,

or the scientist for that matter, does not know or understand about the technology, for example its long-term consequences.

National surveys in Denmark

A number of Danish national surveys were carried out between 1996 and 2000. In December 1996 and 1997 the leading Danish conservative paper *Berlingske Tidende* conducted two small surveys based on the heated public debate about Monsanto's soya. In December 1996, 68 per cent of respondents said that they thought GM foods should be prohibited. In the second survey, which was a follow-up to the first one, 63 per cent wanted the foods prohibited.[12]

In a project initiated by the Danish Board of Technology about 'the food policy of citizens' that aimed at investigating the goals and priorities of Danish consumers in relation to food, two surveys were conducted in January 1998. The first of these included four questions about GM food. In this survey, 62 per cent of the respondents indicated that they fully or partly agreed that it should be prohibited to produce or sell GM foods in Denmark. Some 73 per cent fully or partly agreed that use of GM products was dangerous for the environment because the long-term consequences were unknown.[13]

A survey conducted for Dansk Industri (the Confederation of Danish Industries) in August 1999 investigated attitudes and expectations concerning future technologies. The results showed that Danes generally have positive expectations towards new technologies and their future impacts on society. However, attitudes were generally negative regarding gene technology and chemical production. Almost half of the respondents said they would never buy a GM product, whereas 80 per cent had positive expectations of gene technology in relation to medical applications.[14]

In spring 2000, the Institut for Konjunktur-Analyse (an independent research institute) together with *Ingeniøren* (a weekly magazine for the Society of Danish Engineers) ran a project on views of biotechnology in Denmark. It consisted of interviews with different groups of professionals and a survey with a representative sample of 600 respondents.[15] Amongst other questions, the respondents in the survey were asked about their expectations of biotechnology and gene technology improving our quality of life in the next 20 years, similar to the question about expectations of biotechnology and genetic engineering in the

Eurobarometer surveys. Here, 55 per cent of the respondents said they expected biotechnology and gene technology would improve our way of life and only 10 per cent said it would make it worse. This is very different to the result of the 1999 Eurobarometer. In other respects, for example, attitudes to applications of biotechnology to food, combating diseases, etc., the results were similar to the Eurobarometer findings. The survey focused strongly on trust and credibility, and generally the findings on both were in accordance with the results of the Eurobarometer survey. However, when asked about their trust in the ethics and morals of four Danish biotechnological companies, the respondents were generally positive even though their trust in information about biotechnology from the food and medical industry was rather low.

Conclusions

In Denmark the 'years of controversy' from 1996 onwards were clearly triggered by the soyabean case. The subsequent debate about cloning in spring 1997 was heated too, and gave rise to intense media coverage as well as several policy initiatives. However, public perceptions of the various applications of modern biotechnology clearly indicate that attitudes are the most negative about GM foods and crops, whereas attitudes to cloning of animals are less negative than the European average.

Despite the different character of these events they have one thing in common as triggers for debate. They are examples of concrete applications of modern biotechnology. In this respect, the revival of the biotechnology controversy in the second half of the 1990s resembles that of the 1980s when it was the first industrial applications of GM bacteria in Denmark that triggered the debate and gave rise to the Act on Gene Technology in 1986. Later in the 1980s, the debate was maintained by the application for approval of GM sugar beet. Even the first and much more limited debate about gene technology around 1980 was triggered by reports about an actual application of modern biotechnology, i.e. the first trials with IVF treatment in Denmark.

Also characteristic for the years after 1996 was the high level of interaction between policy and other public spheres. The number of policy-making activities was not significantly higher than in the first half of the 1990s but the activities were aimed at addressing the public perceptions of biotechnology to a much larger extent. Important examples are the moratorium of 1999 and the

BioTik report. NGOs that were almost silent in 1991–96 were very active and several new NGOs emerged in this period. Forms of political activism, which had not been seen in Denmark before in relation to biotechnology, also emerged in this period, such as the blockade against the soya ship in 1996 and actions against field trials in 1999.

The strong criticism that GM foods do not benefit the consumer and only economically benefit the industry itself was expressed almost unanimously in much of the press coverage and in our focus-group interviews. Large multinationals like Monsanto appeared as the villains of the piece. A broader context for the resistance against GM foods was provided by a critical debate about the consequences of the industrialisation of food production (animal husbandry, pesticides, salmonella, etc.), which dates back to the mid-1970s and remained as a hot topic in Denmark throughout the 1990s. The emphasis on moral acceptability, which was found in the Eurobarometer surveys as well as in the media coverage, seemed to be based on a perception of GM foods having long-term and as yet not fully known consequences, and, at the same time, being almost exclusively in the economic interest of the industry.

The recognition of ethical arguments came more slowly in the policy processes due to the dominant risk frame, which became institutionalised in the regulatory activities. It had been prevalent only in relation to human biotechnology. In the wake of the reopening of the biotechnology controversy in 1996–97, ethics was still only at issue in relation to cloning and biotechnology on mammals. More recently, it has become important in relation to food and crops as well and was brought into focus in some of the most prominent policy activities, notably the BioTik report and the subsequent policy initiatives by the Minister of Trade and Industry. However, even though the Danish parliament has recognised that ethical considerations are important in the regulation of biotechnology, there is still no significant shift away from risk-based regulation.

These initiatives seem to be aimed at establishing consensus (a new 'social contract'), like the activities of the 1980s were believed to do. It still remains open, however, whether social consensus based on acceptance of GM foods conditioned by appropriate institutional arrangements and control mechanisms can be achieved. The strong support for veto-like arguments against GM foods, which was found in the Eurobarometer survey and in our focus-group interviews, seems to indicate that the situation in this respect is different from that of the 1980s.

Notes and references

1 Jelsøe, E, 'Information's role in the introduction and social regulation of new biotechnologies', in Dierkes, M and von Grote, C (eds), *Between Understanding and Trust: The Public, Science and Technology* (Reading: Harwood Academic, 1999), pp287–312.

2 Institut National de Recherche Agricole (INRA) and Marlier, E, 'Eurobarometer 39.1 – biotechnology and genetic engineering: what Europeans think about it in 1993', *Report DGXII/E/1* (Brussels: Commission of the European Communities, 1993).

3 Lassen, J, Allansdottir, A, Liakoupulos, M, Olsson, A and Mortensen, A T, 'Testing times: the reception of Roundup Ready soya in Europe', in Bauer, M and Gaskell, G, (eds), *Biotechnology: The Making of a Global Controversy* (Cambridge: Cambridge University Press, in press).

4 BioTik-gruppen, *De Genteknologiske Valg* (Erhvervsministeriet, 1999).

5 Socialdemokratiet, 'Gen-vej til fremtiden – træd varsomt. Debatoplæg om genteknologi', discussion paper (Socialdemokratiet, 1999).

6 Landbrugsraadet, 'Landbrug, fødevarer og genteknologi. Landbrugets holdning til anvendelsen af genteknologi i landbrug og fødevareproduktion', *Landbrugsraadet* (1999).

7 Lassen, J, 'Changing modes of biotechnology assessment in Denmark', in Miettinen, R (ed.), *Biotechnology and the Public Understanding of Science: Proceedings of the UK–Nordic Co-operative Seminar held in Helsinki 25–27 October 1998*, Publications of the Academy of Finland 3/99 (Helsinki: Od Edita, 1999), pp82–90.

8 Jelsøe, E, Lassen, J, Mortensen, A T, Frederiksen, H and Wambui Kamara, M, 'Denmark', in Durant, J, Bauer, M W and Gaskell, G (eds), *Biotechnology in the Public Sphere: A European Sourcebook* (London: Science Museum, 1998), pp29–42.

9 Dr Richard Seed is a physicist and fertility researcher from Chicago, who wanted to raise money for establishing a fertility clinic where infertile couples could have a child by cloning of one of the parents. He was the subject of intense media coverage in the beginning of January 1998 but was considered less-than-serious (if not 'mad'), possibly also because he was an outsider in relation to established medical research institutions and because it was soon revealed that he was in serious need of money.

10 In 1998 researchers at Cornell University found that pollen from maize modified with the bacterium *Bacillus thuringiensis* (Bt toxin) kills the caterpillar of the threatened monarch butterfly. This provoked calls for the GM maize to be banned on environmental grounds.

11 Gaskell, G, Allum, N and Wagner, W *et al.* this volume, pp53–79

12 For a more detailed explanation see Jelsøe, E *et al.* (note 8), p36.

13 Andersen, I E and Iversen, T, 'Borgernes madpolitk – en undersøgelse af forbrugernes bud på fremtidens fødevarepolitik', *Teknologinævnets Rapporter*, 1998/2.

14 Dansk Industri, *Fremtidens Teknologier* (Dansk Industri, September 1999).

15 Institut for Konjunktur-Analyse, 'Danskernes syn på bioteknologi', *Nyhedsmagasinet Ingeniøren* (May 2000).

Address for correspondence

Professor Erling Jelsøe, Department of Environment, Technology and Social Studies, Roskilde University, PO Box 260, DK-4000 Roskilde, Denmark. E-mail Ej@teksam.ruc.dk

Biotechnology in Finland: transcending tradition

Timo Rusanen, Atte von Wright and Maria Rusanen

In the early 1970s modern biotechnology took Finland by surprise. It was considered to be 'big science', unsuitable for the resources of a small country. However, by the end of the 1970s, gene technology had become part of established science in Finland and is now actively funded by institutional bodies. Advances have been made, especially in the field of industrial enzymes which has remained a key area of Finnish gene technology. In the 1980s biotechnology became firmly established in Finland, both as a subject of academic research and for spin-off enterprises. Peer pressure had an important role in controlling biotechnological research before the introduction of formal legislation. In the 1990s, the need for specific legislation was foreseen, followed by the implementation of the Finnish Gene Technology Act.[1]

Political constitution and culture

Finland achieved independence in 1917 after initially being under Swedish rule and, since 1809, an autonomous Grand Duchy in the Russian Empire. Finland is a constitutional republic with a parliamentary system of government. The supreme power is vested in the people represented by the 200-member parliament.[2] Most of the parliamentary decisions are based on proposals from the Council of State (Cabinet). The president's functions and powers are set out in the constitution. The new constitution of Finland, which became law on 1 March 2000, shifted a significant proportion of executive power from the president to the Council of State. EU membership from 1995 onwards has further contributed to this trend. The president appoints the Council of State which must, however, enjoy the confidence of parliament. The president also conducts Finnish foreign policy in cooperation with the Council of the State.[3]

Political parties at the core of Finnish political life are numerous and varied. The non-socialist parties usually hold the majority in parliament. As a rule, changes in government do not [usually] cause any major changes in politics. The consensus between the political parties is reflected in the present Cabinet, the so-called Rainbow Coalition, originally appointed in 1995, and still in power in 2001, including the conservative National Coalition Party, the Social Democrats, the former communist Left Alliance, the Swedish People's Party and the Green League. New political demarcations have begun to appear in an urban–rural dimension reflected by these predominantly urban parties in the Cabinet and the Finnish Centre (formerly known as the Agrarian Party), which has been in opposition since 1995.

Policy on biotechnology

The economic impact of modern biotechnology has not yet matched its symbolic and political importance for industrial R&D in Finland, as Finland recovers from the deepest economic recession experienced by any EU country since the Second World War. Promoting modern biotechnology is a part of public policy. Many universities have research centres focused on modern technology, where biotechnology competes with information technology (IT) research – the most advanced technology in Finland. Compared to the main industries of Finland, traditionally forestry and metals and recently the rapidly growing telecommunications sector, modern biotechnology has made only a small economic impact.

In public policy biotechnology is seen as a tool for future R&D. Modern biotechnology is predicted to be one of the booming industries in the 2000s, echoing the development of IT in the 1990s.[4] However, this vision remains to be realised. So far, the IT sector has continued, and will continue in the near future, to be the major field of industrial of R&D in Finland. This is supported by public policy because Finland aims to become a leader in the information age, not just in Europe but worldwide.[5] Overall expenditure on R&D was 2.9 per cent of Finland's GNP in 1998.[6]

In the private R&D sector biotechnology competes with environmental technology as the second major field of development after IT. On an international scale, there is no domestic industrial basis for biotechnology, for example, in the food or pharmaceutical industries, comparable to IT where the domestic company Nokia is also a major international player. Nevertheless, the funding of biotechnology development by the Finnish state is significant, because relatively little private funding is allocated to the sector. In spite of this lack of private funding, the biotechnology industry is the sixth largest in Europe.[7] The strongest use of biotechnology in Finland is enzyme production, based on well-established fermentation technology. Microbiological know-how as well as pharmaceuticals, diagnostic systems and biomaterials are other advancing fields. There are between 70 and 80 companies active in biotechnology in Finland. Many of them are situated in science parks established with public funding. Six universities have strong biotechnology research departments. Biomedicine is catching up with biotechnology and molecular biology as topics for research. In 1998, there were approximately 180 academic research groups and 19 graduate schools specialising in biotechnology. In December 1998, the Academy of Finland nominated 26 research groups as centres of excellence for the years 2000–05, of which 12 are biotechnology based.[8]

The public policy effort to promote R&D sector reflects the Finnish optimism for technology. There is significant backing for R&D, based on people's experiences of new technologies and trust in technology.[9] Technology is associated with a rapid rise in the standard of living during the era of Finnish urbanisation and expansion of heavy industry in the 1960s and 1970s, culminating in the rise of IT in the 1990s. Disillusionment caused by the potential disadvantages of technological development may only just be starting to appear.

Public policy

The period 1997–2000 has been relatively uneventful regarding biotechnology regulation in Finland, apart from three main legislative events (Table 1). In 1997 the EU Novel Food Regulation was incorporated into Finnish legislation. The other two key events took place in 2000 in the form of the new Patent Law and amendment of the Gene Technology Act. The Finnish Gene Technology Act and the accompanying statutes were changed on 1 June 2000. The trigger was the change in the EU directive on the contained use of GM microorganisms (98/81/EU). At the national level some amendments have also been made to the contained use of other GMOs. The Finnish parliament amended a new version of the Patent Law in 2000 which takes

into account biotechnological inventions and the respective intellectual property rights.

Overall this relatively uneventful period in legislation reflects the position of biotechnology in Finnish society. The main activity is still very much R&D based with relatively few actual industrial applications. Consequently, the legislators have not felt any need or pressure to streamline the existing regulations, which, apparently, have served their purpose, as far as research activities are concerned. There have been no major conflicts between industrial interests, governmental policy and the public at large. Characteristically, the Finnish approach to the situation has been reactive rather than proactive. The legislation follows the developments at EU level rather than trying to identify local or national interests and anticipate future needs.

The institutionalisation of ethics

The first institutional initiatives on gene technology started in 1979, when the Recombinant DNA Expert Group was created by the initiative of the National Board of Health. The Group did not have any binding legal status, and its members all had scientific backgrounds. Its task was to instruct and advise both scientists and authorities in matters related to gene technology. Along with the development of the legislation, the remit of the Group was divided between two new official bodies: 1 the National Advisory Board for Biotechnology (established in 1991 by the Ministry of Social Affairs and Health, and subsequently taken over by the Prime Minister's Office) and 2 the Board for Gene Technology (established in 1995 by the Ministry of Social Affairs and Health). Both are chaired by experts with scientific backgrounds.

The Board for Gene Technology acts as the Finnish competent authority required by the Finnish Gene Technology Act and EU gene-technology directives. The Board must, by law, include ethical expertise, although the board is dominated by members nominated by different authorities (Ministries of Social Affairs and Health, Environment, Agriculture and Forestry, and Trade and Industries). At present one of the seven members is an ethicist.

The National Advisory Board for Biotechnology was given official status by the Finnish Gene Technology Act. The Board has special tasks as a reviewing and evaluating body for gene technology and had a prominent role in formulating the new version of the Finnish Gene Technology Act. Although the work has been mainly technical, the

Table 1. Key policy events in Finland, 1996–2000

Date	Trigger	Events	Outcomes
1997	Passing of EU Novel Food Regulation.	EU regulation is incorporated into Finnish legislation. Novel Food Board is established as the national expert group required by the regulation.	
1999	Dolly the sheep.	Law on medical research on human embryos and fetuses.	Prohibition of human cloning.
2000	The reformulation of EU directive 98/81/EU.	The new version of Finnish Gene Technology Act is passed, superseding the previous one of 1995.	Some amendments (not required by the EU directives) concerning the contained use of GMOs are incorporated in the national law.
	EU directive 98/44/EU on intellectual property rights and biotechnological inventions.	The Finnish Patent Law harmonised with the directive.	Patenting of biological material made possible under certain conditions.
		Kansalaisten Bioturva (People's Biosafety) is established in May: an association critical of biotechnology, especially the applications of gene technology.	Despite its recent establishment, the association has fuelled public debate aiming, for example, to sue the Finnish Board for Gene Technology for negligence in office.

Board also has the task of considering the social and ethical consequences of gene technology. The National Advisory Board for Biotechnology has a more varied composition than the Board for Gene Technology. Among the 18 members, in addition to representatives of different research institutions and ministries, are representatives of formal and semiformal bodies such as conservationists, trade unions, a moderate animal rights movement, consumers, and industries. The Board also includes one ethicist, but no single actual NGO member. This reflects a particular aspect of Finnish society: strong tradition of institutionalisation even of grassroots movements.

The tasks and the composition of both the Board for Gene Technology and the National Advisory Board for Biotechnology reflect the development of the legislation on gene technology in Finland. Progress has been very much driven by the authorities; they have taken the initiative at each step in the process. The Boards act professionally and fairly in fulfilling their legal duties, but their role is clearly either that of an authority (the Board for Gene Technology) or as an advisory body to authorities (the National Advisory Board for Biotechnology). Although membership of the National Advisory Board covers many sectors of society, there are several groups with an obvious interest in the subject matter that are absent. For example, no religious groups are represented – this

in a country where more than 80 per cent of population are church members and where an exceptionally large section of the population (61 per cent) regard themselves as religious. There are no communication experts or social scientists included, neither are there any representatives of the outspoken critics of the gene technology.

In the past, NGOs in Finland have not specifically singled out biotechnology as the target for action. A new NGO critical of the implementation of biotechnology, Kansalaisten Bioturva (People's Biosafety), was founded in May 2000. During its short existence it has managed to introduce a radical element into the public discussion on biotechnology.

Official and public response to controversy

Cloning. The first cloning of a mammal from an adult cell, Dolly the sheep, was both a scientific and media sensation in Finland, as it was elsewhere in the world. The media coverage was more mixed than in the previous reporting of biotechnological inventions. The ethical problems and the possibility of human cloning were highlighted. However, these concerns were not reflected in any official action taken by authorities or legislators. Human cloning was prohibited by a special law, passed in 1999. No special guidelines regarding cloning of mammals were issued. At the time of writing, no projects directly involving animal cloning are apparently in progress, although the necessary techniques are being introduced in several research groups.

Food. The case of transgenic soya shipped to Europe from the USA in late 1996 received extensive media coverage in Finland. However, the event was not considered important initially, it was only when the debate and protests prevalent across Europe became more widely known, that this issue became a major media event. The tone of the discussion was neutral, and the media did not take any particular stand in the debate. The authorities' response was, likewise, rather calm, and the message conveyed to the public was that no GM soya would be imported, at least not intentionally. No special legislative or control measures were introduced. In May 2000 it was, however, revealed that small amount (0.4 per cent) of GM rape had probably contaminated the seeds that had been purchased during the previous year, and, consequently, some GM rape-seed might have been grown in Finnish fields. Although the contaminated crop had been processed, and no GMOs should have been present in fields in 2000, the incident caused some alarm. In fact the publicity coincided with the establishment of Kansalaisten Bioturva.

Medical applications. Gene therapy trials are not specifically covered by the Finnish Gene Technology Law. The Finnish Law on Medicines has been applied, and the viral vectors used in the genetic constructs are considered analogous to live vaccines. Consequently, the official body controlling gene therapy is the National Agency for Medicines. The trials in progress are centred on gene therapy for malignant brain tumours. Genetic testing for hereditary diseases is available on a voluntary basis, for example in prenatal clinics. The lack of legislation and clear guidelines, together with the view that the 'patients' have not been in a position to give informed consent, has caused some debate, mainly among health-care professionals and health scientists. Forensic DNA tests have been applied routinely for identification purposes and for obtaining evidence in criminal cases. The police have publicly expressed a wish that a DNA archive, similar to a fingerprint register, should be established.

Media coverage

Since the nineteenth century, Finland has had a large number of newspapers with very high circulations. Dailies are part of the Finnish way of life. The expansion of the factual and pragmatic Finnish newspapers was made possible in the late 1800s by the traditionally high rate of literacy. It was promoted by the progressive public officials and clergy as a means of disseminating new innovations, such as those in agriculture and health care, in the sparsely inhabited agrarian countryside. In a way the same spirit of enlightenment still exists in the contemporary Finnish press. In the period 1972–96, biotechnology was presented, in general, as a promising new technology and appeared in the press as more pragmatic and less discursive than in many other EU countries. During the latest three-year period (1997–99, Phase 2), the reporting of gene technology in Finnish media has become more multidimensional, compared to reporting in Phase 1 (1992–96) (Table 2).

The media analysis for the years 1997–99 is of two newspapers, *Savon Sanomat* (which represents a consortium of Finnish newspapers) and *Helsingin Sanomat* which has the highest circulation of the Finnish dailies. In Phase 2, a comparison was made between *Helsingin Sanomat* and *Savon Sanomat*. The differences in tone of articles between these papers turned out to be small. The number of articles in Phase 2 is double the number of articles in Phase 1 (Figure 1). If all articles since 1973 are taken into account, some 25 per cent occur in Phase 1 and 49 per cent in Phase 2, representing a significant increase in reporting. Economic prospects are clearly not as dominant in Phase 2 as in Phase 1. Gene technology in contemporary Finnish society acquired wider social, cultural, as well as ethical and moral connotations in media coverage. This might reflect the changing role of technology in society as a whole, as well as the changing public perception of biotechnology in its social setting.

Themes associated with gene technology are no longer associated with potential new sources of wealth as they were earlier. When analysing themes as clusters, 'economics' is less prevalent than various individual fields of application and their effects on everyday life. In Phase 2 there is a significant increase of articles about biomedical issues. This development reflects the progress in gene technology R&D. Another theme becoming more prevalent is 'public opinion'. This develop-ment reflects the more discursive nature of the media debate about biotechnology. A more inter-active debate, although still very modest compared to other European societies, has emerged. However, on biotechnology, a discourse with a more varied participation is appearing in the Finnish press.

Table 2. Finnish media profile, 1992–1999

Phase	1. 1992–96		2. 1997–99	
Frequency (%)[a]	34		66	
Frame (%)	**Progress**[b]	53	**Progress**	27
	Economic prospects	22	Nature/nurture	19
	Accountability	8	Economic prospects	16
	Nature/nurture	7	Accountability	14
			Ethical	12
Theme (%)	**Biomedical**	27	**Biomedical**	34
	Agrifood	20	Agrifood	20
	Economics	10	Public opinion/policy	14
	Genetic identity	9	Genetic identity	9
	Public opinion/policy	9	Economics	5
Actor (%)	**Science**	81	**Science**	58
	Politics	7	Business	12
	Business	5	Media	10
			Politics	6
			Interest groups	5
Benefit/risk (%)	**Benefit only**	57	**Benefit only**	48
	Both	30	Both	29
	Neither	8	Neither	12
	Risk only	5	Risk only	11
Location (%)	**Finland**	83	**Finland**	85
	USA	4	USA	6
	World	2	World	2

a Percentage of corpus in the period; total *n* = 547.
b Bold indicates highest frequency within phase.

Figure 1. Intensity of articles on biotechnology in Savon Sanomat

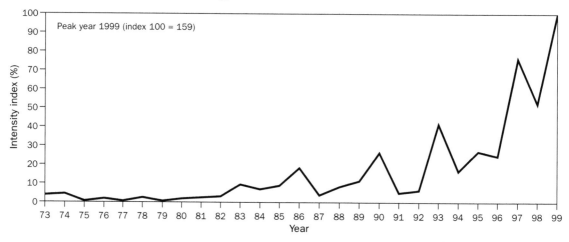

When observing single themes, rather than clusters, the GM food theme is most prevalent in Phase 2. Food issues have become a central theme in the media in Phase 2, whereas earlier they were almost absent. This development reflects the fact that, before 1996, no GM food had arrived on the Finnish market, and GM food was a rather abstract concept, because maize and soya were not common crops in Finland. By contrast, new GM crops, such as potato and rape-seed are very familiar staple crops. Another theme becoming very common is research on the human genome and gene therapy, reflecting the advances in research activities and consequent media coverage.

Frames also reflect the increased multidimensionality in Phase 2. The single most common frame in 1972 to 1996, progress, has given way to an increased variety of frames. In 1992–96, the frame of 50 per cent of articles was progress, in 1997–99 this had dropped to 25 per cent. At the end of the 1990s there was a significant increase in articles with an ethical theme and 'Pandora's box' approach; hinting at possible unknown risks associated with superficial short-term benefits. Consequently, ethical and risk concepts are being taken into consideration. However, this more divergent and critical set of frames has not had much influence on the public's opinion of gene technology. Based on the Eurobarometer survey, the perception of risk remains low in Finland in spite of the changes in media coverage.

In the most recent phase there is a significant number of articles reflecting the dichotomy between nature and nurture in the Finnish press. The discussion about the genetic vs the social origins of various social and cultural issues has been highlighted in the media. The much-publicised findings on the supposedly genetic origins of complex patterns of human behaviour (alcoholism, homosexuality, intelligence, criminal tendencies) seem to have ignited the debate and provoked responses from psychologists and sociologists.

In both phases the most common actors in the articles have been scientists. University scientists are overwhelmingly dominant actors in Phase 1, represented in 80 per cent of articles, but diminishing to 58 per cent in Phase 2. Although science and scientific achievements still have a major role in articles, the actors are from more diverse areas. NGOs have appeared more frequently in the media. Political actors have lost their relative significance. There are more voices representing the commercialisation of biotechnology, but in addition, the public's concerns are more salient. Animal biotechnologies received considerable attention in the Finnish media. This might be connected to the increased media profile of the activities of the animal rights movement.

Risks and benefits

In Phase 1 typically benefits were present in media analysis, but they were considered 'very unlikely'. In Phase 2 opinions are more divergent, almost dichotomous. The benefits are not mentioned at all, or, they are considered as very likely/already present. Articles no longer refer to general benefits, but evaluate them in a more specific way. In Phase 1 the most common benefits are for health and economic growth. In Phase 2 health benefits are still the main category, but economic prospects have become less important (22 vs 8 per cent) at the expense of various other types of benefits (e.g. legal, social equality and consumer associated).

The shift in risk perception has been quite different. In Phase 1 the risks were presented in media articles as being 'very unlikely'. Contrary to the presentation of benefits, the emphasis in Phase 2 articles is more risk conscious: the proportion of articles presenting risks as 'quite likely' or 'very likely/already present' has increased. Health risks remain the most significant single category. Economic aspects are no longer an important risk category, whereas moral concerns and environmental and consumer risks have increased.

Unlike many other European countries, the discussion on GM food actually started in Finland late (1997–99). However, the GM food discussion in the press has remained factual and informative, typical of the style of the Finnish press, and there has been relatively little scaremongering. Plenty of information has been reported in the media about risks and benefits, but very few claims have been made without adequate scientific, social, cultural or ethical backing. This very factual approach may relate to the public's fairly positive attitude towards GM food and the perception of it as low risk.

Summary

The reporting of biotechnology in the media has become more multidimensional during 1997–99. In the earlier phases the media presented the latest news on gene technology. The dominant frame was progress leading to economic benefits, and the main actors were scientists, who concentrated on medical applications, presenting only the benefits and generally seeing the risks as irrelevant. Basic research was idealised. Conducted in laboratories by 'heroic' scientists, this research was concerned with introducing the potentially useful applications into everyday life. In Phase 2, articles on GM food, gene therapy and cloning, although not front-page news, have had a higher profile than basic research. The authors are no longer exclusively scientists, but also lay experts from other fields, such as interest groups and NGOs. The tone remains very factual. The role of the media is by no means a watchdog, but rather an objective informer. There is also a critical view from activist groups such as

Kansalaisten Bioturva, where views are based on arguments rather than obvious ideology and can often be found in the 'letters to editors'.

Public perceptions

In the 1996 Eurobarometer survey, public perception in Finland differed in one important respect when compared to other EU countries. Although, as with other Nordic countries, the level of knowledge about biotechnology and gene technology was high, this awareness was not reflected in the relative scepticism seen elsewhere in Scandinavia. The acceptance of biotechnological applications is high, most applications were regarded as useful, and only a few Finns found them risky. The moral considerations are few; the vast majority actively encourage biotechnology. In that respect the Finnish response is comparable to that of southern European countries.

In 1999, there was a regression towards the European average in all attitudes: perceived usefulness of the given application, risk perception, moral consideration and level of encouragement (Figure 2). Finland is the only country in EU where the majority of the respondents are supporters of biotechnology and have had such a low level of risk perception. However, during the last three years the number of outright supporters has been decreasing in comparison to risk-tolerant supporters and opponents.

In 1996 Finland was the most optimistic country about technology in the EU. How have attitudes since changed? Attitudes remain positive overall, but do not differ greatly from the EU average. People in Finland consider, more often than in most other countries, that modern technology will improve the quality of life. There are three exceptions to this view: technology as applied to the internet, to computers, and to telecommunications. A fourth exception to the positive application of technology is beginning to appear in attitudes towards genetic engineering. This contrasts with the generally optimistic view towards technology that has been evident in Finland until recently. In the cases of the internet and computers, there may be a time lag between the implementation of a technological application and its effects on the way of life or its cultural consequences. After some time the negative consequences begin to appear, such as the ubiquitous ringing of mobile phones and the constant flow of e-mails. Genetic engineering, has not yet had a major impact on people's lives, so the effects of direct experience may be delayed.

The level of knowledge of biotechnology remains high, being well above the European average and below only Sweden, Denmark and the Netherlands. Reactions to the various applications of genetic engineering have, in general, been positive. All the applications were perceived as useful but in the medical applications, the production of medicines and cloning of the human cells the usefulness of gene technology was measured to be just above the EU average. In terms of support for various applications, Finns have the most positive attitude towards genetic testing, followed by bioremediation, human cell cloning,

Figure 2. Finnish attitudes to applications of modern biotechnology

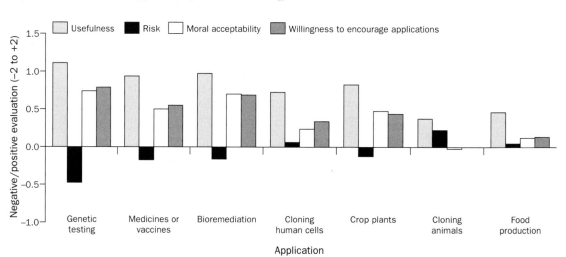

GM crops, GM food and animal cloning. Finns, together with the Dutch, more frequently consider the genetic modification of food and crops more positively than any other nation in the EU. In spite of the very high media coverage of GM-food-related debates, the public remains positive.

An even more significant result is the low risk perception towards the GMOs among Finns. Of the seven applications asked about in the Euro-barometer survey, Finns regarded six of them as being low risk, more than any other nation in the EU. The only exception is cloning animals, which was perceived by Spaniards to be less risky. Finns are the only nation of in the EU that finds gene technology useful without simultaneously anticipating any associated risk.

Consequently, in both the 1996 and 1999 sets of data, Finns have, on average, less ethical and moral concerns than other Europeans. Finns consider the food and crop applications to be morally acceptable more often than other EU nations. In 1999, the high level of moral acceptance is comparable only to that of the Netherlands and Spain. In Finland, cloning animals gives rise to relatively few moral considerations. The difference in other applications is small. In considering the moral acceptability of medical applications, such as using biotechnology for producing medicines, genetic testing or for cloning human cells, Finns equal the European average.

Finnish attitudes, therefore, are a combination of low risk perception and a relatively high perception of usefulness of the biotechnology applications with some ethical considerations. In the case of food applications, the risk perception is especially low and usefulness is perceived as being very high with few ethical considerations. Altogether, these combined attitudes towards gene technology suggest a lot of encouragement, especially for food applications but also for certain other applications, such as cloning animals and use of bacteria for bioremediation.

This view can be interpreted as part optimism, part pragmatism. The low risk perception, in the Finnish case, means there is no special need for the trade-off between the pros and cons when thinking about gene technology. Hence the view is an optimistic one.

In 1999 the Finnish response to biotechnology remained similar to the response in 1996, in spite of the relative regression towards the European average. The views in Finland are similar to those of the southern European countries, with the exception of Greece whose response has changed radically during the passed three years. The response in Finland is in many respects similar to that of the Dutch in 1999.

In Finland the proportion of 'don't know' responses was very low in Eurobarometer 1999, compared to 1996. In fact, it is the lowest among all the EU countries. In most other countries the 'don't know' responses increased when respondents were asked whether they had heard of the application before this survey. This was not the case with the Finnish respondents.

The level of trust remains high towards all actors in biotechnology, particularly in relation to the other EU countries. Some 86 per cent of the respondents trust that newspapers are doing a good job when it comes to GM issues. Results for other actors were medical doctors (92 per cent), consumer organisations (91 per cent), shops (89 per cent), government (81 per cent), ethics committees (81 per cent), farmers (77 per cent), environmental groups (65 per cent), industry (52 per cent), churches (46 per cent). The level of trust in all actors is the highest or second highest among the EU countries, with the exception of the churches, taking third place and, more significantly, environmental groups taking fifth place. Trust in actors is high, regardless of whether an actor is active in the field of gene technology or not, or whether an actor has taken any stance for or against it.

When asked whom they trust most to tell the truth about biotechnology Finns indicated they trust the medical profession and the universities most. The trust in these two sources has remained as high as it was in 1996. The high level of trust towards the universities is exceptional compared with the rest of Europe, but the Finns' trust of consumer organisations and environmental groups is relatively low. This is similar to the response in 1996. In Finland the general public trusts experts to be responsible and truthful. The experts have inherited the same trust that public officers have held throughout the history of Finland. This is based on the fact that the public consider the national administration to be patriotic and uncorrupt.

Conclusions

Very few new events occurred in the Finnish policy and legislation regarding biotechnology during the years 1996–2000. In typical fashion, the legislative processes were reactions to general European trends rather than responses to specific Finnish national concerns. Thus, the new version of the

Finnish Gene Law passed June 2000 was a response to the corresponding reformulation of the EU directive 98/81/EU. Similarly the new Finnish Patent Law represents the adoption of the principles of the relevant EU directives to the Finnish legislation. According to the latest Eurobarometer survey, the acceptance of gene technology remains high amongst the general population. However, opinions are becoming more critical and diverse than found in the previous survey. The accidental contamination of rape-seed by GM variants was reported in May 2000. This raised some concern and coincided with the founding of the first Finnish NGO openly critical towards gene technology.

During the last three years the media picture has become more multidimensional. The media no longer present biotechnology as a single, prosperous new methodology, part of modern progress. Instead, various debates on biotechnology are taking place in the contemporary Finnish press, although these remain modest when compared to the rest of Europe. New topics of debate such as those about GM foods and the nature–nurture distinction, which were not present before 1996, are now appearing. Articles are also being authored by wider variety of actors in society, not predominantly by university scientists as was the case earlier.

The public perception of biotechnology in Finland remains as positive in the period 1996–99 as it was earlier. Most applications are considered as useful and moral considerations are few. The majority of Finns are willing to encourage biotechnology. Especially significant is the very low risk perception, the lowest in the EU in all applications. However, some regression towards the European average can be noticed, reflecting a slight undertone of concern in the otherwise optimistic view of the Finns towards biotechnology. Technological applications in telecommunications have already been met with a similar relative scepticism.

Notes and references

1 Rusanen, T, von Wright, A and Rusanen, M, 'Finland', in Durant, J, Bauer, M W and Gaskell, G (eds), *Biotechnology in the Public Sphere: A European Sourcebook* (London: Science Museum, 1998), pp43–50.

2 Tiitta, A, *Find out about Finland* (Helsinki: Otava, 1996).

3 President of the Republic of Finland <www.president.fi/netcomm> (2001).

4 Laipio, M, 'Finland in the front rank with one in ten of Europe's biotech companies', *Finnish Business Report,* 4 (2000), pp13–14.

5 Science and Technology Policy Council of Finland, *Finland: A Knowledge-based Society.* (Helsinki: Science and Technology Policy Council of Finland, 1996).

6 European Commission, DGXIII, *Biotechnology: User's Guide for SMEs* (Luxembourg: Office for Official Publications of the European Communities, 1999).

7 Laipio, M (see note 4).

8 European Commission (see note 6).

9 EVA: the Centre for Finnish Business and Policy Studies, 'Finns going forth at a different pace: spectrum of Finnish opinion', *Finnish Attitudes 1999* (Helsinki: EVA, 1999).

Address for correspondence

Timo Rusanen, Department of Social Science, University of Kuopio, PO Box 1627, SF-70211 Kuopio, Finland. E-mail timo.rusanen@uku.fi

Biotechnology: a menace to French food

Daniel Boy and Suzanne de Cheveigné

Main events 1996–99

France has had a tradition of quite confidential low-profile regulation of biotechnology which made it one of the most favourable countries towards biotechnology.[1] The period 1996–99 saw a spectacular change in the situation, corresponding to the arrival of this new technology in the public sphere. Media coverage increased massively, public debate in the form of a consensus conference was organised, regulation changed again and again, and public awareness of biotechnology naturally became more acute. As in a number of countries, the cloning of Dolly the sheep marked a turning point. The imports into Europe from the USA of Monsanto's Roundup Ready transgenic soya at the end of 1996 provoked little reaction from the media (with the exception of one daily paper, *Libération*) whereas three months later, Dolly received very intensive coverage. From then on, biotechnology events were regularly covered by the media, often becoming political issues. Before outlining the main events in the French public debate, a reminder of the political situation is necessary.

The political situation

Following elections in May 1997, a socialist majority returned to power, in coalition with ecologists. In the frame of this alliance, a programmatic agreement was signed between the Socialist Party and the Greens. This programme included a number of fairly moderate measures concerning GMOs. In particular, it announced that 'a moratorium on the use of genetically modified organisms would be proposed at the European level'.[2]

In practice, changes in political majority have had little effect on the evolution of public policy. Ecological preoccupations are no doubt stronger in left-wing governments but they have never overridden a certain industrial realism.[3] Nevertheless, it seems that France's particular political situation, with a right-wing president 'cohabiting' with a left-wing government, has set up a sort of competition, each side systematically invoking the precautionary principle. In a number of cases, such as the refusal to lift the embargo on British beef, the rule of prudence set up by the prime minister appears to be partially motivated by fear that the 'presidential adversary' might take political advantage of an error or lack of precaution by the government.

Dolly the sheep

As in many countries, the announcement of the cloning of a sheep was perceived as a major event. In France, it opened up the debate on biotechnology in general. All main newspapers covered the event from 24 February 1997 onwards. The prospect of human cloning was immediately invoked and a large number of opinions were published, including international reaction. The Conseil d'État (State Council) condemned human cloning on 3 March 1998. On the same day, President Chirac asked the National Ethics Committee to outline the limits of what should be authorised. Their advice, against human cloning, was rendered on 22 April of the same year.

The question of animal and human cloning remained in the air throughout the period under study, with newspaper reporting on other animals cloned, on the apparently rapid ageing of Dolly, on Dr Seed's proposal to clone humans, on the *Lancet*'s condemnation of moratoria on human cloning, etc. The ethical discussion around human cloning regularly pits humanistic Kantian references to the uniqueness and dignity of the human person against a utilitarian approach perceived by the French to be dominant in Britain and the USA. Religious references are very infrequent. The cloning of Dolly seems to have served as a concrete example of the possible excesses of biotechnology in general: a first step towards a 'brave new world'. It certainly opened up public discussion in the area.

GM food and crops

During the period under study, GMOs progressively became the main biotechnology issue under discussion. In the autumn of 1996, the first shiploads of transgenic soya arrived in Europe from the USA, in the face of near total indifference from the media. The only exception was *Libération* that published its 1 November issue with the front-page headline: 'Alert: mad soya' (an obvious reference to BSE). In spite of this dramatic treatment the other papers barely picked up on the story (on average one or two articles per paper over the following month, and not even in all papers). GMOs were not yet an issue.

Nevertheless, at about the same time, a legal 'serial comedy' was beginning about transgenic maize. In December 1996, the European Commission authorised the firm Ciba-Geigy (now Novartis) to sell transgenic maize seed. On 14 February 1997, the then right-wing government decided not to authorise the growth of GM maize in France in application of the precautionary principle – a contradiction since its sale had been authorised. In April the European parliament voted to suspend sales of transgenic maize. In November 1997, the new left-wing government authorised the planting of Novartis's transgenic maize after consulting the Precaution and Prevention Committee but forbade that of canola and of sugar beet. In December 1997, another firm, Pau-Euralis, asked to be allowed to grow a new variety of transgenic maize but the Minister of Environment declared that no new transgenic varieties would be authorised until a public debate had occurred. In February 1998, a consensus conference was announced, to take place in June (further details below).

On 30 July 1998, when the consensus conference had presented its conclusions, the government decided to authorise the growth of two new kinds of transgenic maize. In September, a number of associations, including Greenpeace and a radical farmer's union, the Confédération Paysanne, filed an appeal to the Conseil d'État, arguing that authorisation had not been properly given. This resulted in the suspension of the authorisation. In October, after the Conseil d'État had announced that its decision would be handed down in December, the government asked producers to delay putting transgenic maize on the market. In December 1998 the Conseil d'État decided to refer back to the European Court of Justice to be sure it had the legitimacy to rule on such a question. Finally, in November 1999, the European Court ruled that France must accept the sale of transgenic maize, as demanded by the European Commission.

This hesitation surrounding GM maize illustrates the uncertainty of official positions on the matter. At the same time, public opposition was growing. On 8 January 1998, José Bové and two other members of the Confédération Paysanne destroyed stocks of transgenic maize seed and, a month later, received a suspended sentence of five months imprisonment. This was Bové's first public deed, but he went on to become a figure symbolic of the debate on GMOs, crystallising around his 'Astérix' moustache.[4] In June of 1999 the Confédération Paysanne and some 50 farmers destroyed test crops of transgenic rice at the Cirad, a research centre for aid to developing countries, in Montpellier. Then in August they dismantled a MacDonald's restaurant under construction in Millau, in retaliation for the American embargo on Roquefort cheese (a measure that had itself been taken in response to the European embargo on American hormone-fed beef). Bové surrendered to the police, initially refused to pay bail, then finally relented, emerging from prison on 7 September 1998, having received widespread moral and financial support – from American farmers amongst others. After a number of other protest actions, Bové travelled to Seattle at the end of November 1999, where he distributed Roquefort cheese and took part in anti-WTO demonstrations.

The object of Bové's and the Confédération Paysanne's fight has widened progressively from GMOs to globalisation and liberalisation. Their arguments are based on cultural references to national identity, particularly concerning food, defending tradition in face of Americanisation, hence the symbolic importance of the Astérix moustaches. At the same time, the financial interests of GMO seed merchants, particularly Monsanto with so-called 'terminator technology' which prevents germination in seeds from GM crops were strongly denounced. Bové embodies a synthesis between a radical intellectual movement (formed by people who 'returned to the earth' in the late 1960s and 70s) with a restricted audience and a wider, popular – even populist – movement made up of a mixture of organic farmers, hunters, ecologists, traditionalists, etc. It is important to note the active role played in the area by associations, from Greenpeace through to consumer associations, whereas traditional political parties are practically mute, except for the Greens who have difficulty keeping pace.

Another element of resistance to transgenic foods appeared among food wholesalers. Backed by consumer opposition to GMOs and in a strong position in relation to producers, Carrefour and Leclerc supermarkets announced in March 1998 their intention not to use any transgenic ingredients in their products. Nestlé and Unilever announced similar decisions in May which were widely reported. Seed producers and farmers developed lines of non-GM products, for example growing soya in the south-west of France. Other signs of opposition appeared: for instance, in July 1998, the mayor of Issy-les-Moulineaux forbade the use of any transgenic product in school canteens, progressively followed by a number of others.

The consensus conference

The organisation of a consensus conference ('conférence de citoyens') was announced by the prime minister in a declaration on 27 November 1997. The conference was organised by parliament's technology assessment agency, l'Office Parlementaire d'Évaluation des Choix Scientifiques et Technologiques (OPECST) whose president, a socialist, was responsible for a fact-finding mission on GMOs. It was organised closely along the lines of the Danish model:[5] a pilot committee was set up, a panel of 15 lay people appointed, training sessions organised and experts selected. The conference was held in public and was immediately followed by the presentation of a report at a press conference on 22 June 1998. In its conclusions, the panel of non-specialists did not propose a general moratorium on transgenic plants but rather a series of measures to develop scientific research and to improve control over the plants. They also recommended that decision processes be made more democratic. Their conclusions were included in the report of the fact-finding mission but have since received little echo.[6]

Medical applications

The history of medical applications of genetic engineering is quite different from that of GM food. The former have been known to the public at least since the beginning, in 1987, of the fund-raising television show *Téléthon* in favour of a patients' association for myopathy (an inherited muscle disorder) that has come to play a very important role in research in France. Gene therapy, although generally approved, is sometimes questioned: for instance, on 10 February 1997, the first gene-therapy treatment of Huntingdon's chorea about to be performed by INSERM in Paris on human patients was contested because it had not received ethical and administrative authorisation. On the other hand, at the end of December 1999, a team from Necker children's hospital in Paris that succeeded, at least temporarily, in curing immuno-deficient 'bubble-babies' was widely acclaimed.

The human genome project is regularly followed in the media. Concern was expressed because French research, initially well ahead, had fallen back in the race because of insufficient funding. DNA identification has been used in criminal cases since 1996. A high-profile, macabre event took place in March 1998 after the Appeal Court of Paris had ordered (6 November 1997) the exhumation of the body of popular actor and singer Yves Montand to undergo genetic testing following a paternity claim – finally ruled to be unfounded on 19 December 1999. Generally speaking, there is some concern in France about the threat to liberty that DNA profiling can represent and about the financial interests behind gene patenting. At the same time, there is little belief in genetic determination. Psychological explanations for behaviour are strongly favoured over ideas that there could be genes for intelligence, homosexuality or schizophrenia.

Media coverage

The main characteristic of media coverage of biotechnology in France during the period 1997–99 is its spectacular increase in intensity. This is true of all newspapers and magazines including ones that had hardly ever touched on the subject: biotechnology arrived in the public sphere during this period. To quantify the evolution, we carried out a content analysis of the French opinion leader paper, *Le Monde*, in continuation of our previous analysis.[7] Nevertheless, it should be remembered that the whole media landscape has changed qualitatively – more spectacularly than *Le Monde* which had always kept its readers informed of progress in the field. Articles on biotechnology can be found in popular newspapers, women's magazines, health or consumers magazines – practically anywhere in the media spectrum.

We have chosen to continue monitoring the French opinion leader, *Le Monde*, a national newspaper with a circulation of about 500,000. It is a paper of reference, read by most decision-makers – in particular higher civil servants – as well as by teachers and students. It has the largest readership of French dailies among the higher income groups. Politically, it is centre-left. In comparison to other national papers, it is less business oriented (and less to the right, politically) than *Le Figaro*, has less of an environmental bent than *Libération*. Two popular – but in no way 'tabloid' – papers, *Le Parisien* and *France Soir* complete the panorama of the main national newspapers.

Le Monde's archives are available on CD-ROM for the period discussed here. We shall mainly report on the coverage during the three years 1997–99 but they will be systematically compared to the preceding five-year period 1992–96. We carried out a full-text search for the same words as in the previous study (biotech*, geneti*, ADN [DNA], transgen*, genique, genome, manipulation(s) + genetique(s), diagnostique + prenatal, diagnostique + preimplantatoire). The result was sampled one day in four for 1997 and 1998, and approximately one in six for 1999 in succession[8] (i.e. on every fourth or sixth calendar day) and any non-pertinent articles were eliminated.

Figure 1 gives the intensity evolution, extrapolated from the sample, of all articles. This includes those centred on biotechnology, those with a substantial portion on the subject and articles that make only passing, possibly metaphoric, reference to biotechnology. Figure 1 also gives the frequency of only those articles that were centred on biotechnology. The total number of articles in Figure 1 demonstrates a complete change of phase from a baseline of about 200 articles per year to a peak six times higher in 1999. The take-off began in 1996 (the year of the first imports of transgenic maize and soya to Europe), and became clear in 1997, the year of the announcement of the birth of the cloned sheep, Dolly.

In Table 1 we characterise the periods by indicating the percentages of all articles written in a

Figure 1. Intensity of media coverage of biotechnology in Le Monde

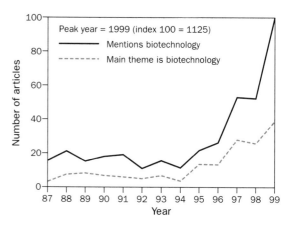

given frame, of all themes identified in the articles,[9] of main actors, risk–benefit ratios and story locations. The general evolution is towards more circumspection in face of biotechnology. The proportion of the articles written in a frame of scientific progress, or, less spectacularly, in terms of economic perspectives has decreased in favour of ethical perspectives. In the most recent period, the frame 'opening Pandora's box' passed the 10 per cent threshold. The frame of public accountability remains low with a score of only 4 per cent, in spite of the organisation of the consensus conference Unfortunately, the conference took place during the Football World Cup which France hosted – and won – so media space for anything else was scarce. The low score for the public accountability frame

Figure 2. Attitudes to applications of biotechnology in France

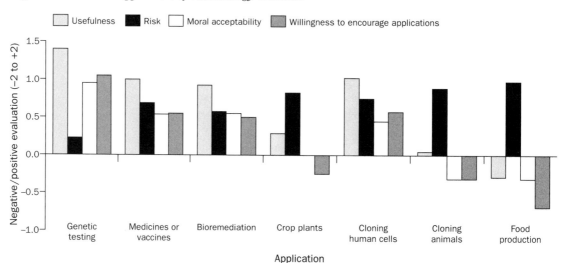

Table 1. French media profile, 1982–99 (threshold for categories: 10 per cent and above)

Phase	1982–91		1992–96		1997–99	
Frequency (%)[a]	22[b]		22		56	
Frames (%)	**Progress**[c]	45	**Progress**	47	**Progress**	38
	Economic	24	Economic	22	Economic	21
	Ethical	17	Ethical	18	Ethical	20
					Pandora's box	10
Themes (%)	**Biomedical**	18	**Biomedical**	24	**Agrifood**	21
	Agrifood	16	Agrifood	17	Biomedical	12
	Generic research	15	Generic research	13	Generic research	14
	Economics	12	Economics	12	Economics	10
					Genetic identity	10
Actors (%)[d]	**Scientists**	41	**Scientists**	43	**Scientists**	35
	Business	21	Business	17	Politics	22
	Politics	17	Politics	15	Business	19
Benefit/risk (%)	**Benefit only**	39	**Benefit only**	36	**Benefit only**	32
	Both	22	Both	21	Risk only	22
	Risk only	15	Risk only	15	Both	19
Location (%)	**France**	51	**France**	46	**France**	43
	USA	19	USA	22	Europe	24
	Europe	18	Europe	21	USA	21

a Percentage of corpus in the period; total *n* = 4649.

b Over 1987–91. Previously, the search was carried out manually, not electronically.

c Bold indicates highest frequency within phase.

d Note a difference in coding procedure between the first two and the last period where only one main actor was retained instead of two.

also reflects the rather Jacobine, 'top–down' character of French society.

As far as themes are concerned, we see food and agriculture overtaking biomedical themes and genetic identification appearing significantly in the most recent period. Among actors, politicians play an increasing role, though scientists keep the largest share. Business actors lag behind in the most recent period. (It should be remembered that *Le Monde* is not a business-oriented newspaper, contrary to *Le Figaro*.) Two important categories of actors are absent from Table 1 since their percentages are too low: interest groups (4 per cent in the most recent period) and moral authorities (1.5 per cent in the same period). These figures reflect the weak influence of environmental and consumer groups on the one hand and of religion on the other – once again that *Le Monde* is an institutionally oriented newspaper came into play. Nevertheless, this is probably characteristic of French society: deeply secular and not very green. Two other categories of minority actors are the European Union (6 per cent) and other international actors (2 per cent) – in spite of much talk about globalisation, in this field as in many others, France

remains quite parochial. The locations counted confirm this: a large proportion of the articles remain centred on France though the share is decreasing. This evolution could be the reflection of a drop in research efforts in the field of biotechnology during the past decade: the country provided one of the first maps of the human genome in 1992 but it ended the decade deciphering less than 2 per cent of it. Finally, an examination of the proportions of articles describing risks, benefits or both confirms a steady trend towards a more negative attitude, although globally speaking, benefits still outweigh risks.

In this new phase of our study, we have paid particular attention to ethical frames and themes. Figure 3 shows the proportion of articles framed in ethical terms over the years. Table 2 shows the percentage of themes that were framed in an ethical perspective. First a comment: the share of moral themes decreases, which means that ethics are shifting from articles centred on such themes to appear in other, more general articles. Biomedical themes are losing their share to cloning but more interestingly also to food and agricultural themes. Regulation is increasingly framed in ethical terms,

Figure 3. Percentage articles framed in an ethical perspective

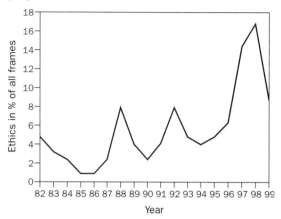

as are questions of genetic identification, although they seem to have peaked in the second period.

The main point observed here, that of the recent reporting of agrifood questions in ethical terms, is also confirmed by counting the coincidence of moral and food themes in articles. The distribution of actors within articles written in an ethical frame is also coherent with this observation (Table 3), if we consider that business is particularly present in the food arena. Scientists lose their share among the actors, mainly to business, although political actors whether national, European or international are slightly on the increase. We also note again the generalisation of ethics: moral authorities are less and less evident in ethically framed articles.

The main conclusion to be drawn here is that moral problems have become less centred on biomedical applications and more on food. This can of course be related to the fact that food applications are more recent than biomedical ones. Nevertheless, it is remarkable that food should be thought of in such terms. This is quite coherent with what we

heard in the interviews we carried out: the spectre of discrimination and of eugenics was never very far from genetic engineering of plants.

We also carried out an analysis of demands during the most recent period to get a better grasp on the dynamics of the construction of biotechnology in the public sphere (Table 4). Food and agriculture provide by far the most demands, confirming the recent importance given to food problems (transgenic foods but also BSE, dioxin in chickens, etc.) by French society. Politicians are the most numerous category making demands. This probably corresponds to their holding a normative discourse: 'X should be doing this or that.' They are followed by the more obvious candidates, media and interest groups. The demands are addressed mainly to business, the 'guilty' actor made responsible for the apparition of transgenic food – Monsanto being a typical example. Politicians come shortly after, scientists lagging well behind.

Public perceptions

The effects of various technologies

Generally speaking, French judgements on the different technologies are slightly more positive than the European average. This is true of computers and information technology (84 per cent positive judgements in France compared with a European average of 78 per cent), telecommunications (85 vs 81 per cent) and new materials (79 vs 64 per cent). The same holds for biotechnology seeing as 45 per cent of French respondents judged that it would 'improve our lives' (vs 40 per cent European average); 25 per cent thought it 'will make things worse' (same as for Europe) and 11 per cent considered that it would have no effect (9 per cent in Europe).

Table 2. Distribution of themes represented in an ethical frame (as a percentage of all themes mentioned in an ethical frame)

	1982–91	*1992–96*	*1997–99*
Biomedical	42[a]	30	10
Agrifood	–	–	17
Generic research	–	–	7
Moral	39	34	19
Regulation	11	12	17
Genetic identity	–	15	10
Cloning	–	–	12

a Values under 5% are excluded

Table 3. Distribution of actors represented in an ethical frame (as a percentage of all actors mentioned in an ethical frame)

	1982–91	*1992–96*	*1997–99*
Independent science	30	36	23
Interest groups	6	–	8
Politics	19	20	23
Moral authorities	28	19	–
Media and publicity	–	–	6
Business	–	7	15
EU	9	9	10
Other	–	–	6

a Values under 5% are excluded

Table 4. Distribution of actors represented in an ethical frame, 1997–99 (as a percentage of all actors mentioned in an ethical frame)

Areas of demand (%)	Agrifood	43
	Cloning	17
	Moral	10
	Biomedical	10
Authors of demands (%)	Politics	25
	Media	21
	Interest groups	17
	Scientists	14
Addressees of demands (%)	Business	34
	Politics	30
	Scientists	14

Two exceptions to this rule appeared: the French are more sceptical than their neighbours about solar energy (71 per cent positive in France vs 90 per cent in Holland, for instance). On the other hand, they are more confident about nuclear energy (36 per cent positive vs 26 on average in Europe and 35 per cent negative vs 44 in Europe). But, in spite of these exceptions, France is positioned in the most positive third of all European countries towards this whole set of technologies.

Applications of modern biotechnology

French attitudes towards different applications vary strongly according to the domain (food, medical, etc.) and to the type of appreciation asked for (risk, utility, moral acceptability and willingness to encourage). Judgements are very reserved about food and crops whereas applications related to medicine are much more positively perceived. This

was already true of the 1996 results, but the contrast has become accentuated.

Foods and crops. The most negative attitudes appear about food, for instance a majority of the French consider that the application is not useful (score –0.30 on a scale from –2.0 to +2.0, whereas in 1996 the positive and negative attitudes were finely balanced with a score of –0.01. Attitudes have become more negative in all of Europe, of course, but in that context France is now among the countries most opposed to transgenic food.

This trend seems to be motivated by a much more pessimistic view of the risks entailed by this application. France is now the country with the most acute perception of food risks with a score of 0.96 vs a European average of 0.59. An analysis of the trend from 1996 to 1999 shows that France and Belgium are the two countries where food fears have increased most. This is probably related to the food crises that had hit the two countries recently (BSE and dioxin in chickens). Not surprisingly, the French find transgenic food less morally acceptable than their neighbours and encourage it less (score –0.69 vs a European average of –0.37).

During the focus groups, a clarification of the notion of risk was asked for. It is important to note that alongside health risks, other types of risks – political, moral or economical – were just as frequently mentioned. Some sample quotes:

- 'social risk, like an uprising of the ultra-religious ... to avoid cloning or loss of identity.'

- 'identifying people for some political or collective use.'

- 'risk in terms of what could happen: eugenics,

"runaway train",[10] "brave new world". There
have been lots of Hitlers... Genetic modification
to have a pure being.'

• 'risk is also cultural for us.'

Environmental risks on the other hand were
virtually absent.

Immediate reactions to the food application
(presented to the focus groups in the same terms as
in the survey) confirm the plurality of risks and
illustrate very negative attitudes:

• Against nature, contradiction, contradictory,
  progress, trafficking, experiment,
  misunderstanding, good and bad, freedom of
  choice, authenticity, medical food, productivity,
  advertising, Third World, argument, fallacious,
  mass, exaggeration, money, modernism,
  consuming, synthetic, against nature,
  standardisation (focus group 1).

• Ersatz, manipulation, trafficking, ambiguity,
  unnatural, loss of marks, bad advertising, anti-
  nature, profit making, money, food production,
  very economic, mistrust, against nature (focus
  group 2).

• Nothing, denatured, asepticised, loss of flavour, of
  odour, of colours, raw milk cheese, loss of the
  natural, loss of authenticity, standardisation of
  food tastes, cultural pauperisation, stereotypes,
  standards, Americanisation, wholesaling, world
  market, globalisation, no differences, planning, a
  number, end of gastronomy, loss of taste (focus
  group 3).

The second application, concerning crops
rendered more resistant to pests, confirms this
trend towards more negative attitudes. In the 1996
survey, the French were very positive towards this
application, with a 'utility' score of 0.75. They still
are positive in 1999 but much less so, with a score
of 0.28. Here again the perception of risk is higher
than the European average (score 0.82 vs 0.36 for
the European average). The contradictions in
public policy in this field in France (like the above-
mentioned saga of transgenic maize) as well as the
rising audience of opposition groups to GMOs
(Greenpeace and la Confédération Paysanne) can
help to explain this trend. The result is that, in spite
of the positive appreciation of usefulness, the
French do not overall consider that this application
should be encouraged (score –0.27 vs 0.33 in
Europe).

Medicine. Among the four medical applications
tested in 1999, two were in the previous survey:
'introducing human genes into bacteria to produce
medicines or vaccines' and 'using genetic testing to
detect diseases we might have inherited from our
parents'. For the first one, the French attitudes
remain, as for all medical application, very positive
(score of 1.00) but less so than in 1996 (1.26).
Here again the perception of risk has increased
from a score of 0.26 to 0.68, ranking France first in
Europe.

The immediate reactions to this application in
the focus groups illustrate the degree of
ambivalence:

• Pasteur, progress, okay, gene therapy, good
  health, disgust, robot, reticence, novel (book),
  fear, hope, unconscious, progress (focus group 1).

• 'Rather positive but watch out for danger if there
  isn't total mastery of the process'(focus group 2).

• 'Will it change the conception we have of the
  human being?'(focus group 3).

In spite of the relative loss of confidence, the
French public are willing to encourage this
application (score 0.54 for a European average of
0.52).

The other application carried through from the
1996 survey concerns genetic testing. It is the only
one for which utility judgements have barely varied
(1.38 in 1996, 1.40 in 1999) even though they have
decreased in Europe (from 1.17 to 1.00). France is
of European countries the most convinced of the
utility of genetic testing. Even though the
perception of risk has increased from a score of
0.12 to 0.23, the application is encouraged with a
score of 1.04 vs a European average of 0.70.

Two new medical applications were presented in
the 1999 survey: 'cloning human cells or tissues to
replace a patient's diseased cells that are not
functioning properly' and 'cloning animals such as
sheep to get milk which can be used to make
medicines and vaccines'. French attitudes differ
quite widely between the two. The cloning of
human cells is judged very positively in terms of
utility (the score of 1.02 is the highest in Europe
where the average is 0.67), in spite of a pessimistic
perception of the risks entailed (score 0.74 vs a
European average of 0.67). Attitudes to the final
application remain very positive in terms of moral
acceptability and willingness to encourage
(respective scores of 0.44 and 0.55 for European
averages of 0.26 and 0.33).

The cloning of animals is perceived in a very different way. The utility score is close to zero (the European average is 0.15). Judgements are very negative in terms of risk (0.87 vs 0.47 in Europe), of moral acceptability (–0.32) and in the general terms of encouragement (–0.33).

Here again, the reactions of the focus groups to these two applications – and to a third one, 'cloning a human adult to allow a sterile couple to have children' – help explain what underlies these judgements. Reactions to cloning entire humans and to animal cloning are remarkably similar:
Humans: unnatural, science fiction, robot, out of human equilibrium, terminator, loss of identity (focus group 2); Brave New World, Italy, total power, hope, despair, runaway train, negative, God, loss of identity (focus group 3).
Animals: danger, no limits, panicky, fast ageing, human robots, risk of misappropriation, frightening, anti-vaccine, an economic argument (focus group 2); incoherence, manipulation, bizarre, long term, unknown, why not?, runaway train, what for?, the anxiety of the poor sheep that are all identical.

Note the last remark illustrating a strong identification with animals. The assimilation of animal to human cloning was very strongly present in the media coverage of Dolly and has clearly remained in public perceptions.

On the other hand, the cloning of human cells was perceived very positively by the focus groups: apparently the 'human' factor was of little importance in this application perceived as a 'medical success' (perhaps 'human embryo cells' would have provoked a more negative reaction). The worries are more about the legitimacy of pushing back ageing than about instrumentalising human components:
Cloning cells: skin, immense hope, questions, life scepticism, prolonging life, why prolong life?, improving health (focus group 2); progress, life, great, positive, beneficial, medical success, ecology, hope, healing, survival, will death become prefabricated?, controlling life, ethics, always ethics, science taking the place of God, take care to master that science, life for everyone (focus group 3).

Environment

The last application, new in the 1999 survey, concerns 'developing genetically modified bacteria to clean up slicks of oil or dangerous chemicals' (bioremediation). The French, like the other Europeans, are quite positive on this point: the utility score reaches 0.92 (European average 0.71), the moral acceptability 0.54 (vs 0.46 in Europe) and the final appreciation 0.49 (0.25 in Europe). But once again it is in France that the risk perception is most acute (score 0.55 vs an average of 0.17).

Conclusions

Perhaps the most important point to emerge is that the French, no doubt more than most Europeans, perceive food and medical applications in very different ways. Their hypersensitivity to risk is a new factor, compared to the 1996 results. It could be explained by a number of elements:

- The relatively recent opening of public discussion. Media coverage was still weak at the time of the previous survey and little opposition was expressed in the public sphere.

- The repercussions of a number of scares related to food safety: BSE, a supposed contamination of coca cola in Belgium, dioxin in chickens, animal feed contaminated with sewage, etc.

- The atmosphere of extreme precaution caused by the competition between the cohabiting left-wing government and right-wing president, each ready to accuse the other of negligence and lack of preparation.

- The popularity of José Bové's opposition both to GMOs and to globalisation.

All these elements contribute to make biotechnology more than a simple scientific question, but one deeply embedded in other social and cultural elements.

Notes and references

1 de Cheveigné, S, Berthomier, A, Boy, D, Galloux, J C and Gaumont-Prat, H, 'France', in Durant, J, Bauer, M W and Gaskell, G (eds), *Biotechnology in the Public Sphere: A European Sourcebook* (London: Science Museum, 1998), pp51–62.

2 Unpublished text of the official agreement.

3 Petitjean, P, 'La critique des sciences en France', *Alliages*, 35–36 (1998), pp118–33.

4 Astérix is the comic-book hero of a tiny Gaul village, at the very end of Brittany, last point of resistance to the Roman invasion of what is now France.

5 Joss, S and Durant, J (eds), *Public Participation in Science: The Role of Consensus Conferences in Europe* (London: Science Museum, 1995).

6 Le Déaut, J Y, 'De la connaissance des gènes à leur utilisation', *Rapport de OPECST, Assemblée Nationale et Sénat* (1998). See also Boy, D, Kamel, D D and Roqueplo, P, 'Un exemple de démocratie participative: La "Conférence de citoyens" sur le sorganismes génétiquement modifiés', *Revue Française de Sciences Politiques*, 50 (2000), pp779–809.

7 de Cheveigné, S *et al.* (see note 1), pp51–62.

8 The 1999 articles were sampled in two stages: initially one day in five, then, out of the initial sample, four days in five.

9 Note that in our previous analysis (see note 1) the calculation of themes was different: we gave the percentages of articles referring to each theme and not the percentage of all themes mentioned that a given theme represents. Both representations are good indicators of evolution but must not be confused.

10 An unsatisfactory translation of 'dérives'.

Address for correspondence

Daniel Boy, Maison des Sciences de l'Homme, CEVIPOF, 54 Bd Raspail FR-75006 Paris, France. E-mail Boy@msh-paris.fr

Biotechnology boom and market failure: two sides of the German coin

Jürgen Hampel, Uwe Pfenning, Matthias Kohring, Alexander Görke and Georg Ruhrmann

Biotechnology in Germany before 1996

Germany was one of the European forerunners in the development of biotechnology, both in the public debate on biotechnology and in the regulation of biotechnology.[1] As early as 1978 the US National Institutes of Health (NIH) guidelines had been incorporated into German regulation. In the same year an initiative of the German government to formulate a 'Gene Law', which would have been a worldwide first, was prevented by critical reactions from the scientific and industrial communities. Whilst biotechnology was only of minor public interest in the 1970s and early 1980s, an intensive debate was triggered in 1984 by the birth of the first German test-tube baby and the attempt by Hoechst to establish a plant for the production of human insulin using genetic engineering methods.

During this period there was a lot of political mobilisation in Germany and, as a consequence of the controversy about nuclear energy, the Green Party entered the federal parliament. The social debates found their counterparts in the policy arena. In order to discuss problems in modern reproduction, medicine and genetic engineering, two commissions were set up in 1984: the Benda Commission, which discussed problems regarding reproductive medicine and medical applications of genetic engineering, and the Parliamentary Enquête Commission on 'opportunities and risks of genetic engineering'. The recommendations of both commissions led to two laws, the German Gene Law and the Law for the Protection of Human Embryos, both passed in 1990. Whereas the Gene Law was closely related to the two European guidelines 90/210/EWG and 90/220/EWG, the Law for the Protection of Human Embryos had no European counterpart and was accepted as a binding regulation, fulfilling regulatory needs, for almost a decade. By contrast the Gene Law was criticised by opponents and supporters of biotechnology alike. As a result of the increasing importance given to German economic competitiveness after East–West reunification, the Gene Law, which was viewed as being too strict and endangering the competitiveness of the industry, was reformulated in 1993. Every opportunity presented by European prescriptions was used to make the law less restrictive.

The German biotechnology boom

Instead of having a strong scientific basis in molecular biology, Germany had a backlog in commercial applications for biotechnology. Although there had been hints from the administrative system as well as from science that genetic engineering and biotechnology would offer new fields for innovation, the chemical and pharmaceutical industries failed to recognise biotechnology as an innovative business sector. Some authors attribute this delay to the dominant role played by synthetic chemistry in German pharmaceutical companies.[2] As a result, the major impulses for the development of biotechnology came from the German Ministry for Research and Technology (BMFT) and were funded with public money. Ongoing attempts by the German government to establish a biotechnology industry in Germany were finally successful when, in the second half of the 1990s, Germany experienced a remarkable biotechnology boom. In order to meet the aspirations of the German government to become the leading force in Europe, the German Ministry for Research and Technology embarked on a very successful programme called the Bio-Regio-Contest in 1996. This programme invited regions to develop concepts in order to improve the social, political, technical, economic and administrative positions of new regional start-up companies and to form and support innovation networks. This contest fostered intense activities in Germany, which were favourably commented on by the media.

The national Schitag Ernst & Young Report 1998 had the promising title *Aufbruchstimmung* ('ready for take off').[3] According to the 1999 Ernst & Young report, Germany had the largest number of start-up companies in the life-sciences industry in Europe, surpassed only by the UK.[4] However, the report also demonstrated that the average size of companies in Germany was quite small. The market turnover of pharmaceuticals produced using genetic engineering methods doubled from DM 883 million in 1996 to DM 1,849 million in 1999 (about UK £276 million to £578 million).[5]

In the years between 1996 and 1999 substantial changes could also be observed at the political level. After 16 years of a Conservative government in 1998, a coalition between the Social Democratic Party and the Green Party formed the new government. Surprisingly, the expectations of a change in biotechnology policy in Germany proved to be wrong, at least in the short term. The new government continued the policies of the previous Conservative government. The general aim of the new government to support economic development of biotechnology was also expressed in German activities at EU level. Key policy events are summarised in Table 1.

Agricultural biotechnology – the story of a failure

The observed biotechnology boom describes the development of new companies in the area of pharmaceutical and medical biotechnology. However, the increasing economic importance of biotechnology did not result in a general decrease in social and political debates on the issues, especially agricultural biotechnology. In the Eurobarometer Survey of 1996, Germany was among the most sceptical countries regarding applications of biotechnology in agriculture and food production.

When the first ships carrying genetically modified soyabeans reached Germany on 6 November 1996, Greenpeace activists mounted a campaign against GM food. Food biotechnology increasingly became a topic of public concern, but raised no heated debate. Intensive media reporting did not take place before January 1997 (see 'Media coverage' below).

Compared with the previous periods, the organisational basis of the resistance was different. Whereas resistance to biotechnology in the earlier periods had been broad-based, only one actor became dominant after 1996: Greenpeace. In March 1997 Greenpeace initiated a shoppers' boycott of GM products and the organisation started to check whether supermarkets were selling GM food.

There was no official withdrawal of GM food from the German markets, but in fact, almost no products labelled as genetically modified were available. In September 1997, Greenpeace listed food companies they thought might be using GMOs in their products and requested declarations from food producers and retail chains that they would not sell GM food. Whilst most companies in Germany tried to avoid public discussion of the topic and applied a 'duck-and-cover' strategy, the German resistance to GM food was also fed by information from other European countries. The British controversy over the results of Arpad Pusztai[6] found its resonance in the German debate. Reports on the refusal of supermarket chains in other European countries to sell GM food served as a trigger for German supermarket chains to change their policy from silence to expressed rejection. Most supermarket chains officially declared that they avoided GM food in their own brands. The attempt by a food company to sell a chocolate bar in Germany direct to the public, evading supermarkets, failed and the chocolate bar was withdrawn from the market in July 1999.

A minor debate on GM food which was symptomatic of the German discussion started in September 1998, when the Zentralverband des Deutschen Bäckerhandwerks (Central Association of German Bakers) declared that, within the next few years, genetic engineering would become an integral part of bread production. Consumer organisations like the Arbeitsgemeinschaft der Verbraucherverbände (AGV) rejected this view. Later this statement was withdrawn. In October 1988, as a consequence of public resistance to food biotechnology, the Raiffeisen-Genossenschaft (Agricultural Association) in Baden-Württemberg demanded GM-free products from its producers. At the largest food exhibition in Cologne in the same month, Greenpeace presented 400,000 signatures they had gathered against GM food.

In December 1999 Greenpeace campaigns shifted from GM food, which was not widely available in Germany anyway, to GM cattle fodder. In summer 2000, Greenpeace started a campaign against the fast-food chain McDonald's which was accused of selling chicken fed on GM soyabeans.

The application of genetic engineering in medicine and diagnosis

The application of biotechnology to human reproduction was the starting point for the debate on genetic engineering in Germany, as already mentioned. The Law for the Protection of Embryos, which had been passed in 1990, seemed to meet the regulatory needs of the general public who saw no need for further debates. This situation changed after the announcement of the advent of the first cloned mammal, Dolly the sheep. At a time when,

Table 1. Key policy events in Germany, 1996–2000

Date	Trigger	Event	Outcome
Autumn 1996	Soya imports (started on 6 November 1996).	The first ship containing GM soya reached Germany. Greenpeace protested.	European dimension added to the domestic debate; government increasingly under pressure from both sides – time-gaining strategy.
November 1996	Bio-Regio-Contest.	The German Ministry for Research, Education and Technology announced a competition between German regions to decide which three regions offered the best concept to develop new biotechnology start-up companies. Almost every region participated.	Successful attempt to change the frame of the biotechnology debate to economics and competitiveness. Start of the German biotechnology boom.
February 1997	Dolly the sheep.	Discussion on ethical limitations and human applicationsof the new discovery.	Short debate, but existing regulation proved to be sufficient to cope with this new development.
May 1997	Novel-Food Prescription Registration comes into force.	Novel-Food prescription regulating compulsory labelling comes into force, but the concrete proposals are passed only in September 1997. Laboratories to detect GM food emerge. Traces of GM food are detected in products. As a consequence the producing companies remove their products from the market. The food industry welcomes uniform regulation but demands further rules to guarantee uniform application and to avoid competitive disadvantages for German companies.	Almost no GM food on the German market.
11 September 1998	German parliament.	New law on the scope of admissibility of genetic tests. The new law legalises genetic tests to be conducted with regard to future criminal prosecutions.	Public consent, new law (§81g of the German Criminal Procedure Law).
From 1998 onwards	Bioethics Convention of the European Council.	Discussion in parliament and amongst the public whether Germany should sign up to the Convention.	Ongoing discussion.
June 1998	Establishment of a reference centre for bioethics.	The creation of a reference centre for bioethics at the University of Bonn is announced. The institute is to be funded by the German Ministry for Research and Education (BMBF) and the German Research Association (DFG).	No direct outcome.
October 1998	Federal Elections in Germany, new government.	As a consequence of the Federal Elections, the German Government coalition changes. The Green Party enters the government.	Initially no change in the policy on genetic engineering.
January 1999	Discussion on biomedical applications, Sloterdijk debate.	The German 'Embryonenschutzgesetz' (Law on the Protection of Human Embryos) strictly forbids any consuming research with embryos. German researchers and research organisations repeatedly lobby for change of the Law. Discussions on medical application, research and prenatal diagnostics take place leading to media hype when the German philosopher Peter Sloterdijk starts a public debate on human reproduction in July 1999.	Discussion on medical applications of biotechnology. No concrete outcome.
November 1999	The German Minister for Health convenes an advisory committee for ethics.	Whereas the first advisory committee established in 1995 concentrated on biomedicine, the new committee will also deal with issues regarding health insurance, diagnostic technology and new therapies.	Ongoing.
March 2000	Parliamentary Enquete Commission on modern medicine.	A new Enquete Commission is established to discuss 'legal and ethical problems of modern medicine', which includes biomedical problems.	Ongoing.
April 2000	Press statement by the Gesamtverband der Deutschen Versicherungs-Wirtschaft.	After several articles in German newspapers, the German insurance association denies that the insurance industry plans to make genetic tests a prerequisite for insurance cover.	Ongoing.

as a consequence of the Dolly story, the problem of the regulation of use of human sperm cells and human cloning sparked an intense public debate in several European countries, the reactions in Germany were rather modest. Human cloning appeared on the agenda but it was more a debate in the arts sections of the newspapers than a political debate; all in all, the impact of this debate appears to have been to be rather low. In April 1997, a commission of the Ministry for Research and Technology chaired by the head of Deutsche Forschungsgemeinschaft (DFG, the German Research Council) and including representatives from the sciences, law, the humanities and theology came together. The commission decided that the existing Law for the Protection of Embryos was sufficient to deal with the problems raised by the technical possibility of cloning. Therefore, contrary to the situation in other countries, German politicians could refer to an existing regulation.

Although the Law calmed the public debate, it increased the resistance of scientific and medical institutions, which considered the regulation too strict and to be preventing research necessary for therapeutic reasons. Every once in a while individual researchers and research associations repeated their demand to weaken the strict regulation and adapt German law to the international standards. They thought this would enable German scientists and start-up companies to be competitive in the international arena. A debate on the change of this regulation commenced. In January 1999, the Minister for Health, Mrs Andrea Fischer from the Green Party, organised a congress to discuss this topic. The discussion led to the establishment of new institutions dealing with bioethics.

A controversial discussion took place on the Bioethics Convention of the European Council, to which Germany was not yet a signatory. Associations of disabled people had especially been opposed to this Convention and organised protests against it. In July 1998, a human chain 4 km long demonstrated to prevent the German government from signing the Bioethics Convention.

While these debates did not evoke the interest of the general public, a lecture by the German philosopher Peter Sloterdijk in July 1999 raised a serious debate which resulted in a series of articles in the weekly newspaper *ZEIT* and other elite papers.[7] The lecture dealt with Martin Heidegger and his *Letter on Humanism* in which he claimed that it had not achieved its goal to civilise mankind. Television channels changed their schedules to broadcast discussions on the opportunities of

modern biotechnology for humans. In his lecture, Sloterdijk mentioned 'Regeln für den Menschenpark' (rules for the human zoo) and talked about 'anthropotechnologies'. He asked whether mankind would end up changing reproduction from 'birth fatalism' to 'optional birth' and prenatal selection. Critics accused Sloterdijk of supporting applications of biotechnology for eugenics and human-breeding purposes. The topic of human reproduction was now permanently on the agenda for public and political discussions.

After the first cases of BSE were detected in Germany, the ministers for agriculture and health resigned in January 2001. The new Minister for Health, a Social Democrat, like Chancellor Gerhard Schröder, seemed to have a more supportive view on medical biotechnology than her predecessor.

Human reproduction was not the only area under regulatory discussion; areas of genetic testing were too. In April 1998, in the largest mass genetic testing programme to date in northern Germany, about 11,000 men were tested to find the murderer of a girl. In order to create a better legal founding for similar activities, a law was enforced in September 1998 concerning the scope of admissibility of genetic tests.

Institutionalisation of ethics

From early on in the preparatory discussions for the Law on the Protection of Embryos, ethical considerations played a major role. In the late 1990s, with new opportunities for medical biotechnology apparent, bioethical problems were the focus of increased importance. For example, in August 1998 DFG announced the establishment of an initiative to improve and increase communication between scientists, politicians and the public, and to support research on bioethics for the next five years. Following the queries that had been raised after the birth of Dolly the sheep, the Deutsches Referenzzentrum für Ethik in den Biowissenschaften (DRZE, German Reference Centre for Ethics in the Biosciences) started looking at related matters in January 1999. Financed by the Federal Ministry for Research and Technology, this centre collects, analyses and archives information, documents and references regarding ethics in the biosciences and in medicine, both nationally and internationally. The centre aims to track any developments in the natural sciences, medicine, legal sciences, the social sciences, philosophy and theology as well as improve the preconditions for ethical judgement. Ethical judgement is not considered possible without a general consensus and this, in turn, is not obtainable without a dialogue between science, the relevant social groups and the political system. DRZE, however, is a documentation and information centre and does not organise consensus conferences or public consultations. To address ethical issues, an advisory committee for ethics was established by the German Minister for Health in November 1999. It includes representatives from medicine, the legal sciences, theology, philosophy, social sciences and psychology. Whereas the first advisory committee established in 1995 concentrated on biomedicine, the new advisory committee also deals with questions of health insurance, new diagnostic technology and new therapies.

Finally, in March 2000, an Enquete Commission of the German parliament was established to discuss 'legal and ethical problems of modern medicine', to include biomedical applications.

Insurance and intellectual property rights

A topic gaining in importance as a result of increasing knowledge of the human genome is the problem involved in the use of genetic information for insurance purposes. The debate in the UK on this topic reached Germany but the outcome was different. In April 1999, the Gesamtverband der Deutschen Versicherungswirtschaft (GDV, Central Association of the German Insurance Companies) confirmed that it was not going to insist on genetic tests as a requirement for insurance. However, according to the German Insurance Law, the result of any test already carried out has to be disclosed. Media reports speculating that the insurance industry planned to make genetic tests a prerequisite for policies was denied by the GDV in April 2000.

Another topic evoking protests by NGOs was intellectual property rights. Although the discussion on regulation was at the European level, national activities also occurred in Germany. In November 1999 the Max-Planck-Institute Society organised a symposium on this topic. In February 2000, Greenpeace bricked up the entrance of the European Patenting Office in Munich, an activity that led to a lot of media coverage although no sustained debate.

Media coverage

The media landscape

Daily newspapers appear to be the most popular and significant printed media in Germany. About 70 per cent of Germans regularly read a local or regional daily newspaper. The five daily quality newspapers (with a circulation of about 1.5 million) and the weekly news magazines are regarded as opinion leaders – which means that they have a strong influence on the agenda of most of the other German papers. This is owing to the number of news agencies used by these media, their tight net of international correspondents and their investigative journalism skills, all of which contribute to their ability to influence the national agenda.

Description of the sample

The German sample consisted of two opinion leaders: the weekly news magazine *Der Spiegel* and the daily newspaper *Frankfurter Allgemeine Zeitung*. *Der Spiegel* is the most important German news magazine with a circulation of more than one million copies. On a political scale, most people would place it among the moderate left papers. The *Frankfurter Allgemeine Zeitung (FAZ)* represents the conservative political spectrum and has a circulation of about 400,000. Both papers have a science section.

The unit of analysis was defined as any semantic complex of journalistic origin dealing with biotechnology in any way. This included written texts as well as pictures, photos, figures and cartoons. In addition, letters to the editors are included, but advertising – such as public relations exercises by the biotechnology industry – were excluded.

For *FAZ* we constructed two 'artificial weeks', selecting two different days of every week at a time. Following this sampling method, one-third of the entire coverage was screened. We screened every second edition of *Der Spiegel*. Each article on modern biotechnology was chosen from the preselected copies. The sampling was conducted by electronic research on CD-ROM in the case of *Der Spiegel* and by online archive research in the case of *FAZ*. The sample consisted of 1531 articles: 1144 from *FAZ* and 387 from *Der Spiegel*. We excluded 169 articles from the analysis as the term 'biotechnology' was only used metaphorically, except for the intensity measures. Therefore, the final sample consisted of 1362 articles, 1035 from *FAZ* and 327 from *Der Spiegel*.

Intensity of coverage

Figure 1 shows the intensity of the German biotechnology coverage from 1973 to 1999. In order to allow comparability between all countries we

Figure 1. Intensity of articles on biotechnology in the German press

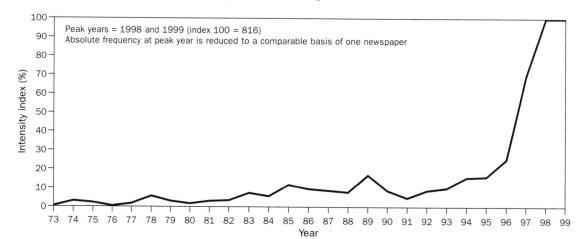

analysed only the frequencies of the daily paper *FAZ*. The peak years, 1998 and 1999, in which 816 of the estimated total of 3432 articles were published, was used as an index year for the development of the coverage. Intensity of coverage is an indicator for journalistic attention and therefore also for public attention to certain issues. Because of the possible effects of media coverage on public attitudes and opinions, we see media coverage as the most important criterion for identifying phases of biotechnology coverage that are of political interest. In our first report we identified three phases of media coverage from 1973 to 1996.[8]

The intensity analysis shows that German biotechnology coverage increased distinctly in the last three years of our analysis. This period, 1997–99, comprises 57 per cent of the whole coverage between 1973 and 1999, compared to only 8 per cent from 1973 to 1984, 15 per cent from 1985 to 1991, and 20 per cent from 1992 to 1996. The following analysis is focused on the comparison of the years directly before and after the so-called watershed of late 1996 and early 1997 which is characterised by certain key events in the area of biotechnology such as the shipping of soya from the USA to Germany in November 1996 (although the coverage did not increase until January 1997), and especially the first cloning of Dolly the sheep in February 1997. We compare the period 1992–96 to that of 1997–99 to look at if and how this presumed watershed is reflected in the media coverage on biotechnology in the later period. We describe these periods by frames, themes, actors, risk and benefit evaluations, and locations and, for the second period 1997–99 also by evaluations of actors and by demands.

The years after Dolly – changes in German biotechnology coverage?

Given the notion that the media coverage on biotechnology from 1997 to 1999 consists of 57 per cent of the whole coverage since 1973 (i.e. almost three times the amount in the preceding period 1992–96, which, in addition is two years longer) the theme 'biotechnology' obviously entered a new realm of public attention in Germany.

The 'pre-watershed' years

The media agenda of the period 1992–96 was characterised by several heterogeneous issues: biomedical (19 per cent) and agrifood issues (15 per cent) being mentioned most frequently (Table 2). Scientific sources were still the most important actors (43 per cent) but industry (18 per cent) played an increasingly important role. Interest groups (5 per cent) could establish themselves for the first time in the mediated public debate.

The sole increase regarding story framing was the topic 'globalisation', which played a role in almost 12 per cent of the articles. The trend of globalisation was illustrated by the fact that, for the first time, a transnational actor – the EU – received considerable attention (5 per cent). The German media coverage of biotechnology in the 1990s became more and more benefit orientated[9] and hence presented less controversy. More than half the articles exclusively mentioned the benefits of biotechnology. A considerably higher proportion (more than 13 per cent of the articles) mentioned neither risks nor benefits, compared to only 5 per cent of articles in which only risks were mentioned.

Table 2. German media profile, 1992–99 (threshold for inclusion: 5 per cent)

Phase	1992–96		1997–99	
Frequency (%)[a]	26		74	
Frame (%)	**Progress**[b]	54	**Progress**	42
	Accountability	13	Economic	21
	Globalisation	12	Ethical	11
	Economic	9	Accountability	9
	Ethical	7	Nature/nurture	8
Theme (%)[c]	**Biomedical**	19	**Biomedical**	21
	Agrifood	15	Genetic research	14
	Genetic research	12	Agrifood	13
	Regulation	12	Economics	12
	Public opinion/policy	11	Public opinion/policy	11
	Economics	10	Genetic identity	10
			Regulation	6
			Moral	6
			Cloning	5
Actor (%)[d]	**Science**	43	**Science**	35
	Politics	18	Business	23
	Business	18	Politics	12
	Interest groups	5	Interest groups	7
	EU	5	EU	5
Benefit/risk (%)	**Benefit only**	55	**Benefit only**	40
	Both	28	Neither	31
	Neither	13	Both	20
	Risk only	5	Risk only	10
Location (%)	**Germany**	33	**Germany**	37
	USA	29	Other Europe	27
	Other Europe	26	USA	24
	World	7	Other countries	9
	Other countries	5		

a Percentage of corpus (which includes only those articles which focus on biotechnology) in the period; $n = 1043$.
b Bold indicates highest frequency within phase.
c Multiple response for three themes (i.e. more than one variable may be coded per article).
d Multiple response for two actors in 1992–96.

According with the notion of a certain globalisation of the German debate, the biotechnology events were placed in a transnational or international environment. In general, in 1998, we characterised the German media debate about biotechnology until 1996 as a pragmatic, problem-orientated discussion about the possible benefits of biotechnology.[10]

The 'post-watershed' years

The years from 1997 to 1999 were dominated by two characteristics: 'renaissance' and 'normalisation'. The renaissance was a revival of ethical and philosophical discussion concerning specific consequences, set up by the concrete implementation of this relatively new technology. On the other hand the media treated modern

biotechnology as a normal and promising industrial technology alongside other technologies.

The renaissance of an ethical and philosophical debate can be seen from the framing of the stories, e.g. the broader context in which the media placed biotechnology themes. The ethical frame was used in 11 per cent of all articles, compared to 7 per cent in the previous period. At the same time the frame nature/nurture reaches a considerable portion (8 per cent) for the first time. This frame concentrates mainly on genetic identity (30 per cent), genetic research (22 per cent) and the biomedical complex (20 per cent). We anticipated that articles on cloning especially would be framed ethically, but this was not the case at all. About 20 per cent of the ethical framing was about articles dealing with biomedical subjects, compared to 10 per cent of articles on cloning (and genetic identity), which is about average within the ethical frame. The same is true for the opposite perspective: of all articles dealing with cloning, 26 per cent are in fact ethically framed, although 38 per cent are presented in the context of progress.

These observations lead to the conclusion that the ethical debate – at least in terms of a more quantitative analysis – is less likely to be an independent public discourse but rather an accompanying consideration amongst all the other possible perspectives. At the same time, 42 per cent of all articles are framed as progress, another 21 per cent are reported under the frame of economical prospects (1992–96: 12 per cent). The economic contextualisation seems to replace the more abstract frame of globalisation, which already showed a strong relationship with economical themes in the former period.

This mix of normalisation of a new industrial technology and consideration of its specific aspects also shows up in the themes of the coverage. Biomedicine (21 per cent), genetic research (14 per cent) and agrifood (13 per cent) are still the three most frequent themes, followed by economic issues (12 per cent) which has become the highest ranking in this category over time. This corresponds to the observation that business actors (23 per cent) play an increasingly important role. Compared to the pre-watershed period some new themes are emerging. This is especially true in the case of genetic identity (10 per cent), which has never been dominant in media coverage. Moral themes (6 per cent), which had disappeared in the previous period, were again as frequent as in the regulation debate from 1985 to 1991. At the same time, the percent-

age of themes dealing with public opinion and policy was slightly lower (11 per cent): regulation issues even dropped from 12 to 6 per cent. Correspondingly, political actors were less frequently mentioned (12 per cent) than before (18 per cent).

The same picture emerges from the risk-and-benefit evaluations. Articles which mention neither benefits nor risks were more than twice as frequent in the second half of the 1990s, whilst articles mentioning only benefits dropped from 55 to 40 per cent, which is still a considerably high proportion. Articles mentioning risks and benefits decreased from 28 to 20 per cent, and those mentioning only risks doubled (10 per cent). Risk evaluations refer predominantly to moral and health risks (Table 3). Compared to the media coverage in the years 1992–96, moral risks are now more frequently mentioned than health risks. Health benefits, with 30 per cent, are the most frequently mentioned benefits, followed by economic benefits. Interestingly, the benefit-and-risk articles clearly mention less economic benefits than before. For the first time economic risks are also considered, whereas in the articles only pointing out benefits, the economic dimension becomes more dominant. Altogether, the discussion on benefits and risks of modern biotechnology is still dominated by the benefits of this technology. In the late 1990s, this discourse is accompanied by the especial consideration of moral risk, which replaces the focus on health and environmental risk.

Actor networks

We complete our picture of the media coverage from 1997 to 1999 by the description of some new

Table 3. Type of benefit and risk evaluations

	1992–96		1997–99	
Benefits only (%)	Research	41	Health	30
	Health	27	Economic	28
	Economic	21	Research	20
Benefits and risks (%)	Economic benefits	42	Health benefits	31
	Health benefits	27	Economic benefits	22
	vs		Research benefits	16
	Health risks	31	*vs*	
	Moral risks	18	Moral risks	29
	Environmental risks	14	Health risks	21
	Consumer risks	14	Economic risks	14
Risks only (%)	Social inequality	(negligible)	Moral	34
			Health	20
			Environmental	13

actor images. First we wanted to know to which actors the media ascribe responsibility for benefits and risks of modern biotechnology. Both benefits and risks are dominated by the actors science and business (benefits – science 58, business 32 per cent; risk – science 46, business 24 per cent). While the dominance of scientific actors is familiar, the importance of business actors underlines the thesis that biotechnology has taken the status of a technology to which people have become more accustomed, and which is increasingly discussed in terms of the economic market. Nevertheless, the discourse clearly shows that there still is a need for reaching decisions on future developments, concrete implementations, and preferences for and aversions to certain applications. We therefore wanted to establish how the main actors in the area of biotechnology are evaluated by other actors ('evaluations'), and which actors play an important role in the discussion about the future agenda of biotechnology ('demands').

'Science' (31 per cent) and 'media and the public' (23 per cent) are the most frequent addressees of evaluations. Both actors are given relatively balanced evaluations (mean 3.7 on a seven-point scale) with a slight tendency towards a 'somewhat negative' image. At the same time, extremely positive and negative evaluations especially of the scientists show that biotechnology is still an ambivalent issue. The most frequent demands concern 'public opinion and policy' (29 per cent) and 'regulation' (16 per cent). Most demands come from the media (24 per cent) and from science (22 per cent), which means that these actors play a considerable role in the public discussion. The most frequently mentioned addressees of these demands are politics and science (both 27 per cent). Interestingly, the same competence in responding to demands is ascribed to scientists and politicians.

Public perceptions

Biotechnology and genetic engineering, in comparison to other technologies, evoked the most critical reactions from German respondents in both 1996 and 1999. In 1996, 36 per cent of Germans had positive expectations of biotechnology and genetic engineering for their own lives whilst 23 per cent feared that the technology would affect their future negatively. The proportion of people thinking that genetic engineering had no effect on their lives was 18 per cent; higher than in any other member state of the EU. Another 22 per cent did not have opinion on genetic engineering. In comparison to other European countries, Germany was amongst the most sceptical.[11]

In 1999, general attitudes towards biotechnology and genetic engineering were very similar to 1996: 38 per cent expressed positive expectations and 20 per cent feared the potential future consequences of genetic engineering and biotechnology, i.e. slightly less than in 1996. One-fifth of the respondents, a higher proportion than in any other European country, thought that biotechnology and genetic engineering would not have effects on their own lives. Some 22 per cent responded 'don't know' to the question on consequences of genetic engineering. Compared with the European development of a substantial decrease in positive expectations from biotechnology and genetic engineering and with virtually no change in the general evaluation of genetic engineering, Germany shifted from being one of the most sceptical countries in 1996 to meeting the European average in 1999.

Almost one-third of the respondents declared that they had never discussed biotechnology prior to the interview and, even though developments in biotechnology had raised significant controversies and intense media reporting over the previous few years, the proportion of people not having discussed biotechnology increased from 24 per cent in 1996 to 31 per cent in 1999.

Applications of genetic engineering

The general lack of discussion about biotechnology is also reflected in the awareness of applications. Only 31 per cent (in the case of GM bacteria for environment protection) and 66 per cent (in the case of GM food) of the population had heard about the different applications before the interview.

Whilst genetic engineering was regarded more or less ambivalently, there was a large difference in the evaluations of applications of biotechnology (Table 4). This difference was greater in 1999 than in 1996.

The use of GM bacteria for environment protection (bioremediation), biotechnological production of medicines and vaccines as well as genetic screening received the highest support in Germany. But not all medical applications were evaluated positively. Whilst the cloning of human cells was evaluated slightly positively, the cloning of animals received very little support from the German public.

As in 1996, agricultural applications were evaluated more sceptically. When looking at transgenic plants for instance, evaluations were

Table 4. German attitudes to applications of modern biotechnology

Application	Year	Useful for society	Risky for society	Morally acceptable	Should be encouraged
Food production	1996	0.18[a]	0.57	−0.08	−0.20
	1999	0.02	0.58	−0.15	−0.32
GM plants	1996	0.55	0.06	0.29	0.18
	1999	0.49	0.15	0.32	0.15
Genetic screening	1996	1.01	−0.01	0.64	0.70
	1999	1.08	−0.24	0.80	0.83
Production of medicines with GM bacteria	1996	0.96	−0.23	0.59	0.64
	1999	1.08	−0.05	0.76	0.84
Cloning human cells for medical purposes[b]	1999	0.55	0.37	0.20	0.25
Cloning animals for medical purposes[b]	1999	−0.01	0.51	−0.30	−0.30
GM bacteria for bioremediation[b]	1999	1.17	−0.17	0.93	0.95

a Arithmetic means, scale −2 to +2 with four categories (−2 = strongly disagree, 2 = strongly agree); *n* is between 700 and 980 cases (excluding missing values).
b Asked only in Eurobarometer 1999.

slightly positive, whereas GM food was still the most rejected application in Germany.

Between 1996 and 1999, the gap between supported and rejected applications of biotechnology increased. Whilst support for medical applications was higher in 1999, rejection of GM food – which could already be observed in 1996 – strengthened.

In the analysis of the reasons for support or rejection of biotechnology, evaluations of risk, usefulness and moral acceptability provide some useful hints.

Genetically modified food was evaluated as being the most risky application of biotechnology in 1999, followed by the cloning of animals. The application was also considered to reap the least benefits and raised the strongest moral objections. On the other hand, transgenic bacteria, the production of medicine using GMOs and genetic testing were seen as being useful, morally acceptable and of low risk. In comparison to the cloning of animals, therapeutic cloning of human cells was seen both as risky but also as useful. It did not raise considerable ethical problems.

In 1996, a regression analysis showed that the evaluations of usefulness and moral acceptability were the main reasons for the support or rejection of biotechnology. Surprisingly, risk had no statistical impact providing that all other dimensions were controlled. In 1999, the correlation coefficients between support and usefulness, even more with moral acceptance, were so high that there seemed to be no clear distinction between these dimensions (the range of Pearson's *r*, an indicator for correlation, is between 0.7 and 0.85). Therefore, the evaluations of usefulness and moral acceptability followed the same pattern as the support for the applications.

On the other hand, the correlation between risk evaluation and the variables for support, moral acceptance, encouragement and usefulness was only moderate, which means that there was a supportive group that evaluated biotechnology or applications thereof as risky, useful and morally acceptable. Consequently, when looking at the conjoint evaluation of usefulness, risk, moral acceptability and encouragement, we found that there are three dominant logics out of the possible 16 combinations (Table 5):

- supporters who think, that the application is useful, not risky, morally acceptable and should be encouraged,
- opponents, who have the opposite view, and
- risk-tolerant supporters, who think that the application is useful, morally acceptable and should be encouraged, but also risky.

Table 5. Supporters, risk-tolerant supporters and opponents by genetic application (respondents with a neutral score (0) were eliminated from the analysis)

	Supporters (%)	Risk-tolerant supporters (%)	Opponents (%)	Residual group (%)
Food production	21.6	13.6	36.5	28.3
GM plants	35.0	16.4	23.0	25.6
GM bacteria for medicine	46.4	26.5	9.2	17.8
Cloning human cells for medical purposes	30.0	23.4	23.6	23.0
Cloning animals for medical purposes	19.1	15.4	38.2	27.3
Genetic screening	50.6	22.8	8.2	18.4
GM bacteria for protection of environment	51.4	25.6	8.2	14.8

The high proportion of risk-tolerant supporters is surprising. Between 31 per cent (in the case of genetic screening) and 45 per cent (in the case of animal cloning) of supporters are risk tolerant. On the other hand, attitudes of opponents are more coherent: they think that the applications are risky, morally unacceptable, not useful and that they should not be encouraged.

Social differentiation

As in 1996, men were shown to be substantially more in favour of biotechnology than women (43 compared to 33 per cent) in the 1999 survey, and younger people were more in favour than older people. Men in the youngest age group, especially, showed more positive attitudes towards biotechnology than any other age group. The 1996 survey showed that even with increasing knowledge there was no difference in the evaluation of biotechnology; increasing knowledge had only one effect: the attitudes became more distinct. In 1999, a substantial difference was found: higher education and better knowledge not only led to reductions of 'undecideds', but there was also increasing support for biotechnology. Some 47 per cent of the respondents with higher education compared to 31 per cent of the less-well-educated respondents expected positive effects from biotechnology for their future lives. Although this does not mean that there is a direct cognitive relationship between knowledge and attitudes, there is a change in the evaluation of biotechnology amongst younger and better educated people.

Trust in social institutions

Few people have direct access to information on biotechnology; most depend on mediated information. This raises the question of trust in the different sources of information.

As in 1996, the most trustworthy institutions in Germany with respect to modern biotechnology were consumer organisations: 29 per cent of respondents expressed that they trusted these most. We found that 17 per cent think that the medical profession is the most trustworthy whilst 14 per cent consider environmental groups to be the most trustworthy. This actor suffered a significant decrease in expressed trust compared to 1996 (22 per cent). Considering the importance of environmental institutions in the political debate on biotechnology, this figure is rather low. Only 8 per cent thought that universities are the most trustworthy. Other institutions, governments and public authorities, the media, industry, religious institutions or political parties were not considered to be of importance.

Another question is whether institutions are, in general terms rather than in relation specifically to biotechnology, considered to be trustworthy or not. The responses to this changed trust question still reflect a remarkable trust gap. Only consumer associations were evaluated as being trustworthy by a majority of the respondents (62 per cent). Half of the public trusted environmental groups and the medical profession. Compared to these institutions, trust in political and religious institutions was extremely low. The media, farmers associations,

201

environmental organisations and universities were somewhere in between. It is remarkable that, with the exception of consumer organisations, there is not a single institution trusted by society and that the political system, industry and the scientific system were trusted by less than 30 per cent of the German population.

Conclusion

For an observer in 1996, the prospects of biotechnology in Germany seemed to be quite positive. Admittedly, the German public were amongst the most sceptical in Europe, but they were not averse to most medical applications of biotechnology. The media reflected the possible benefits of biotechnology in a pragmatic, problem-oriented way. Political regulators made strenuous efforts to weaken the strict regulations of 1990 and to support the development of a German biotechnology industry. Consequently, the German biotechnology boom, the economic take off ranking Germany first in the number of start-up companies in Europe, did not seem to be surprising.

Compared to the situation in other European countries, where the acceptance of biotechnology and its applications suffered a substantial decrease, amongst the German public the perception of biotechnology was remarkably stable between 1996 and 1999. Public perception is still characterised by a 'relaxed scepticism'. Germany, which was one of the most sceptical countries in 1996, was average compared with other European countries in 1999. However, the German biotechnology boom is only one side of the coin – the other is the almost complete failure of GM food and the new debate on medical applications.

Although there are discussions in both areas, the general situation of medical and agricultural applications is different. Compared to 1996, the gap between accepted and rejected applications of biotechnology increased, and the resistance to GM food was even higher in 1999 than in 1996, while medical applications found more support in 1999. It can also be observed, though, that debates in Germany were somewhat delayed.

Recognising the public rejection of GM food in Germany, both the food industry and politics followed a 'duck-and-cover' strategy, which led to a dampened debate on this topic. On the other hand, a new public debate emerged in Germany, leading to a discussion of medical applications of biotechnology, the deeper understanding and limitations of human activities in 'playing God'. The Sloterdijk debate initiated this discussion which is still ongoing. The debate can not be fully understood without reference to German history in the fascist period.

We conclude that the public climate has not generally changed. The process of normalisation, e.g. treating biotechnology as a technology beside others, is still ongoing. The key biotechnology events described above may have had an alarming or warning function and received considerable public attention, but in the long run they did not dominate the debate. In the media, the discussion of the economic uses of modern biotechnology for instance, was more prominent than the discussion on cloning.

The future of biotechnology in Germany seems to be ambiguous. The more positive evaluations by the youngest age group and the stronger support from highly educated people, as well as the support for applications such as genetic fingerprinting and the positive media coverage on biotechnology may be interpreted as a shift from a sceptical to a more positive perception. At the end of the twentieth century, the media still treated biotechnology (and even increasingly so) as a success story but with a careful regard to specific problematic applications. The renewed sensitivity to the moral dimensions of biotechnology and the low trust in institutions dealing with the control and regulation of biotechnology is a strong argument against this view. It is likely that the differentiation between accepted and rejected applications will continue, but it is also likely that the medical applications of biotechnology will replace agricultural biotechnology as the focus of public attention and that the present state of perception and evaluation of different applications will change when abstract promises and abstract fears are confronted by concrete experiences.

Acknowledgement

We wish to thank Mrs Hotzel from the Online Research Unit of the Friedrich Schiller University for her help in sampling the media coverage.

Notes and references

1 Torgersen, H and Hampel, J, *et al.*, 'Promise, problems and proxies: 25 years of European biotechnology debate and regulation', in Bauer, M and Gaskell, G (eds), *Biotechnology: The Making of a Global Controversy* (Cambridge: Cambridge University Press, in press)

2 See for example Dolata, U, 'Nachholende Modernisierung und internationales Innovations-management; Strategien der deutschen Chemie- und Pharmakonzerne in der neuen Biotechnologie', in Schell, Th von and Mohr, H (eds), *Biotechnologie-Gentechnik, Eine Chance für neue Industrien* (Berlin: Springer, 1995).

3 Schitag, Ernst & Young, *Aufbruchstimmung 1998. Der erste Report der Schitag, Ernst & Young Unternehmensberatung über die Biotechnologie-Industrie in Deutschland* (Stuttgart: Schitag, Ernst & Young, 1988).

4 Ernst & Young, *Communicating Value, European Life Sciences 99, Sixth Annual Report* (London: Ernst & Young, 1999).

5 Informations-Sekretariat Biotechnologie <www.i-s-b.org>.

6 Dr Pusztai showed that some rats fed on GM potatoes developed alarming side-effects, including irregular organs and immune-system damage. Before his paper had officially been published, he claimed in a television documentary that the public were being used as 'guinea pigs' for GM food safety. His employers, Rowett Research, immediately suspended him and debate has raged ever since over the validity of his research findings.

7 Sloterdijk, P, *Regeln für den Menschenpark. Ein Antwortschreiben zum Brief über den Humanismus* (Frankfurt/Main: Suhrkamp, 1999).

8 Hampel, J, Ruhrmann, G, Kohring, M and Görke, A, 'Germany', in Durant, J, Bauer, M W and Gaskell, G (eds), *Biotechnology in the Public Sphere: A European Sourcebook* (London: Science Museum, 1998), pp63–76.

9 Ruhrmann, G, Görke, A and Kohring, M, 'Berichterstattung über Gentechnologie in deutschen Tageszeitungen. Ergebnisse einer systematischen Inhaltsanalyse', unpublished report (Münster/Osnabrück: Deutsche Forschungsgemeinschaft, 1992); Kohring, M and Görke, A, 'Genetic engineering in the international media: an analysis of opinion-leading magazines', *New Genetics and Society*, 19 (2000), pp345–63.

10 Görke, A, Kohring, M and Ruhrmann, G, 'Gentechnologie in der Presse. Eine internationale Langzeitanalyse von 1973 bis 1996', *Publizistik*, 45 (2000), pp20–37.

11 Gaskell, G, Bauer, M W and Durant, J, 'Public perceptions of biotechnology in 1996: Eurobarometer 46.1', in Durant, J, Bauer, M W and Gaskell, G (eds), (see note 8), pp189–214.

Address for correspondence

Dr Jürgen Hampel, Centre of Technology Assessment in Baden Württemberg, Industriestr. 5, D-70565 Stuttgart, Germany. E-mail Juergen.hampel@ta-akademie.de

Greece: losing faith in biotechnology

George Sakellaris and Aglaia Chatjouli

Public policy and political context

The politics surrounding biotechnology in Greece since 1997 have been influenced by the broader social context. An important feature has been the spectacular development and increased activity of a number of NGOs, specifically Greenpeace. In the late 1990s, public opinion towards biotechnology changed dramatically in Greece. There are several reasons for this. First, the public became disillusion-ed with new technology in general and biotechnol-ogy in particular. The public expected more in terms of practical applications and progress made. Second, the public was influenced by anti-biotechnology campaigning from activists and in the media. Third, in a relatively religious country, there has been influence by the Greek Orthodox church taking a critical stand on biotechnology.

Initially the socialist government promoted the new technology but, in response to negative public opinion, the government changed its position, intro-ducing policies that were sometimes inconsistent. The adoption of EU directives has been slow and there have been conflicting decisions concerning field trials of GM crops. The Greek initiative regar-ding the European moratorium on the commercial exploitation of GM crops is characteristic of the type of action taken by the government. The influence of NGOs on the government's approach was demon-strated in April 2000, when a former leader of Greenpeace in Greece was appointed Vice-Minister of the Environment. As a result government policy has increasingly opposed the development of biotechnology.

At the other end of the scale, a wave of biotechnology support has emerged. The main sources of support are the Food and Biotechnology Communications Initiative, scientific associations, and initiatives emanating from the American Embassy. These institutions have promoted the interests of biotechnology through a series of conferences and lectures.

However, the biotechnology industry in Greece is almost non-existent, Greece being one of the few EU countries with no homegrown R&D companies.

The multinationals have a presence in Greece and tend to lead and dominate the market. This lack of local R&D innovators means that there are few industrial partners for the scientific research community. Most collaborations are with either the multinationals or companies abroad. This results in the scientific community being uninvolved and isolated from local events. Finally, grants for bio-technology research in Greece are very limited. Greece is probably the only European country with no research programme focusing on ethical, social and legal aspects of biotechnology.

Key policy events in Greece, 1996–99

Almost all the main events in the policy arena can be linked with activist mobilisation and/or consumer and press initiatives (Table 1). The government has tended to follow the mainstream. In 1997, by invoking the EU directive 90/220, local authorities stopped some GM field trials, following strong activist resistance led by Greenpeace. Seed importers reacted to this event, which then became a media story. In 1998 an ethics committee was formed by the government, which was positively received by the key players. This was followed by the Greek Orthodox Church issuing a statement against xenotransplantation, on moral and ethical grounds.

A national consumer day held in 1999 was dominated by the issue of GM foods. Various environmental and consumer organisations came together to argue against the government, although in more measured tones than the activists against GM foods. All in all, a negative attitude towards GM foods has prevailed. This was further com-pounded by the story reaching Greece in March 1999 of Arpad Pusztai's research on the health effects of GM potatoes on rats, leading to GM foods becoming a focus of media attention. At this point, the statutory Foundation for the Protection of Consumer Rights, which had introduced ethical and moral dimensions to the debate, also adopted a negative stance.

The government, with the support of five other European countries, froze all field trials of GMOs

Table 1. *Key policy events in Greece, 1997–1999*

Date	Trigger	Event	Outcomes
October 1997	Strong activist activity, led by Greenpeace, against field trials of GM maize.	Government uses the clause in EU directive 220 stating that local authorities may interact and stop field trials. In two cases local authorities stop them.	Reaction of seed importers (Monsanto, Novartis). Extensive media coverage.
January 1998	Formation of the Committee of Ethics.	Committee is appointed by the government and belongs to the General Secretariat of Research and Technology.	Positive reactions from government and the scientific community.
Spring 1998	Church declaration against xenotransplantation.	The Greek Orthodox Church publishes a statement announcing that xenotransplantation is amoral and against human nature.	There is no official governmental reaction to the statement, but a spokesman declares that government supports any research activity. Some mass media echo the position of the Church.
December 1998	Proprietors of all Greek supermarkets sign a common declaration never to allow GM foods in their stores.	The government does not express any position, but there is a quite strong reaction from multinational companies and importers.	Little impact on public opinion and the media.
March 1999	The 'national day of the consumer' is officially devoted to GM foods.	Many meetings and symposia take place all over the country, dominated by the opinions of environmentalists, activists and consumer organisations. Government participates in most of them expressing scepticism and warning the public of risk and safety issues.	Very heavy coverage by the media, extended articles in the press and many television debates. The general climate is negative towards the use of GM foods.
March 1999	Greek press reports heavily on the British debate on the Pusztai case.	GM foods become headline news for a fortnight. The only state institution quoted is the Foundation for the Protection of Consumer Rights, which adopts an extreme position against GM foods, and also introduces ethical and moral parameters to the debate.	Public acceptance of GM foods is at its lowest level.
June 1999	Moratorium on field trials of GMOs.	Greek government initiative suggests restricting GMO releases. The Greek proposal is adopted by five other countries and all trials more or less come to a halt.	Greek Scientific Society and the Ethical Committee protest against the government's decision, which was taken without any consultation. None of these arguments is widely published or discussed in the media.
August 1999	Greenpeace accuses multinationals of following different labelling policies for Greece and abroad.	Greenpeace releases to the media a detailed list of imported products which are not labelled in Greece but are labelled abroad. The government, through the Foundation of the Protection of Consumer Rights, demands an investigation.	No significant reaction from industry.
March 2000	Formation of the National Authority of Food (Ministry of Development).	The Authority's mandate extends to food safety, the protection of public health and the protection of the consumer.	GM food becomes the main focus of the Authority.

in Greece. There was no consultation with the scientific community or relevant committees who disagreed with the government. In 1999 Greenpeace uncovered a story suggesting that the labelling process in Greece differed from the process adopted by other countries. Whilst the government began an investigation, industry remained silent. In March 2000, the Ministry of Development formed the National Authority of Food, with GM foods as its priority.

Biotechnology in Greece before 1996

The biotechnology business sector has always been of minor importance in Greece. State investment for research in this area has also been limited, with funding never exceeding 9 per cent of the national R&D budget. The General Secretariat of Research and Technology reported in 1995 that for the years 1991–94 the research funding of 0.5 per cent of GNP was the lowest in Europe. Thus there was little business activity in Greece in the domains of fermentation technology, plant genetics, diagnostics, protein engineering and enzyme technology, microbial genetics and marine biotechnology. Despite government claims since 1982 that biotechnology is a key technology, it has not been important economically for Greece. In 1984 the first Greek biotechnology company, Biohellas, was founded with investment capital of 500 million drachmae (about UK £0.9 million). This capital was invested jointly by the state (the General Secretary of Research and Technology), the Agricultural Bank of Greece and the Greek Bank of Industrial Development. The new company, with its own research laboratories, gradually became involved in several projects focusing on the agribiotechnology area. However this was unsuccessful and the company collapsed in 1992. Since then no other R&D biotechnology company has been established in Greece, although there are some companies that use modern biotechnology techniques and products.

This limited business interest, together with low public awareness, meant that there was no pressure for a regulatory framework in biotechnology. In the main, the Greek authorities passively adopted EU directives, seeing no need for local legislation. Three factors are important to understanding the short history of biotechnology in Greece. First the state's lack of initiative to adopt a national policy for biotechnology – any decisions were the result of pressure from the scientific community. Second, the lack of interest from local industry in potential involvement in the biotechnology business. Finally, the public had shown little interest in biotechnology.

In December 1983 Greece adopted EC directives 819.71 and 650.79 on 'environmental policy' and 'protection of consumers' respectively, without any prior consultation with the public or other key players. The Greek Association of Biologists followed this government action with a conference in June 1984, entitled 'Biotechnology and society'. The main topics were the ethical, legal and economic problems arising from the new biotechnological applications. There was no participation by the state authorities, and practically no interest from the public and the media. Until 1987 Greek involvement in European biotechnological research was negligible. Only two Greek proposals were incorporated into the EU research programmes: Biomolecular Engineering Programme (BEP) and Biotechnology Action Programme (BAP). In 1987 the Greek Association of Biotechnology (GAB) was founded. Although there was initial enthusiasm and many people subscribed to GAB, its overall impact was no greater than previous attempts. The state authorities never accepted the GAB as a consultative body and today it is almost inactive.

Many believed that the main reason for the slow development of biotechnology in Greece was the lack of interest in local applications rather than the limited governmental support and funding. A dominant view in the early 1990s was that there was little merit in undertaking sophisticated research without local industrial support, and that this kind of research should be left to countries like Germany, France and the UK. Instead it was proposed that Greek research should be refocused, utilising the natural characteristics of the country such as the sea and the sun. Portugal and Spain were developing similar policies. Finally, however, Greece decided to follow the European research model, committing totally to the research programmes proposed by the European Commission. A research policy for biotechnology based on local circumstances was never developed.

Main events from 1996 to 1999

The presence of Greenpeace in Greece

Since 1996 Greece has seen the most significant change of public opinion in any European country. It is widely acknowledged that the main catalyst for this change is Greenpeace. Greenpeace's activity in Greek biotechnology began in 1997. Two factors have influenced Greenpeace's impact on the public. First, the strong language of the activists: this was the first time there had been public criticism of biotechnology and its applications. The second factor was the popularity of Greenpeace amongst the mass media. Greenpeace was positively reinforced in Greece, by coverage in both television and the newspapers. A consequence of this media attention was that Greenpeace and the wider anti-GM movement attracted support from personalities from various corners of social, political and cultural life. This further enhanced the public's negative view of biotechnology.

GM food

Public reaction and media coverage of biotechnology were mainly concerned with GM food and crops, and these became the main policy issues. Greece was the last European country to adopt the 220 and 258 directives of the European Commission. Their implementation was complicated, for example nine relevant ministries were involved in the issue of field trials. As a result, the top heavy and inflexible system became an easy target for legal and activist challenge. It is not surprising therefore that the trials of GM tomatoes and maize were stopped following the intervention of local and regional authorities, even though the commercial companies had gained legal authorisation for the trials.

The Greek government, to its embarrassment, found itself caught between two opposing camps. On one hand, there was growing public opposition to GM foods, openly supported by the mass media. On the other, the Ministry of Agriculture had to face the disappointment of leading multinationals, who had invested in Greece with a view to establishing a regional base and extending their investment to the wider eastern Mediterranean region and the Middle East. This embarrassing political dilemma was a key trigger leading to the Greek initiative for the European moratorium. The government took the politically expedient choice.

Formation of the Greek Bioethics Committee

The Greek Bioethics Committee was formed in 1998 as part of the Ministry of Development, overseen by the General Secretary of Research and Technology. The role of this committee is to consult the government, and provide information and advice to the policy-makers, the scientific community and the public. It is a body of experts composed of seven members, all men, and all university professors apart from one journalist. Most specialise in the biomedical field and, in general, the committee tends to be pro-biotechnology. Prior to this form of institutionalised ethics, other committees existed that dealt with the general area of medical ethics and were connected with the medical world, with few linkages to biotechnology. Opinions of the Bioethics Committee are reported in the media, but to date it has failed to achieve the advisory role it hoped for.

The Greek moratorium

In June 1999 the European parliament adopted a proposition to suspend new field trials of GM seeds. Although this action was characteristic of European parliamentary practice, it was unusual because the initiative came from Greece. For Greece, this initiative was a purely political decision to avoid damaging the popularity of the party in government, and it was taken without advice or consultation with experts. The scientific community and commercial companies were taken by surprise. This moratorium was finally adopted in six other countries. The opposition party accused the Greek government of using the moratorium as an election ploy, to project an environmentally concerned image. The moratorium was announced just before the European elections of 1998. In the view of the opposition, such a moratorium should have been put in place much earlier.

This initiative marked the beginning of an anti-biotechnology policy by the Greek government, culminating in the nomination of the former leader of the Greenpeace movement in Greece, as Vice-Minister of the Environment, responsible for biotechnology matters. It is important to mention that a key factor influencing the rather unenthusiastic governmental approach to biotechnology, was the limited interest for business development in the country. There are several possible reasons for this. Areas of research at a national level are limited, as is the funding, particularly in the biotechnology field. Thus, scientists are more involved with international research networks than with projects of national priority. A second reason is the limited opportunities for biotechnology applications. In Greece the 'biotechnology industry' is not technologically innovative. Some food and pharmaceutical companies use imported know-how, not having the economic motivation to produce their own. For this reason the industrial R&D departments are very small whilst links between the industry and universities are limited. A third reason for limited business development is the relatively small market. Greece, with a population of 10 million, is surrounded by countries with poor national budgets and traditionally low investment in modern technological applications. Traditionally, biotechnology business is focused on large and rich markets with strong industrial units where the technology transfer is possible. Thus Greek R&D has to compete with more developed countries, and is also disadvantaged by its geographical isolation. Finally, the high costs of the infrastructure and specialised personnel required limit business development. In addition, there is little enthusiasm amongst the public for both the economic and social implications.

All of the above have contributed to what might be called a weak policy, which in turn has fostered a negative public perception. The response of the multinationals involved in biotechnology, especially the food sector, is to try to improve their image by emphasising the potential benefits of biotechnology. However, given the strength of the anti-biotechnology movement, the effect is negligible. It is noteworthy that, although the members of the Greek Bioethics Committee are largely from scientific backgrounds and in general pro-biotechnology, the industry is still unable to mobilise this or other relevant committees.

The present situation

In accordance with EU legislation, there are national regulations for bringing GMOs to market, for R&D as well as for the use of GM microorganisms. Specific activities such as the marketing of plant-protection biotechnology products are also implemented through the EU legislation. The uses of GM microorganisms are also regulated by EC directives, but their implementation in Greece is the responsibility of the Greek state. Environmental impact assessment of such products is currently undertaken by the Ministry of Environment in cooperation with the Universities of Crete and Thessalonica and the National Hellenic Research Foundation. The Ministry of Development, General Secretariat for Energy and Technology provides funds to relevant research institutions. The Ministry of the Environment, Physical Planning and Public Works, General Directorate for Environment is the relevant authority for implementing the EC directives and is also the coordinating body of a national committee working on the subject.

Media coverage

The sample

The coverage of modern biotechnology in the Greek media was investigated through a time-series analysis of four newspapers for the period 1973–99: *Kathimerini* (which means 'daily'), *Eleutherotypia* ('free press'), *Ta Nea* ('the news') and *To Bima* ('the step'). These newspapers are considered to serve as opinion-leaders for the Greek public.

Kathimerini is a national morning newspaper. It is considered to be conservative, although critical of right-wing political parties. *Eleutherotypia* is an afternoon daily newspaper, and more oriented towards the socialists and the left. *Ta Nea* is a national afternoon newspaper, currently with the highest circulation amongst the afternoon papers, and is oriented towards the middle of the political spectrum. Although tabloid in format, its style and content differ from the British tabloids, yet it is less rigid than a quality newspaper. *To Bima* is a morning newspaper, with the second highest circulation amongst the morning papers after *Kathimerini*. Politically it is oriented towards the centre-left, which is where the Greek socialist party sits. As such it is considered to reflect the government's views.

For the period 1974–85, the newspapers were sampled manually. In order to facilitate the process, the newspapers were sampled every other year, including years important in terms of biotechnology news. For the period 1986–96, a database of almost all articles of all Greek newspapers was searched, using selected keywords. The keywords were coded by theme. Those articles with themes of modern biotechnology were selected for analysis.

For the year 1997, all articles were gathered using an online search, and all the retrieved articles coded. Three newspapers were included: *Eleuthertypia, Ta Nea* and *To Bima*. Ninety-two articles were retrieved and were coded. For the year 1998, all articles were inspected manually, and all articles found were coded. The same three newspapers were searched as in 1997. This time 110 articles were found and coded. For the year 1999, both an online keyword search and a manual search were carried out. In 1999, 123 articles were found of which 103 were coded. The articles were included in the analysis if they dealt with biotechnology issues, such as cloning, genetic engineering, GMOs, issues of bioethics, and so on.

Phase structure of media coverage

Media coverage of biotechnology in Greece increased dramatically in the period 1997–99 (Figure 1). A relative index of press coverage of modern biotechnology, for the period 1973–99, is shown.

The period before 1997 is characterised by very low coverage, in fact the lowest in Europe. There are several reasons for the increased coverage from 1997 onwards. First the articles were collected mostly by hand, therefore increasing the sample number and including articles that did not have 'modern biotechnology' as their main focus. Second, the increase in press coverage is marked by a number of key events such as cloning and the introduction of GM foods. In its coverage of biotechnology, the Greek press appears to be catching up with the rest of the European press.

Figure 1. Intensity of articles in the Greek press, 1973–99 (based on average numbers of articles)

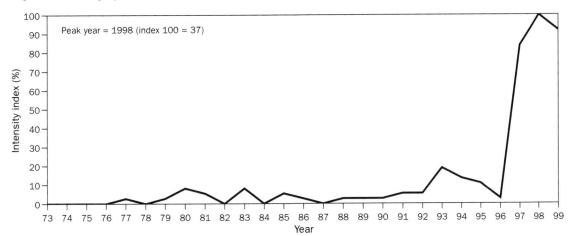

The increase in coverage for the period 1997–99 is coupled with a shift in the overall attitude of the Greek press towards the new technology and its applications. Based on the change of intensity of coverage, but also on the coded variables, the period can be divided into two major phases, pre- and post-1997. Nevertheless, our preference was to further divide the period before 1997 into Phase 1 (1977–91), 'progress at the risk of opening Pandora's box', and Phase 2 (1992–96), 'progress brings more benefits, but at the expense of morality'. Finally, Phase 3 (1997–99) is characterised by 'progress vs public accountability': cloning is heavily covered, while the development of agrifood is associated with risks. Phase 3 is the high-intensity, most informative period, and the main focus of our current analysis.

Phase 1 (1977–91): progress at the risk of opening Pandora's box. This phase is characterised by the low intensity of press coverage in the media. While 63 per cent of articles have progress as a frame, 13 per cent have 'Pandora's box' as a frame and 10 per cent cover nature vs nurture (Table 2). These last two frames, each represent less than 5 per cent of the total articles in the following two phases. The progress frame is dominant throughout the three phases. In spite of the small sample in Phase 1, a variety of themes are represented. The most prevalent is the biomedical theme, found in 46 per cent of articles. Topics raised under this theme include human-based DNA research, gene therapy, reproduction and pharmaceuticals. In Phase 1, biotechnology is not presented as risky. Some 53 per cent of the articles portray the new technology and its applications, mostly in the biomedical sphere, as comprising of benefits only and 27 per

cent of the articles portray the new technology as having benefits and risks.

Phase 2 (1992–96): progress and benefits, but at the expense of morality. In this phase the progress frame also dominates, with a very high frequency of 80 per cent, while most of the remaining articles have a moral frame, indicating a rise in the moral sensitivity of the published material covering ethical issues. The emphasis on progress-related topics is coupled with a picture of biotechnology and its applications having risks as well as benefits, but in some cases only benefits for humanity. In 36 per cent of articles generic research is the theme discussed the most, together with biomedicine (29 per cent) and agrifood (11 per cent).

Phase 3 (1997–99): progress vs public accountability. In this phase, cloning is an often-occurring theme, while progress in agrifood is associated with risks. In this phase the coverage has increased immensely, partly because the biotechnology debate has come to the fore in the public sphere, and partly because the Greek press adopted a style of very detailed and negatively predisposed coverage. In this period, 305 articles were counted and coverage peaked in 1998 (Figure 1).

The themes that emerge in 1997 are agrifood (24 per cent), including issues like GM crops and GM foods, followed by biomedicine (19 per cent), and cloning (19 per cent). This is the first time cloning appears with a relatively significant frequency. Cloning, together with agrifoods, acts as a trigger for media attention. Morality emerges in third place (11 per cent), indicating a more critical stance by the media.

Table 2. Greek media profile, 1977–99 (threshold for inclusion: 5 per cent)

Phase	1. 1977–91		2. 1992–96		3. 1997–99	
Frequency (%)[a]	8		10		82	
Frame (%)	**Progress**[b]	63	**Progress**	80	**Progress**	40
	Pandora's box	13	Ethical	14	Public accountability	29
	Nature/nurture	10				
	Economic prospects	7				
Theme (%)	**Biomedicine**	46	**Generic research**	36	**Agrifood**	24
	Agrifood	10	Biomedicine	29	Cloning	16
	Generic research	10	Agrifood	11	Biomedicine	16
	Moral	8	Other	9	Regulation	12
	Regulation	6	Moral	7	Moral	10
	Genetic identity	6	Genetic identity	7	Public opinion	8
					Generic research	6
Actor (%)	**Independent science**	64	**Independent science**	62	**Independent science**	43
	Business	13	Business	27	Business	20
	Politics	13			Interest groups	11
	Other	5			Politics	8
					Other	8
					Media publications	6
Benefit/risk (%)	**Benefit only**	53	**Benefit only**	71	**Both**	48
	Both	27	Both	23	Benefit only	28
	Risk only	10			Risk only	19
	Neither	10			Neither	5
Location	**USA**	32	**USA**	35	**USA**	19
	Greece	16	UK	14	Greece	17
	UK	16	Greece	10	UK	15
	USSR	5	Sweden	8	World	7
	Japan	5			Europe	5

a Percentage of corpus in the period; *n* = 356.
b Bold indicates highest frequency within phase.

Regulation, public policy and public opinion also begin to appear as themes in 1997, indicating a divergence of views within the media as to the future applications of biotechnology. The frequency of these new thematic categories increases in 1998. Cloning becomes the key theme discussed in the Greek press, followed by agrifoods, morality, biomedicine and regulation. By 1999, issues related to the agrifoods theme receive the most coverage (29 per cent), followed by regulation (16 per cent) and biomedicine (15 per cent).

Overall in Phase 3, a consistently high frequency of the agrifood theme is observed (24 per cent rising to 29 per cent in 1999). Cloning and biomedicine are also important themes, with regulation close behind, emerging for the first time in Phase 3. By 1999 there has been wide discussion of new technologies, their associated benefits, risks and potential applications. The public has a voice and regulation is updated. In addition, Phase 3 marks an increase in concern about the potential risks of

biotechnology (Table 3). The issues seen as carrying both benefits and risks have increased from 23 per cent in Phase 2, to 48 per cent in Phase 3. The risk-only variable has increased from 10 per cent in Phase 1, to 19 per cent in Phase 3. Issues considered as more risky in Phase 3 are concerned with: regulation, agrifood, public opinion and public policy, and morality. Those considered to bring more benefits are biomedicine, generic research, economics, genetic identity and cloning.

The topics covered by the Greek media in Phase 3 indicate a more international scope. New countries are entering the debate, but the USA remains the country linked most frequently with biotechnology stories (19 per cent) with Greece coming a close second with 17 per cent.

In Phase 3, the topic that triggered most attention in Greece and other countries was the production of GMOs in the form of crop plants and food. The debate focused on the underlying science, scientists themselves, industrial involvement, the market for

Table 3. Coverage of risks and benefits by theme in the Greek media

Theme	Risks and benefits (%)	Risk only (%)	Benefits only (%)	Neither (%)
Biomedical	41	2	57	0
Agrifood	41	36	17	6
Generic research	44	0	52	4
Economics	62	0	38	0
Moral	74	17	7	2
Public opinion	59	18	16	7
Regulation	47	39	5	10
Genetic identity	61	3	32	3
Cloning	58	14	24	4
Other	11	17	60	11

and marketing of the products, associated regulation and action of NGOs. Sources of information in the public domain varied from Greenpeace to the government and scientists. The discussion of these issues was concerned mainly with risks and benefits. Throughout Phase 3 the production of GMOs was highly controversial and met with some radical opposition. In the media emphasis was also given to public protest, with interest groups such as Greenpeace being mentioned most frequently.

Closer examination of the coverage of GMOs in Phase 3 indicates 43 per cent present GMOs as having only risks, 41 per cent present them as having both risks and benefits, and 9 per cent see only benefits. The risks mentioned vary, from potential short- and long-term risks to human health and to the environment. Some 62 per cent of these articles were framed within public account-ability, with calls for a slowdown in the pace of development of GMOs and concerns about industry and business profiting from producing or importing products from the USA.

Public perceptions

Eurobarometer data

The Greek Eurobarometer survey was undertaken by the KEME Foundation. There were 1012 inter-viewees in the survey. Paralleling the shift towards more negative media coverage in the last three years, the survey shows that public perceptions have also become more critical of biotechnology.

Biotechnology compared to other technologies

By comparison with other EU countries, Greeks are amongst the least optimistic about the contri-bution of technology to everyday life. Apart from telecommunications the Greeks are significantly below the European mean scores. On solar energy their limited optimism is surpassed only by Portugal and for nuclear power the Greeks are far and away the most pessimistic.

The Greek public have become more pessimistic about the new technologies than they were in the 1996 Eurobarometer survey. This is particular true of biotechnology; here optimism has declined from 30 per cent in 1996 to 19 per cent in 1999. In parallel, pessimism has increased from 19 per cent to 39 per cent. Thus for every optimist there are two pessimists (Table 4). These results place Greece at the bottom of the ranking of those who think that biotechnology 'will improve their way of life', and at the top of the ranking for those who think it 'will make things worse'.

Awareness and knowledge

Asked whether they had heard of seven applications of biotechnology before, a majority had heard of GM foods and of the cloning of animals, two of the most frequently covered applications of biotech-nology in the media. Interestingly, awareness of GM crops is low at 36 per cent, compared to the European mean of 63 per cent. It seems that the controversy over agrifoods has led to only a partial awareness of the production process. Taking all the seven applications into consideration, levels of awareness of biotechnology are at the lower end of the European ranking.

In terms of knowledge there is an interesting contrast between the textbook items and the image items in the Eurobarometer survey. On textbook knowledge the Greek mean score is only marginally lower than the European average. However, the

211

Table 4. Greek attitudes to new technologies

Technology	'Will improve our way of life' (%)		'Will have no effect' (%)		'Will make things worse' (%)	
	1996	1999	1996	1999	1996	1999
Solar energy	69.0	67.7	9.6	5.2	9.3	17.1
Information technology	74.8	70.7	2.9	7.2	13.0	12.5
Biotechnology	30.1	18.6	4.0	5.2	18.7	39.2
Telecommunications	86.3	70.5	3.2	20.9	4.8	2.6
New materials	51.8	46.0	7.3	7.7	16.2	22.6
Space exploration	56.4	49.7	13.1	15.3	11.7	16.6
Nuclear power		6.6		3.0		80.1
Internet		56.8		10.7		15.9

Greeks have the highest score in Europe for menacing images. For example, 51 per cent say that ordinary tomatoes do not have genes while GM ones do (the European overall figure is 31 per cent) and similarly a majority say that GM animals are always bigger.

Attitudes towards specific applications of biotechnology

Figure 2 shows the attitude of Greeks to seven applications of biotechnology. Genetic testing and medicines are widely supported. This is very similar to other European countries and also to the results of the previous surveys. The least supported application of biotechnology is GM foods which are seen as more risky than any of the other applications and perceived to be neither useful nor morally acceptable. Interestingly, Greeks consider GM foods to be less morally acceptable than either human cell or animal cloning.

Table 5 shows that amongst the 'decided public' from 1996 to 1999 there has been a major shift in opinion. Support and risk-tolerant support for GM foods has declined from 50 per cent to 19 per cent. At the same time opposition has grown from 50 per cent to 81 per cent. There has been a similar but less marked shift in attitudes towards GM crops, although here the risk-tolerant group is approximately the same size in 1999 as it was in 1996. The use of GMOs in medicine continues to have more supporters than opponents in 1999. However, there is a 20 per cent reduction in supporters between 1996 and 1999, with a corresponding increase in the opponents. In 1999 genetic testing remains well supported, by nearly three-quarters of the 'decided public' (i.e. those who expressed an opinion). It is interesting to note that in all categories of potential biotechnology applications, the risk-tolerant group was among the lowest when compared to other European countries. In addition,

Figure 2. Average evaluation of usefulness, risk, moral acceptability and willingness to encourage biotechnology applications in Greece

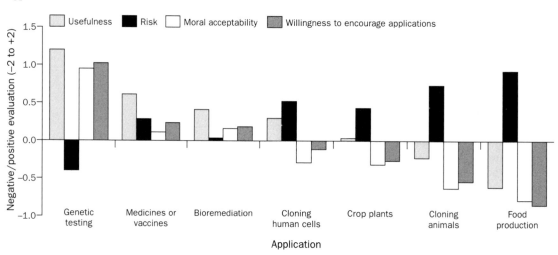

Table 5. Supporters, risk-tolerant supporters and opponents of biotechnology in Greece

	GM food (%)		GM crops (%)		Medicines (%)		Genetic testing (%)	
	1996	1999	1996	1999	1996	1999	1996	1999
Supporter	31.6	12.2	57.7	27.3	66.7	45.4	84.8	72.3
Risk-tolerant supporter	17.8	6.6	19.2	17.9	22.1	26.2	12.1	18.7
Opponent	50.5	81.2	23.2	54.7	11.3	28.4	3.1	8.9

Table 6. Trust in sources of information about biotechnology

Source	Greece (%)	EU average (%)
Consumer organisations	11.1	25.6
Environmental organisations	15.6	14.1
Animal welfare organisations	2.0	3.6
Medical profession	33.2	23.5
Farmers organisations	2.2	2.5
Religious organisations	6.5	1.9
National government bodies	5.2	2.7
International institutions	4.4	3.6
A particular industry	0.6	0.4
Universities	7.1	6.8
Television and newspapers	2.2	3.8
None of these (spontaneous)	6.4	5.7
Don't know	3.7	5.5

in areas of high concern, such as GM food and crops, the risk-tolerant group decreases. Taken in the context of the high scores on the image items, it appears that the Greeks have become increasingly risk averse and that the controversy over GM foods has spilled over into public perceptions of medical biotechnologies.

Risk beliefs

The questions about risk beliefs help to explain the overall judgements of the applications of biotechnology. In Greece 79 per cent, compared to the European average of 57 per cent agree, that 'if anything went wrong with GM foods it would be a global catastrophe'. Likewise 86 per cent see GM foods as 'fundamentally unnatural', and 72 per cent disagree that GM foods 'pose no dangers to future generations'. The strength of these beliefs about 'dread risks' are more pronounced in Greece than in many other European countries.

Trust and confidence

When asked whether they trust specific sources of information about biotechnology, the Greek public do not differ markedly from other Europeans (Table 6). However they do appear to trust the medical profession more than the European average, as well as religious organisations and government institutions. The Greek public find consumer organisations much less trustworthy than other Europeans. This may be explained by the fact that consumer organisations are almost non-existent in Greece. Greek trust in environmental organisations is around the European average. This relates to the high-profile role of environmental organisations in Greece in the last few years, and their contribution to the public debate.

Asked whether key actor groups in the area of biotechnology are doing a good or a bad job for society, the Greeks are well above the European average for most of the actors including medical doctors, newspapers, environmental groups, the government and the church. The one exception is industry for whom only 26 per cent said 'doing a good job' (one of the lowest scores in Europe), with 58 per cent saying 'doing a bad job' (the highest in Europe alongside Sweden). Given that environmental groups, the church and the press are in the opposition camp, it would appear that the biotechnology industry has a mountain to climb.

Conclusions

The Eurobarometer data, the media analysis and the developments in the policy arena, paint a picture of a generally negative environment for biotechnology in Greece. A number of factors have come together to contribute to the present situation. There is no home-grown industry to speak of and the government failed to take a positive lead early on. The NGO campaigns against GM foods, starting in 1997 were supported by an increasingly negative media. Partly in response, the government championed the moratorium on the commercial exploitation of GM crops. All the while public perceptions shifted to an increasingly critical stance. There is a relative lack of optimism about new technologies and while those who have been critical of agribiotechnology are held in high regard, industry is not. Support for GM foods has collapsed and this may have had a carry-over effect to some medical applications of biotechnology.

Address for correspondence

Dr George Sakellaris, National Hellenic Research Foundation, Institute of Biological Research and Biotechnology, Vassileos Constantinou 48, GR-11635 Athens, Greece. E-mail Gsak@eie.gr

Italy: from moral hazards to a cautious take on risks

Agnes Allansdottir, Sebastiano Bagnara, Laura Angotti and Lorenzo Montali

Biotechnology in the Italian public sphere – before the storm

In comparison to many other European countries, the public debate on biotechnology in Italy has been relatively slow to take off. Italy can be considered as a somewhat late entrant into the field of biotechnology, and there are some concerns that it lost an important opportunity for further developments. Up until the watershed, marked by the arrival on the media scene of Dolly the cloned sheep, biotechnology had been an issue of relatively low salience in the public arena. Initially, the issue of rDNA was met with bewilderment by the Italians and was associated with human reproduction and reproductive technologies, which had become highly sensitive social and political issues. After a period of optimism in the early 1980s, which had concentrated on the benefits brought about by the progress of the biotechnology industry, a public debate started that focused on national regulation of biotechnology and, in particular, the ethical and moral issues surrounding its intervention in life. Biotechnology was primarily framed by health benefits and moral hazards. The early 1990s saw a shift in the debate away from the national context, and policy activities were mostly orientated towards implementing European directives and following the European line on the future of biotechnology in general. By the end of 1996, there was a relatively low level of debate in Italy and research indicated that biotechnology was not a salient concern among the Italian public.[1] By the year 2000, the situation had clearly changed, and Italy had become one of the most 'actively cautious' of the European countries, often at odds with the European Community and the European Commission. This chapter attempts to delineate the main factors that caused such drastic shifts in the national debate on biotechnology.

The Italian take on the politics of life

Bioethics has always been an actively contested terrain by secular and religious groups in Italian politics, and this situation was exacerbated after the collapse of the reigning political party in the early 1990s.[2] After the demise of the Christian Democrats – historically the biggest political party in Italy – a series of smaller parties were formed that aligned either with the centre–left coalition or with the centre–right coalition who have been in power since spring 2001. The centre–left coalition, in power from 1996 to 2001, included and represented some of the newly formed Catholic parties, the Reformed Communist Party and the Green Party. As a consequence, the environmental perspective was given a strong political voice. Following tradition, the first Minister of Health in 1996 represented the Catholic point of view, whilst her successors represented more secular and pro-science perspectives.

The seeds of discontent

To some extent, the seeds of the Italian controversy over biotechnology were sown in the summer of 1996, by two unrelated issues that were later to characterise the debate over biotechnology in Italy. First there was the budding debate over food and agricultural applications of biotechnology, and second, there was the publication of a document on the juridical status of the embryo by the National Bioethics Committee (CNB).

That summer, environmental organisations, following other European sister organisations, launched what in Italy was a rather low-profile campaign protesting against the imminent arrival of GM soya in Europe. The national authority, the Minister of Health, was called upon to block the import of Monsanto soya under article 16 of the EC directive 90/220. This protest had little or no immediate outcome in terms of policy and the national media was somewhat indifferent to the issue. However, things were to change when the EU approved the import of Bt maize into Europe and the issues of Monsanto soya and Ciba-Geigy maize were fused into a common cause for concern.[3] The approval was met with criticism amidst accusations that the EC had given in to the pressures of industry and multinational companies at the expense of the wellbeing of citizens. Such critical voices grew stronger when the novel food directive was put in place in January 1997, reflecting a growing questioning of the capacity of the EU to adequately regulate biotechnology. This moment marked a shift in the framing of discussion of national regulation, from uncritically following and implementing decisions on a European level towards a more proactive national stance. There was some significant activity in the policy arena in this earlier period, for example in October 1996, the Scientific Committee on the Risks Deriving from the Use of Biological Agents published guidelines for ensuring safety in gene therapy, that had been produced by a working group of experts set up in 1995.

The second significant issue in the summer of 1996 was the publication of a document on the status of the embryo by National Bioethics Committee. The recommendations effectively advocated that the juridical status of a person should be given to the embryo at the moment of conception. The reactions from the more secular front were strong, exemplified by the Manifesto for Secular Bioethics launched by the financial daily paper, *il Sole24ore*, in June that year. The recommendations sparked off a political debate over the following months, in which it was not only the possibility of biomedical research that was at stake, but there were also strong links to abortion, a topic that has always been a sensitive political issue in Italy. To date there is no national regulation of reproductive technologies as there has been no conclusive political consensus on the issue. In its place there is only a circular issued from the Ministry of Health in 1994 and a number of deontological codes of practice from medical associations.

Dolly sounds the alarm

Early 1997 clearly marked a turning point in this debate, when the announcement of the existence of a healthy cloned sheep named Dolly acted as a catalyst and had reverberations that were both profound and diffused. The possibility of a cloned sheep paving the way for human cloning made the lack of national regulation of reproductive technology intolerable.[4] Debates in parliament followed and several bills on reproductive technologies were put forward. During question time in parliament, the Minister for Health announced a ministerial decree on 5 March banning all forms of experimentation relating to human and animal cloning. The National Bioethics Committee swiftly reported back to the Minister for Health on 25 March.

Initially the ministerial decree banned all forms of cloning, both animal and human, but successive re-enactments became less stringent allowing animal cloning in exceptional circumstances, for example where there is a clear and demonstrable health benefit to humans, or where it might save a species from extinction. However, any kind of experiment relating to cloning of human cells is still banned by ministerial order, which must be re-enacted every three months in anticipation of future national regulations of reproductive technologies.

Hard on the heels of Dolly, the debate over the use of biotechnology in agriculture and food production began to gain momentum. On the advice of the Ministry for the Environment, in the hands of the Green Party, the Minister of Health issued a decree on 4 March banning the cultivation, but not the import, of Bt maize in Italy, bringing Italy in line with Austria and Luxembourg. The ban on cultivation was re-enacted once and then abolished in light of the recommendation of the European Commission in September 1997, and of Novartis's decision to implement a large-scale monitoring plan.

The following months saw increased activity in the policy arena. The Ministry for Agricultural and Forestry Resources initiated a review of biotechnology and agricultural policy after the parliamentary committee for social affairs approved a resolution calling upon the government to block the import of GM soya and maize into Italy, and to provide compulsory labelling in order to guarantee consumers' rights. It reported back to parliament for the first time in October 1997 and strongly advocated a cautious approach, appealing to the protection of national agricultural traditions and national biodiversity.

In September 1997, the Scientific Committee on the Risks Deriving from the Use of Biological Agents, set up in 1992, became the National Commission for Biotechnology and Biosafety (CNBB). Its mandate has been renewed and substantially enlarged in order to encompass the coordination and surveillance of national biotechnology initiatives and activities, and to ease collaboration with the private sector as well as ensuring that the Italian public are kept informed of developments. It has been organised into expert working groups on different aspects of biotechnology, and the overall outcome has been a greater degree of oversight and coordination of both activity and regulation in Italy.

Activities in the arena of formal policy-making were mirrored by growing movements of resistance. In November 1997, a coalition of NGOs called upon Romano Prodi, the then prime minister, not only to suspend all field trials involving GM crops, but also to reopen the debate over intellectual property rights. Table 1 gives an overview of policy developments in Italy.

Getting ready for action

In early 1998, biotechnology was firmly on the Italian agenda with notable developments in terms of business and industry, as illustrated by Novartis's announcement that Italy would become a strategic country for their activities in the biotechnology sector. Up until that moment, it was widely believed that biotechnology in Italy was lagging behind other European countries. The first sustained attempts to promote biotechnology were met with large-scale and organised opposition to gene technology, promoted mostly by the environmental organisations Greenpeace Italia and Lega Antivivisezione. At that

Table 1. Key policy events in Italy, 1996–2000

Date	Trigger	Event	Outcome
June 1996 onwards	Embryo debate	National Bioethics Committee publishes a document on the juridical status of the embryo.	Political debate over embryo research reopens debate over the lack of national regulation of reproductive technologies.
Autumn 1996	Imminent soya imports	First soya imports from the USA give rise to low-key opposition campaign.	The effects are not really felt until the following year.
February 1997	Dolly the sheep	The cloned sheep sends shockwaves through Italian society, not least because there is a long history of policy-makers never reaching a consensus on the thorny issue of reproductive technologies.	The Minister of Health issues a ministerial decree on 5 March banning all forms of experimentation relating to human and animal cloning. The ban has been re-enacted every three months since then, whilst awaiting new regulation of reproductive technologies.
March 1997	Bt maize	The Minister of Health finally heeds warnings and calls from environmental minister over concerns about GM in agriculture.	Italy bans cultivation of Bt maize with a ministerial decree.
April 1997 onwards	Debate on GM food and agriculture	The Ministry for Agricultural and Forestry Resources initiates a review of biotechnology and agricultural policy after the parliamentary committee for social affairs approved a resolution calling upon the government to block the import of GM soya and maize into Italy, and to provide compulsory labelling in order to guarantee consumers' rights.	A report to parliament in October 1997 strongly advocates a cautious approach.
September 1997	Debate on adequacy of regulation and monitoring	The Committee on Risks Derived from Biological Agents becomes the National Committee for Biotechnology and Biosafety with a substantially widened mandate.	More effective coordination and oversight of biotechnology activities in Italy.
March 1998	Directive on property intellectual rights	In March the senate calls upon the government to reopen the patent debate and to resist the implementation of the 98/44 directive.	The Italian government joins the Dutch initiative that calls into question formal aspects of the 98/44 directive.
June 1999	Proposal for a moratorium on GMOs at G8 meeting in Cologne	Italy joins Denmark and Luxembourg in support of the French–Greek unsuccessful call for a moratorium on GM food an the G8 summit. Government reaches an agreement over the implementation of the patenting directive.	The Minister for the Environment refuses to sign, and proposes a national moratorium.
Winter 1999–2000	Furore over GM food	Increased localisation or regionalisation of the debate; some municipalities declare themselves 'GM-free' zones. Retail chains announce plans to go 'GM free'.	The government temporarily suspends seven GM products in December 1999.

moment, the opposition groups joined forces and their efforts were given further visibility with the help of well-known public figures such as Dario Fo, the Noble prizewinner for literature. The voices of the opposition took a generalised stance of rejection towards the most prominent aspects of biotechnology, cloning, GM food, agricultural applications and intellectual property rights, fusing them into one. Campaigns coincided with various forms of protest and resistance.

In March 1998, the senate approved a rather radical resolution calling upon the government to actively engage in blocking the EU patenting directive until it had been radically revised, and to adopt effective monitoring and controls over GM production. It also called for the launch of a public information campaign and for the clear labelling of any foodstuff derived from the use of GMOs. The resolution appealed for the safeguarding of traditional Italian agriculture and food production, for example by preventing national agriculture from becoming dependent upon multinational companies through their introduction of GM seeds.

Active caution and occasional resistance

Since 1992, national regulation had been characterised by the following of European regulation, and this was still the case in 1996. However, around the watershed, Italy began to take an increasingly proactive stance. First, the debate over soya and maize was interpreted as the EC yielding to the pressures of multinationals at the expense of the wellbeing of its citizens. Second, the patenting directive had been a sensitive issue for a long time in Italy and in 1998 a more cautious approach was called for. There was a growing sense of unease over the reflection of Italian interests and viewpoints at a more global level of policy-making. At a time when the country had, to an extent, become politically stronger at the European level following institutional and fiscal reforms.

In July 1999, the Cabinet approved the patenting directive, despite the strong opposition of the Minister of Environment. However, at the time of writing, it has yet to be put before parliament. The Minister of the Environment, together with the Ministers for EU Policies, Agriculture and Health, signed a document calling upon the government to adopt the precautionary principle with regards to cloning, patenting and the labelling of processes. They also called for a moratorium on field experiments and cultivation of GM crops, and for the promotion of high-quality traditional agriculture

instead. At the G8 summit in Cologne, Italy, together with Denmark and Luxembourg, joined the French–Greek initiative calling for a moratorium on GM releases. The meeting coincided with the first real food scares in Italy, triggered by stories of dioxin-containing chicken in Belgium in the summer of 1999. In that context, it was repeatedly claimed that monitoring and control over food production in Italy was more stringent than in other European countries.

The issue of food safety was repeatedly framed by appeals to tradition. In recent years traditional food and wine have gained increasing cultural value in Italy, perhaps best exemplified in the 'slow food' movement. The focus has not only shifted from an international or European level to a national one, but has also become increasingly localised with some of the Italian regions and municipalities forming a coalition of GMO-free zones whilst they wait for new regulations. Traditional food products have become an increasingly valuable commodity, as is made clear by the boost in the markets of local produce. Some of the leading food retailers and supermarket chains have also announced their decision to ensure that their own-brand products are GM free. Both the opposition to and the perplexities about the use of GM in agriculture tend to focus on the products themselves and their potential health risks, whilst the environmental aspects cause less concern. Nevertheless, in December 1999 the Italian government temporarily suspended trials of GM crops and halted commercialisation of GM products already on the market.

Although the year 1999 was to a large extent dominated by the issues of GM food and agriculture, there were some further developments with regard to medical applications. In July, the CNBB set up a working group on xenotransplantation and related risk assessment, and in November supported the Council of Europe's call for a moratorium on xenotransplantation in the absence of adequate risk assessment. The debate over xenotransplantation in Italy has at times been an interesting story of shifts and tensions between discourses of morals and risks and the institutions that deal with those respective discourses.

In addition to xenotransplantation, both the National Commission for Biotechnology and Biosafety and the National Bioethics Commission have issued guidelines on genetic testing, an area that is generally understood to be rather adequately regulated, for example by the Privacy Bill which covers some of the key aspects. Similarly, forensic use of DNA research is favourably regarded. Finally, in an attempt to promote research collaboration with industry, the National Commission for Biotechnology and Biosafety made public the new national plan for development of biotechnology in Italy in August 1999.

The year 2000 saw further controversies with some attempts to promote biotechnology on one hand and rising organised resistance on the other. A biotechnology trade fair in Genoa was considered to be a failure after protests by opponents of biotechnology and the anti-globalisation movement. More recently, the debate in Italy appears to be taking another turn, particularly as regards stem-cell cloning. In early 2001 scientists took to the streets of Rome protesting about the state of Italian science, lack of funds and the slowness of institutional reforms. In particular, concerns are currently being raised over the freedom of scientists to carry out research, which is seen by some as being hampered by religious concerns.

The 'Italian Way' of stem-cell cloning is emblematic. When discussions about the feasibility of stem-cell cloning arose, the Minister of Health set up an *ad hoc* expert commission which recommended harvesting stem cells from adult tissue rather than from embryos. The scientific or technical viability of this technique is still not clear, but it would probably be considered as ethically sound if the thorny issue of the use, and in particular the creation of embryos for research, was bypassed. The Vatican is against the creation of embryos for harvesting stem cells. However, this does not mean that the Vatican is generally against biotechnology, in fact the opposite has often been the case. For example, the Vatican is in favour of xenotransplantation on grounds of its potential to save lives that may otherwise be threatened by the shortage of suitable human organs for transplantation. Similarly, the Accademia Pontificia della Vita is in favour of applying biotechnology in agriculture and food production as a possible way to relieve world hunger.

Media coverage

The Italian media landscape is largely dominated by television. Traditionally, newspaper readership is rather low, with a marked preference for local or regional papers. There is no daily tabloid press in Italy, but the national dailies do comprise styles and features that in some other countries might approximate the more popular press. Currently 52 daily newspapers are published in Italy, and of them *il Corriere della Sera* has the highest circulation.[5] At

times the Rome-based and slightly more left-wing alternative opinion leader, *la Repubblica*, attempts to close the gap. Traditionally, all Italian media propagate particular points of view and *Corriere della Sera* is located around the centre of the political spectrum. The paper is sometimes seen as tending towards the perspective from Milan, the country's financial and industrial capital.[6]

A surge in media coverage

Before the storm, Italian press coverage of biotechnology was rather less intense than in some other European countries where the onset of debate was earlier. Our longitudinal monitoring of coverage between 1973 and 1996 shows clear and distinct phases both in terms of intensity of attention and in the content of coverage. The 1970s saw some bewilderment, but by the early 1980s there was optimism fuelled by the potential of industrial opportunities, although later somewhat marred by moral and environmental concerns. In 1992 representations of biotechnology in the Italian press entered a new phase.[7] The scene clearly changed when Dolly the cloned sheep suddenly appeared on the international media scene.[8] The rise in intensity of coverage of biotechnology after this is striking and has remained high ever since (Figure 1).

The index of intensity of media coverage of biotechnology was constructed using a set of keywords and the search engines of the online electronic archives of *Corriere della Sera*. Each article could be retrieved under more than one keyword, therefore when constructing the index an article was counted once.[9] This index can be taken as a proxy for media coverage in general, and also as an indicator of the salience of the issue on the public agenda. The index gives no indication as to the content and tone of the actual coverage. To analyse the content of the media debate, a random sample of 200 articles per year was drawn from a list of headlines of all the articles relating to biotechnology that were published by *Corriere della Sera* from 1997 to 1999. The sample of 600 articles was subsequently analysed. Each article was could be coded as being dedicated primarily to biotechnology, as a story that included biotechnology, or as a story where there was only a passing reference to or metaphoric mentioning of biotechnology or its associated keywords. The proportion of articles in this last category has greatly increased in recent years. This might be interpreted as evidence of a wider diffusion of the relevant terminology that has

Figure 1. *Intensity of articles in the Italian press, 1973–99*

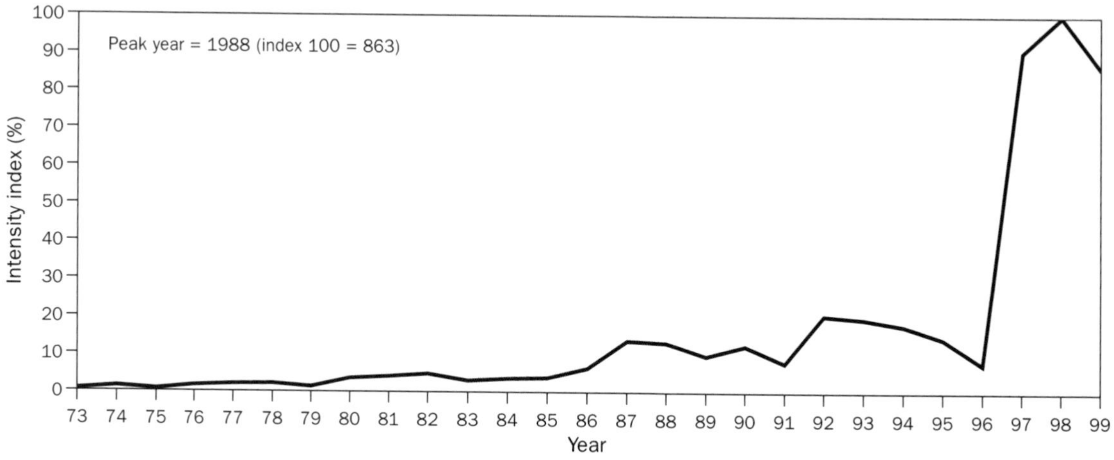

by now become a part of everyday language and has connotations far removed from any scientific notion of what biotechnology might entail. As an example, the language of genetic modification is at times used to talk about politics and political parties, and to describe the characteristics of high-profile football teams. The articles that made only a passing reference to biotechnology, or any of the other keywords we searched for, were excluded from the analysis presented in this chapter.

Changing frames and representations

Comparing the content of press coverage of biotechnology over the last three years with the previous phase clearly indicates a change. A more detailed examination of the key categories of analysis within single years led us to regard 1997 and 1998 as a phase of transition, while the parameters changed sufficiently to regard 1999 as a separate phase. The analysis is summarised in Table 2.

The term 'frame' refers to the overall or dominant framing of the discourse in the articles analysed, and might be conceptualised as a container within which the diverse themes of biotechnology can be discussed. In other words, frames set the boundaries of the discourse. In general terms, biotechnology in the Italian press tends to be framed in terms of 'progress'. It is commonly claimed that ethical framing dominates discussions and representations of biotechnology in Italy, but our analysis indicates that actually ethical framing is clearly retreating. At the same time, economic framing has become more prominent, echoing the early 1980s. A framing of unforeseeable

consequences and forces unleashed, as represented by the myth of Pandora's box, is steadily rising; an interesting return to the debate in the 1970s.

From 1973 to 1996, Italian press coverage of biotechnology was dominated by biomedical themes, comprising a third of all themes discussed between 1992 and 1996. After Dolly, the genetic identity theme became more salient and even more prominent than biomedical themes, accounting for a quarter of all themes in the transition phase of 1997–98. By 1999, the relevance of themes altered as agriculture and food were in the spotlight along with 'public opinion and policies'. In other words, the changes in the predominance of themes are even more marked than the changes in overall framing of discourse. There are interesting parallels in those shifts as the moral theme, previously of rather high salience in the Italian media representations, had practically disappeared by 1999, mirroring the decline in ethical framing of the discussions. Beyond the relevant salience of themes, the associations between themes are worth considering. A telling finding is that in the first wave, 73 per cent of moral themes were associated with biomedicine, but only 20 per cent in 1999, indicating diminishing concerns over moral hazards. In the wave of coverage before the watershed, the theme of regulation was associated mostly with biomedicine (48 per cent compared to 26 per cent in 1999), but by 1999 regulation was discussed in relation to themes of food and agriculture, as were themes of public opinion and policies. A more political representation was clearly gaining ground over biomedical science.

Table 2. Italian media profile, 1992–99 (threshold for inclusion: 5 per cent)

Phase	1992–96		1997–98		1999	
Frequency (%)[a]	20		51		29	
Frame (%)	**Progress**[b]	55	**Progress**	70	**Progress**	58
	Ethics	12	Ethics	10	Economic prospects	17
	Nature/nurture	11	Economic prospects	6	Pandora's box	13
	Pandora's box	8	Nature/nurture	5	Ethics	5
	Economic prospects	8	Pandora's box	5		
Theme (%)[c]	**Biomedical**	34	**Genetic identity**	25	**Agrifood**	21
	Agrifood	19	Biomedical	18	Public opinion/policy	18
	Moral	12	Cloning	12	Genetic identity	17
	Genetic identity	11	Agrifood	12	Biomedical	16
	Public opinion/policy	8	Public opinion/policy	11	Regulation	11
	Regulation	8	Genetic research	6	Cloning	6
	Economic	5	Moral	6		
Actor (%)	**Science**[d]	43	**Science**	40	**Science**	36
	Business	17	Politics	36	Politics	34
	Politics	12	Business	6	Business	9
	Media	11	Media	5	Interest groups	8
					Media	7
Location (%)	**USA**	41	**Italy**	46	**Italy**	53
	Other Europe	26	USA	23	USA	18
	Italy	25	Other Europe	16	Other Europe	17
Benefit/risk (%)	**Both**	51	**Benefit only**	45	**Benefit only**	42
	Benefit only	36	Neither	22	Neither	27
	Risk only	11	Both	20	Both	17
			Risk only	13	Risk only	14
Benefit actor (%)			**Science**	52	**Science**	48
			Politics	27	Politics	36
			Business	10	Business	9
Risk actor (%)			**Science**	53	**Science**	39
			Business	16	Business	34
			Politics	14	Politics	16
Benefit type (%)[e]	**Health**	43	**Research**	29	**Legal**	28
	Economic	16	Health	26	Research	25
	Research	16	Legal	22	Health	23
	Social equality	7	Economic	7	Economic	12
					Environment	6
Risk type (%)	**Moral**	41	**Moral**	45	**Health**	42
	Environment	16	Health	23	Moral	23
	Social equality	16	Environment	9	Environment	23
	Health	12	Research	8		

a Percentage of corpus; total *n* = 502.
b Bold indicates highest frequency within phase.
c Results from response counting (i.e. more than one variable may be coded per article).
d Results from response counting for 1992–96.
e Results from response counting for types of benefits and risks.

The overall frames and themes of discussion cannot be separated from the main actors in the debate. From 1973 onwards, scientific actors were clearly the protagonists but their role as has steadily weakened and their place is increasingly being occupied by political actors who, from 1997, have been almost as visible as scientists (Table 2). As the media debate changed in 1999 other actors, most notably interest groups, have entered the scene.

The location of the action being reported is an interesting indicator of change, with the media gaze displaying an increasingly national focus – from a quarter of all locations in the years before the watershed, to up to over half of all locations in 1999. Hence, the focus shifted from elsewhere (mostly the USA and Europe) to Italy as biotechnology became a pressing national issue.

Hopes and fears or normalisation

Biotechnology is often represented by hopes of benefits and fears of costs or risks. Before the watershed, half of all articles carried risk and benefit arguments, while in later years over 40 per cent of articles carried only benefit arguments; moreover, the proportion of articles mentioning no consequences, neither risk nor benefit, rose drastically up to 27 per cent in 1999. These findings might look somewhat odd in the context of a growing debate and controversy. The most plausible explanation is that the turning point of the debate has broadened the scope of press attention to biotechnology, as well as lowering the threshold of media coverage of the issue. Therefore, it stands to reason that a random sample of articles from recent press coverage is more likely to include some kinds of articles that would not have found their way into newspapers in earlier times.

Risk and benefit arguments in the media can be interpreted as indicators of basic values, through the dreaded or desired outcomes of actions that are reported in the narrative. Before the watershed, both medical applications and food and agricultural applications were most closely associated with risk and benefit arguments. However, by 1999 medical applications were associated either with a 'benefit only' argument, or with a 'neither risk nor benefit' argument. At the same time, food and agricultural applications were increasingly associated with risk arguments.

Media stories tend to attribute blame and praise to social actors. Our analysis of the media coverage shows that reported risks are now increasingly attributed to industrial or business actors, whereas those who are considered to bring benefits are increasingly political actors; at the same time, the proportion of scientists seen to bring benefits is declining (Table 2). It is evident that the actors responsible are linked to the kinds of consequences they bring about.

The consequences of biotechnology in the Italian press used to be reported in terms of opposition between health benefits and moral hazards. After 1997, benefits in terms of scientific research overtook health, and increasingly the consequences were framed in terms of legal benefits. In contrast, when it comes to visions of negative consequences of biotechnology, health risks have become much more prominent, and by 1999 were the most frequently mentioned types of risks. At the same time, while the moral hazards have halved, there is now more concern over environmental impacts. This corresponds to the decline in the ethical framing of the debate and the decreased importance of the moral themes. In general, it may be said that medical applications are increasingly associated with health benefits, some moral hazards and benefits for research enterprise, whilst agrifood applications are associated with economic gain and threats to health.

Table 3 shows a sharp rise in the frequencies of associations between the themes of food and agriculture and the presence of controversy in the article. Although the overall proportion of the reporting of or mentioning of controversies remains quite stable over time, biomedical themes are increasingly represented as being non-controversial. These findings indicate a process of normalisation and acceptance of medical applications, and a growing controversy over food and agriculture: a useful reminder about the caveats that should be used when talking about press coverage of biotechnology in general.

The increasingly controversial coverage of food applications of biotechnology has not dented positive coverage of medical applications of biotechnology, and if anything our research suggests the contrary: biomedical applications of biotechnology seem to be enjoying an increasingly favourable press coverage in Italy. In our view, the analysis of coverage in *Corriere della Sera* is indicative and converges with how the debate has evolved and unfolded in other national media. Attention has certainly become more intense, and the central and rather balanced position of the paper analysed in our research might therefore reflect the overall trends and tones of the media debate.

Table 3. Controversy in articles on biotechnology

	Biomedical themes (%)	**Agrifood themes (%)**	**Overall presence of controversy (%)**
1992–96	50.3	28.7	46.0
1997–98	52.6	52.9	48.8
1999	33.3	70.0	48.3

Public perceptions

The perceptions, hopes and concerns over biotechnology amongst the Italians have been explored using both quantitative and qualitative approaches. The latest Eurobarometer survey, fielded in November 1999, used a stratified and statistically significant random sample of the Italian population to interview 1005 respondents. This section reports on the results from the latest Eurobarometer survey in Italy, comparing and contrasting with earlier surveys. The key findings are then contextualised through a more qualitative inquiry. A series of six focus-group discussions were carried out between September and December 1999, to explore better the dimensions of public concerns without the constraints imposed by survey research.[10]

Declining enthusiasm and rising scepticism

In general terms, public perception of biotechnology in Italy has become more negative in recent years. The term 'biotechnology' has lost some of its positive connotations: in 1999, 42 per cent of the Italian sample believed that biotechnology would improve their way of life in the next 20 years, compared to 59 per cent in 1996. It is perhaps more indicative that in 1999, 27 per cent of the Italian respondents said that biotechnology would make things worse, compared to a mere 10 per cent in 1996. Given a list of new technologies, such changes occur only for biotechnology and genetic engineering. Only Greece, Denmark, Norway and Austria show a greater proportion of

opponents or sceptics among the general public than Italy. The term 'biotechnology' might carry multiple semantic connotations, but our qualitative research suggests that the primary anchors are cloning, exemplified by Dolly, and GM food. In contrast, in public discussions just before the watershed, the primary anchors tended to be biomedical themes.

Given the growing debate and a dramatic explosion of press coverage from 1996 to 1999, it is a somewhat surprising finding that the proportion of Italians who had never talked about biotechnology before their interview had not really changed from 1996 to 1999 (58 per cent in 1996 compared to 56 per cent in 1999). In other words biotechnology does not seem to be a topic of conversation for half of the Italian public. In a separate set of questions, respondents were asked whether they had previously heard of each of seven applications of biotechnology. With regards to the numbers of applications they had previously heard of, Italians are close to the European average. The best known applications are GM food (69 per cent, slightly below the European average) and animal cloning, mostly as associated with Dolly (62 per cent had heard of this application compared to an average of 57 per cent of Europeans). Only 26 per cent of the Italian respondents had heard of bioremediation using GM bacteria.

Differentiation of applications

Italian public perceptions of different applications of biotechnology are clearly differentiated.

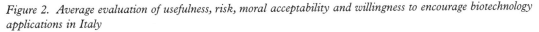

Figure 2. Average evaluation of usefulness, risk, moral acceptability and willingness to encourage biotechnology applications in Italy

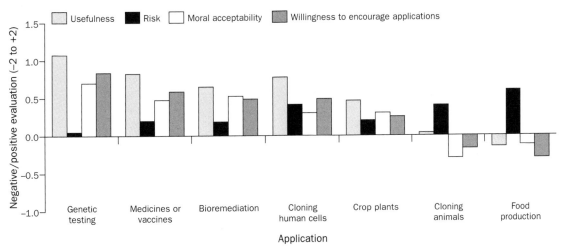

Respondents in the Eurobarometer survey were asked whether they thought each of seven applications of biotechnology was useful for society, risky for society, morally acceptable and whether the applications in question should be encouraged (Figure 2).

The Italians are clearly in favour of medical applications. Genetic testing for heritable diseases such as thalassaemia is strongly supported, perceived as being useful, not associated with risk and is morally acceptable. The same pattern of perceptions holds for other medical applications too, such as vaccines where the benefits are clear, the risks are low and there are no moral obstacles; consequently, the level of encouragement for this application is high. The Italians reject both cloning of animals and, in particular, GM food; both applications are seen as morally questionable and are perceived as carrying risks for society. The perceived benefits of animal cloning are seen as slight and GM food is seen as pointless.

The findings from qualitative inquiry into public concerns add interesting dimensions to these findings. In discussion with members of the public, GM food is largely portrayed as a pointless addition to an already satisfying food market: 'We all share the same experience of food that has never given any trouble why go and change the taste of food or make the tomato more nutritious? We don't need it.' A recurrent theme in discussions is that GM food, associated with multinationals and an American way of life, is a menace to the cultural traditions of the country. Italians are rather traditional consumers who value their culinary traditions highly. Indeed the results of the survey show that the willingness to consume GM products is low in Italy (0.74 on a four-point scale, compared to the European average of 0.94) and is close to the most sceptical European countries of Greece, Norway and Austria.

Few say they would buy GM fruit (19 per cent) or GM cooking oil (17 per cent) if it tasted better, and in discussions the following statement about being a potential consumer of GM products was quite typical: 'Well, maybe after at least 20 years, when I can be sure that nothing will happen to me.' In particular, doubts are raised over the adequacy of current risk and safety assessments, since adverse effects might be delayed and the form that they take may be hard to predict. They are therefore untestable within such a short time span. Such unknown risks tend to be unacceptable in the absence of clear benefits: 'Maybe growing tumours, maybe other chronic diseases that nobody can even

imagine, deranged DNA, who knows?' This is a recurrent theme across differing social groups and across the country. This does not mean that the Italian public demands a risk-free world, rather that public concerns over risk might not always match the framing of risk proposed by the authorities. Such arguments might be embedded in ancient cultural ideas, for example about food and contagion that have been further reinforced by popular understanding of medicine and diseases. The fact remains that such concerns cannot simply be dismissed as erroneous. The public is also quick to make links to BSE and other related issues.

These points become more evident when comparing public perceptions of animal cloning with the cloning of human cells for therapeutic purposes (see Figure 2). The public does not reject the technique of cloning, in fact support for cloning of human cells is rather high. It is seen to be morally acceptable and, although there are some perceived risks, the benefits to human wellbeing are seen to be sufficient to justify these risks. Similarly, the cloning of animals is also perceived as risky, but in sharp contrast, its benefits seem unclear and fraught with moral questions. In discussions with the public, the cloning of Dolly was perceived as an example of scientists 'playing God' and the transgression of natural boundaries risking dire consequences. Morals and risks might be separate expert domains, but in the public mind they overlap and interact, and sometimes morals are deployed as buffers against risks: 'There is no need for violence against nature, nature should be respected.... Man tickles nature, tickle today and tickle tomorrow, at some point nature will rebel.'

The distinguishing feature which makes the Italians stand out together with Spain, Portugal and the Netherlands is their acceptance of GM crops in contrast to GM food. The differentiation between applications becomes more evident when comparing levels of support or rejection for single applications (Table 4). Of the respondents who took a position, twice as many are in favour of genetic testing as those in favour of GM food. Furthermore, the opponents outnumber the supporters for the two most prominent applications, GM food and animal cloning.

Shifts in public opinion from 1996 to 1999

Four of the seven applications used in the 1999 Eurobarometer were carried over from the 1996 survey and provide a good basis for time-series comparisons. However, because there were some

Table 4. Levels of encouragement of different applications

	GM food	*Cloning animals*	*Crop plants*	*Bioremedi- ation*	*Cloning human cells*	*Medicines*	*Genetic testing*
Encourage (%)	32	34	48	49	55	58	65
Discourage (%)	54	39	25	17	19	17	11
'Decided' (%)	76	73	73	66	74	75	76

changes in the ways that the questions were asked in the two surveys, and because the 1999 survey included the filter question, 'Have you heard of ...?' before each question, the proportion of 'don't know' answers has risen. To overcome this problem it was decided in all countries to use only those respondents who replied to the questions about utility, risk, moral acceptability and encouragement of the seven applications; these respondents are referred to as the 'decided public'.

Between 1996 and 1999 there was a decline in those categorised as straightforward supporters of GM food, and at the same time the proportion of opponents grew drastically (Table 5). However, this was less so for GM crops. There has not been a corresponding rise in opposition to medicines and genetic testing, and the proportion of those who now recognise the potential risks seem willing to accept them. Thus, slightly dented support for medical applications has not been substituted by rejection, but by support through the awareness and acceptance of the perceived risks. Similarly, there is slightly more risk-tolerant support for GM crops, but no changes when it comes to GM food. For medical applications, the risks might be acceptable when the benefits are evident, but the same cannot be said about GM food.

Unease and diffidence

In general, Europeans feel insufficiently informed about modern biotechnology (82 per cent). Notwithstanding all the reservations expressed, 72 per cent of Italian respondents say they feel insufficiently informed. Those figures are still high, but it is interesting to note that this puts Italy close to the Netherlands and Portugal, countries where public opinion is on average more favourable than in Italy. Qualitative inquiry reveals a profound sense of uncertainty and lack of knowledge about modern biotechnology and all our focus groups felt the need for more transparency and to be kept informed.

It is not clear to whom the public might turn in search of further information, or who they would trust to tell the truth about biotechnology. Consumer organisations came highest in the list of trusted actors, with 29 per cent of respondents saying they would trust them to tell the truth. This is higher than the European average of 23 per cent. Next, the medical profession was indicated as a source of truth by 20 per cent of respondents, slightly lower than the European average of 24 per cent. Environmental associations came third with 13 per cent, which is slightly lower than the EU average of 15 per cent. Finally, only 2.4 per cent of respondents named national governmental bodies as a trusted source, a finding that is common across Europe.

The Italians seem somewhat reluctant to bestow trust upon social actors. The 1999 survey included a series of questions asking whether certain actors were thought to be 'doing a good job for society or not', as a proxy measure for trust. In general, fewer Italians seemed willing to agree with statements that actors are 'doing a good job', but interestingly

Table 5. Changes in public support between 1996 and 1999

	GM food (%)		*Crop plants (%)*		*Medicines (%)*		*Genetic testing (%)*	
	1996	**1999**	**1996**	**1999**	**1996**	**1999**	**1996**	**1999**
Supporter	29.5	18.7	50.8	38.1	48.1	36.2	55.1	45.3
Risk-tolerant supporter	31.3	30.7	35.0	39.7	43.2	52.3	42.1	49.7
Opponent	39.3	50.6	14.3	22.2	8.7	11.5	2.7	4.9
'Decided'[a]	52.9	44.8	63.0	43.9	60.6	48.2	69.1	53.6

a Percentage of 'decided' respondents for each application 1996 and 1999.

differences for 'not doing a good job' were much weaker. In this regard the Italians appear to be sceptical. Unsurprisingly, medical doctors are seen as doing a good job, but at 57 per cent, this is substantially lower than the EU average of 72 per cent. Medical doctors are closely followed by consumer organisations at 56 per cent, but again this is drastically lower than the EU average of 73 per cent. Shops are in third place at 52 per cent, compared to the EU level of 61 per cent. Clearly the efforts of some of the major retail chains to ensure that their own-brand products are GM free has enhanced their image. If retailers and consumer organisations are seen as being on the side of the public, industry is increasingly seen as the adversary, with only 21 per cent of respondents believing that they are doing a good job and 40 per cent stating that they are not (although 39 per cent said they didn't know). The government fares somewhat better than industry, with 37 per cent supporting the job its doing, compared to 28 per cent that disagree (again, 35 per cent were unsure).

The picture that emerges resonates with findings for focus-group discussions. The public are in general sceptical and cautious. Consumer organisations are perceived as signalling problems and defending the public. In a way, their credibility is grounded in their lack of real power and the absence of economic interests. This is in opposition to perceptions of industry, and in particular of multinationals, who are seen as being somewhat too powerful in this 'mad economy'. There is some diffused unease over the perceived lack of sensitivity towards public sentiment. Such concerns are repeatedly linked to themes of things moving too fast and developing out of control.

The Italians tend to be somewhat more cautious than the average European: 47 per cent agree that cloning animals should be introduced more gradually and 50 per cent say the same about GM food. In particular, 61 per cent of Italians believe that if something went wrong with GM food, the consequences would be catastrophic. Thus, in summary, the Italian public is not against science and technology but is simply cautious: 'Science cannot stop, it cannot be blocked, but science should transform without destroying.'

What lies ahead?

Four years ago biotechnology was just beginning to enter the public arena in Italy, but by the year 2000 Italy had become one of the countries most opposed to biotechnology in Europe, in particular in the

areas of agriculture and food production. This has been evident in terms of policy activities as well as in growing public opposition that cannot merely be blamed on ignorance. Further, the controversy and cautious stance cannot simply be attributed to religious or moral concerns. On the contrary, the moral framing of the debate has given way to a more secular orientation towards risks. This is evident in both the media debate and in how the debate has evolved and unfolded in the political arena. The debate over GM food has taken on strong connotations concerning the defence of culture and identity, while for the public at large the environmental impact of biotechnology is simply of less concern.

In recent years, the role of moral issues has declined, whilst the framing of issues in terms of safety and risk has gained more salience. This might also be due to changes in the semantic connotations of those key terms of the public debate where the discourses of risk have been broadened to enable a more ethically flavoured framing than before. Although framing in terms of risk and safety does not carry the same kind of political controversy as moral threats, policy-makers should still be aware that there is often a substantial gap between expert or scientific framing of risks and safety and the public's formulation of the same issues.

The public is still rather confused about existing regulation, which is no surprise given the fact that there is still no national regulation of reproductive technologies, due to the difficulties of reaching a clear political consensus on those issues. Italians tend to be conservative and to favour traditional products, in particular when it comes to food, and our research indicates a deep unease and diffused scepticism amongst the general public about futile products being thrust upon them.

Those political parties campaigning against GM products, such as the Green Party, and those who have campaigned for the freedom of research, such as the Radical Party, have both been instrumental in bringing biotechnology on to the public agenda. However, neither were rewarded in terms of numbers of votes in the recent general elections. Nevertheless, science has remained on the political agenda, and concerns over the general state and future of science in Italy have fused with the debate on biotechnology. This has been the case with regards to GM food, but perhaps more importantly, with regards to biomedical research. Only the future will show whether the present administration can effectively implement the institutional reforms necessary to enhance the national science base that were set in train by the previous administration. Since the centre–right gained a majority in the elections of spring 2001, things might well be set to change. Indeed, at the time of concluding this chapter, the government led by Silvio Berlusconi has confirmed its intention of reversing the previous government's blanket opposition to GM crops and to encourage biotechnology in Italy.

However, given public resistance, changes might be slow to come about. In the meantime, the Italian public remains cautiously hopeful and sceptical, torn between support for developments that might relieve human suffering and increase general wellbeing and diffidence towards the powers of industry and the vanity of science seen as going against the natural order.

Acknowledgements

Some aspects of the work reported in this chapter were made possible by a grant from the University of Siena, PAR '99 progetto di ricerca 'Biotecnologie e il pubblico: il ruolo della comunicazone' awarded to Professor Sebastiano Bagnara. The authors of this chapter wish to thank Professor Francesco Paolo Colucci, University of Milan, Bicocca for his comments on the focus-group work.

Notes and references

1 Allansdottir, A, Pammolli, F and Bagnara, S, 'Italy', in Durant, J, Bauer, M W and Gaskell, G (eds), *Biotechnology in the Public Sphere: A European Sourcebook* (London: Science Museum, 1998), pp89–99.

2 See Mazzoni, C M (ed.), *Una norma giuridica per la bioetica* (Bologna: Mulino, 1998).

3 Lassen, J, Allansdottir, A, Liakoupulos, M, Olsson, A and Mortensen, A T, 'Testing times: the reception of Roundup Ready soya in Europe', in Bauer, M W and Gaskell, G (eds), *Biotechnology: The Making of a Global Controversy* (Cambridge: Cambridge University Press, in press).

4 See Neresini, F, 'And man descended from sheep: the public debate on cloning in the Italian press', *Public Understanding of Science*, 9 (2000), pp9359–382, for an analysis of actors' strategies in establishing mammal cloning as a social and scientific fact and the links made to the debate over embryos and reproductive technologies.

5 The daily circulation figures for *Corriere della Sera* were around 600,000 in late 1999. 'Censis 33', *Rapporto sulla Situazione del Paese* (Rome: Fondazione Censis, 1999).

6 Some might have reservations over the choice of *Corriere della Sera* as the publication analysed. During the time period of our analysis there were some criticisms that the paper might have been unduly supportive of the industry's attempt to shape public opinion towards biotechnology in early 1998. In any case the paper remains an elite opinion leader.

7 Allansdottir, A *et al.* (see note 1).

8 Einsiedel, E, Allansdottir, A and Allum, N C *et al.* 'Brave new sheep: the clone named Dolly', in Bauer, M W and Gaskell, G (eds) (see note 3), for a study into press reactions to Dolly the sheep.

9 The index of intensity of press coverage of biotechnology had to be calibrated as the search engines of the online archives of *Corriere della Sera* have become more sensitive, yielding a greater number of hits than in previous years. This was done by reconstructing the index for 1995 and 1996 and comparing that with previous results. The numbers reported are thus proportionate to earlier coverage, and for 1997–99 should not be read as actual numbers.

10 The groups were organised in a way that attempted to take into account some important dimensions of segmentation: levels of education, levels of income and social positioning and political orientation. Comparing and contrasting religious and social outlooks and exploring geographical differences between the north and the south of Italy. The focus-group discussions were framed by a common protocol and the transcriptions were analysed following an agreed common code of analysis in collaboration with public concerns working group (see Wagner, W, Kronberger, N and Gaskell, G *et al.* in this volume, pp80–95).

Address for correspondence

Agnes Allansdottir, University of Siena, Department of Communication Sciences, Via dei Termini 6, I-53100 Siena, Italy. E-mail: Allans@media.unisi.it

The Netherlands: controversy or consensus?

Jan Gutteling, Cees Midden, Carla Smink and Anneloes Meijnders

National landscape

The Netherlands is a small but densely populated nation (1999: 462 inhabitants per square km), with relatively strong population growth compared to other European countries (0.7 per cent). The lack of space and high population density have placed pressure on the industrial and agricultural sectors to intensify. A strong science-based agriculture and the economies of scale have enabled the Netherlands to become one of the major European food-exporting countries. Other areas of industry for which modern biotechnology is relevant are the chemical, environmental and pharmaceutical sectors. The Netherlands occupies a relatively central position in Europe from a trade point of view, and the main harbour (Rotterdam) and airport (Amsterdam) are significant distribution nodes.

Since 1994 a coalition of Social Democrats (D66) with the Labour Party (PvdA) and the Liberal Party (VVD) has been in power. During the last few years, in contrast to most other European countries, the Netherlands has known a period of constant economic growth (3 per cent or higher) and a decrease in unemployment. The Netherlands is currently thriving. In 1999 the GNP was 14 per cent above the average of the EU at 66,884 Dutch guilders (UK £18,523) per inhabitant. This prosperity stands in sharp contrast to the situation in 1990 when the Dutch GNP was 14 per cent below the EU average. The economic success of the Netherlands is related to international developments such as economic growth in the USA. It has also been attributed to the particular socio-economic complex of the Netherlands, known as the polder model. The polder model has four distinctive characteristics: **1** the relationship between government and 'social partners' (that is, employee and employer organisations) is based on consensus; **2** social partners agree on wage restraints; **3** a strict control of costs related to social security is enforced; and **4** government and the social partners participate in an active labour market policy.

In 1999, when asked whether they were satisfied with the democracy in their own country, 80 per cent of Dutch people said they were. Some 73 per cent reported a favourable attitude toward the EU. Both indicators are relatively high compared to other European countries. The Netherlands also differs from other European countries on several socio-cultural indicators. The proportion of the electorate holding membership of a political party is only 2.5 per cent, the lowest of all European countries. Dutch membership of labour unions is lowest of all northern and western European countries. Only 40 per cent of the Dutch align themselves with a particular religion. On the other hand, membership of NGOs such as Amnesty International, Red Cross, Greenpeace, World Wildlife Fund and Médecins Sans Frontières is much more popular in the Netherlands than in other European countries. Of those organisations, only Greenpeace actively opposes modern biotechnology.[1]

Public policy

Since the 1980s, the Netherlands has invested strongly in the development of biotechnology. After the breakthrough of rDNA, the focus was on fundamental research. At the beginning of the 1980s, the stimulation of innovation became part of government programmes. This was complemented in the late 1980s with the stimulation of industrial biotechnology R&D. From the beginning of the 1990s, fundamental research has been attuned to industrial priorities on one hand, with attention to market pull (specifying market priorities) for biotechnology on the other.

Policy developments between 1980 and 1991

Perhaps because of the signals coming from the self-imposed moratorium on rDNA research by scientists at the Asilomar Conference in 1975 (Dutch scientists participated and reported back), Dutch policy concerning biotechnology has always been two-sided. On one hand it has aimed to harness the potential benefits, and on the other hand it considers potential risks. In 1981 the Brede

Committee was established to advise the government on benefits and risks of rDNA research. One of the first discussions in parliament on rDNA research concerned the approval for building a high-risk (CIII) laboratory, for which permission was granted in 1981. The most important social actor then was the Royal Academy of Science (KNAW), which was promoting rDNA research. Recombinant DNA pharmaceuticals (e.g. insulin, 1982) were introduced without any public debate or new regulations. The government used the existing law on pharmaceuticals and followed FDA guidelines. The early government attention to social considerations was reflected in the commissioning of a series of studies on social aspects (including public perceptions) of biotechnology in 1985. One of the NGOs that started considering biotechnology at an early stage, was the animal welfare movement. In 1985 they initiated a study on biotechnology and animals. In addition, they were actively pushing for the development of a new law on animal welfare, which was finalised and adopted in 1993, and which included a chapter on transgenic animals. A specific directive on animal welfare was passed in 1997.

The first food-related biotechnology product to reach the Netherlands was the growth hormone BST, which was developed in the USA for increasing milk production in cows. In 1987, the Ministry of Agriculture conducted a consumer attitude study on BST; in 1988 the issue was discussed in parliament. BST was never allowed on to the Dutch market, and an EU moratorium came into effect at the beginning of 1990. The first approval for field tests (of a potato with virus X resistance) was given in 1988. It was contested by an environmental movement, the Foundation for Nature and the Environment, but approved in court by the highest judicial authority (the Council of State) in 1989. Action groups calling themselves 'Angry Potatoes' destroyed the field tests for the first time in August 1989, and several times after that. These activities, however, did not succeed in mobilising the public to any great extent.

In parliament, questions both about the usefulness and the risks of biotechnology continued to be asked. The issues were mostly related to animal biotechnology (animal welfare and ethics) and agricultural biotechnology (safety for health and the environment, patenting, market demand and consumer acceptance). Around 1989, the debate also increased outside parliament. The two main issues were transgenic animals and food: the former because of the announcement in 1989 of the development of transgenic cows (the first calf was born in 1990); the latter because of the application of rDNA techniques in the development of cheese rennet (chymosin), in 1988, and the subsequent request for government approval in 1989.

During this period, attention was paid to potential public acceptance problems and subsequently demands for public information were made. A government-initiated study in 1988–89 showed that public awareness and knowledge of both traditional and modern biotechnology was still rather low. The government supported various initiatives for multi-actor workshops and debates on biotechnology topics, and installed both an ethical committee on animal biotechnology and a committee on environmental safety. Also, since 1991, the government has subsidised the Consumer and Biotechnology Foundation whose main goal is to support knowledge-based opinion forming about biotechnology by NGOs, especially the consumer organisations, and to take part in the debates. A government-funded, broad public information campaign was started in the early 1990s and ended in 1998.

Policy developments since 1991

Chymosin was approved by the government, and consumer organisations and food producers on the Advisory Committee of the Food Law agreed that labelling would not be necessary (1991). However, the dairy industry decided not to use it because of the potential reaction from the important German export market. The birth of the first transgenic bull 'Herman' in 1990 raised a lot of debate, both in parliament and in the newspapers. Although a new law on animal welfare had been under discussion since 1987, it was not yet prepared for this development, so no adequate legislation was available until the law was in place in 1993. After this, parliament asked the government to revise the decision not to approve research on transgenic cattle. In 1992, parliament decided that under stringent restrictions the breeding programme involving Herman could continue, in order to produce a certain amount of milk containing lactoferrin.

In 1993, just after the new Law on Animal Welfare was in place, a consensus conference on transgenic animals was organised. In 1995, another consensus conference considered human genetic screening research, and in June 1997 the Health Council published their advice on gene therapy. One of their recommendations was, that in the near future, the use of GMOs in humans should be regulated by law. Also, gene therapy research in humans should be regulated by protocols.

Table 1. Key policy events in the Netherlands, 1996–2000

Year	Event
1996	Law on medical testing passed, including a moratorium on hereditary research.
1997	The European rule on New Foods, EC directive 97/258/EG, became effective.
1998	Genetically Modified Organisms Regulation. Includes technical guidelines for activities with GMOs. This supersedes the 1993 regulation. Law passed prohibiting prenatal gender choice for non-medical reasons. Law passed on medical scientific research using humans. Regulates the conditions under which research using humans is allowed. An independent Platform Medical Biotechnology financed by the Ministry of Health is established. Public debate on cloning, initiated by the Ministry of Health.
1999	Establishment of review committees on medical scientific research with humans. Addition to the Food Law; regulations on the use of the label 'made without gene techniques'. Initiative for a public debate on xenotransplants, initiated by the Ministry of Health. Establishment of the Forum Genetics and Healthcare by a patients' organisation (VSOP), the Ministry of Health and Foundation Future Scenario's Healthcare.
2000	Regulation in the Food Law on GM essences and additives. Implementation of EC directive 50/2000.

Table 1 presents the key policy events in the Netherlands related to modern biotechnology for the period 1996–2000. In 1996, GM soyabeans came on to the European market. The Ministry of Health approved the use of this soya in the Netherlands. In April 1997, the Ministry issued, within the framework of the Food Law, a labelling directive on the use of GM soya and maize in products. However, in October , the courts decided that the Food Law could not be used to differentiate between products, and the directive was rejected. This did not bring about material changes because from November 1997 onwards, the labelling of GM soya had been directed by European regulations. In practice, however, only a few such products that are labelled can be found in the supermarkets.

Generally speaking, in the Netherlands there has been no major societal concern about GM food. However, in the past few years international concerns are having an effect on traders and grocers. In order to avoid difficulties, Dutch traders, grocers and processors have started to source GM-free foodstuffs. In addition, Dutch NGOs have become more critical about GM food and government policy towards it. Following the advent of the first mammal to be cloned from an adult, Dolly the sheep, in 1997, pharmaceutical companies have become increasingly aware of their societal responsibilities. As a result, they founded bioethical commissions to deal with the social questions. At the end of 1998, the independent organisation, Platform Medical Biotechnology, was established, financed by the Ministry of Health. The goal of the Platform is to offer a contribution to responsible decision-making with regard to development and application of medical biotechnology. Furthermore, a forum on genetics and healthcare was established by a patients' organisation (VSOP), the Ministry of Health and the Foundation for Future Scenarios in Healthcare. The Forum's aim is the communication and exchange of knowledge. In 1999, the Ministry of Health initiated a public debate about xenotransplantation. In addition, the Dutch government organised a social debate in 2000 about gene techniques. An interdepartmental note on modern biotechnology was published in 2000, and based on this a national public debate on GM food was held in 2001.

Media coverage

Six major national newspapers and at least one newspaper in each region serve readers throughout the country. Circulation figures for Dutch newspapers indicate that in recent years the total annual circulation is approximately 4.49 million copies (the country has about 6 million households). The current trend is that the circulation of national dailies is increasing and that of regional newspapers is decreasing. Some 89 per cent of all newspaper sales are subscriptions. For the average person in the Netherlands, newspaper reading is a daily ritual, with most people spending on average half an hour a day reading at least one newspaper. Although all Dutch national newspapers offer a variety of reports, they are distinguishable by the type of information they publish. The popular, general-interest newspapers emphasise human-interest stories, entertainment, sporting events, and practical information. The second group, the so-called 'quality' newspapers, offer readers more policy-oriented information on social, political and cultural issues, organisations and their key actors. The popular national newspapers have a higher circulation than the quality national dailies. No tabloids are published in the Netherlands.

Our media study on biotechnology focuses on the coverage in *De Volkskrant* (the People's Newspaper). *De Volkskrant* ranks third in the circulation statistics and has the largest circulation of the quality newspapers. More than two-thirds of its readers can be categorised as middle or upper class. Overall, the *De Volkskrant* readership is better educated than the Dutch public in general. Additional analyses indicate its readership is also different from the popular newspapers' readership in this respect. As the leading national Dutch newspaper, on 2 October 1975, *De Volkskrant* adopted editorial bylaws. These included a declaration of the newspaper's identity:

> *De Volkskrant* is a national daily newspaper, which has the objective of informing readers in as fair and as versatile a manner as possible. *De Volkskrant* arose from the Catholic labour movement. For that reason, among others, *De Volkskrant* wants to be progressive and to plead for the oppressed and those whose rights are violated. *De Volkskrant* is independent is its opinions. In particular, *De Volkskrant* aims to stimulate developments leading to a more humane society.

In 1977, *De Volkskrant* launched a half-page weekly column on scientific issues, expanding this in 1981 to a full section entitled 'Science and society' appearing in the Saturday edition. In 1988, this section was renamed 'Science'. Basically, *De Volkskrant*'s editorial policy on science is to treat all issues objectively. Since 1998, *De Volkskrant* has also had a daily internet edition.

Several methods of selecting articles on biotechnology were applied. For issues published prior to 1993 we used microfiches containing exact copies of the 'paper' version of the newspaper. For issues published between 1993 and 1997 we used the CD-ROM version of *De Volkskrant*, containing all relevant information. For issues published since 1998 the content of *De Volkskrant* is available through an online database with restricted access.

In total, 2286 articles were selected (Figure 1). We observed a particularly sharp increase of biotechnology coverage from 1993 onwards. This increase may partly be due to the change of scanning technique (microfiches vs electronic), but it is very likely that the intensity of publishing has increased since 1993 as well. Table 2 presents a breakdown of the articles since 1993. We used two 'biotechnology windows' for analysing the data, 1993–96 and 1997–99. In the international project, 1996 and 1997 are seen as the 'watershed years' when Roundup Ready soya and Dolly the sheep changed the symbolic landscape of modern biotechnology in Europe. The data have been analysed according to frames, themes, actors, risk and benefit information, and location.

Media analysis of biotechnology

Overall, we observed a consistent presentation of biotechnology in the two periods, with only

Figure 1. Intensity of articles on modern biotechnology in De Volkskrant, 1973–99

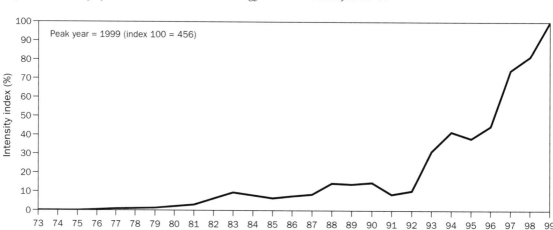

Table 2. Dutch media profile, 1987–2000 (threshold for inclusion: 5 per cent)

Phase	1987–96		1997–2000	
Frequency (%)[a]	72		28	
Frame (%)	**Progress**[b]	32	**Progress**	32
	Ethical	23	Accountability	24
	Accountability	23	Economic	18
	Economic	17	Nature/nurture	9
Theme (%)	**Biomedical**	21	**Biomedical**	17
	Agrifood	19	Agrifood	14
	Genetic identity	18	Genetic identity	13
	Generic research	13	Public opinion	10
	Economics	9	Economics	9
			Moral	7
			Generic research	6
Actor (%)	**Independent science**	37	**Independent science**	32
	Business	21	Politics	16
	Politics	17	Business	15
	Media	9	Media	13
	Interest groups	7	Interest groups	10
Benefit/risk (%)	**Neither**	61	**Neither**	40
	Benefit only	21	Benefit only	29
	Both	12	Both	18
	Risk only	7	Risk only	12
Location (%)	**Netherlands**	53	**Netherlands**	49
	Other Europe	20	Other Europe	26
	USA	19	USA	16
	Other countries	8	Other countries	10

a Percentage of corpus (excludes articles which mentioned biotechnology only metaphorically) in the period; total $n = 1059$.
b Bold indicates highest frequency within phase.

moderate changes in any of the variables, when comparing the period 1993–96 with the period 1997–99. In the period 1997–99, progress was by far the dominant frame, as it was in 1993–96. Public accountability and economic opportunities did not change either. The ethical frame, however decreased from appearing in 24 per cent of articles in the first period, to only 10 per cent in the second. In the period 1993–96, no other frames were dominant in more than 5 per cent of the articles.

Regarding the description of risks and benefits of modern biotechnology, the number of articles including risks and benefits increased by 21 per cent in the period 1997–99 compared to the previous period. Articles, which described only benefits showed the largest increase (8 per cent), followed by articles with both risks and benefits (6 per cent) and articles with only descriptions of risks (5 per cent). When we look in particular at the location of the biotechnology activity in the articles, the Netherlands and the USA were mentioned slightly less frequently in the period 1997–99 than before

(7 per cent), and other European countries slightly more frequently (6 per cent).

In Table 3 we present a more detailed analysis of the actors mentioned in articles in the period 1997–99 relating to risks or benefits of modern biotechnology. Independent scientists and business actors are mentioned more frequently in relation to the benefits of modern biotechnology. On the other hand, media and published opinions in the media, and interest groups (including NGOs) are more prominent in articles referring to risks.

In summary, we conclude that the coverage of modern biotechnology in general is still rather positive. It is framed most frequently as progress, with biomedical themes mostly referred to by independent scientists who present more of the beneficial effects of biotechnology than in the previous period. This may indicate that the Dolly/soya watershed observed in other European countries has not been replicated in the Dutch opinion-leading newspaper.

Table 3. Actors in articles on risks and benefits in De Volkskrant, 1997–99

Actors related to risks (%)		Actors related to benefits (%)	
Independent science	32	Independent scientists	45
Politics	12	Politics	13
Business	6	Business	25
Media and public voice	25	Media and public voice	9
Interest groups	16	Interest groups	1
Moral authorities	2	Moral authorities	1
EU	5	EU	2
Other actors	3	Other actors	4

Public perceptions

The 1999 Eurobarometer survey was conducted with a special focus on modern biotechnology compared to other technologies. Here we present some of the findings for the Dutch representative sample participating in this study.

Table 4 gives the frequency distributions of the expected effects on society of eight areas of technology. The data indicate that the Dutch have rather optimistic expectations about the role of technology. Apart from the enduring pessimism with regard to nuclear power, biotechnology scores lowest on positive expectations and highest on negative expectations. Uncertainty about biotechnology is still rather high compared to other technologies. However in comparison to other European countries, the Dutch respondents had lower 'don't know' answers (16.7 per cent vs 25.6 per cent for Europe). Compared to the European mean, the Dutch score for modern biotechnology is on the positive side. Approximately 53 per cent of the Dutch sample expect biotechnology to improve their way of life, compared to the European mean of 40 per cent. Almost 20 per cent of the Dutch expect biotechnology to make things worse, compared to the European mean of 25 per cent.

Attitudes towards applications of biotechnology

Respondents were asked to judge seven applications of biotechnology on their usefulness, risk, moral acceptability and whether they should be encouraged. From the results it can be concluded that the most favourable applications are genetic testing, the use of biotechnology to produce medicines and the use of GM bacteria to clean up polluted areas (bioremediation). People are most opposed to the production of new foods and the cloning of animals to produce medicines. On average people feel that these applications should not be encouraged. For example, GM food is opposed by 43 per cent while 49 per cent offer support, but the stronger views of the opponents lead to the negative overall score. Concerning animal cloning 43 per cent are opposed, while 39 per cent agree that it should be encouraged. For crops almost 35 per cent think these applications should be discouraged. However 57 per cent think they should be encouraged, while 8 per cent do not know. The reactions to the cloning of human tissue are remarkable. People are more positive towards this than to animal cloning (66 per cent are willing to encourage and 25 per cent disagree). The percentages of 'don't know'

Table 4. Expected effects of eight technologies in the Netherlands, 1999

Technology	Will improve our way of life(%)	Will have no effect (%)	Will make things worse (%)	Don't know (%)
Solar energy	90.2	7.1	1.1	1.6
Computers	86.2	3.8	6.3	3.8
Biotechnology/genetic engineering	52.7	10.7	19.9	16.7
Telecommunications	86.5	7.4	3.8	2.3
New materials	82.8	6.3	2.2	8.6
Space exploration	56.4	28.3	5.6	9.7
Internet	77.0	9.7	7.7	5.6
Nuclear power	23.6	15.4	49.9	11.1

Table 5. Dutch attitudes to applications of modern biotechnology

Application	Year	Useful for society	Risky for society	Morally acceptable	Should be encouraged
Food production	1996	0.70[a]	1.00	0.70	0.50
	1999	0.47	0.64	0.38	−0.09
Transgenic crops	1996	1.10	0.70	0.90	0.80
	1999	0.76	0.58	0.47	0.22
Medicine	1996	1.50	0.90	1.10	1.10
	1999	1.22	0.46	0.84	0.82
Genetic testing	1996	1.40	0.70	1.10	1.10
	1999	1.38	0.15	1.05	1.00

a Arithmetic means, scale −2 to +2 with four categories (−2 = strongly disagree, +2 = strongly agree).

responses are low in the Netherlands across all applications.

Generally speaking, biotechnologies are regarded as morally acceptable in the Netherlands. Moral concern is greatest for the cloning of animals (38 per cent), the production of GM foods (28 per cent), the protection of crops (26 per cent) and the cloning of human cells (25 per cent). Risks are perceived with regard to all applications by a majority of the respondents with the highest scores on GM foods (72 per cent) and the lowest on genetic testing (56 per cent). The level of perceived risk is generally above the European average.

In general the majority of Dutch people see biotechnology as useful with the least useful being the cloning of animals (61 per cent) and the most useful, the production of medicines (85 per cent) and genetic testing (89 per cent). The Dutch see GM foods as more useful compared to the average European consumer.

Comparisons with Eurobarometer 1996

When we compare the mean scores of the four applications also measured in 1996 (Table 5) the following picture emerges. In general, the level of public support for biotechnology applications has decreased since 1996, with the biggest decrease in support for food applications. Moral acceptance shows a slight decrease across all applications as do perceived risks and usefulness. The decline in support for these applications of biotechnology appears to be the result of lower perceived usefulness and moral acceptability, notwithstanding lower levels of perceived risk. But, perhaps the striking finding from the survey is the levels of confidence in key actors involved in biotechnology. Asked if government, consumer organisations, shops and environmental organisations are doing a good job

for society or not, the Dutch respondents show among the highest levels of confidence in all these groups, compared to other European countries.

Conclusions

Overall, the government takes a favourable position towards modern biotechnology, and is prepared to support and finance potentially beneficial applications or research, but at the same time taking possible risks into consideration. In general, laws and policies regarding the judicial aspects of modern biotechnology and its applications are incorporated into existing regulation as much as possible. The government is willing to listen to social organisations as part of the process of developing regulations, and at times incorporates proposals or modifications from these groups. Such NGOs are usually critical of biotechnology developments. The public's voice can be heard through consensus conferences and public debates, as well as in the media.

In our analysis of the Dutch opinion-leading newspaper, we conclude that the coverage of modern biotechnology between 1996 and 1999 is, in general, still positive. Coverage is framed most frequently as progress; themes are mostly biomedical with reference to independent scientists. This coverage is mostly concerned with presenting information about the beneficial effects of biotechnology. Comparing these findings to the previous periods (the years before 1996), differences in newspaper coverage are not very great. This suggests that the Dolly/soya watershed that was observed in other European countries has not been replicated in the Dutch media.

Compared to the European average, Dutch attitudes towards modern biotechnology are positive. Some 53 per cent of the Dutch have positive expectations of biotechnology, compared to the

European mean of 40 per cent. Compared to the position in 1996 the level of support for particular applications of biotechnology has decreased, with the strongest decline for GM foods. Hence, despite positive expectations, the Dutch are in general less supportive of biotechnology applications than they were. They are more concerned about moral acceptability, but perceive less risk. However, this shift to a less supportive position is not as dramatic in the Netherlands as it is in other European countries.

Comparing both the Dutch media and the public opinion data to developments in other European countries, we may conclude that, in 1999, the Netherlands was relatively positive towards biotechnology. Five or even ten years ago, it would have been unthinkable to suggest that the Dutch would be positive about a modern strategic technology that was causing so much public controversy in neighbouring countries. The days of wide public opposition to nuclear technology in the Netherlands seem be in the distant past.

What is the explanation for this rather unexpected phenomenon? One obvious explanation is the current state of affairs in the Netherlands, from the socio-economic, political and cultural perspectives. The 'polder model', successful in a socio-economic sense, has led to an unprecedented economic prosperity, and may have had an impact on other aspects of social life as well. For example, the consensus drive that directs socio-economic developments, may also be behind developments in modern biotechnology, resulting in NGOs having a participatory rather than controversial role in policy making. These NGOs also have a wide visibility and support across the country, as can be seen from their relatively high membership rates. As the Eurobarometer survey shows, the Dutch public, in contrast to many other European countries, have high levels of confidence in consumer organisations and in government. Thus there is no sense of urgency to mobilise wide public opposition towards this particular type of technology.

Notes and references

1 Social and Cultural Planning Office, 'The Netherlands in a European perspective', *Social and Cultural Report 2000* (The Hague: SCP, 2000).

Address for correspondence

Dr Jan M Gutteling, University of Twente, PO Box 21, NL-7500 AE Enschede, the Netherlands. E-mail j.m.gutteling@wmw.utwente.nl

Norway: biotechnology and sustainability

Torben Hviid Nielsen, Trond Haug, Siv Frøydis Berg and Arve Monsen

Norwegian biopolitics

Norwegian biopolitics is a European *Sonderweg*: a specific national solution to a general problem. The two EU directives from 1990, on contained and released use of GMOs, are enforced in Norway. However, as a non-member of the EU, the Norwegian parliament passed two additional and comprehensive Acts in 1993 and 1994: an Act relating to the production and use of GMOs (the Gene Technology Act) and an Act relating to the application of biotechnology in medicine (the Biotechnology Act).[1]

Both Acts are 'conditionally approving', i.e. they intend to exploit the potential of biotechnology *and* avoid the risks and moral concerns, but they were also intended – and they are still considered – to be more restrictive than the EU directives. These restrictive Acts correspond to a sceptical public opinion, and reflect a highly ambivalent attitude to the field.

The public discourse on political regulation of modern biotechnology has passed through three distinct and successive phases (Figure 1). First, a phase of initiation, dominated by three independent discourses regarding risk, R&D, and moral concerns;

Figure 1. The Sonderweg of Norwegian biopolitics, 1976–2000

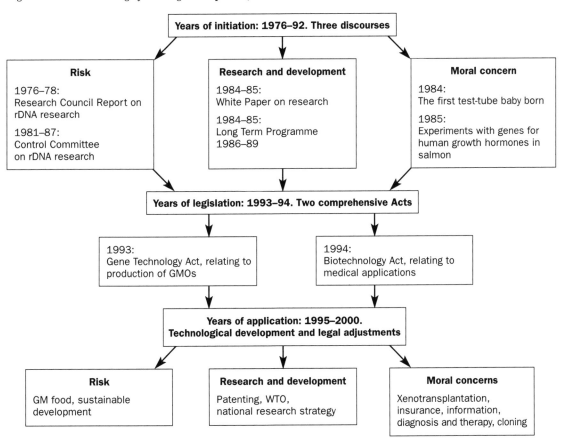

second, a phase of legislation, where the comprehensive Acts combine and condense the three preceding discourses; and third, a phase dominated by technological development, experiments, actual applications and legal adjustments.

Public discourse

Phase 1 (1976–92): years of initiation

The years prior to the parliamentary approval of the two comprehensive Acts were characterised by three distinct discourses with different actors and interests. As early as 1976, the Research Council worked to 'contain' the threat of biohazard as controllable risk. Without much publicity, the government and parliament were able to make biotechnology an R&D priority in 1984. It was not until the end of the 1980s that biotechnology became an open and controversial political issue, when experiments with GM salmon and the birth of the first Norwegian test-tube baby were announced in the media.

Risk. The international research community initiated the process that gave rise to the first regulation of Norwegian biotechnology. On 10 September 1976, the European Science Foundation called for a meeting in Amsterdam. Its *ad-hoc* committee on recombined DNA research suggested establishing a European 'umbrella body' in the European Molecular Biology Organization's (EMBO) Standing Advisory Committee on Recombinant DNA. It also proposed the establishment of 'national advisory bodies' responsible for the interpretation of recommendations and a code of practice, advising on research and overseeing implementation. At the General Assembly of the European Science Foundation (ESF) on 26 October these recommendations were approved.

In the same year, the Research Council nominated a committee chaired by Søren Laland, the first professor of biochemistry at the University of Oslo. As a starting point, the mandate was limited to following international developments and elucidating the potential for research in Norway. During this work, the mandate was extended to discussing actual risks, evaluating the needs for control and regulation, and outlining administrative enterprises of control.

The committee's report on rDNA research recommended establishing 'a permanent organ with both advisory and controlling functions regarding all use of rDNA technology and rDNA

products in Norway'. The recommendation differed on two central points from that of the ESF. First, the Norwegian committee found legal regulation unnecessary 'in a country like ours, where the circumstances are this transparent'. Instead, it was suggested that the affected authorities be obliged to report all planned experiments to a committee for evaluation and approval of experiments. Second, the committee recommended the revised guidelines from the American National Institutes of Health (NIH), rather than the British system of security recommended by the ESF because the NIH guidelines were 'very detailed, and therefore much easier to maintain'. Three years later, in autumn 1981, the Research Council appointed the first control committee, Control Committee on rDNA Research.

Research. In the second discourse, the Labour government's White Paper on research in Norway identified biotechnology as one of five major priority areas in 'a united and long-term general priority of national research contributions'. The White Paper mentioned the great importance of biotechnology (defined as medicine, agriculture and environmental protection), but stressed the possibilities of sea farming, a 'large and quickly expanding enterprise ... an area in which we both have naturally given advantages' and 'a considerable industry or activity, where cultivation of marine animals and marine plants has just started'. Corresponding to this, the government's Long Term Programme 1986–1988 accentuated 'the use of modern biotechnology to utilise our resources in the sea and in sea farming'.

The science community had thus closed or 'contained' the risk debate, and R&D had been given priority even before the new biotechnology and gene technology was put on the national political agenda.

Moral concern. An important precursor for moral concerns regarding biotechnology was the research on genetic modification of salmon. In 1985 Norwegian scientists integrated the human gene for growth hormone into the salmon genome, but not until the press conference announcing the final success were journalists informed that the gene came from a mammal. When the national broadcaster later uncovered the true human nature of this gene, the transgenetic project was scandalised as such. The 'super salmon' became an important breakthrough for Norwegian gene technology, but it functioned at the same time as a major catalyst for latent scepticism towards the same technology.

The new biotechnology did not, however, turn into a politically controversial issue until parliament debated the Act relating to artificial procreation on 25 May 1987.[2] In the summer of 1984, the first Norwegian test-tube baby was born at the Region Hospital in Trondheim – and in the very same year about thousand pregnancies were initiated with the help of artificial insemination.[3]

The main themes in the parliamentary debate concerned morally motivated and ethically grounded considerations. Much of the debate resembled a second round of the controversies on elective abortion in the 1960s, but the horizon was new. In the 1960s contraception and abortion detached sexuality from reproduction. Now IVF had facilitated fertilisation entirely detached from human bodies. Risks were no longer connected to failure of laboratory tests or their unforeseen consequences but to unwanted moral and social changes. The prospects of prenatal and germ-line screening made possible a 'selection society' scenario, and unexpected consequences and use of abortion were the main issues in the debate. The parliament asked the Labour government to present a White Paper in order to facilitate an ethical debate and to suggest legislation for research communities. The major concern put forward by the parliamentary majority was that medical use of biotechnology could transgress 'natural' or 'social' boundaries in an undesirable and/or unintentional way. Ethical guidelines were called for because ethics was considered basically as the right to say 'no'; a potential veto which – *vis-à-vis* a risky technology – could legitimately suspend routine politics.

The new biopolitics was marked by a rupture from the traditional demarcations between left and right, progress and conservatism, modernity and tradition. The Progressive Party (FrP), the Conservative Party of Norway (H) and the Norwegian Labour Party (AP) were most supportive of biotechnology. The value-conservative Christian Party (KrF), the rural-based Centre Party (SP) and the Socialist Left Party (SV) were most sceptical. These different attitudes were also reflected in the changing of governments, especially the shift from the Labour government (1990–97) to the coalition government in 1997–2000, consisting of the Christian Party, the Centre Party and the Liberal Party (V). After March 2000, Labour replaced the coalition government in power.

Phase 2 (1993–94): years of legislation and politics of Norwegian biotechnology law

In 1989, when Prime Minister Gro Harlem Brundtland (AP) presented to parliament the requested statement on guidelines for biotechnology and gene technology, the dominating themes were the many possibilities for industry and food production and potential environmental problems. She stressed 'the large number of perspectives and possibilities … about which there can be no doubt', and further claimed that, so far, research and practice had only to a small extent 'affected areas that are regarded ethically controversial in the public debate'. However, the possibilities had to be measured against 'the unwanted consequences', and the parliament also had to decide on the 'limitations and the control needed'.[4] In the debate that followed, the opposition tried to reintroduce the agenda of artificial insemination.

Two comprehensive Acts. The legislation followed a prolonged public debate and several White Papers, but was finally timed to be passed by parliament before the second referendum on membership of the EU on 28 November 1994. The Gene Technology Act was passed on 2 April 1993, and the Biotechnology Act followed on 14 June 1994.

Three legal forms and types of regulation. The two Norwegian Acts are intended to provide a balance between reaching potentials and avoiding risks and moral concerns by way of 'conditional approval'. They regulate on the level of the product, the process, as well as the entire research programme, i.e. the three agendas described by Shelia Jasanoff as dominating American, British and German culture.[5] Both Acts phrase the conditions in three legal formulations.

First, a set of legal standards is specific to the Norwegian Acts. The Gene Technology Act has the stated aim of ensuring that the manufacture and use of GMOs takes place in an ethically and socially justifiable way, in accordance with the principle of sustainable development and without detrimental effects on health and the environment.[6]

The Biotechnology Act states the need to ensure that the application of biotechnology in medicine is used in the best interests of human beings in a society where everyone plays a role and is fully valued. This should take place in accordance with the principles of respect for human dignity, human rights and personal integrity, without discrimination on the basis of genetic background and based on ethical norms relating to Western cultural heritage.[7]

The two sets of legal standards are both standards of prevention, extending protection and responsibility from individuals to collectives and allowing for a substitute representation of interests. Nevertheless, they differ somewhat concerning content and implications. The Act regulating non-human use is written in the context of recent sociopolitical and scientific discourse, whereas the terminology in the Act regulating medical use refer to eighteenth-century natural law and the later declaration on human rights.

The comprehensive enrolment of ethical values and norms as conditions is characteristic of the Norwegian legislation of biotechnology. Except for the claim that 'possible negative consequences for the wholesomeness for human beings and environ-ment are to be limited',[8] no equivalent was in existence at the time, neither in the EU directives nor in other nations' legislation.

As a starting point, the two sets of legal standards have a formal significance. They form part of the attempt of the framework laws to anticipate future technological possibilities that could not be specifically foreseen and therefore are not regulated in the detailed form of casuistry. However, the political process concerning the legislation gives reason to understand the intentions with the legal standards as substantial extra demands in addition to the casuistry and the EU directives. When the Gene Technology Act was presented to parliament, it was accentuated that, 'In Norway we have stressed that other considerations than environmental and health issues can be made current to cases concerning postponement.... In our opinion, this Act leaves the way open for the possibility to make even further restrictions, at least as far as this does not come into conflict with EU.'[9] In accordance with this, the Minister of Health emphasised that the total legislation of biopolitics placed Norway among the most restrictive countries in Europe.

A second legal formulation common to the two Acts is the enumeration of detailed casuistic requirements (listing of actual fields of application) and preconditions for contained and exposed use of GMOs, artificial insemination, fetal diagnosis, genetic testing, gene therapy, etc. There are minor differences compared to the EU directives, especially regarding the classification of GMOs and the definition of released use, but the casuistic requirements are basically identical.

Finally, both Acts delegate a considerable influence over the interpretation and application of the legal standards to the Norwegian Biotechnology Advisory Board. The Board provides a forum for negotiations, formation of consensus, and compromises. The circumstances and interests considered legitimate are indicated by the Board's composition of professionals, public officials, interest representatives and NGOs.

In summary, Norwegian biotechnology and gene technology legislation is characterised by special legal standards in combination with the casuistic preconditions which are essentially identical to the EU directives. Legislation is also characterised by the influential advisory board as an administrative procedure. The legal forms do not equalise the domains of regulation, but together they regulate the products and procedures of biotechnology, as well as the entire research programme. They intend to balance the three early discourses by avoiding risks and initiating R&D within ethical limits.

Phase 3 (1995–2000): years of application, technological development and legal adjustments

The three discourses from the initiation years are repeated in the years of application, but the debate has transgressed the former limits of the research community, and the spheres of politics and morality. The first phase was related to the level of utopias, dystopias and potentialities, whereas the second phase was on the level of choices concerning actual entities, technology and knowledge. During the most recent decade, techniques from biotechnology have become daily routine – not least for diagnostic purposes in hospitals, but industrial production is still small-scale and agricultural use virtually non-existent.

Risk. It had been easier to give general priority to R&D than to implement possibilities of production. The research policy was more successful than the industrial policy. Expectations and investments are still higher than production and revenue, but in the years following the legislation, biotechnology has increasingly taken the step from experimental laboratories to hospital routines and to the marketplace, and thereby renewed the problems behind the three independent discourses that preceded the comprehensive Acts.

• The issue of sustainability and biodiversity posed by agricultural biotechnology and GM food can be seen as a new horizon for risk – now 'released' into the environment rather than 'contained' in the laboratory.

- Early medical diagnosis, DNA profiling, the mapping of the human genome and the possibility of cloning have reinforced ethical considerations – now as the 'right not to know' and the 'right to privacy'.

Research and development. Patenting (EU), free trade (WTO) and priorities in the strategic R&D plans have repeated and reinforced biotechnology as research and development priorities. The Research Council's R&D report from 1995 accordingly summarised the industrial use of biotechnology as 'proportionately modest': 'The domain has developed at a slower pace than what was hoped some years ago. Especially, it is difficult (to) acquire large concerns with international experience. Among 30 and 40 concerns are users of biotechnology today, all mostly traditional biotechnology.'[10] The consultants Ernst & Young's international reports from 1998, found that Norwegian production was ranked 11th in Europe.[11]

The 1995 R&D report repeated that biotechnology was 'on the threshold of implementation'. The approximately 400 new applications for patents each year were considered circumstantial evidence. It was therefore suggested that the budget for research and development should be doubled, which in 1993 held 669 million Norwegian kroner (about UK £50 million), in the period up to 2005. The new strategy mentioned the 'identification of the possibilities in the market' as an important goal in itself. However, the use and regulation of biotechnological know-how has been, and still is, regarded as a problematic area.

The committee reporting on patent issues in 1989, agreed on two crucial conditions: product patents on humans, human organs and human genes were regarded as ethically unsound, and patents on naturally occurring microorganisms should not be allowed. The question of implementation of the EU patent directive, passed in 1998, was considered unacceptable by a coalition government of Christian, centrist and agrarian parties, but the new Labour government recommended approval in March 2000.

Moral concern. During the late 1980s, moral concerns regarding experiments with human growth hormones in 'super salmon' and the use of IVF had been the spur for the legislation. Legal standards with a semi-ethical content are specific to the laws, but the prolonged legislative process ended up as a

kind of 'trial and error process', from the ethically formulated concern back to legal standards of a more political nature.

The first major official policy document was presented within the sphere of 'normative' philosophical ethics. It contrasted consequences with emotive arguments, 'utility' with 'duty', and it referred to classical philosophers such as Jeremy Bentham (1748–1832) and Immanuel Kant (1724–1804).[12]

The second official policy document focused on the descriptive values and attitudes of the population, as indicated by opinion polls. 'Ethical guidelines' were interpreted as a 'set of moral principles', on which there should be 'broad agreement … among the general public whatever their political or religious beliefs'.[13]

In the third attempt, however, the interregnum Conservative government[14] and the new Labour government[15] both altered the terrain by referring to a new concept of 'mixed ethics', which they claimed would solve the conflict between 'utility' and 'duty', as well as be broadly acceptable to the population, i.e. would be normatively right as well as descriptively true.

All the three successive attempts left their traces in the preliminaries to the Acts, but none of them ended up as a key concept in the final texts. In the end the politicians replaced the attempts to define ethical conditions, which they themselves had asked for, with legal standards of a more political nature.

Xenotransplantation was one of the subjects brought up when cloning of 'higher organisms' was prohibited in 1997. In December 1999, the christian democratic government appointed a committee to consider all aspects concerning xenotransplantation, and at the same time proposed a temporary prohibition of all clinical experiments on humans involving xenotransplantation.

In 1998, insurance companies' right to request and use genetic information was discussed in a White Paper. Two years later, on 7 June, the report was finished, but is at time of publication still not debated by parliament.[16] A narrow majority of the committee wanted to repeal the existing prohibition regarding use of genetic information in evaluation of risk, and claimed that, in principle, there was no distinction between genetic information and other information regarding health. The committee thus favoured the insurance companies' right to collect genetic information. The report immediately provoked critical reactions from all political parties. The politicians feared a so-called 'selective society', and the Norwegian Federation of Organisations of

Disabled People (FFO) called the report a 'war declaration'.

Until the beginning of 2001, BSE, or mad cow disease, was almost exclusively a public issue concerning the question of Norwegian membership of the EU. Ethical, and thus 'natural', livestock rearing became the main theme, and BSE and Belgian Blue were treated as a necessary and unavoidable consequence of industrial, large-scale livestock production.

The news of the shipping of American GM soya in 1996 resulted in demonstrations and symbolic protests from environmental and consumer organisations. This soon led to new directives concerning conditions of production, marketing and labelling. However, in 1999 the Norwegian Food Control Authority spot-checked 300 different products from Norwegian grocery stores, and a large number of the products turned out to contain GM ingredients. Neither the consumers nor the producers were until then fully aware of the presence of 'GM food' in stores, and both groups reacted with surprise and disappointment.

Media coverage[17]

Although television is by far the most frequently used information channel, the printed press occupies a strong position in Norway: in a population consisting of 4.5 million people, over 90 per cent of over-13s read at least one newspaper on a daily basis.

Aftenposten, which is analysed and discussed in this section, is a national newspaper based mainly on subscription. It has a circulation of 284,000 and a daily readership of 803,000 on week-days, second only to the tabloid *Verdens Gang* (circulation 374,000; daily readership 1,342,000).[18]

The readers of *Aftenposten* are both more optimistic (40 vs 32 per cent) and less pessimistic (28 vs 36 per cent) regarding biotechnology and gene technology than the population at large, but the readers of the two tabloids *Verdens Gang* and *Dagbladet* are also slightly more optimistic than the population at large. The readers of *Verdens Gang* are thus 34 per cent optimists vs 32 per cent, and 32 per cent pessimists vs 36 per cent, and the readers of *Dagbladet* are 39 per cent optimists vs 32 per cent, with the same number of pessimists (36 per cent) as the population at large.

The most pessimistic or sceptic readers are in the category of reading 'other newspapers', which constitute 40 per cent of the population, and where both the 'Christian' (*Vårt Land*) and the agrarian (*Nationen*) press belong. Here the optimists are 26

vs 32 per cent of the general public, and the pessimists 40 vs 36 per cent. The most sceptical segment of the population is, however, the 5 per cent that indicated that they did not read any newspapers at all. Here optimists are 22 vs 32 per cent and pessimists 56 vs 36 per cent.[19]

Neither the widely circulated tabloid press *Verdens Gang* and *Dagbladet*, nor *Vårt Land* and *Nationen*, associated with the Christian and the Centre parties respectively and with much smaller readerships, have been analysed in a comparative way. Earlier and more sporadic analyses of *Vårt Land* and *Nationen* indicate, however, a much more critical and sceptic coverage than the more balanced or even positive *Aftenposten*, which is opinion-leader among the political and cultural elite.[20]

The following media profile includes the years 1994–96 (which have not been previously reported for Norway) and the first six months of 2000. Three phases are distinguished: 1994–96 (progress), 1997–99 (accountability) and 2000 onwards (economic).[21]

A balanced valuation of biotechnology

A comparison between the numbers of positively and negatively oriented articles shows a predominance of the former (33 per cent with a positive tone set by the author *vs* 28 per cent with a negative tone). Still, neither the positive nor the negative valuation clearly stands out as dominant in *Aftenposten*'s coverage of biotechnology (32 per cent of the articles are both somewhat positive and somewhat negative). The balanced coverage throughout the whole period is mainly due to the in-house journalists: 36 per cent of their contributions may be characterised as balanced, 34 per cent are positive and 26 per cent are negative. Conversely, the negative articles constitute the majority of the contributions sent in by other authors (40 per cent), while the positive and balanced ones come to 35 and 25 per cent respectively.

Phase structure: from progress, through accountability, to economics

Identification of the journalistic framing of the articles and the changing intensity of coverage in the years 1994 to 2000 (Figure 2) reveal three phases, each with a distinctive character.

Phase 1 (1994–96): progress. This period was characterised by a low intensity of articles dealing with biotechnology issues. In 1994 and 1995 the

Figure 2. Intensity of articles on biotechnology in the Norwegian press

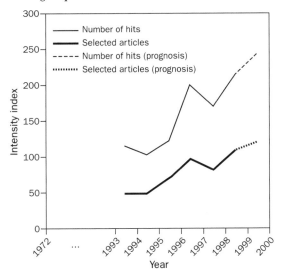

numbers were especially low (8 per cent), whereas a noticeable increase was registered in 1996 (12 per cent). Moreover, the discursive framework was heavily oriented to progress, but even here a change took place in 1996. The progress frame, which was represented in over 40 per cent of the articles in 1994 and 1995, dropped to 29 per cent in 1996. Also, frames expressing worry and anxiety – 'Pandora's box' and 'runaway' – made their entrance in this year. A significant change took place in several of the categories in 1996. Regarding themes, food dominated, not medicine as in previous years, and articles containing a negative valuation outnumbered the positive ones. An examination of the headlines in 1996 confirms this tendency: especially in the last six months, concern was expressed in relation to novel food. The EU's sanction of GM maize and news of the arrival in Europe of the first shipload of GM soya were reported and discussed frequently.

All in all, progress appears to have dominated the phase as a whole, but the impression blurs somewhat when the benefit/risk category is taken into consideration. Stories reporting both benefits and risks as possible consequences of the new biotechnology predominated, which must be seen as an expression of ambivalence. Progress dominated, but it was accompanied by doubts. The changes in 1996 heralded a new phase.

Phase 2 (1997–99): accountability. The year 1997 inaugurated an intensity of growth to such a degree that the trend registered over the last six months of

the previous year was further reinforced. This increase continued in the following years. Even the small decrease in 1998 covered a higher number of articles (82) than the peak year in the previous phase (68 in 1996). The main trigger responsible for this increase was the breaking of the Dolly-the-sheep story in January 1997: the world was informed of the first successful cloning of a mammal from the cells of an adult sheep at the Roslin Institute in Edinburgh. The news immediately provoked debates in the Norwegian parliament and lead to a prohibition law on cloning as early as March. *Aftenposten* reported on the matter frequently and covered the debate that followed. This is one of the main reasons for the significant change in framing occurring in the coverage these years – from progress to accountability. Just as clearly, the debate on regulation of GM food and GM crops was another contributing factor to the stage shift – a question that has been ever-present in the Norwegian biotechnology debate since the end of 1996. The predominance of risk-only stories completes the picture presented above: Dolly and GM food as manifestations of biotechnology were no longer understood as vague, future possibilities, but as 'the real thing' – here and now.

Phase 3 (2000–): economics. A prognosis made for the year 2000 shows interesting results.[22] The indications are tentative, but the change in journalistic framing is convincing and suggests that a new agenda is in the making. Cloning and GM food are being superseded by medicine and economics as main frames in *Aftenposten*'s coverage of biotechnology. Furthermore, the business category makes its first appearance as main actor, and the number of positive articles by far outweigh the negative ones. Obviously, the announced completion of the mapping of the human genome has contributed to this change. A look at some of the news headlines attests to this, and illustrates the connection often made between the Human Genome Project and economic prospects: 'New billion-industry when all the genes are identified', 'The gene-economy is here', 'Vital importance for the pharmaceutical industry'. Last, but not least, benefit-only stories take prominence in the press coverage for the first time.

This new and still uncertain trend might indicate a more general and also more international change towards the growing application of biotechnology and gene technology in industry.

From scientific progress to accountability and regulation, from accountability to economy – this is the historical record of changes in the years 1994 to 2000. In the following section, the continuities in the debate will be brought into focus: what are the general characteristics of *Aftenposten*'s coverage of biotechnology over this period?

Scientists' agenda: medicine and food

Medical articles have the highest frequency in the theme category, followed by food and agriculture. In the evaluation and benefit/risk categories, a distinct pattern is discernible. A positive evaluation comprises 44 per cent of all articles on medical issues, with only 22 per cent negative. Also, 37 per cent of these articles mention benefits exclusively, while 23 per cent are categorised as 'risk-only' articles. The reverse is true for the food category: 56 per cent of the stories are negative and 13 per cent positive. As for benefits, they are mentioned in 10 per cent of the instances, while risk issues cover 47 per cent.

This trend is unambiguous, especially taking into consideration that the Norwegians underwent quite an intense debate on abortion and IVF, which triggered a negative tone in many of the medical articles. Regarding themes and valuations, *Aftenposten*'s coverage mirrors the preferences of the Norwegian population: positive on medical applications of biotechnology, but negative on GM food and agriculture (see 'Public perceptions' below).

As for actors, a main assumption was the existence of a correlation between journalistic framing and type of actor mentioned, e.g. the change from 'progress' in phase 1 to 'accountability' (regulation) in phase 2, meant that a corresponding shift in the actor category from 'science' to 'politics' was expected. This turned out not to be the case. As can be seen in Table 1, 'science' operates as the dominant actor in both phases, which means that the scientists must be considered agenda-setters or opinion-leaders in the media coverage of biotechnology and gene technology. These scientists will have an influence on changes in the framing as well – especially when they announce breakthroughs of worldwide importance. The breaking of the news about Dolly the sheep then, probably contributed to the change in framing from progress to accountability, while the news about the completion of the mapping of the human genome initiated another change, this time to economics.

This last observation further confirms the trend discussed in relation to themes above: the coverage tends to be positive for the greater part when the scientific breakthroughs can be related to medical issues; the positively oriented articles constitute 53 per cent in the year 2000.

General patterns in press coverage

We can conclude that no major trends, whether in the positive or negative direction, easily suggests themselves regarding the coverage of biotechnology in *Aftenposten*. However, two more general patterns can be detected that deserve special mention. These patterns concern a different type of valuation than that discussed so far, as they occur at issue-level and within the first few days following a general announcement. Furthermore, they apply to the Norwegian newspaper coverage in its entirety. In the first pattern, valuation develops in cycles, while in the second, it operates simultaneously in several directions.

Biotechnology framed as scientific progress, technical ability and moral undesirability. Norwegian press coverage of the story on Dolly the sheep underwent three, very common stages, each with a specific framing. In the first stage *scientific progress* was accentuated and the stories were informative and descriptive rather than critical. For instance, *Aftenposten* and *Dagbladet* reported: 'Cloned sheep – a breakthrough for the scientists'; 'British scientists have cloned sheep'.

The second stage elaborates on the – often science-fiction-like – technical possibilities awaiting us as a consequence of the scientific breakthrough described in the first stage. We are told that Norwegian scientists possess, like Dr Frankenstein, the knowledge it takes to clone humans. In another article, it is claimed that 'Human cloning is in the offing'.

However, in the third stage, scientific progress and the technical possibilities are often transformed into something morally undesirable. *Aftenposten* wrote that the Norwegian politicians reacted to the lack of legal regulation and would 'ask for a ban on cloning in Norway'. *Dagbladet* reported on the sceptical opinion regarding cloning in an article called 'The fear of Dolly'. The triumph of progress has, the journalist claimed, once again created its own negation.

Biotechnology framed as knowledge of disease and as the potential for better health. Regarding medical applications, the Norwegian newspapers often alternate between framing biotechnology and gene technology as diagnostic knowledge into unavoidable disease as

Table 1. Norwegian media profile, 1994–2000 (threshold for inclusion: 5 per cent)

Phase	1994–96		1997–99		2000–[a]	
Frequency (%)[b]	29		50		21	
Frame (%)	**Progress**[c]	37	**Accountability**	32	**Economic**	29
	Accountability	20	Progress	31	Accountability	23
	Ethical	17	Ethical	12	Progress	20
					Ethical	15
Theme (%)	**Medical**	37	**Medical**	34	**Medical**	37
	Agrifood	33	Agrifood	24	Regulation	21
	Generic research	14	Cloning	12	Agrifood	17
	Genetic identity	7	Generic research	11	Generic research	11
Actor (%)	**Science**	37	**Science**	44	**Business**	28
	Politics	28	Politics	24	Science	21
	Business	17	Business	15	Politics	20
Benefit/risk (%)	**Both**	44	**Risk only**	36	**Benefit only**	37
	Risk only	28	Both	31	Both	32
	Benefit only	25	Benefit only	28	Risk only	30
Valuation (%)[d]	**Negative**	36	**Both**	38	**Positive**	53
	Both	31	Positive	31	Negative	27
	Positive	31	Negative	25	Both	20
Location (%)	**Norway**	62	**Norway**	53	**Norway**	51
	USA	13	USA	14	World	18
	World	9	Britain	8	USA	14
			World	8	Britain	6

a Prognosis for the year 2000, based on coded articles from January through June.
b Only values of corpus in the period; $n = 570$.
c Bold indicates highest frequency within phase.
d The valuation category is based on tone as set by the author of the article.

well as therapy, i.e. as a possibility for recovering health. On 6 November 1998, *Aftenposten* wrote that genes contain 'your own medical record, before illness actually occurs', and *Dagbladet* claimed that 'A gene test will reveal your future'. The yoke of unavoidable disease is, however, often turned into the possibility for freedom and health: on 12 January 1998, both *VG* and *Dagbladet* presented on their front pages the news that it was now possible to order eggs, sperm and a surrogate womb separately over the internet, and so combine them at will. In another article from 8 March the same year, *VG* offered busy women of today the possibility of freezing their own eggs, so as to give birth whenever it suited their careers.

Public perceptions

Informed scepticism

Already during the preparation of the two comprehensive Acts, national surveys found that the

Norwegian public met new biotechnology and gene technology with severe reservations and scepticism. Norwegian politicians, journalists and public administrators have ever since emphasised the harmony or concordance between the restrictive laws and the sceptical public – sometimes provoking circular arguments, explaining the one with the other.

The three Eurobarometer surveys during the 1990s have all confirmed this image and elaborated on it by depicting the combination or coexistence of very low expectations with relatively high knowledge of biotechnology and gene technology. The scepticism is informed.

In 1999, with 32 per cent 'optimists' expecting biotechnology and gene technology to improve our way of life and 37 per cent 'pessimists' expecting things to get worse, Norwegian expectations ranked second last among the 16 nations (surpassed only by Greece). However, with 54 per cent correct answers on the knowledge scale, Norwegians were also well above the EU average in 'cognitive' knowledge. Other northern European nations like

Denmark and the UK share the combination of low expectations and high knowledge, while a number of southern European nations like Spain and Portugal are characterised by the opposite combination of high expectations and low knowledge (Table 2).

However, the low Norwegian expectations of biotechnology and gene technology are not merely an expression of a general techno-pessimism or enmity. Norwegian expectations of the four most positively considered technologies were on a par with the European average. In 1999, 75 per cent of EU citizens and 72 per cent of the Norwegians were optimists about telecommunications, solar energy, and computers and the internet, while only 5 per cent of EU citizens and 6 per cent of Norwegians considered themselves pessimists. Nevertheless, Norwegian expectations towards the three new technologies generally regarded most negatively, were strongly more negative than the European average: 50 per cent of EU citizens and 41 per cent of Norwegians were optimistic about space exploration, 41 per cent of EU citizens and 32 per cent of Norwegians were optimists about biotechnology and gene technology, and 28 per cent of EU citizens and 14 per cent of Norwegians were optimists about atomic energy.

It is more surprising however, that low expectations also declined steadily during the 1990s. The 1993 survey had 8 per cent more optimists than pessimists, the 1996 survey had 4 per cent more optimists than pessimists, while the pessimists outnumbered the optimists by 5 per cent in the 1999 survey. The gradual increase in acceptance often expected of new technologies had not taken place.

During the same decade European expectations had – although from a much higher point of departure – declined at a similar rate. In 1993, the EU had 25 per cent more optimists than the Norwegians, in 1996, 22 per cent and in 1999, 23 per cent. The distance or discrepancy between the higher expectations of Europeans and the lower of Norwegians has thus remained the same.

Lack of knowledge is a very widespread explanation for the low expectations and the deep scepticism in the population. Researchers, industrialists, entrepreneurs and educators are often united in the 'scientistic' expectation, that if people had only known better, they would have been more accepting. Thus, concerning the 1993 Eurobarometer, the semi-official INRA report interpreted 'support for biotechnology/genetic engineering, as well as "optimism" regarding it, as a positive function of what is known on the subject'.[23]

Three sets of findings seem, however, to contradict this widespread scientism and its strategy of enlightenment. First, as already mentioned, a ranking of the nations does not indicate any close relationship between knowledge and expectations or acceptance (Table 3). Second, within most of the European nations the correlation between knowledge and expectations is positive, but low. The Norwegian data from 1993, 1996 and 1999 have all been analysed and published,[24] and the

Table 2. General expectations and knowledge of biotechnology and gene technology, 1999

Expectation that biotechnology will improve our way of life (% respondents)		Knowledge of biotechnology (% correct answers on 10 questions)	
Spain	41	Netherlands	64
Netherlands	33	Denmark	63
Portugal	26	Finland	58
Belgium	24	France	56
France	19	Belgium	55
Luxemburg	19	**Norway**	54
EU	18	United Kingdom	53
Germany	18	Luxemburg	53
Italy	16	**EU**	52
Ireland	11	Germany	51
Finland	11	Italy	49
United Kingdom	4	Austria	49
Austria	3	Greece	48
Denmark	−1	Spain	48
Norway	−5	Ireland	48
Greece	−20	Portugal	38

Positive values, respondents encouraged, definitely agree and tend to agree; negative values, respondents discourage, definitely disagree and tend to disagree.

Table 3. General expectations of biotechnology and gene technology: Norway and EU, 1991–99

Norway	1991	1993	1996	1999
Optimists (%)	–	36	34	32
Undecided (%)	–	36	36	30
Pessimists (%)	–	28	30	37
EU	**1991**	**1993**	**1996**	**1999**
Optimists (%)	50	48	46	41
Undecided (%)	38	37	34	36
Pessimists (%)	11	15	20	23

Table 4. Norwegian attitudes to applications of biotechnology and gene technology in medicine and agriculture, 1996 and 1999

Applications	Year	Positive[a] (%)	Undecided (%)	Negative[b] (%)
Introducing human genes into bacteria	1996	57	23	20
to produce medicines or vaccines	1999	57	14	29
Using genetic testing to detect hereditary	1996	54	19	27
diseases	1999	53	15	31
Transferring genes from plant species into	1996	39	15	46
crop plants to make them more resistant to	1999	32	18	50
insect pests				
Using modern biotechnology in the	1996	31	15	54
production of foods	1999	25	13	62

a Positive, respondents encouraged, definitely agree and tend to agree.

b Negative, respondents encouraged, definitely disagree and tend to disagree.

low positive correlations point to two other explanations:

- With increased knowledge the decline in the numbers of 'undecided' is greater than the increase in optimists. With increased knowledge more people have a point of view and take a stand, either as optimists or as pessimists.

- A relatively large segment of the population combines high knowledge with scepticism and pessimism towards biotechnology and gene technology.

Third, a simultaneous decline in expectations and a small increase in knowledge have marked development during the 1990s. Over time, expectations have declined in spite of a minor increase in knowledge.

Medicine and agriculture

Further examination of these low general expectations reveals a huge difference between the medical applications regulated by the Biotechnology Act of 1994 and agriculture (or food production) regulated by the Gene Technology Act of 1993 (Table 4).

Production of medicines and vaccines is more acceptable than genetic testing for hereditary diseases, but the two medical applications posed by the survey in 1996 and 1999 both found an overwhelming majority in favour of encouragement.

Scepticism towards food production is stronger than that towards plant pest resistance, but the two agriculture applications mentioned by the survey in 1996 and 1999 both have a smaller, but marked, majority against encouragement.

Applications in the field of health are encouraged but those in food production are not. The general decline in support from 1996 to 1999 hit both, but food more than medicine, so the difference has increased.

Analyses of the Eurobarometer data indicate that the Norwegian public – in spite of the low level of overall encouragement – share the apparent general pattern of public perception where 'usefulness' is considered a precondition for support, whereas some risk seems to be acceptable so long as there is a perception of usefulness and no moral concern, and 'moral doubts' can be used as a veto irrespective of views on use and risk.[26]

The *Sonderweg* of the Norwegian legislation and regulation might have anticipated or found procedures to handle and administrate the way the three criteria, i.e. usefulness, risk, and moral acceptability, combine to constitute overall encouragement.

The Gene Technology Act prescribes for deliberate release of GMOs so that 'significant emphasis shall also be placed on whether the deliberate release represents a benefit to the community and a contribution to sustainable development' (§10) – as the public seems to consider 'usefulness to society' as a precondition for encouragement.

- Risk assessment is an important part of the approvals procedure, but neither the law nor public opinion demands zero risk. The law prescribes 'no risk of detrimental effects on health and the environment' (§10). Moreover acceptable risks should be weighed against benefits, and alternative and the best-available technologies.

- The public seem to consider moral acceptability in the same absolute, duty-ethical, Kantian sense as the legal standards in the Norwegian Acts, which have also increasingly found their way into international declarations and agreements.

Traditional 'blue' critique and modern 'green' scepticism

Norwegian scepticism is so widespread and apparently persistent because it is made up of and combines a 'traditional' and a 'modern' segment of the population, respectively backed by 'blue' and 'green' values and expressing heterogeneous and partly incompatible concerns.[26]

In 1996, general expectations of biotechnology divided the Norwegians into three almost equal thirds. Then, 36 per cent were 'optimists' in the sense that they expected modern biotechnology to make daily life better; 29 per cent were 'pessimists' in the sense that they expected biotechnology to make daily life worse, and 35 per cent answered 'don't know' or expected 'no effect'.

The optimists share the characteristics that are generally expected to be found among entrepreneurs. The typical optimist is a well-educated young man with an urban residence. He combines good knowledge of biotechnology with a perception of low risk. He places himself to the right of the traditional political spectrum.

The 'undecided' and the 'pessimists' are at first glance less distinct groups. Nevertheless, a cluster analysis reveals that the pessimists are made up of two hitherto rather unnoticed or neglected but highly distinct groups, named 'traditional' and 'modern', and constituting 12 per cent and 16 per cent of the population. The traditional and the modern pessimists differ from the optimists by an over-representation of women with rural residences and perceptions of high risk regarding modern biotechnology. Apart from these three common characteristics, the two types of pessimists show systematic and marked contrasts. The traditional is older, the modern younger. The traditional completed education after primary school, the modern after university. The traditional has little knowledge, the modern extensive knowledge of biotechnology. The traditional inclines towards the centre and right of the political spectrum, whereas the modern is oriented towards the left. The traditional is strongly religious, the modern strongly non-believer; and the traditional is materialist, the modern postmaterialist.

The Norwegian data indicate the traditional and the modern sceptics as two well-defined and consequently separated types. The profiles do, however, also indicate that the modern sceptics generally share more characteristics with the optimists than with the traditional sceptics. It is neither socio-economic background, nor education or knowledge of biotechnology, but gender and general values such as political orientation, religion, attitude towards modernity and perception of risk that distinguish the 'modern sceptic' from the 'optimist'.

Traditional and modern sceptics share the assumption that modern biotechnology will make our way of life worse, but this shared assumption is backed up by different arguments and conclusions.

The 'blue' argument has no external references. It is closed and centres on its own values. It questions technological intervention in nature as such. Its modality is 'in the "nature" of things'. Without rebuttals, an alteration of values alone can change the conclusion.

The 'green' argument on the other hand refers to (perceived) uncertainty and risk as its principal warrant. The backing to this argument evaluates uncertainty against knowledge and risks against benefits. Its modality is conditioned: 'at the present stage' of technology and knowledge. The rebuttal makes it possible to reach another conclusion: with increased and certain knowledge and/or less (perception of) risk, the argument might transform into or lead to the same conclusion as the optimists.

The concerns behind the arguments are as different as the social groups expressing them are distinct. The 'blue' argument is backed by moral (or religious) values, the 'green' by uncertainty and risk. The blue critique is Faustian. The whole enterprise of biotechnology is perceived as a modern covenant with Mephisto. Even in the form of a technical success, modern biotechnology pawns the soul. Insight into the nature of nature is problematic as such. The green scepticism is more 'Frankensteinian'. Insufficient knowledge of the consequences, not the insight itself, is problematic. The danger is the possibility of the technology going its own uncontrolled way, and thus turning into a monster or demon. Experiments with life might be unforeseen and unintentionally take the power from its creator.

Modern biotechnology is met and surrounded by a pre-industrial critique of intervention in nature's own order as such, as well as a post-industrial critique of the new technologically created and partly unintended risks. The classic diffusion model of technological innovation is thus contradicted or falsified by the lasting and wide-spread mobilisation against the technology. Two types of opposition modify the mobilisation model: one in favour of the old order of tradition, the other directed against the new risks.

Acknowledgement

Our thanks to Nick Allum, Øyvind Giæver, Helge Torgersen and Marianne Ødegaard for comments on an earlier draft. Parts of this article are based on Hviid Nielsen, T, Monsen, A and Tennøe, T, *Livets tre og kodenes kode: Fra genetikk til bioteknologi, Norge 1900–2000* (Oslo: Gyldendal, 2000).

Notes and references

1 Ministry of the Environment, *Act No. 38 of 2 April 1993 Relating to the Production and Use of Genetically Modified Organisms* (Gene Technology Act); Ministry of Health and Social Affairs, *Act No. 56 of 5 August 1994 Relating to the Application of Biotechnology in Medicine* (Biotechnology Act).

2 Ministry of Health and Social Affairs, *Act No. 68 of 12 June 1987 Relating to Artificial Procreation.* In 1994, this Act was incorporated in the Biotechnology Act (see note 1).

3 An important precursor to the controversy was the disclosure by the national broadcasting agency of the experiments with human genes in salmon in 1985.

4 *Stortingets Forhandlinger* (1988–89), pp3696–703.

5 Jasanoff, S, 'Product, process, or program: three cultures and the regulation of biotechnology', in Bauer, M (ed.), *Resistance to New Technology* (Cambridge: Cambridge University Press, 1995), pp311–31.

6 Gene Technology Act (see note 1), §1.

7 Biotechnology Act (see note 1), §1-1.

8 EU directive 90/219/EU on the contained use of genetically modified microorganisms.

9 *Stortingets Forhandlinger* (1992–93), p473. Spokeswoman Anne-Lise Dørum quoted.

10 Research Council, *Perspektivanalyse og handlingsplan for bioteknologi 1995–2005* (Oslo: 1995).

11 Ernst & Young, European Biotech 97: 'A new economy', *The Fourth Annual Ernst & Young Report on the European Biotechnology Industry* (Stuttgart: Ernst & Young International, 1997), p17.

12 Norges Offentlige Utredninger (NOU 1990: 1), *Modern Biotechnology. Health, Safety and the Environment*, spec. VII.

13 Norges Offentlige Utredninger (NOU 1991: 6), *Man and Biotechnology*, spec. IV. Quotes from p44.

14 Ministry of the Environment, *Concerning Biotechnology, Parliamentary Proposition No. 8* (1990–91).

15 Ministry of the Environment, *Additional Proposition Concerning Biotechnology, Parliamentary Proposition No. 36* (1990–91).

16 Norges offentlige utredninger (NOU: 21/22), *Forsikringsselskapers innhenting, bruk og lagring av helseopplysninger [The obtaining, use and storage of health information by insurance companies]*.

17 While the policy section above covers the period 1976–2000, the section on media coverage concentrates the attention on the years 1994–2000. Accordingly there is no correspondence between the 'phases' referred to in the two sections.

18 The statistics in this section were obtained from: Forbruker & Media <http://www.gallup.no/menu/media/aviser/Aviser001/sld008.htm>; Statistisk Årbok 2000

<http://www.ssb.no/aarbok/tab/t-070130-306.html>.

19 The data are from the Norwegian Eurobarometer, 1999.

20 Solli, J, *Dolly de Luxe, Report 5/00* (Trondheim: Senter for Bygdeforskning, 2000); Magnus, T, *Mat i Media, Report 6/00* (Trondheim: Senter for Bygdeforskning, 2000); Dahl, A J, *Dolly i mediene* (Trondheim, 2000); Dahl, A J, *Dokumentarium over Artikler Skrevet om Kloning i Norske Aviser i Perioden 23 Februar 1997 – 1 Juni 1999* (Trondheim, 2000).

21 The newspaper articles on biotechnology and gene technology, covering the period from 1994 through June 2000, were obtained electronically. Of 1066 hits, 517 were selected for coding and analysis.
The relatively big discrepancy between the number of hits and the selected articles is due to a number of reasons: we decided to omit articles printed in the more locally oriented evening edition of *Aftenposten*; we excluded hits which turned out to be irrelevant; many stories which mentioned biotechnology only in passing were left out.

22 The prognosis (120 articles) is based on coded articles from January through June 2000 (66 articles)

multiplied by 1.8, expressing the relationship between the first and last six months of each year.

23 INRA/European Coordination Office, *Biotechnology and Genetic Engineering, What Europeans Think About It* (European Commission, 1993).

24 The Norwegian 1993 data are reported and discussed in Hviid Nielsen, T, 'Modern biotechnology – sustainability and integrity', in Lundin, S and Ideland, M (eds), *Gene Technology and the Public* (Lund: Nordic Academic Press, 1997), pp102–20. The 1996 data are reported in Hviid Nielsen, T, 'Nyt om bioteknologi og opinion: fire intervensjoner', *Working Paper No. 108* (Oslo: Centre for Technology and Culture, 1998); and the 1999 data are reported in Lund, M, Hviid Nielsen, T and Kalgraff Skjåk, K, *Norske holdninger til bioteknologi* [*Norwegian Attitudes to Biotechnology*] (Oslo: Norsk samfunnsvitenskapelig datatjeneste, 2000).

25 Biotechnology and the European Public Concerted Action Group, 'Europe ambivalent on biotechnology', *Nature*, 387 (1997), pp845–7.

26 See also Hviid Nielsen, T, 'Behind the color code of "no"', *Nature Biotechnology*, 15 (1997), pp1320–1.

Address for correspondence

Professor Torben Hviid Nielsen, Centre for technology, innovation and culture, University of Oslo, PO Box 1108 Blindern, N-0317 Oslo, Norway. E-mail t.h.nielsen@tik.uio.no

Poland: arrival of the Gene Law

Andrzej Przestalski, Bolesław Suchocki and Tomasz Twardowski

Introduction

So far, biotechnology in Poland has not left the laboratory stage. The principal actors on the scene are the scientific community, carrying out the research and promoting biotechnology, and the government, financing science and creating legislation. The legislation, though actively developed in the late 1990s, by mid-2001 had reached a form that facilitates industrial and agricultural applications of biotechnology and market presence of GM food. The Gene Law was passed by parliament on 11 May 2001 and signed by the president on 10 July.[1] Until very recently the press coverage of biotechnology had been characterised by a definite technological optimism. In the 1970s to mid-1990s, coverage was restricted to reports of Western developments in biotechnology. Only in recent years has some kind of debate started, covering risks and moral aspects of biotechnology, although the focus on benefits is still dominant.

Public policy

GMO release and related events

Between 1996 and 2000, the role that biotechnological issues played on the public scene increased noticeably. In January 1997, commercial companies sought government permission to introduce GMOs into the environment. In March of the same year, a meeting of the Ministries of the Environment and Agriculture was held, with several high-level administrative officers and scientific advisors present. This led to preliminary approval for GMO release in Poland, for the purpose of scientific experiments, to be conducted under strict supervision of competent authorities. In summer 1997, three GMO plants (maize, rape and potato) were approved for release into the environment. In 1998 there were 20 releases (maize, rape, cucumber, beet and potato), and in 1999 ten such releases (maize, rape and potato). In 1996 the first genetic screening for cancer was carried out on a limited number of volunteers. The community of biotechnologists together with the Biotechnology Committee prepared a third report on the state of biotechnology, which was published at the end of 1997.[2] In September 1999 the First Congress on Biotechnology was held in Wrocław.

In 1996 an important actor entered the biotechnological scene: the 'Green' movement, related to and supported by international NGOs such as Greepeace. Critical of biotechnology in general, it started by protesting against Poland's involvement in the import of transgenic food products from the USA to Europe and the rumoured release of transgenic carp in Poland. In the spring of 1997, the Greens focused their interest on the cloning of Dolly the sheep. In June 2000 they published a report, *What's for Dinner, Mamma?*, warning against GM food.[3] These events had a significant impact on the biotechnological awareness of the general public and were indirectly one of the reasons why biotechnology became an issue raised frequently by the press.

Legislation

This short period was also significant from the legislative point of view. In November 1996, a new parliamentary law concerning environmental protection was debated. A separate section of the law was devoted to biotechnology. It provided for a competent authority to grant permits for GMO releases – an authority that would cooperate closely with the Ministries of the Environment and Agriculture. In September 1997, the Polish president signed the law. At the end of 1997, Polish experts prepared a draft of the Gene Law, based on EU directives 90/219 and 90/220, which two years later (December 1999) was presented to the government. The ministerial draft of the Polish Gene Law proposed by the government in May 2000 resulted in some visibility. It was heavily criticised both for poor integration with EU directives and for its inadequate scientific background. Table 1 outlines the key policy events.

There were other steps towards the implementation of EU directives. In October 1999 the government published technical directives

Table 1. Key policy events in Poland, 1996–2000

Date	Trigger	Event	Outcome
June 1996	GMO committee	Formation of the experts committee for the elaboration of technical guidelines under the auspices of Ministry of Agriculture; the interministerial counselling board for GMOs was established (Ministry of Agriculture, Ministry of Health, Ministry of Environment Protection and State Committee for Scientific Research).	This body took responsibility for evaluation of GMO release in the environment (risk evaluation and risk management).
Summer 1997	GMO release	Three releases of GM plants (maize, rape and potato).	Experiments were done according to EU standards under strict supervision of experts appointed by Ministry of Agriculture.
September 1997	Legislation of GMOs	President signs a new law concerning environment protection including several aspects of biodiversity and introduction of GMOs to the environment (article 37a of the law). Commercial GMO planting under this law is not possible.	The only legislation concerning GMO release and contained use; very significant for the development of biotechnology in Poland.
November 1997	National Gene Law proposed	The expert team elaborates the project of a Gene Law presented to competent state authorities and to the government. The project is based on EU directives 90/219 and 90/220.	No interest expressed by the government (see May 2000).
Summer 1998	GMO release	Twenty releases of GM plants (maize, rape, cucumber, beet and potato)	Experiments carried out according to EU standards under strict supervision of experts appointed by Ministry of Agriculture.
Summer 1999	GMO release	Ten releases of GM plants (maize, rape and potato).	Experiments supervised by experts appointed by Ministry of Agriculture; administrative restrictions were the reason for the reduction in the number of experiments.
June 1999	Survey of public attitudes to GMOs and biotechnology	On limited scale the Eurobarometer was reproduced; first solid data on public perception available in Central and Eastern Europe (CEE).	Conclusions: two-thirds of Polish society ready to accept GM food; 90 per cent want state supervision and legislation of biotechnology; high similarity of Poland with USA.
September 1999	First National Congress on Biotechnology	Special day-long session dedicated to legislation and biosafety; summary of national biotechnology (state of the art) produced.	Serious interest by mass media and public; special report mailed to parliament stressing the urgent need for biotechnology legislation.
	Elaboration of the National Biosafety Programme	Within the frame of the Global Environment Facility project, with international cooperation.	Establishment of the national frame programme for biosafety.
October 1999	Establishment of the first GMO information office in CEE	Initiative of scientists, with financial support from the European Federation for Biotechnology and the EU.	Lots of interest from mass media; significant output on information policy.
	Food labelling	Government published technical directives concerning labelling, introduction into environment and trade of GMOs. No commercial planting of GMOs is possible under this law.[4]	The law comes into force on 23 April 2000.

Table 1. Key policy events in Poland, 1996–2000 (continued)

Date	Trigger	Event	Outcome
December 1999	Gene Law	Presentation to the government of the draft of the Polish Gene Law by a team of biotechnologists and lawyers.	High media coverage, but the project has not been accepted.
April 2000	Food labelling	According to the law (published 22 October 1999) the government published technical directives concerning labelling, GMO release and trading. Labelling law comes into force.	Labelling does not occur until end of June.
May 2000	Biosafety Protocol	Biosafety Protocol (Rio de Janeiro Convention) signed by Polish delegation (Nairobi, Kenya)	Common misinterpretation that global Gene Law was formulated; 50 ratifications required for international law.
	Green's report	Polish Greens published a report, *What's for Dinner, Mamma?* (a significantly different English edition was published simultaneously on the Internet).	Much less public attention than for the first report (dated 1996); the report warns of GM food dangers; limited mass media coverage.
	Gene Law	Presentation by the government of the ministerial draft of the Polish Gene Law.	High coverage given, but the project was heavily criticised for lack of unification with EU directives and lack of scientific background; work in progress.
June 2000	Biotechnology legislation	According to a declaration by the Polish government, Poland will adjust national legislation to EU standards by the end of 2002.	Much public discussion in mass media, parliament and in scientific societies.
10 May 2001	Biotechnology legislation	Polish parliament (Sejm) passed the Polish Gene Law.	Much public discussion in mass media, parliament and in scientific societies.
11 July 2001	Biotechnology legislation	Polish president signed the Polish Gene Law; this law comes into force on 25 October 2001.[5]	Restrictive character of the law catalysed many critical comments from scientists and industrialists; surprisingly, the 'Greens' are not happy with the legislation either.

concerning labelling, deliberate releases of GMOs, and a prohibition on any commercial planting of GMOs. The law came into force in April 2000. Since then the labelling of GM food has been mandatory. A new law (1 January 1999) concerning environment protection covers several aspects of biodiversity and the deliberate release of GMOs into the environment. The Polish Gene Law covers biotechnology and genetic engineering and will be in force by the end of 2001 (within three months of the president's signing it). Therefore, the Polish biotechnological scene finally has the Gene Law. This will mark the transition of biotechnology from the laboratory to industry, agriculture and market.[6]

Ethical committees

The late 1990s witnessed the establishing of a system of ethical committees in Poland. Although the scope of their interests is beyond science, their existence is one of the preconditions for the development of biotechnology. Two ethical institutions have been created: one on animal issues and the other on humans. This was a governmental initiative, motivated both by the desire to accommodate the Polish law to that of the EU and by pressure from scientists themselves.

Until 2000, ethical questions concerning research on animals were left to the university authorities (rectors) or non-university institute authorities (directors). In fact there were no special ethical guidelines; instead, ethical questions were taken into consideration more or less systematically and intuitively as one of the criteria used for the approval of scientific projects. Yet some universities in the 1990s established their own ethics committees. In 1997 parliament passed the Animal Protection Law, but it took three years (until May 2000) for the National Ethical Committee for Experiments on Animals, as well as 16 local ethical committees, to be established under the law. They started work in October 2000. Ethical institutions concerning research on humans are closely linked to medical academies. In the 1990s, medical academies had their own ethics committees for clinical and experimental research which acted more or less independently from each other. In addition, there was a chain of committees for supervision of research on humans at national and local levels established by the Minister of Health and Social Care. In 1999 these were replaced by a system of ethical bodies including Bioethical Committees at Medical Chambers, Bioethical Commissions at Medical Academies and Bioethical Commissions at Medical Research Institutes.

Media coverage

The newspapers chosen as representative of the coverage were a national daily, *Rzeczpospolita*, with a circulation of 210,000, and a national weekly, *Polityka*, with a circulation of 210,000. Both are opinion leaders and address an educated audience.

The characteristic feature of the Polish press coverage of biotechnology to date is technological optimism. In the 1990s, however, the level of optimism started to decline: a trend which continued in the latest phase of coverage (1997–99). The indicators of change in press attitude in the phase 1990–96 included the diminishing framing of general and consumer benefits and of economic prospects, and the emergence of ethical issues, which implies a consideration of concerns and risks (Table 2). While these trends have not reversed the general optimism about biotechnology, they have contributed to a more balanced image of biotechnology.

The phase 1997–99 shows a continuation of the trend. The sample consisted of 158 articles published in both newspapers. The coverage stabilised at a relatively high level. The most frequent theme in the press at that time was one that had not existed before: cloning (28 per cent). The second most frequent was ethical issues (17

Table 2. Polish media profile, 1973–99 (threshold for inclusion: 5 per cent)

Phases	1973–79		1980–89		1990–96		1997–99	
Frequency[a] (%)	10		20		32		38	
Frame (%)	**Progress**	56	**Progress**	75	**Progress**	79	**Progress**	60
	Ethical	15	Economic prospect	12	Economic prospect	7	Nature/nuture	8
	Economic prospect	13	Runaway	5	Ethical	6	Pandora's box	8
	Nature/nurture	8					Ethical	8
	Pandora's box	5					Economic prospect	7
							Runaway	6
Theme (%)	**Medical**	36	**Generic research**	39	**Medical**	51	**Medical**	48
	Agriculture	26	Medical	27	Animal	15	Generic research	8
	Generic research	18	Animal	8	Generic research	14	Animal	8
	Ethics	8	Public opinion	7	Agriculture	5	Agriculture	6
	Animal	5	Agriculture	6	Genetic identity	5		
	Regulation	5						
Actor (%)	**Scientific**	77	**Scientific**	82	**Scientific**	83	**Scientifc**	70
	Political	8	Industry	11	Industry	9	Industry	11
							Political	5
Benefit/risk (%)	**Benefit only**	49	**Benefit only**	66	**Benefit only**	66	**Benefit only**	52
	Both	41	Both	27	Both	28	Both	32
	Neither	8	Neither	5	Neither	5	Neither	9
							Risk only	8
Location (%)	**Other Europe**	36	**USA**	26	**USA**	36	**USA**	48
	USA	18	Other Europe	21	Other Europe	17	World	11
	USSR	13	France	8	UK	10	UK	10
	UK	10	UK	7	France	5	Other Europe	8

a Percentage of corpus in the period; $n = 207$
b Bold indicates highest frequency within phase.

per cent) and then human genome (16 per cent) and gene therapy (16 per cent). The biotechnological events were located (if any location was given) in the USA (48 per cent), the UK (10 per cent), other European countries (11 per cent), and rest of the world (11 per cent). Poland was a location in 5 per cent of the articles. The composition of actors involved reflects that of the themes: main actors were universities (54 per cent), government research institutions (12 per cent), scientists in private laboratories (10 per cent), hospitals (4 per cent) and government (2 per cent).

Articles that do not mention any benefits amount to 17 per cent, while those with no risks mentioned represent 61 per cent. Those that contain no negative valuation form 17 per cent of coverage and those containing no positive evaluation form 61 per cent (Table 3). Nevertheless the trend is obvious. The signs of a new, more critical and reserved tone of the phase compared to the preceding ones are: articles with no benefits mentioned, 17 per cent (compared with 10 per cent before); articles with economic benefits mentioned, 11 per cent (previously 20 per cent); articles with consumer benefits mentioned, 6 per cent (previously 11 per cent). Articles mentioning all other benefits except health, moral and research dropped in number while those mentioning risk increased in number. Economic, health, moral, military and research risks are mentioned more often, while those concerning social equality and environment have remained at the previous level. 'Pandora's box' and 'runaway' frames of articles are now found considerably more often. Similar changes are evident in television coverage of biotechnology.

Public perceptions

Student responses

In 1999 a third wave of a survey conducted every 18 months interviewed 400 students of health promotion, public health and general medicine

from the Medical Academy and of social sciences from the Adam Mickiewicz University in Poznań. They were chosen as those who will shape the image of biotechnology in Poland in the future. The questionnaire used was the Eurobarometer 52.1, augmented by some additional questions. This allowed us to make comparisons with former research done in Poland indicating there was a differentiation in attitudes across practical applications of biotechnology (scientific laboratory vs mass application in everyday life) towards the field of application. An additional knowledge test was also included in the questionnaire.

The applications of biotechnology regarded as most useful were genetic testing for hereditary diseases (53 per cent) and production of medicines and vaccines by implanting human genes into bacteria (58 per cent). Yet while the conviction of the former was relatively steady, a scepticism towards the latter is emerging.

Thirty per cent of respondents regarded other applications of biotechnology as useful, for example increasing the protein content of food, prolonging durability, improving taste, transplanting plant genes to crop plants in order to make them resistant to insecticides, development of GM animals for laboratory studies, and implanting human genes into animals such as pigs for transplants. What is more, the usefulness of these applications, as perceived by the respondents, tends to slowly increase, and opinions of accompanying risk tend to drop. This optimistic tendency applies least of all to transplantation of plant genes to GM crops.

Perceptions of the moral acceptability of biotechnological applications divide into two categories. The first contains genetic testing, production of drugs and vaccines and transplantation of plant genes into crop plants: those viewing them as morally acceptable outnumber those who do not by more than 20 per cent. The other group containing the remaining applications is considered morally acceptable by the majority of respondents too, but the preponderance is less than 20 per cent. Generally, moral acceptance of biotechnology

Table 3. Tone of press coverage in Poland

	1973–79	*1980–89*	*1990–96*	*1997–99*
Slightly critical (%)	20.5	8.3	10.7	21.5
Somewhat critical (%)	2.6	4.8	0.8	12.0
Quite critical (%)	–	3.6	3.1	4.4
Very critical (%)	2.6	2.4	–	1.3

seems to be growing. It has dropped only with regard to using biotechnology for food production and implanting of human genes into bacteria. The moral evaluation of genetic testing has not changed between 1996 and 1999.

Objectively there is no direct relation between objective usefulness of a technology and a degree of risk accompanying it. There are technologies of great practical importance that carry hardly any risk or no risk at all, e.g. practical use of solar or wind energy, and those that carry great risk, e.g. chemical weapons or atomic energy. In everyday consciousness, however, the two phenomena seem to be perceived as not fully independent. When there is concern about perceived danger, a certain level of risk (including moral risk) ascribed to a phenomenon leads to diminished perceived usefulness. This seems to be the explanation for the difference of perceived usefulness in the case of genetic testing and transplantation of animal organs to humans. It could also explain why the sequence of six applications of biotechnology, arranged by the respondents according to their diminishing utility, is identical to that arranged by them according to their growing risk. This holds equally for other European countries.

Besides the evaluation of usefulness, risk and moral acceptance of the six biotechnologies, the respondents were asked their general attitude towards them. Their opinions allow us to judge whether they support various applications. Support for biotechnology tends to decrease in general, with the exception of using GM animals for laboratory studies and inserting human genes into animals to grow organs for transplantation. Applications that receive definite support are genetic testing (26 per cent) and production of medicines and vaccines by inserting human genes into bacteria (30 per cent). Comparing the percentages of respondents opposing particular biotechnology applications with those having moral reservations against them shows a varied pattern, but in circumstances of moral concern, there is very little chance of support.

The general public

At the same time we prepared and organised the first national survey of public perceptions of biotechnology, carried out on a representative sample in March 1999 by a professional public-opinion institute. The questionnaire was related to that of Eurobarometer 1999 but was considerably shorter and focused on GM food. The general public in Poland is much more in favour of novel technologies than in EU countries. The acceptance of GM food is similar to that of North America: about two-thirds of the population are ready to accept it, if the production and distribution is under strict supervision by law. Some 80 per cent of those who accept novel foods expect government supervision and labelling. Labelling seems to have an autonomous value for the respondents: it is appreciated not only for its role as source of practical information, but also as a privilege and expression of consumers' right to information and choice. As far as moral issues are concerned, reservations exceed acceptability only in the case of xenotransplantation (39 per cent) and GM food production (47 per cent). In other applications moral acceptance prevails: ecology (81 per cent), plant protection (66 per cent), production of new drugs and vaccines (65 per cent) and transgenic animals (56 per cent).

The survey showed that young, educated people are more ready to accept GM food than the adult public as a whole. On the other hand, the levels of acceptance of specific biotechnology applications among medical students are lower than in the general public. The differences are due to their type of education and levels of knowledge. A significant contribution to the body of opinion of the general public is made up of respondents who have not heard of biotechnology before. For instance, only six out of ten respondents have heard of biotechnology applied to food production. The result is that some of the responses may not be consistent and some lack cohesion. Some 70 per cent think genetic modification of food is useful and should be supported, but only 47 per cent think it is acceptable to alter nature in order to improve the quality of food. Only 32 per cent of the respondents do not see any risk for human health and environment in biotechnology applications, while 50 per cent do see such a risk.

In summer 2000 the survey was repeated. The only significant change was that the percentage of those who would buy GM food for a lower price diminished by 10 per cent (from 36 per cent).

Conclusions

Pressure from the scientific community, the need to adjust the Polish legislation to that of the EU, as well as economic considerations (applications for deliberate releases of GMOs by commercial companies) have contributed to moving the legislation process towards the first parliamentary reading of the Gene Law in 2001. In 2000 a new coherent national system of science-related ethical committees was initiated. The past trend of optimistic press coverage of biotechnology has been eroded and a new trend of scepticism in the press is noticeable. The opinions and attitudes of the general public, for the first time revealed in a representative national survey, show a lot of inconsistencies. Two-thirds of the general public are ready to accept GM food, although 40 per cent have never heard of it before and only 47 per cent consider it morally acceptable.

Notes and references

1 Michalska, A and Twardowski, T, *GMO a środowisko* [*GMOs and the Environment*] (Poznań: Edytor, 1997).

2 *Official Journal*, Dz. U. 25 July 2001, no.76, pos. 811.

3 Jermak, M, Kruszewska, I and Aken, J van, *Co na Obiad, Mamo?* [*What's for Dinner, Mamma?*] (Mure: ANPED, 2000).

4 *Official Journal*, Dz. U. 28 October 2000, pos. 962.

5 *Official Journal*, Dz. U. 25 July 2001, pos. 811.

6 Twardowski, T and Michalska, A. KOD: Korzysci, Oczekiwania, Dylemati Biotechnologii (Poznań: Edytor, 2001).

Address for correspondence

Professor Tomasz Twardowski, Institute for Bioorganic Chemistry, Polish Academy of Science, ul. Noskowskiego 12, 61-704 Poznań, Poland. E-mail twardows@ibch.poznan.pl

Representation of biotechnology in Portugal

Jorge Correia Jesuíno, João Arriscado Nunes, Carmen Diego, Pedro Alcântara, Susana Costa and Marisa Matias

Historical and political background

According to an eminent sociologist, Portuguese society can be described as 'semi-peripheral' within the world system, in the sense that the scientific–technological complex in Portugal is still undeveloped, in contrast to the consumption models which are much closer to those of the more advanced societies.[1] This situation is largely due to the inheritance of the fascist regime that ruled Portugal from 1926 until 1974. Science and technology were one of the casualties of the long dictatorship of that regime. Many of the best and most prestigious figures in Portuguese science and culture were evicted from universities because of their opposition to the regime. However, many of them were able to work and contribute to scientific and cultural developments while in exile. The educational system consisted mainly of a poorly staffed network of primary schools, which tended to promote the conservative ideology of the regime. Illiteracy was widespread and only a small fraction of the Portuguese population had access to secondary schools and universities. After the Second World War, gradual industrialisation led to a demand for qualified workers and managers. This trend forced the government, in the early 1960s, to make educational reforms based on a considerable expansion of the secondary and higher education systems.

The revolution in 1974 opened the way for the democratisation of Portuguese society. After this, successive attempts were made to reform the educational system and to encourage the return of many scientists, scholars and intellectuals. In spite of such efforts Portugal remains today, in terms of R&D, below the European average. The general expenditure on R&D as a percentage of GDP rose from 0.43 per cent in 1988 to 0.63 per cent in 1992. This growth has been accompanied by a change in the relative position of universities and state laboratories. From 1982 to 1988 R&D units in the university sector increased by 88 per cent.[2]

A factor that contributed significantly to the development of the Portuguese scientific system was membership of the EEC in 1986. Since then an ever-increasing push towards internationalisation can be observed in the Portuguese scientific communities. Another important turning point was the creation of the Ministry of Science and Technology in 1995. This led to a government strategy for science and technology, and to the creation of a national science and technology system. This system is composed of a network of research units, most of them located at or associated with public universities.

Research in the private sector was almost always insignificant in spite of the very rapid growth in the number of young, highly qualified scientists emerging from graduate programmes. Biomedical and life-sciences research was based on previous lines of work, carried out by scientists who had trained abroad and returned to Portugal. A small number of high-quality research units, with a strong emphasis on molecular biology and genetic research, were set up. In spite of these developments and of the considerable growth in the number of projects, researchers and graduate students, there was little impact on the development of related industries. Although there are some start-up companies in this area, biotechnology is still a weak sector in the Portuguese economy. This lack of visibility and strength may help to explain the negligible impact of biotechnological issues on public opinion.

Public policy

During the 1980s, new concerns arose in Portugal about the opportunities as well as the risks arising from rDNA techniques. These extended to issues related to human genetics in general, and in particular those associated with medically assisted reproduction and genetic manipulation, both somatic and germline. In the mid-1980s, an attempt was made by the leadership of the Ministry of Justice to set up a committee to deal with the scientific, ethical and legal issues raised by the emerging techniques of molecular genetics. The committee failed to complete its work which led, in 1990, to the creation of the National Committee for Ethics in the Life Sciences, modelled on the French Comité Consultatif National d'Ethique pour les Sciences de la Vie et de la Santé.

Both the composition of the committee and the scope of its activity conspired to limit its influence and its capacity to promote public debate. Largely dominated by scientists and doctors of a strict Catholic persuasion, the committee was purely advisory, and only acted upon specific requests from the government, parliament, professional associations and groups of citizens. On several occasions, the committee was asked to draft advice on issues such as transplants of tissues and organs, experiments on cadavers, clinical tests of new drugs, medically assisted reproduction and organ donation. In 1994, a statement on the legal protection of bio-technological inventions, including references to gene therapy, was drafted as a comment on a directive from the EU. This was the first opportunity for the committee to pronounce on a variety of issues. These included the acceptability of gene therapy, the differences between 'genetic engineering for improvement' and 'eugenics', and, more generally, the conditions under which procedures and products could be patented. Over the following years, the committee was asked to advise on issues such as research on embryos, the legal protection of biotechnological inventions, and the definition of 'genetic identity' or cloning. Key policy events are outlined in Table 1.

The activity of the committee had little effect on the drafting and implementation of specific legislation; its authority among the scientists was to say the least, of a superficial nature, and no significant initiatives were taken to promote public debate beyond the limited field of scientists and bioethicists. Although Portugal has signed all the major international conventions and declarations on human genetics and on bioethics and, as a member of EU, is expected to transpose these directives into national law, this has rarely happened in the case of genetics. There remains a legislative void which has had the effect of withdrawing from public visibility issues which should be discussed in parliament. One consequence is the continuing process, for all practical purposes, of self-regulation of genetic research and genetic testing by its practitioners, and the lack of effective means for making their practices publicly accountable.

A further feature of the political and regulatory culture is the lack of institutionalisation of scientific advice to parliament and government. Scientists are not well organised and do not campaign publicly for stronger participation in advising policy makers.

This means that many of the public issues involving science and technology are not included in the governmental or parliamentary agendas, and, as a consequence, are not recognised as public issues. As a result, both Portuguese scientists and citizens are kept at a distance from debate and government decision-making.

Relationship between government and scientists

This divide between scientists and political actors is clearly illustrated by the BSE controversy. As shown by Gonçalves: 'Instead of being collaborative, their mental relationships were marked, from the outset, by mistrust and confrontation ... [which could be interpreted] as a further manifestation of the semi-peripheral condition of Portuguese society ... which could be paradoxically aggravated by the Portuguese membership in the EU.'[3] Indeed the centralisation of regulatory action at the EU level, may well contribute to a reliance by Portugal on scientific research from more advanced member states, thus alienating the advice of less recognised national scientists. Another illustration of the divide between scientists and political and administrative power, as well as the problems they face in making a coherent policy, is the controversy surrounding GMOs and, in particular, GM foods.

The analysis of the GMO story in Portugal, once again demonstrates the ambiguities of the govern-mental actors as well as their problematic relation-ships with the scientific community. Indeed, in the EU as a whole, GM issues are not exempt from perplexities and internal contradictions, both within as well as between European countries. The diffi-culties of trying to achieve a common policy are justified because so much is at stake. In Portugal however, the GMO debate is far from being central to the political agenda. For example, following the imposition of the directive 90/220/EC, the GM issue was addressed by only a small number of scientists working mainly in molecular biology. These scientists tried to raise awareness of the potential risks involved.

The effort of the scientists was in contrast to the indifference of the political actors who, as a rule, tend to espouse a certain mistrust towards scientists and to rely on the scientific authority of more advanced countries. When public debate on GMOs arose in other European countries, neither the main political parties nor the media in Portugal were prepared to take positions on this issue. Authorisations were granted by the Ministry of the

Table 1. Key policy events in Portugal, 1990–2000

Date	EU	Portugal
1990	Directive 90/220/EC on the deliberate release into the environment of GMOs.	
1992		Transposition of directive 90/220/EC. Release into the environment of 12 GMOs for research purposes.
1994	Approval for the first time of commercialisation of a transgenic plant (tobacco).	
1996	Thirteen EU members are against the approval of transgenic maize produced by Novartis.	
1997	*January:* The EU authorises Novartis to commercialise the transgenic corn. Health and environmental concerns receive less attention then economic and commercial interests. *April:* European Parliament asks the European Commission to suspended the authorisation granted to Novartis.	*February:* Greenpeace and Quercus (an NGO) temporarily succeed in preventing the unloading of 15,000 tons of transgenic maize imported from the USA. They surround the ship *Pacificator* in the harbour of Lisbon and paint on the hull 'No X corn'.
1998	*April:* The EU approves Monsanto's Bt maize in Europe. Approval of directive 1139/98 establishing the labelling rules for food containing GM soya or GM maize. *July:* Social and Economic Committee of the EU approves the final revisions to directive 90/220. *September:* The Environmental Committee of the European parliament asks the Commission not to oppose Austria and Luxembourg's anti-GMO stance. It also proposes a moratorium on GMO release into the environment.	*February:* Setting-up of an interministerial council of experts to advise the government on GMO issues. *May:* Experimental tillage of GMO eucalyptus in an area of 3000 m².
1999	*June:* European ministers of the environment agree on draft amendment to directive 90/220/EC establishing a moratorium on the approval of new GMOs. *December:* European parliament prohibits the use of GMOs in their canteens and restaurants.	*March:* Deco (consumer association) publishes a study denouncing the detection of transgenic ingredients in non-labelled commercial foods. *May:* Demonstration by Quercus at the door of the prime minister's residence, demanding legislation on the labelling of food products containing GMOs. *November:* 65 Portuguese associations approve two joint declarations asking for an end to GMO crops and the effective labelling of every food product containing transgenic ingredients. *December:* The Ministry of Agriculture suspends the authorisation of commercial GM crops granted to two varieties of GM maize. The remaining 15 requests previously submitted were frozen. The reasons given were based on preventing potential environmental risks.
2000	*January:* Approval in Montreal by 130 countries of a Biosecurity Protocol.	*February:* Parliament approves a law based on the precautionary principle. Growing, trading and importing of transgenic food is suspended until the revision of directive 90/20/EC, scheduled for 2001.

Environment for the release of 12 GMOs for research purposes.

The role of NGOs

The Portuguese public had to wait until February 1997, when Greenpeace demonstrated against the arrival of GM soyabeans from the USA in Lisbon harbour, before awareness of the issues was raised. A year later, in February 1998, the government set up an interministerial Council of Experts with representatives from four ministries: Agriculture,

Environment, Health, and Science and Technology. The Council's mission was to advise the Government on GMO issues. In spite of growing criticism of both the status and composition of the Council, and the lack of government initiative, in February 1999, two varieties of transgenic corn were released for sale.

Meanwhile, environmental organisations launched a more explicit strategy to oppose government ambiguities. In November 1998, 65 NGOs, constituting the Portuguese Confederation of Environmentalist Associations, signed two declarations on GMOs, appealing for the effective implementation of the internationally accepted precautionary principle.

In December 1999 a press release from the Ministry of Agriculture confirmed that the two seed varieties that had been previously authorised for sale were to be withdrawn from the national catalogue; the law was suspended for one year. This decision was a surprise. Ten months after the authorisation the government was reconsidering its position. But no technical justification was given, suggesting that the decision was political rather than scientific. The government even bypassed the Council of Experts. Several factors may have contributed to this decision. Up until then, Portugal, together with Spain, had been the only countries not to suspend authorisation, so the decision might have a desire for alignment with European policy. In addition, Portugal had held the EU presidency in the first semester of 2000, which meant it was involved with the Montreal meeting where a Biosecurity Protocol was to be signed. From this, it could be concluded that the 'politically correct' decision coincided only by accident rather than design with the arguments conveyed by the NGOs.

In February 2000 a debate on the GMO issue took place in parliament. Two projects were examined: one proposed by the Ecological Party and the other by Bloco de Esquerda (Bloc of the Left), a party on the left of the political spectrum, represented by only two members. It was the proposal of this latter party that was approved. The two projects were similar in their purposes, which were the application of the precautionary principle and the proposal of a five-year moratorium until 2004, independently of the revision of the directive 90/200/EC. But they differed in important aspects, for example the Ecological Party proposed excluding the suspension for scientific purposes, whereas the Bloc of the Left did not. Another significant difference is related to the organisation of a public debate. This was aimed at including the Portuguese citizens in the decision-making process, but, once again, it was not included in the final approved version. However, with the development and implementation of new technologies and the recognition of an increasing number of irreversible impacts on the environment, human health and food, a new demand for regulation emerged. This was a desire to unite decision-makers and those affected by the decisions. However, whereas in most of European countries the GMO issue was giving rise to consensus conferences aimed at closing the gap between scientists, citizens and political actors, and

as a means of widening the democratic processes in society, this is not the case in Portugal. In Portugal, where the recent democratisation still requires stabilising, such practices are given a lower priority. Nevertheless, a dialogue among experts, stakeholders, regulators, and the public in general seems to be emerging as an indispensable citizenship demand. In this sense, democratic values could provide the means by which to construct this dialogue, making sure that each group can bring their own interest and values to the process and yet reach a common understanding of the problem and the potential solutions. So, in this sense, participation seems to be not only a normative goal of democracy, but it is also a requirement for rational decision making in situations in which evaluating uncertainty is part of the management effort.

Media coverage (1992–99)

The Portuguese media corpus consists of articles retrieved from only one daily national newspaper: *Público*. It was selected because it is an opinion-leading publication in terms of its scientific and technical coverage. It is mostly read by a highly educated audience (it is one of the newspapers widely read by the country's elite). Perceived as prestigious, it is a reference point for the other press publications. In terms of political orientation, it is situated to the centre left. It has an average daily readership of 77,000. *Público* was the first daily newspaper to include a section with special editors and journalists for science, technology and environment, introduced in 1990.

The articles were selected manually as there is no computerised research facility available for *Público*. All the science articles from January 1992 to December 1999, were systematically analysed in terms of the keywords defined by the project. Due to the relatively low number of articles found, it was decided to analyse all of them instead of selecting a sample. Thus, the qualitative analysis refers to the corpus of articles about biotechnology from 1992 to 1999, consisting of 678 articles, 303 for Phase 1 (1992–96) and 375 for Phase 2 (1997–99). The media profile is shown in Table 2.

Phases of coverage

It was not until the final year of Phase 1 (1992–96) that biotechnological events really began to emerge in the Portuguese media. As Figure 1 shows, the period from 1992 to 1995 is relatively stable with a low percentage of published articles about biotech-

Table 2. Portuguese media profile, 1992–99 (threshold for inclusion: 5 per cent)

Phase	1. 1992–96		2. 1997–99	
Frequency (%)[a]	45		55	
Frame (%)	**Progress**[b]	80	**Progress**	67
	Public accountability	11	Public accountability	21
	Ethical	7	Ethical	6
Theme (%)	**Biomedical**	55	**Biomedical**	44
	Moral	9	Agrifood	13
	Regulation	8	Regulation	11
	Generic research	8	Cloning	10
	Agrifood	8	Moral	8
Actor (%)	**Independent Science**	66	**Independent Science**	71
	Business	9	Business	9
	Politics	9	Politics	5
	Multinationals	5		
Benefit/risk (%)	**Benefit only**	72	**Benefit only**	60
	Both	22	Both	33
	Risk only	6	Risk only	7
Location (%)	**USA**	46	**USA**	42
	Other Europe	36	Other Europe	32
	Portugal	10	Portugal	12
	Other countries	5	Other countries	9

a Percentage of corpus in the period; *n* = 678.
b Bold indicates highest frequency within phase.

Figure 1. Intensity of articles on biotechnology in Público, n = 678

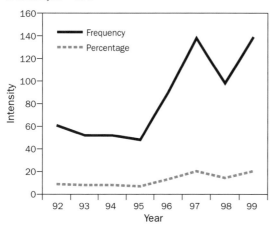

nological issues. From 1996 to 1999, a significant increase took place with the number of articles increasing to nearly three times the previous average.

Phase 1, 1992–96: scientific progress. The phase of media coverage from 1992 to 1996 contains 45 per cent of all the articles. This phase is dominated by the progress frame: more than three-quarters of the articles in this period are linked to the idea of

scientific progress. The public accountability (11 per cent) and the ethical frames (7 per cent) play a less important role. These values show the emerging need for public discussion around the ethical principals and the consequent need for regulation that should guide the practice and applications of new scientific discoveries. However, the media discourse is dominated by the celebration of scientific progress and the minimisation of risks both for human health as well as for the environment. Such progress is linked essentially with biomedical issues (55 per cent), related in the first place to diagnosis, testing and predictive medicine and second, to pharmaceuticals, gene therapy and reproductive technology. Also, of some importance are the subjects related to generic research (8 per cent) and agrifood (8 per cent). The moral questions related to biotechnology and how to regulate the potential outcomes also play a relatively important role (9 per cent for both).

The scientific actors are the most important ones in biotechnology (66 per cent), followed by business (essentially private laboratories and to a lesser extent, industry, 9 per cent) and political actors (9 per cent). The appearance of political institutions such as the government and the parliament (the only political actors referred to in this phase) is related to regulatory mechanisms imposed by the developments of biotechnology, in which they have a crucial and elementary role. Less frequent references are made to the multinational organisations, a sign of the trend of globalisation (5 per cent).

The public perception is globally influenced by a positive evaluation of biotechnology: 72 per cent of the articles within this period refer only to benefits from the new technology, about 22 per cent show benefits and risks, and a few (6 per cent) present only risks. The benefits are mainly related to research and health, while the negative aspects are, essentially, related to morality and to health, and to a lesser extent the environment and research.

Phase 2 (1997–99): decreasing optimism. This phase comprises 55 per cent of all the articles. The progress frame is, as in the previous phase, the central idea that organises the biotechnology issues – the celebration of new developments and scientific progress. However, in this period its relevance decreases from 80 per cent in the previous phase to 67 per cent in this phase, while the frame of public accountability assumes a larger importance, increasing to almost twice that of the previous phase (11 to 21 per cent). The articles concerning ethical issues maintain the same relevance in the media coverage (6 per cent). The significant increase of the public accountability frame can be seen as an indication of the crucial need for public control and the establishment of regulatory mechanisms. It can also be seen as indicating a need to motivate public participation in the debate on the ongoing developments of biotechnology, such as those related to GM food and cloning. The emergence of cloning as a theme for the first time, in 10 per cent of the articles and the increase in the agrifood theme from 8 to 13 per cent are the principal changes between the phases. The bio-medical themes decrease from 55 to 44 per cent, but are still significant. Within biomedical themes, diagnosis, testing and predictive medicine are highest, followed by pharmaceuticals, gene therapy, reproductive technology and also xenotransplan-tation, which appears for the first time in this phase. Regulation (11 per cent) and moral (8 per cent) themes both maintain essentially the same frequency.

In comparison with the previous period, the role of the independent scientists (universities, research institutions and hospitals) increases from 66 to 71 per cent, while the importance of the political actors

decreases from 9 to 5 per cent. However, the government and the parliament become more involved, as well as the political parties, obtaining some media visibility only in this period. The business actors maintain the same frequency (9 per cent), but with some significant differences. For example, the private laboratories and the industries show a significant increase in Phase 2, and the actors related to agriculture production appear for the first time. Their appearance is due to the emergence in this period of the agrifood issues, that is the production and the consumption of GM food, and the associated controversial implications for human beings and the environment.

The perception of biotechnology continues to be clearly positive, but optimism tends to decrease along with growing signs of concern. The frequency of articles mentioning only benefits is much lower in Phase 2 (72 to 60 per cent), while those referring only to risks remain practically the same (7 per cent). However, the number of articles that discuss both the risks and the benefits of a certain application or development increased significantly from 22 to 33 per cent. This means that the discussion in the media is becoming more explicit, as more details are known about the consequences of the different applications.

The benefits are mainly related to research and health but with a change: while the probability of benefits for research is becoming known, the probability for health implications is uncertain and not quantified. This distinction is important because it means that, in spite of research progress in the biomedical field, the effective application of biotechnology to healthcare remains indefinite or in the distant future. The new gene discoveries linked to Alzheimer and Parkinson diseases, which affect large numbers of people worldwide, are good examples. Research has led to the understanding of their causes and of mechanisms that may open a path to cure, but as yet there is no known gene therapy or pharmaceutical cure.

As research and health are the principal bene-ficiaries of biotechnology, it is unsurprising that the majority of responsible actors are scientists in universities and research institutions (75 per cent), followed by scientists in private laboratories (the best represented actors within business). The political actors (8 per cent) are relatively important in connection with regulatory mechanisms and ethical positions concerning the applications of biotechnology in the biomedical field, agrifood and cloning. Negative judgements are concerned mainly with moral issues and health risks. These are both evaluated as either 'very likely in the future' or 'already present'. The environmental risks are considered less obvious and not projected into the future. For consumers, risks are evaluated as 'very likely' or 'already present' or having 'unknown impact in the future'.

Responsibility for risks is attributed in first place both to scientists (50 per cent) and to business (40 per cent), and in second place, to the politicians. The scientists are mainly associated with ethical issues about biomedical and cloning themes, while the risks linked to business are essentially in agrifood field. Politicians (9 per cent) are held responsible for regulatory mechanisms, considered to be inadequate or even absent, when it comes to ethical problems in the biomedical field.

Regulation is the principal area of demand (72 per cent), and the political actors are the principal addressees of that demand (51 per cent). The need for a rigorous public policy for the development and applications of biotechnology, especially those linked directly to human beings (cloning, reproductive technologies, xenotransplantation and gene therapy) is clear. There is a call for the political actors, essentially the government, to come to the front line of the public debate. This call comes from moral authorities (11 per cent) such as ethics committees, and some religious organisations and interest groups (16 per cent) such as the medical and legal pro-fessions. The agrifood and environmental themes demand public regulation too, but with much less visibility. This demand is led mainly by environ-mental organisations. The work undertaken in the scientific organisations such as universities and research institutes (15 per cent), and in the business areas such as private laboratories and some agrifood industries (12 per cent), are also targets of the environmentalists, who demand political prudence in the applications of biotechnology.

The peripheral status of Portugal within Europe is clearly reflected in the area of biotechnology. Research in the private sector is insignificant, but a small number of high-quality research units, linked mainly to public universities have achieved developments in the biomedical field and other areas related to industry. However the impact of these developments on Portuguese society and the economy has been very small; only a few companies have emerged in this field. This explains the low number of articles concerning biotechnological issues with a Portugese location in the two periods of analysis: 10 per cent in Phase 1, and 12 per cent in Phase 2. In both phases the news refers mainly to events in the USA (46 and 42 per cent) and to other countries in Europe (36 and 32 per cent), with a large UK representation.

Public perceptions

Eurobarometer surveys

The surveys reveal some important differences from 1996 onwards. In Portugal, as in the other European countries surveyed, the level of optimism regarding biotechnology tends to decrease dramatically. In 1996 it reached a peak of 54 per cent, decreasing to 33 per cent in 1999. Of note is the significant increase of 'don't know' responses. This could be interpreted as a symptom of some confusion amongst the public. Another interesting finding concerns the free associations made by the respondents to the word 'biotechnology'. It is most frequently associated with health and cloning, whereas GM food and the environment are evoked by no more than 2 per cent of the respondents. There are also important changes concerning the support for biotechnological applications. There is a systematic and consistent drop in risk-tolerant supporters (those who think that an application is useful, morally acceptable and should be encouraged, although they see it as risky as well) from 1996 to 1999 in all four applications. This is paralleled by an increase in opponents in 1999 compared to 1996 (Table 3).

The most dramatic change took place in the application of biotechnology to food where risk-tolerant supporters drop from 45 to 30 per cent and opponents rose from 28 to 45 per cent. The percentage of supporters remains stable: 27 per cent in 1996 and 26 per cent in 1999. For crops a similar reversal in positions between risk-tolerant supporters and opponents is observed. In medicines and genetic testing, risk-tolerant supporters decrease from 1996 to 1999, but there is a corresponding increase not only in opponents, but also in the percentage of supporters. However, in comparative terms, the percentage of risk-tolerant supporters continues to be one of the highest, and the percentage of opponents one of the lowest observed in the surveyed European countries. This result suggests that Portuguese citizens appear to reflect the general attitudinal trends taking place in Europe – but in more radical terms.

Conclusions

The three aspects examined – policy, media and public perceptions, point to the same conclusion.

Table 3. Portuguese attitudes to applications of modern biotechnology

Application	Year	Supporters (%)	Risk-tolerant supporters (%)	Opponents (%)
Food production	1996	27	45	28
	1999	26	30	45
GM crops	1996	43	47	10
	1999	46	35	19
Medicines	1996	35	60	6
	1999	42	47	11
Genetic testing	1996	40	58	3
	1999	58	38	4

Portugal is a peripheral or rather a semi-peripheral nation within the European context. Biotechnological issues so heatedly debated in more economically developed European countries, arrive in Portugal later and the debate is weaker. The Portuguese public give priority to problems of security that in more developed countries are already solved. This can also be observed in the results of the Eurobarometer.

The media have a decisive role in establishing the socio-political agenda for the general public. However, they do not promote these debates by putting them on the front pages, instead they seem to limit themselves to echoing what has happened in other European countries and the USA. This is not surprising, as the political actors themselves are not actually engaged in a debate on the issue and seem to be devoid of a clear strategy.

Although important changes took place after the 1974 revolution in Portugal, particularly the institutionalisation of a democratic regime, forms of public participation are still under construction. In addition, the relationship between science and politics still lives in the shadow of the past. Whereas, in some nations the constitution of a politics of science, or the integration of scientific advice into political decision-making may have been routine for several decades, in Portugal this process is still evolving. This reinforces the semi-peripheral nature of Portugal, which in some way contributes to legitimising top-down political decisions.

As far as the application of biotechnology to food and crops is concerned, Greenpeace activists, other environmental protection organisations and small farmers have demonstrated their opposition to the large enterprises that hold the monopoly. They have tried to draw attention to the unpredictable consequences of biotechnology for the environment and for humans and claim that biodiversity is being threatened. However, the

public debate in Portugal has been a virtual one. This virtual debate, in which the public has been an absent actor, has some important characteristics. Scientists were divided about the effects of GM foods, in terms of risks and benefits to the environment and human health. This may have contributed to the public's confusion, to the lack of a clear political strategy underlying the decision-making process, and to the role of NGOs in leading the opposition of GMO imports. The division amongst scientists may also lie behind the sporadic rather than sustained nature of the attempts by the media to draw the public's attention to the uncertainty and eventual risks as well as benefits of GMOs for human health and for the environment. In addition, the low profile of industry together with the lack of information and public discussion about the risks and benefits means that questions concerning the desirability and feasibility of product labelling, plus criteria for thresholds of GMO applications have not been addressed. All in all, the enterprises in Portugal have not had a coordinated strategy.

In fact, the reversal of the Seed Law (see Table 1) was justified in the name of science, of risk and the probability of accidents occurring. However, an alternative approach, taking the structural limitations of the country into account, which would safeguard national interests and preserve existing agriculture in Portugal, would be to develop a national strategy that was not disruptive to the rest of Europe. On the other hand it is possible to identify some of the conspicuous absences or limitations that characterise the situation in Portugal regarding human genetics in general and genetic testing in particular. These include the absence of public debate beyond some limited initiatives, which, despite the broad disciplinary inclusiveness, tended to remain confined to scientists and experts. The absence of comprehensive regulatory arrangements, with the exception of a limited input from the Society for Human Genetics which led to the regulation of specific issues regarding some forms of genetic testing, is striking in Portugal. Also, although a body for advice on ethical issues exists, it seems to have a limited influence on practitioners of human genetics. Finally, the reliance of the scientists and physicians involved in genetic testing on self-regulation, based on the model of the medical deontological code is a far-reaching limitation. As for the potential or actual threats to privacy and to equity and, more generally, to citizens' rights arising from the uses of genetic identification and genetic testing, the debate barely exists at all.

Notes and references

1 The concept of semi-periphery, formulated by Wallerstein: Wallerstein, I, *The Politics of the World-Economy* (Cambridge: Cambridge University Press, 1980). It was subsequently used by Boaventura de Sousa Santos [Santos, B S, *O Estado e a Sociedade em Portugal (1974–1988)* (Porto: Afrontamento, 1990)] to describe the Portuguese social formation, referring to an intermediary position, located between central and peripheral states. This is a consequence of the inequalities arising from the appropriation of the economic surplus, on a world scale. The function of the intermediary countries, like a 'transmission belt', could contribute to reduce the disparities and conflicts between countries located in opposite poles and, depending on the subjects, those semi-peripheral countries can be central and simultaneously peripheral.

2 Gonçalves, E, 'The importance of being European: the science and politics of BSE in Portugal', *Science, Technology & Human Values*, 25 (2000), pp417–88.

3 Gonçalves, E (see note 2).

Address for correspondence

Professor Jorge Correia Jesuíno, ICTE, Avenida das Forcas Armadas, P-1600 Lisboa, Portugal. E-mail Correia.Jesuino@iscte.pt

Sweden: the lid is on, but for how long?

Björn Fjæstad, Susanna Öhman, Anna Olofsson, Marie-Louise von Bergmann-Winberg and Nina Seger

The period 1973–95: public debate, media coverage and government regulation

Already from the beginning of the era of modern gene technology, both the economic potential and the possible hazards were recognised by various actors in Sweden. A number of Cabinet ministers were briefed as early as in 1974 by a group of prominent scientists. In 1975, the Royal Swedish Academy of Sciences appointed a working group to look into the possibilities and risks associated with the recent advances in molecular genetics. In 1977, the Swedish pharmaceutical company KabiGen (today a part of Pharmacia) started to collaborate with Genentech and the following year signed a contract with the American company regarding development of bacterially produced human growth hormone. Towards the end of the decade, media exposure became intense concerning the physical risks of rDNA technology, and public awareness soared. In a representative survey in 1978, as many as 58 per cent of the Swedish public reported having heard about a planned 'risk laboratory' (or 'safety laboratory') for rDNA research in Uppsala which was the main focus of the publicity. In a follow-up question, as many as 45 per cent of the respondents wanted the research to be prohibited by law.[1] Some headlines in the newspapers at the time were very provocative, such as 'God knows what monsters you have in your test tubes'. Nuclear power had been successfully introduced into the political debate a few years earlier, and generally the same forces were behind the anti-rDNA initiatives. Some of these politicians and critics had probably been alerted by the 1974–75 research moratorium that led to the Asilomar conference, and also used it as an argument against the technology.

On 1 January 1980, by an act of parliament, rDNA experiments were explicitly brought in under existing legislation. This considerably calmed the debate. The number of stories covering gene technology in *Dagens Nyheter*, Sweden's most influential newspaper and the focus of our media study, dropped by half between 1979 and 1981. After this, the public discourse on gene technology in the first half of the 1980s was focused on ethics, especially in reference to human reproduction and genetic prenatal diagnosis.[2] The second half of the decade was, in turn, dominated by a discussion about the regulation of gene technology. The technology now slowly started to become a routine political issue, but the attempt in the 1988 general election by the Centre Party to put biotechnology, especially herbicide-resistant plants, on the political agenda failed.

During the late 1980s and early 1990s, several government commissions and committees presented proposals regarding how to best regulate gene technology. Some of the more stringent regulatory procedures from 1980 were eventually relaxed. On the other hand, the Recombinant DNA Advisory Committee was made a government agency in its own right, a rather strict law on animal protection was adopted, and gene technology on human sex cells became prohibited. Toward the mid-1990s, the public focus shifted to health aspects and medical uses of gene technology. GM food was not yet a heated issue.

After several years of continued public inquiry, and in preparation for the European Economic Space agreement with the EU – later replaced by Sweden's joining the EU – the parliament adopted a comprehensive Gene Technology Law, which took effect on 1 January 1995. Again, when the new legislation was put in place, the number of articles in *Dagens Nyheter* fell markedly, about 40 per cent from one year to the next.

In our previous media study,[3] during this whole period, from 1973 to 1996, the positive stories in *Dagens Nyheter* outnumbered the negative ones. However, since the negative stories tended to be more negative than the positive ones were positive, the overall score is slightly on the negative side. Over the years, the coverage in *Dagens Nyheter* went from negative to neutral. For the 1990s as a whole, the mean score is very close to zero. However, regarding the subject area 'crops, livestock and food', the opposite occurred. In the early 1980s, the stories in these areas were clearly positive, turning just as clearly negative in the

1990s. The reason for this most probably is that the topics covered changed from basic research on rape-seed and sugar beet to commercial animal fodder and actual food products sold in the supermarkets and put on dinner plates.

In spite of the largely neutral overall score, the general impression of the actors involved, from all camps, seems to be that the media coverage was quite negative, judging from our interviews with key players. The reason for this, in all likelihood, is that the positive stories mostly consisted of factual and non-emotional reports on scientific and/or economic advances. These positive stories, usually without pictures, were mostly placed on the business pages, in the general news section, or on the science page. They were largely written by wire agencies or by in-house news journalists. The negative and critical stories, on the other hand, were more emotional, were placed on the editorial and opinion pages, and were to a large extent written by external contributors, quite a few of whom were well-known politicians, debaters and columnists.

The Eurobarometer of 1996

In the 1996 Eurobarometer on biotechnology, Sweden came out as one of the most sceptical countries in the EU. The Swedes tended to think of genetic engineering as an inappropriate 'tinkering with life', having existential, far-reaching, unknown, and not-easily observed consequences. Genetic engineering was not seen as very helpful for the average citizen, except for the medical applications, and was perceived as a 'top-down' technology.

Interestingly, the most common answer by far to an open-ended question about what comes to mind when the term biotechnology including genetic technology is mentioned, was Belgian Blue, volunteered by as many as 13 per cent of the sample. This race of cattle with double muscles in some places is the result of a natural mutation many decades ago, and not of genetic technology. However, it looks quite unnatural and is infamous among the public in Sweden for hardly being able to carry its own weight and needing caesarian sections for the majority of births; Swedish agrarian insurance companies even refuse to insure it. Belgian Blue is also seen as an EU project, since it was only allowed into Sweden due to EU rules. The negative attitudes to Belgian Blue cattle thus seem to colour the attitudes to both gene technology and the EU.

As in all the other countries in the Eurobarometer survey of 1996, one of the major findings in Sweden was that public support (encouragement) of genetic technology applications does not co-vary with the perceived risk and is only half as strong with perceived usefulness as with the moral acceptability of these applications.

Gene technology in Sweden, 1996–2000

'A total overreaction', said the headline in a leading national newspaper on 19 May 2000. It was immediately followed by an introduction in bold: 'The rape is harmless. Professor condemns decision to destroy crops.' This fairly recent top news story reported the inadvertent import, selling and sowing of 14 tons of rape-seed with a 0.4 per cent content of GM rape-seed. The publicity came after a few years of rather scant Swedish public debate on biotechnology. There already was a repose after the Gene Technology Law took effect in January 1995, and when the Cabinet in October 1997 commissioned the Minister of Education and Research to appoint a parliamentary commission with very broad authorisation to look into biotechnology, the public discussion became even calmer. As will presently be seen in the report from the media arena, this does not mean that our newspaper under study, *Dagens Nyheter*, did not write very much about gene technology during the late 1990s – on the contrary – but that the publicity was less emotional and less conspicuous than before. The sudden media outbreak in the spring and summer of 2000, however, can be interpreted to mean two things. First, below the surface there is an apparent preparedness in the media to react to controversies in the field of gene technology, meaning, in turn, that the journalists seem to believe that there is a potential and readily aroused interest and apprehension among the public as far as this technology is concerned. Second, in spite of the publicity, which continued in bits and pieces until July when the rape was destroyed by order of the Agency for Agriculture, the story died out after each instalment, implying that genetic engineering finally is a mature media topic not very different from any other kind of (bad) news.

Of course, looking back, the major international biotechnology event during the latter part of the 1990s was Dolly the sheep. In Sweden, just as in most other countries, this sheep – the first mammal cloned from an adult – caught the eye of the public as well as the mouths of the professional opinion-mongers for a few weeks in February 1997, mainly as a possible precursor of human cloning. But because human cloning was still very hypothetical, and since reproductive issues probably are not as emotionally loaded in Sweden as in some other parts of Europe, and also due to religion being relatively less salient in Sweden, the Dolly issue more or less petered out after a couple of months.

The case of Dolly may or, perhaps more likely, may not have been a major factor behind the above-mentioned Cabinet decision in late 1997 to set up a parliamentary commission on biotechnology. Another influencing factor could possibly have been the fact that Swedish television's main channel devoted an entire Saturday afternoon in October 1997 to a large-scale public hearing on genetic engineering. A more probable background, however, was the debate during the winter of 1996–97 on the legalisation and import of GM maize and soya. The trigger behind this debate was the EU's approval of GM maize and the shipping of GM soya from the USA to Europe. During the period from November 1996 to January 1997 the topic of GM food, which so far had been a non-issue, leapt into the attention of the Swedish public.

At this publicity outbreak, we in the Swedish research team quickly established a comprehensive and continuous press search and located some 350 stories about GM maize and soya in Swedish dailies and magazines during this short period. More than half of these articles discussed the EU decision. As many as a third of the articles mentioned health risks associated with GM food – risks that simply do not exist according to the Swedish Food Agency. Surprisingly few (4 per cent) of the articles mentioned ethical or moral considerations, i.e. the very aspects which are the most important according to the 1996 Eurobarometer survey with the general public which, by coincidence, was fielded immediately before and to some extent during the publicity period. Only 4 per cent of the articles had a positive tone, and as many as 43 per cent were clearly negative; the rest being balanced or without evident evaluation.

During this three-month period in the winter of 1996–97, many actors made their voices heard. The most active NGO was Greenpeace, and its very critical views were almost unanimously supported by those representatives of the general public who were interviewed in newspapers or on television or radio. (However, neither before nor after this contribution have the NGOs been markedly visible in the Swedish public debate on gene technology.)

Several prominent politicians made public statements on the issue, among them two Cabinet members. The minister of agriculture spoke of the need for a certain restraint, but at the same time

she was clearly open to the future potential of genetic engineering. The minister of the environment, for her part, wanted the GM soya and maize to be stopped. This albeit small but obvious difference in uses of language within the Cabinet itself might also have hastened its decision half a year later to appoint the Parliamentary Commission on Biotechnology to thoroughly examine the topic. The fact that all seven parties in the parliament were represented in the commission shows even more the official importance attached to biotechnology.

The brief to the commission, issued by the minister of education and research, was entitled 'Biotechnology in society – possibilities and risks',[4] and the commission adopted the name Commission for Biotechnology (Bioteknikkommittén). The tasks mentioned in the brief include ethical considerations, risk evaluation, scientific development, the formation and dimensions of public perceptions and attitudes, the need for popular education, industrial applications, prospects for Swedish industrial development in the field, and public control of biotechnology. The commission was charged with proposing concrete changes in regulatory content and structure. A first report was published in June 1999 and dealt with the structure and tasks of the Gene Technology Advisory Board. The final report, including a 21-point biotechnology policy (outlined in the conclusion to this chapter), was presented on 1 December 2000.

Three other government commissions relevant to biotechnology were also appointed in 1997, but with much narrower agendas. One looked into alternative methods for experiments on animals and the future use of animals in experiments.[5] This commission observed that the development of GM animals for scientific experimentation might lead to an increase in experiments using animals, thus stricter legislation was called for. On the other hand, an EU Commission meeting in April 1997 recommended a 50 per cent cut in the number of animals used for experiments until the year 2000. In its report, 'Experiments on animals' which was published in 1998, the commission seconded this proposal.[6] Alternative methods have also been recommended and supported by the Swedish Central Board for Experiments on Animals (Centrala försöksdjursnämnden).

The second government commission concerned xenotransplantation, i.e. the transfer of organs and tissue from animals to humans.[7] It evaluated the ethical, medical, legal, and animal protection aspects of xenotransplantation, and discussed potential risks for infections between species, the ethics of xenotransplantation, xenotransplantation to children, transplantation from GM animals, the organisation of clinical tests, as well as the registration and supervision of the patients involved. In Sweden, several research groups study aspects of xenotransplantation; and experiments involving pig kidneys, pig livers, nerve cells from pigs, and insulin-producing cells from pigs have been carried out, some already in the early 1990s. The commission's report, 'From one species to another – transplantation from animals to humans', was published in 1999.[8] A special board rather than the Agency for Health and Social Affairs was proposed to be the main overseer of xenotransplantation.

The third commission named in 1997 investigated ethical aspects of research in general. The aims for this inquiry were to review education in research ethics and to propose how to raise the awareness and impact of ethical considerations in the research process. The commission looked into the structure and tasks of the present committees for research ethics. It discussed the balance between gaining new knowledge and performing ethically sound research, as well as the need for public access. The final report, 'Good practice in research', was published in 1999.[9]

It is probably fair to say that the reports and other activities of all these four government commissions have had a significant impact only within the select group of persons and institutions which follow and/or debate biotechnology for economic, regulatory, or ideological reasons – or from inveterate habit.

The specific topic of how to use genetic information has been discussed in a number different forums during the late 1990s. A report written on behalf of the Ministry for Health and Social Affairs proposed legislation on genetic integrity, prohibiting employers and insurance companies from asking for or using genetic information in connection with employment or buying insurance. It also proposed prohibiting employers from making inquiries to find out whether genetic tests have been done in the past or about genetic diseases in the family. An input into this proposal was the convention adopted by the Committee of Ministers of the European Council in 1996 to prohibit discrimination due to individual genetic makeup. This convention takes effect when five states, at least four of which are member states, have ratified it. However, since legislation preventing insurance companies from judging individual insurance risks would be contrary to

other laws regulating the insurance business, the proposal was never put to parliament. Instead, in May 1999, the Swedish government and the Swedish Insurance Federation (Sveriges Försäkringsförbund) made an agreement, in which the Federation undertook to ensure that member companies would not demand that prospective clients undergo genetic examinations as a condition for taking out an insurance policy for the next two years. It has long been expected that the Cabinet will appoint a parliamentary commission to look further into genetic integrity, but this has not yet been done, probably due to difficulties in defining the brief to the commission.

During the winter and spring of 1999, the tabloid *Aftonbladet*, Sweden's largest daily news-paper, ran a long series of articles on biobanks. The newspaper had realised that Sweden's hospitals house a total of 80 million biosamples of various kinds: blood samples, biopsies, and others, comprising, at least in principle, information about the complete genetic makeup of all residents of Sweden. The series of articles influenced the Minister for Health and Social Affairs to ask the Agency for Health and Social Affairs to propose a piece of legislation. The resulting proposal, presented in May 2000, states that the biobanks should become more readily accessible to science but also that the rights of the individuals concerned to be informed and to decide over their biosamples should be strengthened. Furthermore, all biobanks were proposed to be registered by the Agency for Health and Social Affairs which would oversee the activities of the banks. The Biobank Law would prohibit the selling of genetic information, but it would allow handling fees to be charged. In August 2001, the Cabinet remitted the government bill to the Council of Legislation; the next step being its introduction to parliament. The proposed law is to take effect on 1 July 2002. The prosed law, however, was heavily criticised by prominent scientists, not only in medicine but also in ethics and law, as being hastily drafted, promoting neither patient interests nor research possibilities.

A consortium of government agencies and other bodies working with biotechnology (among them the Gene Technology Advisory Board, the National Board for Health and Welfare, the Karolinska Institute, the National Institute for Working Life, the Medical Products Agency, the Stockholm Cancer Association, the Swedish Council for Planning and Coordination of Research, and the Occupational Safety and Health Administration), organised a consensus conference, referred to as a 'panel of laypeople', on human genetic diagnostics in mid-October 2000. Interestingly, the Swedish way of conducting the first consensus conference in biotechnology had some national variations. The organising committee thus tended to represent the establishment. As usual in these contexts, the panel was selected by a polling agency, but the panel chairman and its rapporteur was named beforehand by the organising committee. The panel was then offered the opportunity to dispense with the chairman and the rapporteur, but chose not to. In the list of experts available to the panel from which to choose, environmental groups, consumer organisations, labour unions and employer unions were not represented. Of the 11 experts who were chosen to be heard, nine were from universities, research institutes or academic hospitals and two from patient organisations. The event, which included hearings open to the press and the general public, cannot be said to have received extensive publicity, nor has it had any visible impact on the public debate. Among the conclusions of the panel, published in November 2000, were the following:

- Sweden should promptly accede to the European Council's convention on human rights in biomedicine.

- A government commission to investigate and propose laws protecting citizens against discrimination due to genetic makeup should promptly be appointed.

- Insurance companies and employers should be prohibited by law to request genetic information, employers also to receive or use such information.

- Research based on material in biobanks can generate knowledge that is valuable to promoting public health. However, legislation is needed to protect the right of the individual to decide upon the use of his/her samples. If the individual withdraws his/her consent, the samples should be destroyed.

- Government should register and control all biobanks, public and private. Individual scientists should not have monopoly of any one biobank.

- When genetic tests are performed, personnel trained and experienced in genetic counselling should be at hand before, during and after the procedure.

- Forensic genetic testing is useful in the conviction of criminals and the acquittal of innocent people. However, forensic genetic testing should only be used for serious crimes.

On the regulation scene, the period 1996–2000 was thus one mainly of inquiry and reflection. Hardly any major decisions were taken, but future decisions were prepared. About 50 MP's bills were submitted and rejected during this period. Most of them called for stricter legislation: more demanding conditions for deliberate release of GM organisms and even a five-year moratorium for deliberate release and certain areas of research. Some of the bills also dealt with the Swedish position in the EU and in other international organisations. Not one of the MP's bills was passed.

A fairly new and interesting aspect of the recent public debate is genetic engineering as a disadvantage in commerce. From the beginning, the very reason for the support given to gene technology by government, business and other actors was the huge economic prospects. Due to the lack of unequivocal public acceptance, the situation has now taken an ironic twist. In December 1999, when the Swedish–American corporation Pharmacia-Upjohn announced its merger with Monsanto, the reaction was mainly negative. But the pessimists were not Greenpeace activists nor from other NGOs, but the stock-market commentators. Monsanto was plainly not seen as an attractive partner, and it was held that the stock owners of Pharmacia-Upjohn would lose from the deal. The reason given was that Monsanto was judged to be a high-risk business due to its strong commitment to gene technology.

A few months later, the large Swedish–Finnish forest group Stora Enso decided to refrain from genetic engineering in all its commercial practices. For instance, no GM trees are henceforth to be used commercially by Stora Enso, and no research 'aiming at a specific practical application of a GMO' is to be undertaken. The reason stated was that such procedures would be contrary to 'business ethics'.[10] Immediately, this decision was criticised by, among others, forest scientists, for voluntarily abstaining from a large future potential, both economically and ecologically.

In the human medical research field, considerable media attention was paid in June 2000 to the announcement of the success of the Human Genome Project, with on-stage participation by US President Bill Clinton and Professor Craig Venter from Celera Genomics. However, after a single day, the topic disappeared from the headlines. The short-lived public attention was very similar in style to the one seen a couple of weeks later when the Øresund Bridge was inaugurated.

In agriculture, field trials continued during the late 1990s. Since 1989, 73 applications for field trials with GM crops have been granted by the Swedish Agency of Agriculture. Of these, 26 concerned potatoes (changes in starch composition), 30 concerned rape (herbicide resistance), 16 concerned sugar beet (herbicide resistance) and one concerned apples. Only one application has been rejected.

Media coverage, 1997–2000

The coverage of gene technology in our chosen newspaper, *Dagens Nyheter*, continued to grow during 1997–99. In fact, these are the top three years by volume. *Dagens Nyheter* is Sweden's largest morning newspaper and the unambiguous top agenda-setter and opinion leader in Swedish public debate. It is 'independently liberal' and has a readership of more than 1 million people, corresponding to 17 per cent of all adults in the country. In contrast to our study of its contents during 1973–96, where all articles dealing with 'the intervention, handling, and/or analysis at the level of the gene(s)' were analysed, the empirical material in this study is a sample. First, all articles concerning gene technology were gathered from an online archive. This gave a total number of 567 articles, from which a sample of 100 per year was randomly selected for analysis.

The total number of articles on gene technology published by *Dagens Nyheter* from 1973 to 1999 is shown in Figure 1. The coverage of genetic engineering follows a wave-like pattern, where all but one new crest is higher than the last. The constant increase of coverage over time is also mirrored by the fact that nearly every trough in the graph is higher than the previous one. Over the years, genetic engineering is becoming an ordinary topic in the public debate, with a continuously higher background level of media reporting also when nothing spectacular is happening.

The waves represent different subject areas being in main focus at different periods in time. In our previous study of *Dagens Nyheter*'s reporting of gene technology (up to and including 1996), four phases were identified; now followed by the one under recent study: the safety phase (1974–80), concerning physical safety and risk; the ethical phase (1981–85), focusing on ethical considerations, mainly in connection with prenatal diagnostics; the regulation phase (1986–90), highlighting regulatory measures; the health phase (1991–96), focusing on progress in health research and genetic diagnoses; and the food phase (1997–99), with an emphasis on agriculture and foodstuffs.

The new empirical material is compared below with the last phase of the earlier study (however, for reasons of international comparison, the last phase of the earlier study begins with 1992 instead of 1991). Table 1 shows the Swedish media profile.

During the fourth media phase – the health phase – several applications of genetic engineering were put into practice, especially in biomedicine and forensics (such as genetic fingerprinting). This meant that the benefits of genetic engineering often were explicitly mentioned. The phase is thus clearly characterised by progress. Scientists were the most dominant actors, and the articles were often published on the general news pages and the science pages. Politicians, too, were frequent actors in articles concerning regulation and genetic testing/identification. An increasing number of stories

Figure 1. Intensity of articles in the Swedish press, 1973–99.

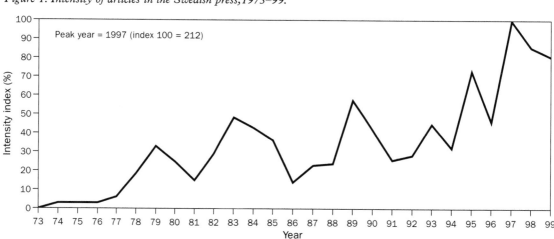

Table 1. Swedish media profile, 1992–99 (threshold for inclusion: 5 per cent)

Phase	1992–96		1997–99	
Frequency (%)[a]	45		55	
Frame (%)	**Progress**	56	**Progress**	32
	Accountability	14	Accountability	28
	Ethical	12	Economic	18
	Pandora's box	11	Pandora's box	10
	Economics	5	Ethical	5
			Runaway	5
Theme[b] **(%)**	**Biomedical**	41	**Agriculture/food**	27
	Agriculture/food	12	Cloning	16
	Regulation	12	Regulation	11
	Genetic identity	11	Economics	10
	Moral	9	Biomedical	9
	Other	6	Public opinion	8
	Genetic research	5	Moral	7
			Genetic research	7
Actor[c] **(%)**	**Science**	53	**Science**	37
	Politics	18	Business	27
	Business	8	Politics	13
	Other	8	Media	6
	EU	5	EU	6
Benefit/risk (%)	**Benefit only**	44	**Neither**	39
	Neither	25	Benefit only	27
	Both	18	Both	19
	Risk only	13	Risk only	16
Location (%)	**Sweden**	51	**Sweden**	49
	USA	19	Other Europe	24
	Other Europe	18	USA	17
	World	6	Other countries	7
	Other countries	5		

a Percentage of corpus in the period; $n = 545$.

b Multiple response for three themes (i.e. more than one variable may be coded per article).

c Multiple response for two actors in 1992–96.

covered issues and events outside of Sweden, and even though Sweden still was the most common location by far, the USA gained space compared to earlier phases.

This picture changed markedly in the second half of the 1990s. Even if progress was still the most frequent frame in this fifth phase, public accountability was almost as frequent; the economic frame was also more common than before. Looking at the themes, the reason for these changes in framing is obvious: biomedical research, the most common theme by far during the health phase, has now become just one theme among many others. What characterised this fifth phase was a diversity of themes covered by media. However, one theme was more common than others: GM food and other agricultural applications. For this reason, we call this most recent phase the food phase. Cloning,

which was not included in the analysis before 1997 when it was a largely unknown concept among laymen, was also a theme covered in a relatively large number of articles.

The change of focus from medical applications to food has meant a change in the general structure of the newspaper coverage. In the food phase, benefits no longer dominated but instead there were more neutral stories mentioning neither risks nor benefits. Scientists were still the most common actors but they did not dominate the way they did before Dolly and GM food. For the first time since the end of the 1970s, industry and business returned as an actor in the debate.

About half of the coverage dealt with events in Sweden just as during the health phase, but a quarter of the coverage in the food phase was about events in Europe. The trend evident in the earlier

Table 2. Actors responsible for benefits and risks, and demands made about gene technology in the Swedish media, 1997–99

Responsible actor	Benefit (%)		Risk (%)			
	Science	56	Science	60		
	Business	37	Business	22		
	Politics	6	Politics	8		
Demands	**Author (%)**		**Addressee (%)**		**Area (%)**	
	Interest groups	21	Business	28	Agriculture, food	49
	Politics	20	Science	21	Regulation	14
	Business	19	Politics	19	Cloning	12
	Media	18	EU	19		
	Science	10				

study showing an increasing coverage of the USA has, at least for now, halted.

In the study of 1997–99, some additional variables were measured (Table 2). One such new aspect was to look at which actors were considered responsible for the benefits and the risks, respectively, of genetic engineering. The results are not surprising: the actors judged to be responsible for the benefits are the same as those responsible for the risks – and the same as the actors who are most commonly covered. In more than half of the articles where risks or benefits were mentioned, the responsible actor was a scientist.

Other new variables focused on demands made in connection with gene technology. The most common area of demand was GM food and agriculture-related issues: almost 50 per cent of all demands concerned this field. The demands were made by interest groups, politicians and representatives from the business sector. Demands were most often addressed to business enterprises, scientists, politicians and the EU.

In the period 1997–99, there were as many negative as positive articles on genetic engineering published in *Dagens Nyheter*, each article being judged by the extent it gives a favourable and a unfavourable impression, respectively, of gene technology. The mean score was very close to neutral. The coverage actually became both less negative and less positive compared to the previous period. In other words, the average story giving a negative impression of gene technology was less negative than before, and the average positive story was less positive. This means that the publicity around the subject did become less emotional and less evaluative than during earlier years. This is still another confirmation of our finding that, in Sweden, gene technology has matured and become one media topic amongst many.

The Eurobarometer of 1999

To monitor the public perception of genetic engineering in Sweden, we use data mainly from the 1999 Eurobarometer on biotechnology. A general question was asked about the way science and technology change our lives. Eight different areas of science and technology were listed: solar energy, computers and information technology, space exploration technology, telecommunications, nuclear energy, the Internet, new materials and substances, and biotechnology/genetic engineering (split ballot). For each of the areas, the respondents were asked if they thought it would improve our way of life in the next 20 years, if it would have no effect, or if it would make things worse. Optimism about the consequences of genetic engineering is on the lower half of the technologies offered. This list is headed by telecommunications, where 86 per cent think it will improve their way of life, followed by 85 per cent for computers and information technology, 81 per cent for solar energy, 79 per cent for the Internet, 72 per cent for new materials and substances, 70 per cent for biotechnology, 61 per cent for space exploration technology, 58 per cent for genetic engineering, and 33 per cent for nuclear power. There is a gender difference in all areas, women being less optimistic than men. It is problematic to compare the figures from 1996 and 1999 concerning biotechnology and genetic engineering since the translation had been changed by the data collection agency between the two surveys, but if anything, the Swedish public seems to have become more optimistic about new technologies.

Attitudes to different applications

Responses to the survey question on attitudes to applications were more complex. Respondents were asked if they ever have heard of each of seven different applications of biotechnology and whether or not they thought the applications are useful, risky, and morally acceptable, and finally whether they should be encouraged or not. The application best known to the public is the use of biotechnology for enhanced qualities in food (81 per cent). This is followed by modifying crop plants (74 per cent), genetic testing (67 per cent), bacterial production of medicines (60 per cent), cloning human cells (59 per cent), cloning animals for production of pharmaceuticals (45 per cent), and using bacteria for environmental purposes (bioremediation)(36 per cent). The proportion of the Swedish public having heard of different applications is higher than the European average for all applications except for cloning animals.

Of the seven different applications, the medical applications are given the highest support (Table 3). Some 63 and 62 per cent, respectively, of the sample agree or strongly agree that genetic testing and bacterial production of medicines should be encouraged. This is followed by cloning human cells, using bacteria for environmental purposes, modifying crop plants, cloning animals and use of

biotechnology for enhanced qualities in food production. Thus, the Swedish public is still negative about GM food and animal applications. The proportion of respondents who have expressed an opinion about biotechnology (the 'decided public'), is substantial and varies between 75 per cent and 86 per cent for different applications. Figure 2 shows mean scores for usefulness, risk, moral acceptability and encouragement.

As in 1996, the regressions between the applications and sociodemographic variables are rather weak (multiple R varies between 0.13 and 0.26). The general trend is the same: women are slightly more negative about food, animal and environmental applications. Respondents with higher knowledge are more positive (to the medical and environmental applications), and so are people with higher technology optimism (to the medical, food and environmental applications). Education, age, political affiliation and income contribute only in a minor way.

In the 1999 Eurobarometer, the Swedish public is the most knowledgeable of all in Europe, with a mean of 6.7 correct answers on a ten-point scale.

Table 3. Percentage respondents who agree or strongly agree that an application should be encouraged (n = *1000*).

	GM food	*GM crops*	*Medicines*	*Cloning human cells*	*Genetic testing*	*Cloning animals*	*Bioremediation*
Encourage (%)	28	40	62	53	63	33	42
'Decided' (%)[a]	86	85	82	81	83	78	75

a The 'decided public' are those respondents who expressed an opinion about an application, i.e. the 'don't know' responses are excluded.

Figure 2. Attitudes to applications of biotechnology in Sweden, 1999 ('don't knows' coded as 0)

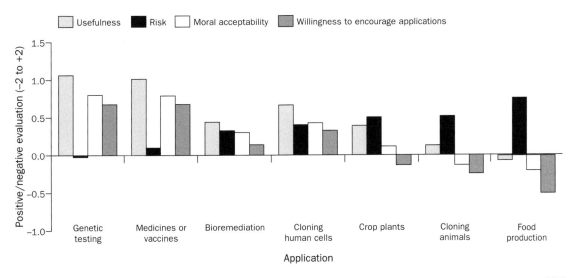

275

We have also calculated the degree to which the respondents' propensity to support the various applications is explained by their views on usefulness, risk, and moral acceptability of the same applications. The answer remains the same as in 1996, and the pattern is the same for all seven applications: moral acceptability is the strongest predictor by far (average beta = 0.49), followed by usefulness (average beta = 0.33). Risk has a low and sometimes non-significant predictive value (average beta = 0.08). This indicates that the risk dimension is quite independent of the other three response variables and has practically no predictive value.

To compare the results between the 1996 and 1999 Eurobarometers, 'response logics' were created. A filter question was introduced in 1999: 'Have you ever heard of the application?', raising the rate of 'don't know' answers. Therefore, logics to compare 1996 and 1999 are based only on the 'decided public', i.e., those who expressed an opinion. Three of 16 possible logics are used: consistent supporters (those who say that the application is useful, not risky, morally acceptable, and should be encouraged), risk-tolerant supporters (those who say that the application is useful, risky, morally acceptable, and should be encouraged) and consistent opponents (those who say that the application is not useful, risky, not morally acceptable, and should not be encouraged). Four applications are used for the time series in Table 4: food, crop plants, medicines and genetic testing.

Among the decided public, genetic testing and GM medicines are given overwhelming support, quite similar to 1996. Use of genetic engineering

for improving crop plants is opposed by almost 40 per cent in 1999, a substantial increase since 1996. Food applications are opposed by almost 60 per cent, the same as in 1996.

Table 5 shows the logics of 1999 applied to the whole sample. The picture is confirmed: a majority of the public supports the medical applications with very few consistently opposed. A sizable proportion, a fifth to a third of the public, are consistently against food and crop applications, seeing them as not useful, risky, not morally acceptable and not to be encouraged. But, still, this is far from a majority of the sample. Actually about the same share of the public supports these applications, and as many as two out of five citizens in our sample have either answered 'don't know', not given an answer to all four questions, or answered with a more complicated – perhaps even moderated – response logic than the three straightforward ones reported in the table.

Trust

The respondents were also asked, for each of a number of professions and groups involved in modern biotechnology, if they thought these 'do a good job for society'. Some 73 per cent of the sample say consumer organisations do a good job, and 72 per cent think the same of medical doctors. This is followed by ethics committees (61 per cent), environmental organisations (59 per cent), shops (52 per cent), and newspapers and magazines (51 per cent), parliament (41 per cent) and industry (21 per cent).

Table 4. Time series for four applications based on three main logics: consistent supporters, risk-tolerant supporters and consistent opponents

Logic	GM food		GM crops		Medicines		Genetic testing	
	1996	*1999*	*1996*	*1999*	*1996*	*1999*	*1996*	*1999*
Consistent supporters (%)	18	17	39	27	50	44	52	51
Risk-tolerant supporters (%)	24	24	34	34	43	46	40	41
Consistent opponents (%)	58	59	27	39	8	10	8	9

Table 5. Logics for applications based on the whole sample, 1999

	GM food	GM crops	Medicines	Genetic testing
Consistent supporters (%)	9	15	28	32
Risk-tolerant supporters (%)	13	19	29	26
Consistent opponents (%)	32	22	6	6
Other logic (%)	29	27	16	17
Don't know/no answer (%)	17	17	21	19

We also asked which one of 12 types of organisations, professional groups or institutions the interviewees trust most to tell the truth about modern biotechnology. Most trusted in Sweden were consumer organisations (23 per cent), followed by the medical profession (22 per cent), environmental organisations (17 per cent) and universities (14 per cent). This is an increase in the support for consumer organisations by more than 10 percentage points from 1996. Considering the fact that Sweden more or less lacks national consumer organisations, this increase could be interpreted as a rise in public concern.

A number of other public concerns were also addressed in the interviews. Thus, 30 per cent of the public would be prepared to take part in public discussions or hearings about biotechnology, and 38 per cent would sign a petition against biotechnology. Some 83 per cent would take time to read articles or watch television to be informed about biotechnology; and only 3 per cent say that they already are sufficiently informed. Of the respondents, 69 per cent would pay more for non-GM food, but at the same time as many as 51 per cent would be happy to eat GM sugar if all traces of the genetic modification has gone; 27 per cent would eat eggs from chickens fed on GM corn; 26 per cent would buy cooking oil containing a small amount of GM soya; and 23 per cent would buy GM fruit if it tasted better.

Focus-group interviews

Four focus-group interviews were conducted during the autumn of 1999 and beginning of 2000. To avoid reaching mainly metropolitan cosmopolites, we did not conduct the interviews in Stockholm or any other big city but in a regional centre, Östersund, with a population of 58,000 inhabitants. In order to achieve fairly homogeneous groups, the interviewees were segmented according to age and education, the result being two younger groups (25–36 years), with and without higher education, respectively, and two more elderly groups (37–68), also with and without higher education. The reason for wanting homogeneous groups was not to identify differences between segments, but rather to make the interviewees feel at home and that they could speak openly about the subject. All four groups contained at least two men and two women.

The analysis of the focus groups indicates that Sweden's own regulation of genetic technology is seen as satisfactory, but that there is doubt that the EU, or the USA and other foreign countries for that matter, have the same rigid control. On the other hand, this new technology is seen to develop so fast that both Swedish legislation and other regulation is believed to lag behind. It is generally felt that those in charge of regulation cannot really know enough about gene technology when the scientists themselves are uncertain about the long-term consequences.

There was consensus in the focus groups that there generally is satisfactory control of cloning and other developments in the medical field in Sweden. Every new pharmaceutical drug is believed to be carefully tested before it is released on the market. Both genetic testing and medical research are judged to be acceptable applications of gene technology, and if these new methods can save people's lives, then it is acceptable to carry out tests on animals, although as few laboratory animals as possible should be used. It is even deemed acceptable to breed pigs to get organs for xenotransplants, as long as the pigs live a happy life until the time comes when their hearts are required. Women more often advocate 'animal rights': that it is wrong for humans to place themselves above animals. An interesting and unexpected distinction that was evident in the interviews, was that xenotransplants are not acceptable for the interviewee herself or himself ('I would not like to have a pig's heart inside my own body'). But if xenotransplants could save the life of a close relative, for example, or one's child, then it would be perfectly acceptable. Thus, the conclusion is that the isolated medical effect in itself is seen as laudable, but that the very feeling of being 'part pig' is repulsive to almost all participants.

Cloning is not acceptable to most interviewees, not even for making human organs so that ill people can recover. There is a feeling of cover up and secrecy: the public does not know how much cloning is actually applied to animals – and humans. The interviewees strongly felt that the public is not given enough information about the latest results of research in genetic engineering. This has the effect that it is not mainly knowledge but feelings about biotechnology that are expressed in the interviews. For instance, there is agreement in the four groups that there is practically no use at all for cloning, not with animals and absolutely not with humans. If a couple cannot have children of their own, cloning should not be an alternative for moral reasons. It is the 'disposition of nature' that some couples will have lots of children and others will have none. If the scientists proceed with cloning, there may be a risk that 'nature and the animal world will strike back in revenge', or even that 'cloned armies will take over and rule the world'. Nature has given us human reproduction, and it should not be substituted by cloning: 'What right have we to play God?', 'If cloning is accepted, the result will be that there are only perfect humans living in the world with no place for disabled persons or people with diseases', 'Is there a risk that, in the future, we will be forced to give birth only to "perfect" babies?'

The food industry is not trusted by our interviewees. Although Sweden has its own regulation for GM food, it is felt to be hard to control what kind of food will be imported to Sweden from countries with less or no regulation. There is also a fear of laws not being followed. As an example, they mention the Belgian Blue bull which has been imported to and now bred in Sweden. Another problem is with crops: what will happen if GM crops are spread by the wind and mixed with non-GM crops, or if they get mixed when transported from one country to another?

Our focus-group participants doubt that the labelling of GM foods reflects the actual content of GM ingredients: 'The food industry is not acting responsibly and is only after our money.' They do not think that GM labelling actually works today, but if it did, some of the interviewees would choose non-GM food even if it were more expensive than the GM food. Others would choose the GM food mostly because of the price. If it were much cheaper than ordinary food, they believe people would probably buy it, and it would also be too much trouble finding out what GM food really is. As it is currently, with no labelling system really felt to be working, 'We're probably already eating GM food,' say the younger participants, 'and the question is how it will affect us, and even more how it will affect our unborn children.'

A positive aspect of GM food is that it could reduce world hunger: 'With crops that are resistant to bugs and other pests, we could produce more food to give to those on the planet who starve', 'What will happen if there are too many people on this planet? The world's resources may not be enough.'

Ethics in Swedish media

Since evaluative moral and ethical considerations dominate the public perceptions as gauged both in the Eurobarometer survey and in our focus interviews, it is of special interest to look at how ethics have been highlighted in the media arena over the years.

The first ethics debate, in the first half of the 1980s, focused on human reproduction, especially genetic prenatal diagnosis. One central question was whether selective abortion meant that handicapped persons are considered to be of less value. In 1993–94, the movie *Jurassic Park* sparked an ethics debate regarding how far science should be allowed to go: are humans to play God? The same ethical question was asked the same year in a debate regarding a real research project where Swedish scientists wanted to cross species boundaries and insert an antifreeze gene from fish into trees. Again, in 1997 an agricultural company wished to insert antifreeze genes into potatoes. Both these transgenic projects were cancelled, probably as a result of the public debate.

The cloned sheep, Dolly, also led to an ethics debate. Ethics has also been on the regulatory agenda since the early 1980s, and when the Swedish Gene Law took effect in 1995, it contained an element not present in the rest of the EU or any EU directive: that consideration is to be paid to ethical aspects, in particular concerning transgenic animals. The influence in this direction probably came from Norwegian legislation passed one year earlier.

Looking at the Swedish media data, it turns out that irrespective if we look at ethics as a theme or as a frame, the incidence peaked already in the early 1980s and has tended to decrease ever since (Figure 3). Thus it cannot be said the agenda-setting newspapers concentrate increasingly on the ethics aspects; rather the opposite is true.

Although we cannot substantiate it, it is our strong impression that the Swedish journalists, who are used to reporting real dangers and actual disasters, in stressing physical risks rather than ethical questions and considerations, may have underestimated the mood and continued moral concern among the public. It is also our impression that many of the biotechnology proponents seem to prefer a debate centered on physical risks rather than one on ethical issues. The reason for this preference, which, given the goals of the proponents, may be misguided or not, seems to be the lasting belief that fear of physical risks can be effectively counteracted with information.

Into the future

On 1 December 2000, the Swedish Parliamentary Biotechnology Commission delivered its final report, 476 pages long, to the Minister for Education and Research. It should be noted that

Figure 3. Ethics as a frame and a theme in Swedish media reporting on biotechnology

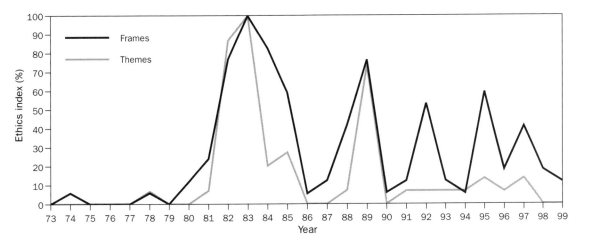

the Commission, representing all seven political parties in parliament, was in agreement as to almost all considerations and proposals, making these likely to be carried in parliament – provided the proposals get that far. The Commission presented its proposed biotechnology policy for the future in a snappy 21-point summary, further abbreviated and edited here:

1. The Swedish Genetic Technology Advisory Board should be restructured into a Biotechnology Inspectorate, whose primary function would be to monitor important and new applications, and conduct supervision, including ethical assessments.

2. A Technology Council should be established to carry out evaluations of biotechnology and other technologies, disseminate information, and stimulate dialogue between researchers, politicians, and other citizens.

3. A law should be introduced for biotechnology applications regarding humans, e.g. gene therapy, cloning, and pre-implantation genetics.

4. Legislation should be introduced regulating research using patients and other volunteers; the law should include research ethics committees and their activities.

5. Compulsory labelling should be required for all products from genetic technology, at all stages of the production process.

6. Sweden should press for an EU directive on the management of human biological material and living animal tissue.

7. Sweden should also work to ensure that the assessment of GMO products is developed into a technology-neutral risk and benefit assessment.

8. Central funding for biotechnology research and postgraduate programmes should be greatly increased. Priority should be given to the function of genes and their importance for normal life processes and diseases in humans and other organisms.

9. Increased funding should be provided to developing countries to enhance their benefits from biotechnology.

10. The risk that very large biotechnology companies abuse their market dominance must be monitored carefully.

11. Research into the risks to the environment caused by biotechnology should be supported through directed programmes.

12. In order to gather background knowledge before GMOs are released on to the market, experimental release into the environment should be implemented and evaluated.

13. Deliberate release of GMOs with antibiotic-resistant genes should cease.

14. Since genetic technology has meant that experimental animals can be used for new purposes, research into the replacement of such animals should be stimulated.

15. Cost-free advice about commercial development should be provided to inventors.

16. Cooperative links between research and industry must be stimulated, e.g. through increases in industrial postgraduate programmes, in combining research institutions and companies in innovation centres, in personnel exchanges, and in special incentives for academic scientists.

17. In order to facilitate future patents and commercialisation of research results, it should be considered making applications for research funding temporarily confidential.

18. School teaching of biotechnology needs to be strengthened.

19. A national pedagogic resource centre for the development of methods and skills in teaching biotechnology should be established.

20. Special courses in natural science, technology and ethics at academic level should be offered to those who come in contact with biotechnology in their professional lives.

21. The training of physicians, nurses and other health-care groups should include increased study of genetics, molecular genetics and ethics. Educational programmes to train genetic counsellors should be established.

On grounds of principle, the most interesting points probably are the proposed government regulation of some aspects of research (proposals 4 and 17). Measures which are seen as encroachments on the freedom of science are always controversial. On the other hand, in a number of the points the Commission emphasises biotechnology as a national priority (8 and 15–21) and takes a clear stand in favour of experimental release of GMOs into the environment (12). The Commission also states that biotechnology should not be seen as fundamentally different from other technologies (7 and, to some extent, 2). If this last point can help reduce the burden of biotechnology being seen as more unnatural than other technologies, it may be of great importance toward a wider public acceptance of agricultural and food applications.

Responses to the proposals of the Commission have so far been rather few and restrained. However, from industry, some negative reactions have been voiced, stating that further regulation and additional regulatory bodies would not help Sweden's competitiveness in the field. The pro

tempore Director General of the Royal Swedish Academy of Engineering Sciences wrote in the editorial of the academy's magazine under the headline 'Superfluous biotechnology policy':[11]

> All technical development comprises a considerable amount of chance, where it is impossible for anyone to foresee the development. Legislation which is too exaggerated, even if well-meaning, does not take this into account. Sometimes politicians should have patience and let time pass by, in order for ordinary people to accept new technology rather than regulate in detail and promote everything to politics.

From political quarters, the comments so far seem to be that the report is fairly well balanced between push and pull, i.e. between support for industrial and medical development and uses on the one hand, and regulatory control on the other.

Greenpeace Sweden had by mid-2001 not published any comment on the Biotechnology Commission report of December 2000, the main reason stated being shortage of personnel. Instead, the NGO reports having lately given priority to the ecological aspects of GM animal fodder (soya and maize), one object being to minimise the import of such fodder into Sweden.

The Swedish clergy has not been very visible in the GM debate over the years, but the head of the Church of Sweden, Archbishop K G Hammar, said in an interview in June 2001 that he found the negative attitudes against GM food strange. He said that he himself felt no fear of GM food: 'Mankind has always exerted influence on food-stuffs. And what is really the difference compared to ordinary plant improvement?'[12]

It is, of course, not feasible to accurately predict the effects, if any, of these 21 proposals on public awareness and acceptance of gene technology, but judging from our earlier research, the Swedish public debate has calmed down considerably each time new regulation has been put in place. It may thus well be that factors which may seem to be restraining industry, for instance the creation of the Biotechnology Inspectorate (reminiscent of two analogous government inspectorates of manufacturers of chemical substances and of banks and insurance companies), actually paves the way for marketable GMO products. The political skill of politicians is not to be underestimated.

Acknowledgement

The Swedish national study was funded by the Mid Sweden University, the Freja Foundation, the Magn Bergvall Foundation, the former Swedish Natural Science Research Council (now the Swedish Research Council) and the Erinaceidæ Foundation.

Notes and references

1 Fjæstad, B, 'Människorna och den tekniska utvecklingen: Allmänhetens attityder', in Sörbom, P (ed.), *Attityder till tekniken: Uppsatser skrivna för och diskuterade vid ett symposium arrangerat av Ingenjörsvetenskapsakademien och Riksbankens Jubileumsfond, april* (Vällingby: Liber förlag/Allmänna förlaget, 6, 1978).

2 Fjæstad, B, Olsson, S, Olofsson, A and Bergmann-Winberg, M-L v., 'Sweden', in Durant, J, Bauer, M W and Gaskell, G (eds), *Biotechnology in the Public Sphere: A European Sourcebook* (London: Science Museum, 1998), pp130–43.

3 Fjæstad, B, *et al.* (see note 2).

4 *Biotekniken i samhället – möjligheter och risker* (Dir. 1997:20).

5 *Alternativa metoder till djurförsök och försöksdjursan-vändningens omfattning i framtiden* (Dir. 1997:43).

6 *Djurförsök* (SOU 1998:75).

7 *Överföring av organ och vävnad från djur till människa* (Dir. 1997:44).

8 *Från en art till en annan – transplantation från djur till människa* (SOU 1999:120).

9 *God sed i forskningen* (SOU 1999:4).

10 Troedsson, H, 'Skogsbioteknik hos Stora Enso – Tillämpningar och principiella ställningstaganden', *Kungl Skogs- och Lantbruksakademiens Tidskrift*, 139 (2000), pp45–50.

11 Deiaco, E, 'Överflödig bioteknikpolitik', *IVA-Aktuellt*, 9–10 (2000), p2.

12 Rönnberg, P, '"Människor skapar problem – inte den nya tekniken"', *IVA-Aktuellt*, 5 (2001), pp8–9.

Address for correspondence

Professor Björn Fjæstad, Department of Social Science, Mid Sweden University, SE-83125 Östersund, Sweden. E-mail bf@fof.se

Biotechnology in Switzerland: from street demonstrations to regulations

Heinz Bonfadelli, Urs Dahinden, Martina Leonarz, Michael Schanne, Colette Schneider and Sandra Knickenberg

Swiss policy on biotechnology

The extent and form of Swiss public debates on biotechnology have been greatly influenced by the Swiss system of direct democracy, which allows citizens to launch a campaign to collect signatures for a so-called 'popular initiative' at the federal level. Provided they manage to gather the necessary number of signatures (150,000 within a specified time), any group of citizens may submit an initiative. It then has to be debated by the national parliament and the government, who can support or reject the initiative or write a counterproposal with similar, but typically less radical, aims. A national referendum on the initiative has to take place within five years of its submission. If there is a counterproposal, both suggestions have to be voted on.

Phases in the history of Swiss public policy

There was almost no political or public debate on biotechnology during the 1970s and 1980s in Switzerland. At first the federal government had no intention of creating a specific, superposed law on biotechnology. This ended in 1987 with the sub-mission of the so-called Beobachter Initiative to restrict the abuse of reproductive medicine and gene technology in humans (accepted in 1992 as Article 24novies of the national constitution with 74 per cent voting in favour). This first piece of legislation was motivated by a growing awareness of the lack of regulation in biotechnology, particularly that applicable to humans. The period 1987–98 is char-acterised by controversy, triggered by the submission of the Beobachter Initiative and continuing up to 7 June 1998, when the Swiss electorate rejected the second 'gene protection' initiative (Gen-Schutz Initiative, GSI) by a majority of 66 per cent. This phase was accompanied by an increasingly contro-versial public debate that forced the government to change its original laissez-faire approach and to accept at least a certain amount of regulatory policy. In the second policy phase (1998 onwards), after the rejection of the GSI, the policy process has focused on the development of the so-called Gene

Lex Package, dealing with non-human biotech-nology. In the next section, we will give a more detailed description of the key policy events in the period from 1997 to 1999 (Table 1). The policy debate before this period has been described in an earlier publication.[1]

The Gen-Schutz Initiative (GSI)

The main biotechnology policy event in the period from 1997 to 1999 was the referendum on the GSI, which took place on 7 June 1998. Most other events in this area were more or less closely related to this referendum. Originally submitted in 1992, the GSI was intended to protect living organisms and the environment from genetic manipulation. By 25 October 1993 the necessary number of signatures had been gathered. The initiative called for the prohibition of **1** the production and sales of GM animals, **2** the release of GM plants and animals, and **3** the issuing of patents on GM plants and animals. The year 1997 was characterised by the Swiss parliament's attempts to develop an indirect counterproposal to the GSI. Swiss industrialists and government decided to follow the strategy of not directly opposing the GSI, but rather planning and running a propaganda campaign for additional legislation. The pro-genetics lobbyists in parliament got together to draft a Gene Law to address the problem of regulating those areas of gene technology not already covered by existing Swiss legislation. On 4 March 1997, the parliament issued a first draft of the Gene Law with the additional Gene Lex Package – modifications to various other laws, mainly within environmental legislation, but also those concerning for example agriculture and animal rights. Public opinion polls showed that the GSI had a realistic chance of being supported by a majority of the population. Since the Gene Law was not developed as a direct counterproposal to the GSI, the Swiss were not able to vote on it. In December of the same year, the federal govern-ment produced a second draft of the Gene Law in record time. The speed with which the government worked was interpreted as an expression of its

Table 1. Key policy events in Switzerland, 1997–2000

Date	Trigger	Description	Outcome
4 March 1997	First draft of Gene Law (Gene Lex) by Swiss parliament, Gen-Schutz Initiative.	Survey results showed that the Gen-Schutz Initiative had a realistic chance of being supported by a majority of the population. Pro-genetics lobbyists in parliament draft Gene Law.	Because the Gene Law was not developed as a direct counterproposal to the Gen-Schutz Initiative, the population were not be able to vote on it.
17 April 1998	Foundation of a national ethics committee for non-human applications of gene technology.	The federal government selects members for the ethics committee for non-human applications of gene technology.	The founding of this committee only two months before the referendum on the Gen-Schutz Initiative is criticised as a public-relations stunt to placate critics of gene technology.
7 June 1998	National referendum on the Gen-Schutz Initiative.	After an intensive press and advertising campaign, the referendum on the Gen-Schutz Initiative takes place.	The initiative is rejected with a 67 per cent majority.
7 May 1999	Official destruction of GM maize fields.	Due to traces of GMO in the seeds, 200 hectares of maize fields had to be destroyed.	The federal government writes a directive defining a benchmark for non-GM seeds that may contain up to 0.5 per cent GM material.
1 July 1999	Directive for benchmark of GMO-free food.	A federal directive stating what can be labelled as GM-free food (less than 1 per cent of GMOs) comes into force.	The directive is well received because it can be implemented.
19 January 2000	New draft of Gene Law.	The federal government publishes a new draft of the Gene Law, to be debated in parliament in autumn 2000. It is not a single law, but a package of additions to various other laws, mainly to environmental law, but also to others (agricultural, animal protection etc.).	The draft is supported by most organisations including the pharmaceutical industry and farmers, but criticised by the agricultural industry and environmental organisations.

willingness to take the concerns of the Swiss population seriously and to develop strict regulations for gene technology.

The federal government became particularly active shortly before the vote on the GSI: it set up the Swiss Ethics Committee on Non-Human Gene Technology (ECNH) on 27 April 1998, an expert committee with the task of advising the authorities in the field of non-human biotechnology and gene technology. The federal government was responsible for selecting the members and the chair of the committee. The size of the committee was limited to 12 members from outside the government, with half of them university-trained ethicists. This last-minute step to set up a committee (two months before the referendum) was criticised as a tactical move to wrong-foot the critics of gene technology.

Scientists oppose the GSI

In a unique event, several hundreds of genetics researchers and sympathisers gathered on 28 April 1998 to march in a demonstration against the GSI.

The event, labelled as the 'demonstration of the professors', received much media attention, but was also criticised as a public-relations stunt. From then on, this date has been known as the 'day of genetic research' and was celebrated again in the years 1999 and 2000. In October 1998, after the vote on the GSI, an association called Science et Cité ('Science and Society') was founded by a group of major scientific institutions. Its goal was the promotion of dialogue between scientists and the public. According to its statute, the association does not take sides in controversial issues but promotes quality debate. Although its foundation had no direct link to the issue of gene technology, the referendum on the GSI was seen as justifying the existence of such an institution.

The long-awaited vote on the GSI took place after a very intensive press and advertising campaign. Because the biotechnology industry and researchers in Switzerland believed their very existence was threatened, a vigorous campaign was mounted. The anti-gene-technology movement also had considerable financial means at its disposal.

To the surprise of most political observers, the initiative was rejected by a large majority of Swiss voters (66.6 per cent), although as usual the turnout was low: only 40.6 per cent actually voted.

After the vote, the government took its time on the Gene Lex Package. On 19 January 2000 it published a new draft of the Gene Law, to be debated in parliament in autumn 2000. Issues addressed in the draft were the protection of humans and the environment, ethical responsibilities, and requirements for informing the public. The draft does not ban completely nor impose a moratorium on the release of GM crops. However, it insists on strict monitoring and restrictions. Furthermore, it is not the farmer who can be held liable for damages arising from GM crops within 30 years, but rather the producer of GM seeds. The Law is in many points comparable to EU regulations but more restrictive on two points. First, the notion of the 'inherent dignity of living being' has to be respected. Second, the release and trade of GMOs can be prohibited where this is in the 'dominant public interest'. The Gene Lex Package has been supported by most organisations, including the pharmaceutical industry and farmers, but criticised by some branches of the agricultural industry and by environmental organisations.

In 1999, 200 hectares of maize fields had to be destroyed due to traces of GMOs in the seeds. The federal government had issued a directive defining a benchmark for non-GMO seeds: they may contain up to a maximum of 0.5 per cent GM material. There has been considerable public discussion about this benchmark. At the same time (mid-1999) a governmental body (Federal Council for Science) held a consensus conference – called Publiforum – on genetic engineering and food. One aim was to try to overcome the gulf that had grown between entrenched fronts. However, the Publiforum, in a close vote (a majority but not a unanimous decision), recommended a moratorium on GM crops. This radical recommendation led some politicians and scientists to question the methodology of consensus conferences. On 1 July 1999, a federal directive on the labelling of GM-free food came into force, requiring that GM-free food must contain less than 1 per cent of GM material. The directive was well received, partly because it could be applied in practice.

Developments in the year 2000

On 9 May 2000, the World Wildlife Fund Switzerland published a study of the economic impacts of GM crops, which created a stir. The study concluded that GM crops cannot benefit Swiss farmers economically. Gensuisse, a lobbying organisation of the pharmaceutical industry, criticised the methodology of the study. It backed up its criticisms by referring to another study by the ETH (Federal Institute of Technology) which had come to the opposite conclusion.

On 13 June 2000, the Ministry of Environment launched an International Symposium on Gene Technology. The plan was to hold four workshops annually. The invitation to Jeremy Rifkin, an American opponent of gene technology, to attend the first workshop was heavily criticised by the pro-gene technology lobby, including the Nobel prize-winner Professor Rolf Zinkernagel. The first workshop of the symposium proved to be so controversial that the Federal Government withdrew as the main sponsor.

In November 2000, various environmental, consumer and farmers' organisations took up the call for a moratorium on the application of gene technology. This development must be seen against the background of recent BSE scandals. BSE is perceived to be an example of the negative consequences of insufficient attention to risk prevention in food production.

Media coverage

The Swiss sample from 1997 to 1999 consists of articles from two qualitative newspapers: the *Neue Zürcher Zeitung* (*NZZ*) is an elite, liberal daily newspaper with an opinion-leading function (readership: 8.4 per cent) and the *Tages-Anzeiger* is a politically independent daily with great impact in the wider Zürich region (readership: 14 per cent). For the sampling procedure, artificial weeks were created with 42 issues per year. A full-text search (keywords: gentech* / biotech* / Klonen / Dolly / transgen* / Genschutz*) generated a sample of 347 articles in total (188 for the *NZZ*, 159 for the *Tages-Anzeiger*). It has only been possible to search the *NZZ* electronically for the past three years, so the absolute number of articles on bio-technology found are restricted to a comparatively short period. However, an amazing total of 1170 articles were produced in just three years (412 in 1997, 406 in 1998 and 352 in 1999).[2] Table 3 shows data for the *NZZ* for reasons of continuity with our previous analysis,[3] and is based on the full sample from the two newspapers. During the period 1997 to 1999, 139 articles (74 per cent of the total) had biotechnology as their main focus; the remaining 26 per cent mention biotechnology indirectly.

Impact on the media agenda

The GSI led to many articles being published between 1997 and 1999. There was a significant increase in the number of articles after 1996, with a peak in 1998 partly because the GSI was then put to the vote. Since June 1998 the number of articles has remained high, but the slight decrease is indicative of a certain fatigue after a long and heated debate in the media and in the public arena.

Certain fields of biotechnology have been the subject of intensive discussion in Swiss political institutions and the media. In order to vote on a popular initiative the public needed relevant information, and each party in the debate made use of the media to spread their opinions. This explains the increase in the number of articles in the media on biotechnology over the past few years, together with a considerable public awareness of issues involved. It is no longer just the political aspects that have put biotechnology high on the media agenda, but also economic and scientific concerns. Figure 1 gives an overview of the production of all the articles (in percentages) over the past 20 years. Seven articles were excluded which mentioned biotechnology merely in passing or metaphorically.

Reporting biotechnology: 1988–99, political debates

The media debate before 1988 has been described in an earlier publication.[4] From 1972 to 1988, a scientific pattern prevailed. From 1988 to 1996 there was a clear shift to political reporting, and from 1996 to 1999 the political viewpoint was emphasised. Here we concentrate on coverage from 1988 to 1999 which can be divided into two phases. Phases 1 and 2 do not differ a great deal with regards to the themes, actors and frames (Table 2). This reflects a focus on political reporting during the period, owing to the two popular initiatives in 1992 and 1998. Differences in the themes correspond with the different focuses of the two initiatives. In 1992 biomedical and regulatory themes dominated, which reflected what people had to decide on in the poll which dealt with such issues as reproductive technologies. Phase 2 included a slightly wider variety of themes, which ties in with the broader discussion among the public. The themes concerned not only the topic of the 1998 initiative, which included mostly non-human issues, but also other aspects of biotechnology. This appears to correlate with the increasing importance of biotechnology for society as a whole. New topics, like cloning and GM food, were becoming more feasible and thus scored high in media coverage. The public accountability frame increased its topicality by 10 per cent from Phase 1 to Phase 2. Public opinion also became more important.

These findings suggest there is a widespread need to discuss where responsibility lies in biotechnology and how the field should be regulated. These questions are no longer seen as issues for politicians and professionals alone. There has been a decline in the number of articles that mention neither risks nor benefits. This indicates that the media is concerned with pondering the pros and cons of biotechnology and that actors are tending

Figure 1. Intensity of articles in the Swiss press, 1973–99.

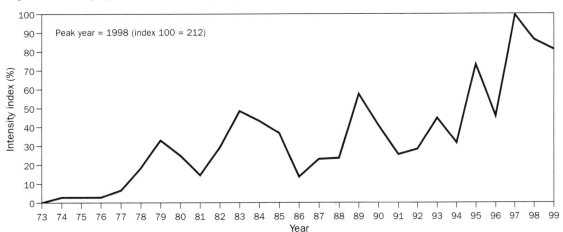

Peak year = 1998 (index 100 = 212)

Table 2. Swiss media profile, 1988–99 (threshold for inclusion: 5 per cent)

Phase	1. 1988–96		2. 1997–99	
Frequency (%)[a]	45		55	
Frame (%)	**Accountability**[b]	25	**Accountability**	35
	Progress	22	Progress	21
	Ethical	10	Economic	12
	Economic	10	Pandora's box	10
Theme (%)	**Biomedical**	19	**Agrifood**	21
	Regulation	19	Regulation	17
	Genetic research	18	Biomedical	13
	Agrifood	16	Public opinion	13
	Public opinion	7	Genetic research	10
	Economics	7	Economics	7
	Genetic identity	7	Genetic identity	7
	Ethics	6	Cloning	7
			Ethics	5
Actor (%)	**Science**	34	**Science**	43
	Politics	26	Politics	22
	Business	17	Business	18
	Interest groups	13	Interest groups	8
	Media	6	Media	6
Benefit/risk (%)	**Neither**	37	**Neither**	28
	Benefit only	26	Both	25
	Risk only	23	Risk only	25
	Both	14	Benefit only	22

a Percentage of corpus (excludes 7 articles which mentioned biotechnology only metaphorically) in the period; total $n = 342$.
b Bold indicates highest frequency within phase.

to take a clear stand for or against the technology or to favour or oppose specific fields of application. The variables that link the actors involved with particular benefits or risks are worth examining. Scientists seem to take the strongest stands on both fronts and are accordingly viewed as either scapegoats or trustworthy experts who can bring salvation, for example, from diseases, famine, environmental pollution and social inequity.

Letters to the editor: clear positions and powerful votes

Letters to the editor can be seen as textual sources full of rich, moral and ethical discourse. They are a reflection of how the public understand and view a particular issue. In addition, they provide access to opinions outside the domain of professional journalists and experts. Letters to the editor are neither representative nor unfiltered pieces of information. Each letter has to fulfil the criteria set by the editorial department. It will not be printed if it does not appeal to the editor or fails to conform in terms of content or length. In the worst case of editorial manipulation, a newspaper may use the

choice of the letters they print to represent their own views on a specific issue. Furthermore some people regularly write letters and therefore have a greater chance of spreading their opinions. Others never write and they may only express their views in interpersonal exchange. Some organisations and lobby groups use the letters page as a platform for reaching a large number of readers and thus gain a large audience for airing their interests. The high proportion of letters to the editor found in the sample provides an opportunity to look more closely at their specific modes of argumentation.

We found 72 letters referring to biotechnology in our sample from the *Tages-Anzeiger* and *NZZ* newspapers covering the years 1997 to 1999 (Table 3). Most of the letters were written prior to the vote on the GSI, and there was a clear peak shortly before the vote in June 1998. An analysis of the letters shows a wide range of views on biotechnology and the GSI. Most writers were explicit about their views: 47 per cent evaluated biotechnology negatively and 31 per cent positively. Some 15 per cent of the letters mentioned neither benefits nor risks and only 7 per cent presented both benefits and risks. This finding suggests that either

Table 3. Letters to the editor (n = 72): most important features

Frame (%)		
	Accountability	45
	Ethics	14
	Pandora's box	13
	Progress	7
	Runaway	7
	Globalisation	6
Theme (%)	Agrifood	29
	Regulation	24
	Public opinion	10
	Genetic research	9
	Ethics	9
	Biomedical	8
Actor (%)	Science	42
	Interest groups	22
	Media	14
	Industry	13
	Politics	8
Benefit/risk (%)	Benefits only	47
	Risk only	31
	Neither	15
	Both	7
Benefits type (%)	No benefits mentioned	60
	Health	26
	Economic	8
	Research	6
Risk type (%)	No risks mentioned	44
	Environment	18
	Moral	17
	Consumer	7
	Health	6
	Social inequality	6
Negative evaluation (%)	Science	15
	Interest groups	13
	Industry	10
	Politicians	8
	Media	6
Positive evaluation (%)	Science	10
	Interest groups	5

most people who write letters to the editor have a clear position for or against biotechnology or that letters portraying unambiguous views have a greater chance of being published. Another feature of the letters is that they often referred to individuals. The letter writers appear to have had no reservations about declaring their disapproval, in particular, of scientists, who, along with research institutes and universities, were most frequently singled out for criticism, followed by NGOs, industry and politicians. Scientists, and occasionally NGOs, were also sometimes praised by letter writers. Those in

favour of biotechnology tended to see its benefits in health, economics and research. Those against envisaged it entailing dangers for the environment, consumers, health and social equality, and tended to support their position with moral arguments.

Public perceptions I

Decreasing media exposure and selective media influence

The first Eurobarometer survey in Switzerland (based on the 1996 Eurobarometer survey on biotechnology) was carried out between the end of May and the beginning of June 1997. This was almost a year before the very controversial GSI and about three months after the media hype surrounding the birth of the first mammal cloned from an adult, Dolly the sheep. The second Eurobarometer survey took place in summer 2000, about two years after the Swiss population rejected the GSI. Therefore the first survey took place at a time when the public debate about biotechnology was becoming more intense and more controversial, whereas the second survey took place during a fundamentally different phase. In 2000 there was little public debate about biotechnology and there were no referendums on the agenda. Thus there was much less media coverage of the issues and decreased involvement by the Swiss public.

This is reflected in the results of the survey. Almost 80 per cent of Swiss citizens (Europe 53 per cent) surveyed in the first Eurobarometer in 1997 had heard something in the media about biotechnology. In spring 2000, less than 60 per cent of the Swiss surveyed answered the same question with 'yes'. A similar pattern was found for those respondents who often or always read articles about biotechnology: it dropped from 27 per cent in 1997 to 19 per cent in 2000. Correspondingly, the proportion of those not interested in the media coverage of biotechnology increased from 29 per cent in 1997 to 36 per cent in 2000.

The survey showed that 43 per cent of Swiss respondents in 2000 felt they had been influenced by the media coverage of biotechnology. Of those, 26 per cent had become more critical of biotechnology and 17 per cent developed more positive attitudes towards it. But this perceived media effect is mediated strongly by each individual's own original attitude towards biotechnology: 40 per cent of those in favour of biotechnology report that the media had influenced them to view biotechnology even more favourably whereas 44 per cent of those originally opposed to biotechnology shifted towards viewing it even more negatively. Thus both groups seemed to look to the media to reinforce their attitudes. These findings tie in with a conclusion from research on media effects – that different people use the same media content very selectively to support their existing attitudes. Such predispositions function as cognitive frames that guide how people process new media content and the arguments presented for or against biotechnology.

Increased expectations but moderate support

In Switzerland, expectations of what biotechnology could offer society were quite low in 1997, comparable to those of some other European countries such as Germany or Austria. Only 37 per cent thought that biotechnology would improve our way of life. In comparison, almost a third of the respondents expected biotechnology to have negative effects. By 2000, the Swiss increased their expectations of the benefits of biotechnology by about 20 per cent to 59 per cent. In the year 2000 there are few countries where people have such positive expectations, although findings were similar in the Netherlands and in Spain.

There was also a shift in attitudes to biotechnology, but the effect is smaller – only 10 per cent. The segment of the population holding positive attitudes towards biotechnology rose from only 19 per cent in 1997 to 30 per cent in 2000, but those against biotechnology (41 per cent) still outnumber those with positive attitudes (30 per cent). Furthermore, attitudes towards biotechnology seem to be more pronounced in Switzerland in comparison to other European countries, as can be seen in the lower amounts of 'don't know' answers when asked about expectations of biotechnology. This may be a result of the more intensive processes of public communication in Switzerland.

In Switzerland, this gradual build-up and moulding of attitudes towards biotechnology, can be largely attributed to the long-term and well-funded campaign against the GSI by the pharmaceutical industry. This campaign strongly emphasised the positive potential of modern biotechnology, and the importance for the Swiss economy of having no restrictions to biotechnology research. Above all the combination of four strategies contributed to the success of the campaign. The first strategy was to suppress controversial topics such as the risks of GM food and crops and the patenting of live organisms. The second was an emphasis on positive topics such as scientific progress and future medical

applications. The third was to suggest moral blame for denying hope to the suffering, and a final strategy was the successful redefinition of the GSI as a gene 'protection' initiative to a 'hindrance' initiative.

Acceptance of biotechnology in Switzerland is significantly higher among younger people (partial correlation with age $r = -0.16$). Gender and level of education have not been found to be linked significantly to the level of acceptance. Nevertheless, there was a trend until 1997 for biotechnology to be accepted more by men and better educated respondents than by women and people with lower educational back-grounds. Furthermore, biotechnology tends to be strongly supported by people holding positive attitudes towards technology in general ($r = 0.40$), and rejected by those who are concerned about eco-logical issues ($r = -0.09$). If these two dimensions are compared – expectations on one hand and acceptance on the other – it appears that biotech-nology is associated above all with health and medical applications. In contrast, people's personal attitudes towards biotechnology still seem to affect cognition concerning risk and moral judgements about which they feel much more ambivalent.

Qualitative and quantitative shifts in knowledge

The aforementioned increase in positive expectations about biotechnology can also be related to respondents' knowledge about applications of biotechnology. About 60 per cent (EU, 73 per cent) said they knew that biotechnology could be used in food production, 55 per cent (EU, 50 per cent) said it is used to make medicines or vaccines and the same proportion knew about genetic testing (EU, 59 per cent). Although there is considerable awareness of a few specific applications of biotechnology, the general knowledge level appears to be quite low. On average, only half of the population gave correct answers to the ten textbook-type knowledge questions used in the Eurobarometer survey. Across the EU only 35 per cent of the respondents in the European countries knew the correct true/false response to the statement, 'Ordinary tomatoes do not contain genes, while genetically modified tomatoes do.' In Switzerland 43 per cent marked this statement correctly as false.

Lack of information is not only evident in an objective sense, but the Swiss also feel it in a more subjective way: 75 per cent rejected the statement 'I feel sufficiently informed about biotechnology'.

Interestingly there was no significant change in the mean knowledge score between the two surveys at the European level (approximately 50 per cent), but in Switzerland respondents demonstrated a decrease in knowledge, getting an average of 62 per cent of the ten knowledge questions right in 1997, but only 53 per cent in 2000. This shift can be interpreted as assimilation to the European level. According to the so-called knowledge-gap hypothesis, conflict about a topic in a society leads to a more intensive information flow which in turn has positive effects in so far as people are more motivated to seek new information. As a consequence, existing knowledge gaps between different social groups with different educational backgrounds will decrease as a function of the more homogeneous information flow. But if one compares the two partial correlations between knowledge and education (controlled for region, sex, age, political interest and attitudes towards ecology and technology) they were 0.22 ($P < 0.01$), about the same for both points in time. But there is evidence of an increasing knowledge gap when one looks at the knowledge agenda. For example, in answer to the question, 'Do people remember biotechnology as a recent media topic?', in the year 2000 only 47 per cent of those with little education claimed to remember it in comparison with 71 per cent of those with higher education. The comparable values in 1997 were 70 per cent for the lower and 89 per cent for the higher educated respondents. Thus, the knowledge gap, measured as a difference in knowledge between those with less and those with more education, increased slightly from 19 to 24 per cent as a function of a decreasing level of conflict about biotechnology in the public arena.

Attitudes to specific applications

In the first Eurobarometer survey, seven specific applications had to be evaluated by the respondents. Four of these applications: food production, GM crop plants, medicines and vaccines, and genetic testing, remained the same in both surveys. In 2000 respondents were also asked about three new applications: cloning human cells and tissues, cloning animals, and developing GM bacteria for bioremediation. For each application, respondents had to evaluate usefulness, risk to society, moral acceptability and whether it should be encouraged.

People appeared to distinguish between the different applications of biotechnology and make different evaluations accordingly. This result corresponds with the findings of the first Eurobaro-meter survey. Medical applications such as genetic testing, genetically engineered medicines or vaccines and also the development of GM bacteria to clean up oil slicks or dangerous chemicals, are considered by the majority of respondents to be useful, involving little risk and to be morally acceptable and even desirable. In contrast, GM crop plants, GM food and the cloning of animals tend to be evaluated negatively. Swiss citizens do not expect clear benefits from these applications, the risks involved seem to be quite high and many do not consider these applications to be morally acceptable. As a consequence, the majority believes that these applications should not be encouraged.

GM food and crops tend to be evaluated more negatively in Switzerland than in the other European countries. But interestingly, the negative evaluation of GM food in Switzerland has diminished slightly since 1997 and come closer to the European average. A reverse trend can be observed concerning GM crops. Here the evaluations have become more negative. In Switzerland GM food is considered the most risky application, as in the other European countries, whereas genetic testing seems to be viewed as the least risky.

The production of GM foods tends to be rejected strongly by a majority of Swiss consumers. More than half of the respondents think that the production of GM food is totally unnecessary. For two-thirds GM food is seen as fundamentally unnatural, as a threat to the natural order of things. Every second respondent claimed to dread the idea of GM food. Only 27 per cent agreed somewhat or strongly agreed with the statement that the risks from GM food are acceptable. As a consequence, 57 per cent would pay more for non-GM food and 67 per cent would refuse GM fruits, even if they tasted better.

Attitudes to actors in the field of biotechnology

How do Swiss respondents view the different people and groups involved in discussions about modern biotechnology? Do they think that these groups are doing a good job for society? In general, most of these groups get quite a good rating. Some 70 per cent of the respondents in Switzerland think that the consumer organisations which monitor the products of biotechnology, the medical doctors who keep an eye on its health implications, and the environmental groups campaigning against biotechnology are doing a good job for society. Similarly about 60 per cent evaluated positively groups like the media for their reporting on biotechnology, farmers for deciding which types of crop to grow, shops for making sure food is safe, and ethics committees for handling the moral aspects raised by new technology. In comparison to these quite optimistic evaluations, only about 45 per cent of the respondents think that 'the government bodies trying to regulate biotechnology' or 'the branches of industry developing new biotechnological products' are doing a good job. The church received the worst assessment for their response to biotech-nology, with only 34 per cent commending it.

Summary

To sum up, future-oriented expectations of biotech-nology in 1997 were polarised and significantly more negative in Switzerland than in the other European countries. Three years on and after a very heated and costly, but ultimately successful campaign against the GSI by the biotechnology industry, this has changed. The majority (59 per cent) of Swiss respondents to the Eurobarometer 2000 survey, believe that biotechnology will improve their way of life in the next 20 years, and only 15 per cent believe it 'will make things worse'. Although people's personal acceptance of biotechnology has also increased by 10 per cent, the opponents of biotechnology in Switzerland still outnumber its supporters by a margin of 10 per cent, with 40 per cent opposing and 30 per cent supporting it.

Public perceptions II

In addition to the survey, we held focus groups in order to get a more in-depth view of the attitudes widespread among the Swiss and the type of arguments they used to justify them.[5] Here are a few, typical results.

Biotechnology: ambivalent evaluations prevail

Biotechnology has polarised Swiss public opinion in the past. This has given rise to the impression that there are only wholehearted supporters or opponents of this technology. However, the reality is more complex and Swiss attitudes tend to be much more diverse and ambivalent. The Swiss population tends to distinguish clearly between the various applications of biotechnology.

Applications of biotechnology in the agricultural and food domain were predominantly rejected. This attitude was not justified with the specific risks of biotechnology, but rather with a general rejection of industrial agriculture: 'I'm convinced that nature is absolutely perfect. I don't like it when men think they can make it more perfect. I'm scared by this development.'

In addition to this 'leave nature alone' argument, some participants also took a more pragmatic stand, saying that GM food currently offered no advantages with regard to either quality or quantity. The hope that global famine could be solved by means of biotechnology was mentioned several times, but not judged to be very realistic because participants thought that farmers would become increasingly dependent on seed-producing companies.

Attitudes in the medical realm were less clear cut. There was strong rejection of GM animals for medical experiments in laboratories. Genetic testing of adults to yield diagnostic information was viewed quite favourably, but such tests were only considered as beneficial as part of the treatment of a specific disease. Merely knowing about an inherited tendency with a probability of developing an illness without having a means of treating it was considered to be rather unhelpful and abstract information.

Several focus-group participants were able to talk about their own experiences with biotechnology (genetic tests) or transplantation. Their experiences added another more personal quality to the focus-group exchange, which was often on a rather general and political level. The discussions showed a consensus in the groups that individual health was so important that there should be no restrictions (e.g. forbidding the use of biotechnology in medical research) that might limit treatment possibilities. Any moral or ethical dilemma should be addressed at the individual level of the person concerned, but not at a general political level: 'If you need it, you would be willing to apply any technology that is currently available. But if you don't need it, you are rather sceptical and you might say "no", and prevent progress in developing other possibilities. I consider this very dangerous.'

Rejection of biotechnology was rarely justified by reference to specific biological or technical risks. Rather, objections tended to be based on moral or ethical concerns. These ethical arguments were not related to strictly religious values, but were about nature and respect for the natural world: 'We don't have sufficient evidence, and that creates fears, for you, for your children and grandchildren and for the environment. For me it means a big ethical intrusion into God's creation. I'm not a believer at all, but that's my view. And one could say with Goethe: "I can't get rid of the ghosts that I called upon."'

While the technical risks of biotechnology were not a dominant issue, the risks to society were addressed quite often. Genetic tests gave rise to concerns about the privacy of that information. GM crops were discussed with respect to their economic impact on the farmers, and the possibility that they would make farmers increasingly dependent on seed-producing companies.

Conclusions

Compared to other countries, biotechnology has been publicly debated very intensively in Switzerland. Two popular initiatives and the subsequent referendums (1992, 1998) on biotechnology are probably the main reasons for this public interest. One would expect, as a result of these intensive debates, that the process of individual opinion formation would be highly advanced and that attitudes would be rather stable. However, our findings from both the surveys and the focus groups suggest the contrary, that public opinion is rather labile. The following quotes, an answer to the question about who can be trusted to tell the truth about biotechnology, illustrates the prevailing uncertainty and lability:

'Nowhere is it written very clearly, what it actually is. You don't know whether you can believe or not. It is not explained properly.'

'Yes, indeed, there is a lack of orientation.... And this ambivalence makes me uncertain. Therefore, when I think about biotechnology, I'm always thinking about uncertainty.'

There are several sources of this uncertainty. One is the very complexity of the technology itself, while another is the ongoing dynamics of biotechnology with new technological developments raising new and challenging questions for society.

Compared with other European countries the public debate on biotechnology in Switzerland has been relatively intense. However, since the referendums in 1992 and 1998, the debate has, to some extent, slowed down. There has been less coverage in the media and as a result, people now have less knowledge about the facts (textbook knowledge) and the opinions (awareness of biotechnology). Currently, the public debate in Switzerland is no longer characterised by street demonstrations, but rather by legal and technical discussions typically taking place in regulatory and administrative offices. This relative calm could be interpreted as meaning that the issue of biotechnology has lost its potential for stimulating public debate. The future is, of course, uncertain, but we are not convinced that the public debate on biotechnology has come to an end in Switzerland, rather it is likely to gain new momentum and continue to arouse strong feelings amongst the Swiss public.

Notes and references

1 Bonfadelli, H, *Gentechnologie im Spannungsfeld von Politik, Medien und Öffentlichkeit* (Zürich: Institut für Publizistikwissenschaft und Medienforschung der Universität Zürich, 1999).

2 TV/radio programme guides mentioning biotechnology were not counted, neither were any comments on the front page or the first page of a section referring to an article within the same newspaper issue. Letters to the editor were counted according to keywords, i.e. letters containing the keyword 'Dolly' were counted as one entity per issue, no matter how many letters there were.

3 Bonfadelli, H, Hieber, P, Leonarz, M, Meier, W A, Schanne, M and Wessels, H-P, 'Switzerland', in Durant, J, Bauer, M W and Gaskell, G (eds), *Biotechnology in the Public Sphere: A European Sourcebook* (London: Science Museum, 1998), pp144–61.

4 Bonfadelli, H *et al.* (see note 3).

5 The four focus groups had a total of 29 participants (6–8 per group). Participants were recruited by phone from a random sample of households and selected according to the following quotas: sex, age, education and attitudes towards biotechnology (supporters, opponents and mid positions). The discussion was led by a moderator and covered the same areas as the survey.

Address for correspondence

Professor Heinz Bonfadelli, IPMZ – Institute of Mass Communication and Media Research, University of Zürich, Kurvenstr. 17 / Postfach 201, CH-8035 Zurich, Switzerland. E-mail: h.bonfadelli@ipmz.unizh.ch

United Kingdom: spilling the beans on genes

George Gaskell, Martin W Bauer, Nick Allum, Nicola Lindsey, John Durant and Julia Lueginger

Policy, media and public perceptions before 1996

Since the early 1970s UK biotechnology policy-making progressed through four principal phases, paralleled by a similar phase structure in media coverage. The first phase, 1973 to 1980, was dominated by the issue of health and safety of laboratory workers involved in rDNA technology. In this period media coverage, of which there was relatively little, concentrated on scientific progress. The second phase, 1981 to 1989, was dominated by the policies to support the economic potential of the new biotechnologies, and by an increase in the intensity of media reporting with an emphasis on the economic prospects and benefits. The third phase, 1990–96, saw the growing importance of policy-making at the European level and the need to deal effectively with a growing number of sector-specific applications. In the media, intensity of coverage continued to increase with more diverse themes. Biotechnology was represented as a pre-eminent example of the harnessing of science to wealth creation, tempered by concerns about risks, ethics and public accountability. Research on public perceptions as evidenced by the Eurobarometer survey of 1996, and by qualitative interviews, suggested that biotechnology had yet to capture the attention of the British public. While there was broad support for new technologies, biotechnology attracted both differentiated opinions (medical applications were supported but transgenic animals were widely opposed) and feelings of moral unease. Moral and sociopolitical considerations such as the consequences of tampering with nature, and where the new science was taking society, appeared to weigh more heavily in the public mind than issues of scientific risk and safety.[1] Table 1 shows the key policy initiatives in the UK.

The watershed years: growing controversy and escalating debate

Three significant events in the years 1996–99 had a dramatic impact on biotechnology in the public sphere in Britain, an impact that spilled over into the international arena. In different ways these events set the agenda for policy-making, dominated media coverage and drew the attention of the public to biotechnology. Dolly the sheep, the BSE crisis and the GM food debate started a new chapter in the history of biotechnology in Britain.

Dolly the sheep

In February 1997, a Scottish research group, the Roslin Institute presented to the assembled world media an unusual 18-month-old female sheep. Baptising the sheep with the name of Dolly added to the news event. The journal *Nature* made Dolly their story of the week by calling what the researchers considered 'adult nucleic transfer', the more culturally resonating 'cloning'. What followed this successful animal cloning was a worldwide debate about the morality of human cloning involving the American president, the Pope, and many other heads of state declaring moral outrage.

In response to the cloning of Dolly the sheep, the Human Genetics Advisory Commission (HGAC) and the Human Fertilisation and Embryology Authority (HFEA) undertook a public consultation on cloning issues, and reported in December 1998.[2] This report introduced an important distinction ruling out human reproductive cloning but strongly recommending that embryo research using cloning techniques be allowed. However, six months later, in a controversial rebuttal of the primary advisory bodies' suggestion, the government announced a moratorium on the use of cloning techniques for the development of medical treatments in research. Instead, a new independent advisory group, the Therapeutic Cloning Group, chaired by the Cabinet's Chief Medical Officer was set up to reassess the potential therapeutic benefits of allowing research using cloning techniques (including stem-cell research). In April 2000 the recommendations of the HGAC and HFEA were reiterated by the Nuffield Council on Bioethics[3] and in August the Therapeutic Cloning Group finally published the same conclusions.[4] The report

Table 1. Key policy events in the UK, 1996–2000

Date	Trigger	Event	Outcomes
1996	The House of Commons Select Committee on Science and Technology report, *Human Genetics: The Science and its Consequences* (July 1995).	The Human Genetics Advisory Commission (HGAC) and the Advisory Committee on Genetic Testing (ACGT) are established to address scientific developments and social and ethical implications of biotechnology (HGAC) and the requirements that should be met by suppliers and users of genetic testing services (ACGT).	Both committees are superseded in 1999/2000 by the Human Genetics Commission (HGC).
December 1998	Dolly the sheep (February 1997).	The HGAC and the Human Fertilisation and Embryology Authority (HFEA) publish the report, *Cloning Issues in Reproduction, Science and Medicine*, following public consultation.	The HFEA and HGAC rule out reproductive cloning but strongly recommend that embryo research using cloning techniques be allowed.
February 1999	Media accusations during the GM food debate that the government is suppressing the results of research on the environmental impacts of GM crops.	The Advisory Committee on Releases into the Environment (ACRE) publish the report, *Impact on Wildlife of Genetically Modified Crops*.	The report warns of the dangers to wildlife if GM foods enter the food chain. Fears of an accelerated decline in the bird population are raised. The report causes more heat in the UK press.
May 1999	Government announcement of a review of the framework for overseeing developments in biotechnology (December 1988).	Office of Science and Technology publish the report, *The Advisory and Regulatory Framework for Biotechnology: Report from the Government's Review*. The review is written jointly by the Cabinet Office and the Office of Science and Technology. It is released in conjunction with a public consultation on developments in the biosciences.	The report announces two new overarching commissions: the HGC and the Agricultural and Environment Biotechnology Commission (AEBC), which, together with the Food Standards Agency (FSA), will provide strategic advice to the government and to the existing advisory bodies on biotechnology. The commissions are to be constituted by experts in consumer issues and ethics as well as scientists. Three existing committees are dissolved and their remits handed over to the HGC.
June 1999	Dolly and GM food debate.	The government announces a moratorium on the use of cloning techniques for the development of medical treatments in research. The announcement is contrary to recommendations the previous year from the HFEA and the HGAC.	A new independent advisory group is set up to assess the potential therapeutic benefits of allowing research using cloning techniques.
September 1999	Pressure from the media and NGOs during the GM food debate.	ACRE is reformulated after allegations that its membership is biased towards the biotechnology industry.	The work remit of the committee remains unchanged.
November 1999	GM food debate – media and NGO pressure; withdrawal of GM food from many supermarket shelves; destruction of GM test sites.	Government announces a voluntary moratorium on commercial GM crop plantings until 2002.	The commercial climate for agricultural biotechnology becomes even more adverse. The government continues with field trials of GM crops despite daily attack from environmental groups.

Table 1 (continued). Key policy events in the UK, 1996–2000

Date	Trigger	Event	Outcomes
November 1999	*May 1997*: James report (*The Food Standards Agency - An Interim Proposal*) *January 1998*: White Paper (*The Food Standards Agency: A Force for Change*) *January 1999*: draft Food Standards Bill.	Following three years of debate and various food controversies such as BSE, *E. coli* and GM foods, the Food Standards Act 1999 is passed providing the legal basis for the setting up the FSA.	The FSA is formally established in April 2000. Its functions are to provide advice to the public and the government on food safety, nutrition and diet; to protect consumers through effective enforcement and monitoring of food standards; and to support consumer choice through promoting accurate and meaningful labelling.
April 2000	GM foods and BSE controversies result in lack of trust in government bodies and in the regulatory process.	The FSA announces that it is to become the first non-parliamentary government body to hold all its board meetings in public, and to organise consultative meetings with the public across the country.	The HGC and AEBC announce that they too are to hold consultative meetings, and from 2001 to hold all board meetings in public. This marks a new era of openness and transparency in British policy-making.
August 2000	Moratorium on the use of cloning techniques for the development of medical treatments in research.	Therapeutic Cloning Group recommends that research using embryos in stem-cell therapies (including cell nuclear transfer techniques) should be allowed.	A free vote on the use of cloning techniques in embryo research is due to be held in Parliament. Changes to the 1990 Human Fertilisation and Embryology Act are drafted.
October 2000	Application by the Association of British Insurers (ABI) to use the results of genetic tests for Huntington's disease in applications for life insurance.	The Genetics and Insurance Committee approves the use of the test. The UK becomes one of the first countries to 'sanction' the use of genetic tests for insurance purposes.	The ABI prepares applications to the committee for more tests (for example some types of breast cancer and Alzheimer's disease). The HGC forms a sub-group to re-evaluate the social and ethical issues surrounding genetics and insurance.

called for changes to be made to the Human Fertilisation and Embryology Act of 1990, in order to allow scientists working on stem-cell therapies to carry out research on human embryos less than 14 days old. The UK government accepted all the recommendations, which were supported by parliament in December 2000, despite a European parliament vote to ban all forms of human cloning throughout Europe.

BSE and vCJD

The first confirmed case of BSE, so-called mad cow disease, occurred in 1984 with the epidemic reaching a peak of 36,000 cases in 1992. BSE was widely assumed to be the bovine form of scrapie, an encephalopathy that had infected sheep for centuries. Since scrapie had not infected humans

the consensus of scientific opinion was that BSE would not do so either. However, the consensus was far from unanimous: at least one high-profile food scientist voiced concern at the possibility of a human catastrophe. In response to such concerns politicians, acting on scientific advice, repeatedly reassured the public that there was no threat to human health from the consumption of British beef.

In March 1996 the crisis for the beef industry became a public crisis when the Health Minister announced that a new form of Creutzfeld-Jacob Disease (vCJD) had been identified in humans, and that the most likely source of this disease was BSE-infected beef. As an immediate consequence, beef consumption in Britain collapsed and a European ban of British beef exports came into effect.
The BSE Inquiry chaired by Lord Phillips and running to 4000 pages was published in October

2000.[5] According to *New Scientist* the report 'provides a harrowing look at how science was mismanaged, misused, misinterpreted and miscommunicated to the public'.[6]

The BSE fiasco raised many concerns beyond the frightening prospect of vCJD – concerns that are likely to have a lasting impact on public attitudes to agriculture, food safety and scientific risk assessment. To their shock, the public learned that modern farming methods had turned cattle into cannibals; BSE was spread in meat and bonemeal, a cattle feed made from the remains of dead animals. They learned that there were risks beyond the grasp of science and that statements by scientists and politicians about the absence of risk could not always be trusted. And they learned that what one eats today may lead to dire consequences in years to come.

The GM food debate

Despite headlines in the early 1990s like 'Franken-stein's tomato' or 'Genetic time bomb', before 1996 GM foods had been more or less unnoticed by the British public. The UK was one of the first European countries to introduce food products of modern biotechnology into the consumer market: so-called vegetarian cheese (made using chymosin derived from GM yeasts) in the early 1990s, and GM tomato paste in 1995–96.

Then in autumn 1996 North American comm-odity crops (so-called Monsanto soya and Ciba-Gigy maize) containing unsegregated mixtures of conventional and GM material were imported into various European countries. The problem was that while the USA had adopted the principle of functional equivalence, in Europe, process-based regulation had left the issue of labelling unresolved. The UK media reported on the arrival of the Monsanto soya at some length, and there was a certain amount of public debate involving special-interest groups (such as farmers, consumer organ-isations, and environmental organisations) as well as policy-makers and politicians.

Over the next two years an increasingly vocal coalition of critics of GM food emerged, including: Greenpeace; Friends of the Earth; the Soil Association and other supporters of organic farming; consumer groups (including the Consumers Association); the Vegetarian Society; and some influential public figures. A number of events served to keep the issue of GM foods on the public agenda. These included the announcement in April 1998 by the food retailer Iceland (whose chairman was a board member of Greenpeace) that none of its own-label products would contain GM ingredients; the decision in June by Prince Charles (a part-time organic farmer) to call for a public debate on the merits of allowing GM crops to be grown in Britain; the call in July by the independent advisory body English Nature for a three-year moratorium on the commercial planting of GM crops in Britain; the decision in August to ban GM foods from the House of Commons restaurants; and the screening, also in August, of a television documentary featuring the unreviewed work of a Scottish scientist, Arpad Pusztai, on the health effects on rats of GM potatoes. Finally, in September 1998 (after several years of difficult negotiation), EU regulations took effect regarding the labelling of foods containing GM ingredients. By this time, the scene was set for conflict between supporters and opponents of food biotechnology in the UK.

By early 1999, GM foods began to climb the political and news agendas when for the first time GM food became a party political issue with the prime minister and the leader of the opposition clashing in the House of Commons. Then on 12 February 1999, the *Guardian* published a letter, orchestrated by the environmental group Friends of the Earth, from 20 international scientists supporting the (still unreviewed and unpublished) work of Pusztai. This 'triggered' a national debate in the UK media that embraced not only Pusztai's work but also more general questions concerning the safety of previously approved GM foods, the labelling of GM consumer products, the environ-mental impacts of GM crops, the relative merits of intensive vs organic farming, the role of large multi-national corporations in the global agricultural economy, the (im)partiality of government ministers responsible for biotechnology policy, and indeed the uncertainties inherent in the scientific process itself.[7] The intersection and accumulation of these events have had a profound effect on the trajectory of biotechnology in Britain.

Medical biotechnology: case-by-case policy-making

In contrast to many other European countries, the UK has always followed a pragmatic case-by-case approach to biotechnology regulation. In the past decade a complex network of departmental and interdepartmental advisory committees, agencies and commissions have arisen to deal with various aspects of the spectrum of biotechnological issues and implications. While there was an impasse over GM foods, it was business as usual for policy-making on medical and related biotechnologies.

In 1996, the government responded to a House of Commons Select Committee report on science and technology by establishing an overarching body, the HGAC, designed to address the scientific, social and ethical implications of medical biotechnologies. This committee has been principally concerned with reproductive issues and the implications of genetic testing for employment and for insurance. In 1996, the Association of British Insurers issued a voluntary code of practice stating that its members would not request any genetic tests as a condition for obtaining insurance. However, recognising that insurance companies were designing guidelines for the use of genetic test results (eight conditions were specified including Alzheimer's, hereditary breast cancer, hereditary colon cancer and Huntington's disease), particularly for life insurance, and that there was no legislation to regulate such procedures, the HGAC recommended that the government implement a moratorium on the use of genetic testing for insurance products until a formal mech-anism for evaluating the scientific and actuarial evidence had been established. The government responded by entering into a voluntary agreement with the insurance industry that genetic tests would not be used (1997), and later launched the Genetics and Insurance Committee in 1999. Having established guidelines for the insurance industry, the committee received, and subsequently approved, its first application (2000) to use the results of a test for Huntingdon's disease in calculations for life insurance premiums. In the meantime, despite concern that the industry had been flouting its own code and using test infor-mation prior to committee approval, the govern-ment has not introduced any statutory regulation or ban. However, despite the fact that a system of approval is now in operation, unease over the use of genetic test results for insurance purposes has prompted a new committee, the recently appointed Human Genetics Commission (successor to the HGAC) to reconsider whether it is socially and ethically tolerable.

Another controversial area has been that of xenotransplantion. The Advisory Group on the Ethics of Xenotransplantation, following two years of deliberation, reported in 1997 that while xeno-transplantation could be acceptable, certain criteria would have to be met and, in the meantime, clinical trials should be temporarily proscribed due to lack of evidence on safety. As a result, a permanent body, the UK Xenotransplantation Interim Regulatory Authority (UKXIRA), was established the same year to oversee the development of xenotransplantation in the UK and to advise the Department of Health on issues of safety, efficacy, acceptability and animal welfare. Any proposal to undertake a trial or procedure involving xenotransplantation in the UK must now be submitted first to the UKXIRA for consideration.

A new era of policy making: openness and transparency

In 1998 the government decided that a review of the regulatory framework of biotechnology was necessary. In May 1999, a report in conjunction with public consultation[8] led to the termination of three existing committees (including the recently appointed HGAC) and the establishment of two new overarching commissions: the Human Genetics Commission (HGC) and the Agricultural and Environment Biotechnology Commission (AEBC) (Figure 1). These two commissions, in conjunction with the recently established Food Standards Agency (FSA), have been designed to provide strategic advice to the government and to the existing advisory bodies on biotechnology and to consider the wider social and ethical issues. They are constituted by experts in consumer issues and ethics as well as scientists and lay representatives. At present there are 18 regulatory/technical bodies that advise the government on biotechnology.

Following three years of debate, a government White Paper, and various food controversies such as BSE, *E. coli* and GM foods, the Food Standards Act was passed in January 1999 providing the legal basis for the setting up of the FSA which was formally established in April 2000. Its functions are to provide advice to the public and the government on food safety, nutrition and diet; to enforce and monitor food standards; and to support consumer choice by promoting accurate labelling of food. However, in addition, the FSA has made history in UK policy-making, by being the first non-parliamentary committee not only to hold all its board meetings in public, but also to hold consultative meetings around the country. In an effort to promote greater openness, transparency and trust in the regulatory process, the HGC and the AEBC have announced that they too will hold consultative meetings with the public and open board meetings from 2001 onwards.

Figure 1. The UK regulatory structure for biotechnology and related areas

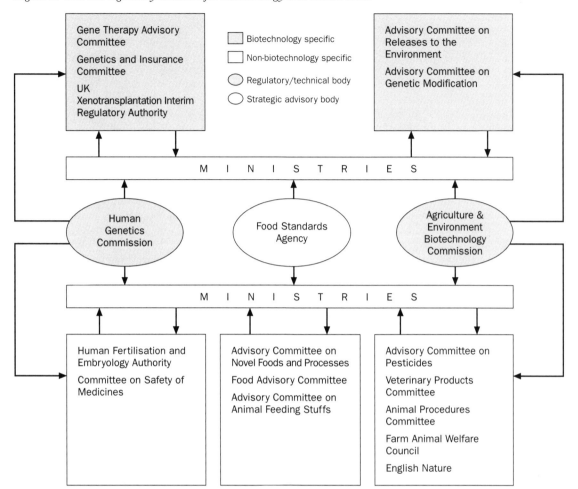

Biotechnology in the media

Figure 2 shows the intensity of press coverage of biotechnology in the UK from 1973 to 1999. Data are taken from *The Times* until 1987 and from then on the *Independent*, the newspapers of record that have opinion-leading functions for other media operators.

In the 1990s, the long-term trend changes in 1991 and again 1996. Before 1992 the average daily issue carried one article on biotechnology and related topics, by 1996 it had risen to three articles to reach four of five articles by 1999. The trend hides a particular peak in February 1999 when the GM food debate occurred. Durant and Lindsey analysed the dynamics of the debate[9] and found that all but the right-wing quality press adopted an active campaigning tone. During the two days when the

Pusztai story first appeared, most of the coverage was attributed to political journalists and no articles were written by science and technology journalists. GM food was linked to BSE and to organic farming in more than 10 per cent of articles. GM foods became a political issue and the acronym 'GM' entered common parlance. Having orchestrated the trigger event, a letter to the *Guardian* regarding the Pusztai research, briefings from NGOs informed much of the ensuing media coverage.

The high level of news coverage for biotechnology, in contrast to many other European countries, may be explained by both internal and external factors in the news system. 'Gene talk' may be particular resonant to the English public, as this invites in various ways celebratory references to what is seen to be a science in which Britain excels and to scientific heroes such as Darwin (by 2000

Figure 2. Intensity of articles in the UK, 1973–99

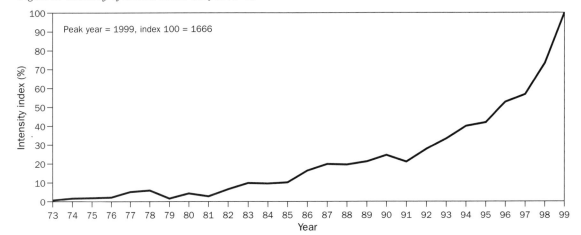

Darwin's effigy has come to replace Dickens on the £10 note). The general trend of increasing media coverage suggests that the 'gene' has reached glamour status in the UK media, and now serves as a peg for other news stories and for advertising. Genetics now has intrinsic news value.

The UK has high stakes in biotechnology. Professional public relations from industry and issue entrepreneurs (such as Greenpeace and other NGOs) keep it in the news. But at the same time, the intense competition among national broadsheet newspapers, the *Guardian, Independent, Telegraph* and *The Times* (the so-called 'quality' press) and, separately, the *Daily Mail* and the *Daily Express* (known as 'tabloid' or 'popular' newspapers), make for a volatile market for news attention. In a form of positive feedback the news value of biotechnology stories increases in a relentless search for what may be the cutting-edge story in a highly contested market of uncommitted readers. This dynamic is visible in the GM food debate as described above but was also evident in the Monsanto soya story of 1996–97 and Dolly the sheep in 1997.

Overall, the coverage can be characterised by the framing of the stories, the themes that are addressed, the actors that attract attention, and by the presence or absence of risk and benefit discourse. Table 2 compares the frames of biotechnology in the quality press before and after the watershed years of 1996–97 and an interesting change is observed. In the first period, reflecting a generally supportive press, progress and economic issues were dominant, with a newly emerging concern for ethical issues. In the second period progress continues to be a dominant frame (down by 16 per cent) with the new frames of nature/

nurture and public accountability. In 1996 we predicted that the ethical frame would become one of the dominant ways of discussing biotechnology.[10]

The replacement of the ethical frame by public accountability may reflect a maturation of the debate. A move from general and explicit ethical concerns to more concrete considerations where ethical positions are implicit, for example, how and by whom decisions should be taken, and how to deal with dilemmas that have implications for the distribution of resources. In the first period the most common themes are genetic identity (genetic fingerprinting and privacy issues) and medical applications (pharmaceuticals and diagnostics), both of which were widely supported in the 1996 Eurobarometer survey.

By contrast in the second period, 1997–99, the term 'medical' loses much of its news value to the more controversial 'agrifoods'. 'Genetic identity' and references to 'public opinion' are also important themes. The rise in reportage about public opinion demonstrates the increased politicisation of the debate and represents a reflexive turn in media coverage. The media increasingly adopted the role of advocates and opinion leaders in the debate, and of commentators on the positions taken by themselves and other media outputs, while at the same time legitimating their advocacy with reference to public opinion and their part in it.

With respect to coverage of the risks and benefits of biotechnology, the dominant benefit orientation of the pre-watershed years declines. In parallel, coverage that focuses on neither risks nor benefits increases from 20 to 43 per cent. This is because biotechnology – reported in the emerging frames of nature/nurture and globalisation, and themes such

Table 2. UK media profile, 1993–99 (threshold for inclusion: 5 per cent)

Variable	1. 1993–96		2. 1997–99	
Frequency (%)[a]	57		43	
Frame (%)	**Progress**[b]	**39**	**Nature/nurture**	**26**
	Economic	25	Progress	23
	Ethical	17	Accountability	18
	Nature/nurture	9	Economic	11
	Accountability	9	Pandora's box	7
			Runaway train	7
Theme (%)	**Genetic identitiy**	**25**	**Agrifood**	**26**
	Medical	22	Genetic identity	17
	Economic	15	Public opinion	17
	Agrifood	13	Medical	12
	Regulation	10	Regulation	11
Actor (%)	**Business**	**32**	**Business**	**27**
	Scientific	28	Politics	23
	Politics	21	Media	10
	Media	7	Scientific	9
	NGOs	6	NGOs	6
Benefit/risk (%)	**Benefit only**	**42**	**Neither**	**43**
	Both	28	Benefit only	57
	Neither	20	Both	17
	Risk only	10	Risk only	13
Location (%)	**UK**	**64**	**UK**	**57**
	USA	21	USA	21

a Percentage of corpus in the period: $n = 311$
b Bold indicates highest frequency within phase.

as genetic identity – is often presented in matter-of-fact claims and not in terms of the risks and benefits of outcomes. Interestingly, of the articles that mention exclusively risks or benefits, the ratio of 'benefit' articles to 'risk' articles drops from 4:1 in the first phase to 2:1 in the second phase. In parallel, the ratio of articles mentioning both risks and benefits to those mentioning only risks changes from 3:1 to 1:1. For the reader of the press there is a greater emphasis on risks in the period 1997–99.

While the NGOs are not prominent actors in the media window, their influence on the course of events should not be underestimated. As with the Pusztai case and some other episodes it was NGOs, working behind the scenes, whose research and briefings stimulated the media's interest.

Overall, there has been a change in the representation of biotechnology in the media. The period 1997–99 sees a decline in the bigger picture or framing in terms of economic progress and a rise in articles about nature/nurture and public accountability. In parallel, agrifoods replace medical themes and in so doing coverage is more likely to feature a risk discourse.

Quality versus popular press

Table 3 shows that many of these trends are more evident in the quality than in the popular press. Historically the UK press has been bifurcated between the elite quality market, and a popular mass market. More recently there has been a trend towards convergence towards a common middle ground.

Although our data reveal differences in the profile of biotechnology in the quality and popular press, the differences are not dramatic. The quality press is more diverse in the framing of the issues and in the actors mentioned. While the dominant frames are common to both, in the popular press they are more accentuated. It is in the themes that the differences are apparent. In the popular press, genetic identity is the dominant topic, far ahead of medical applications. The quality press features agrifood, genetic identity and the reflexive turn of the media. This suggests that the controversy over GM food is something of an elite issue in the UK. The quality press has more risk-focused coverage, 13 per cent as compared to 5 per cent, but around

25 per cent of all coverage is benefit-focused in both types of press.

While business and political actors are in focus in the quality press, in the popular press the media/public opinion and political actors take centre stage. It seems paradoxical that in the popular press 'public opinion' is not a theme, but the 'media' is a significant actor. The popular press is also more likely to take the lead in the 'reflexive turn'. This came about because some of the popular press took an explicit position against GM food, resulting in a battle between various papers as to who was in the vanguard of protecting the public, leading to cross-references and critical commentary on the positions of other press outlets.

Public perceptions

The analysis of the media coverage of biotechnology for the years 1997–99 depicts two features that may be expected to have had a considerable impact on public perceptions. First, there has been a consistent upward trend in the volume of media coverage, which following Leahy and Mazur's version of the agenda-setting hypothesis would be expected to cultivate negative attitudes.[11] Second

was the 'GM food debate' in February 1999, when the issue of GM foods became a political issue and press coverage changed to a campaigning style and moved to the front pages. With these developments it might be expected that the issue of GM foods in particular, and possibly biotechnology in general, would be highly salient or at least considerably more salient than in 1996 when the last Eurobarometer was conducted, and that a trend of increasingly negative attitudes would be observed. Indeed, the findings from the 1999 survey, and contrasts with 1996, show that while opposition to GM foods has increased and support for medical biotechnologies has held constant, as an issue for the general public biotechnology is of no more interest than it was in 1996.

Awareness of biotechnology

Notwithstanding the political and media controversies, for the majority of the British public the survey shows that biotechnology is not very salient. Asked 'Before today have you ever talked about biotechnology?', 59 per cent of the British public said 'No, never'. Somewhat surprisingly this compares to 52 per cent in 1996. For those who

Table 3. Framing of biotechnology in the quality and popular press, 1997–99

	Quality press		**Popular press**	
Framing (%)	Nature/nurture	26	Nature/nurture	44
	Progress	23	Progress	32
	Public accountability	18	Public accountability	12
	Economic	11		
	Pandora's box	7		
	Runaway train	6		
Theme (%)	Agrifood	26	Genetic identity	40
	Genetic identity	*17*	Medical	19
	Public opinion	17	Agrifood	16
	Medical	12	Research	9
	Economics	6	Public opinion	7
	Regulation	11		
Actors (%)	Business	27	Media	30
	Politics	23	Politics	25
	Other	15	Business	16
	Media	10	Other	12
	Independent science	9	Independent science	10
	NGOs	6		
	International	6		
Risk and benefits (%)	Neither	44	Neither	54
	Benefit only	27	Benefit only	28
	Both	17	Both	14
	Risk only	13	Risk only	5

Sample size: n(quality) = 115, n(popular) = 129; listings only include categories with 5 per cent and above.

said they had talked about it, we find no greater reported frequency than in 1996; only 6 per cent said they talked about it frequently. At first sight these findings seem implausible, but it accords with our experiences conducting a series of focus-group discussions in the summer of 1999. The participants were chosen from amongst those whom we thought would be well informed. They were all regular readers of four of the national papers which had been prominent in the GM food debate. But, to our surprise, relatively few of the participants showed more than a passing familiarity with the topic of biotechnology, although many said that they thought they should be more interested and informed.

While biotechnology may not be a popular conversation topic, the volume of press coverage appeared to have had an impact on levels of awareness. As many as 80 per cent had heard of GM foods and between 50 and 60 per cent had heard of cloning, genetic testing and pharma-ceuticals. The contrast between these high levels of awareness and low levels of discussion would suggest that, on the topic of biotechnology, the mass media are the dominant source of information and likely to be influential in opinion formation.

The impact of the media coverage is evidenced in the section of the survey dealing with scientific knowledge. As in 1996, this comprised a number of questions dealing with textbook or factual know-ledge, the sort of facts one might learn at school or from a television documentary. Three of these questions were also designed to test for the existence of menacing images of biotechnology. The changes is textbook knowledge from 1996 to 1999 are relatively small, but the findings for the menacing image questions are dramatic. In 1999, 30 per cent gave the correct true/false response to the question 'Genetically modified animals are always bigger than ordinary ones', down 10 per cent since 1996. A similar decrease was found for the statement 'Ordinary tomatoes do not contain genes, while genetically modified ones do', with correct answers dropping from 40 to 31 per cent. The third menacing image question designed for the survey in 1996 and replicated in 1999, addresses the central issue of the Pusztai controversy that led to the GM food debate. Respondents were asked to respond to the statement, 'By eating a genetically modified fruit a person's genes could also become modified.' In 1996 some 55 per cent of Britons disagreed with this statement, but by 1999 the figure had dropped to 36 per cent.[12] It would be naïve to attribute these changes in beliefs in the monstrosity, adulteration and infectivity of GM

foods solely to the Pusztai controversy. For example, our qualitative research as early as 1996 showed that public concerns about GM foods were anchored in the BSE crisis. But the high-profile controversy over Pusztai's findings may have served to crystallise a latent concern.

Attitudes to technologies and biotechnology

The 1996 survey showed that the lack of enthusiasm for biotechnology could not be attributed to a rising tide of technological Luddism. Some 77 per cent of respondents thought that computers and IT, telecommunications, solar energy, new materials and space technology would 'improve our way of life in the next 20 years'. By contrast only 58 per cent of the British public thought the same of biotechnology and genetic engineering.

In 1999 we find that optimism in other tech-nologies has held almost constant with 78 per cent agreeing that the five specified technologies would improve our way of life. But, over the three years, optimism about biotechnology and genetic engineering declined by some 12 per cent to 46 per cent overall. And to put this into perspective, in 1999 the British public was only a little more opti-mistic about biotechnology than civil nuclear power, 46 and 41 per cent respectively.

This question also revealed a convergence of attitude, and by implication in connotation, of the terms 'biotechnology' and 'genetic engineering'. In 1996 a split ballot asked half the respondents about biotechnology and the other half about genetic engineering. These showed levels of optimism of 73 and 43 per cent respectively. For whatever reason the then more recent nomenclature 'biotechnology' was seen as more attractive than 'genetic engineering'. Perhaps few understood what biotechnology was in 1996. But by 1999 the comparable figures were 52 and 41 per cent respectively, showing the transient nature of verbal repackaging.

Attitudes to specific applications of biotechnology

In the context of the explosion of media coverage, declining optimism about biotechnology, a relatively high level of awareness of the specific applications covered in the survey, and a greater prevalence of menacing images of GM foods, how would the British public view a range of applications of biotechnology? In 1996 we found differentiated attitudes to various applications of biotechnology. There was broad support for medical applications, ambivalence over agrifood biotechnologies and opposition to GM animals for research and xenotransplantation. The pattern of attitudes for the seven selected applications in the 1999 survey is shown in Figure 3.

The first point to note is that there is a considerable degree of differentiation in attitudes across the seven applications. The traditional medical biotechnologies of genetic testing and the production of medicines are widely supported. These are seen as useful, low risk and morally acceptable. The same pattern holds for bioremediation. At the other extreme, GM foods are not seen as useful, they are perceived as both risky and morally unacceptable, and are not supported. The two cloning applications are perceived very differently, showing that cloning per se is not rejected but that the form and uses to which it is put are the issue. The cloning of human cells and tissues for medical purposes is much more acceptable than the cloning of animals for similar medical purposes. While the two are perceived as equally risky, the cloning of human cells and tissues is seen as more useful and, perhaps crucially, it is morally acceptable, whereas the cloning of animals is seen as morally unacceptable. In 1996 we found that the absence of moral acceptability acted as a veto and this holds in 1999 for the two cloning applications. Cloning of animals is seen as morally unacceptable and is opposed, while the cloning of human cells and tissues is seen as morally acceptable and is supported. Perhaps the fundamental concern is the distinction between whole vs part organism cloning. The former is seen to be one step away from the cloning of human beings and

eugenics, a scenario which we found in qualitative interviews to be almost universally rejected. Finally it is interesting that opposition to GM foods is much greater than opposition to GM crops. This suggests that the food safety concerns (c.f. the terms of the Pusztai controversy) are far more influential in determining public attitudes than are the environmental impacts of GM crops that have featured so prominently in the campaigning of various opposition groups.

Support and opposition for applications in 1999

Given that a relatively high number of respondents were not prepared to express an opinion on some of the applications, an alternative way of looking at the levels of support in 1999 is to contrast the percentages of those who agree or agree strongly that a particular application should be encouraged, with those who disagreed or strongly disagreed. Using the whole sample as the baseline, Table 4 shows the percentages of supporters and opponents (the 'decided') and of those who did not express an opinion, the so-called 'undecided'. Here the same ranking of applications holds as in the mean scores shown in Figure 3.

It can be seen that almost half the British public expressed support for genetic testing (47 per cent), closely followed by 42 per cent supporting medical biotechnologies. The government's proposals for the cloning of human embryos may have been encouraged by these findings. For these applications, as for bioremediation and the cloning of human cells, a

Figure 3. Average evaluation of usefulness, risk, moral acceptability and willingness to encourage biotechnology applications in the United Kingdom

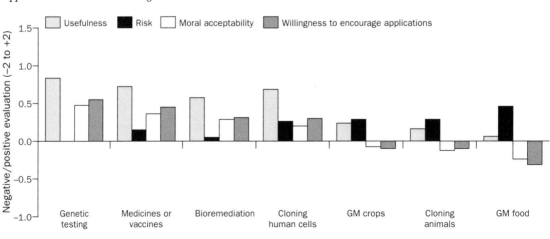

Table 4. Percentages of supporters, opponents and 'undecided' for applications of biotechnology

	GM food	GM crops	Medicines	Genetic testing	Human cell cloning	Animal cloning	Bioremediation
Encourage	25	28	42	47	41	26	34
Oppose	42	32	15	13	21	30	14
Undecided	33	41	43	40	38	44	52

majority of the decided are supportive. For GM crops and cloning animals the decided public is almost equally divided for and against. By contrast a majority are opposed to GM crops, cloning animals and GM foods. It is also of note that GM foods attract the highest ratio of opponents to supporters (1.7 to 1) and, reflecting the recent media coverage of the issue, the lowest percentage of 'undecided' respondents at 33 per cent.

Changes in opinion, 1996–99

The changes in the question wording and format from 1996 to the 1999 survey led to an appreciable decline in the percentages of 'decided' respondents. This makes simple time-series comparisons based on the entire sample invalid. In order to make justifiable comparisons the following analysis is based on only those respondents who expressed an opinion on all four of the attitudinal dimensions, that is use, risk, moral acceptability and encourage. With responses on the four attitudinal dimensions we can construct subgroups of the public taking one of the three following 'logics': support, risk-tolerant support and opposition.

The first finding to note is the impact of the awareness filter question and of the different interviewing practice on the percentages of decided respondents, a decline of almost a half from 1996 to 1999. In terms of the distribution of the logics, as might be expected, the support for GM foods has tumbled. Opposition has increased from 33 to 53 per cent, and the sum of supporters and risk-tolerant supporters has declined from 66 to 46 per cent. Whereas a majority of the decideds supported GM foods in 1996, by 1999 the majority were opposed. For GM crops there is a 21 per cent increase in opposition and a corresponding 21 per cent decline in the two forms of support, but overall the supporters are in the majority.

However, the controversy over GM foods and crops has not spilled over into concerns about the use of modern biotechnology for medical applications. For pharmaceuticals and genetic testing there is virtually no change over the three-year period. The level of opposition has remained

almost constant at about 6 per cent for medicines and 4 per cent for genetic testing. Equally the sum of supporters and risk-tolerant supporters is constant at over 90 per cent for medicines and for genetic testing. Hence over the period 1996 to 1999, public attitudes have become more differentiated. Medical applications have retained a high level of support while GM foods are now rejected by a majority of those with better-formed attitudes, and for GM crops there is a significant decline in support and increase in opposition. The 'great GM debate' has polarised public perceptions of biotechnology. Only the brave would argue for any short-term possibilities for the introduction of GM foods. The advocates of GM foods have failed to persuade the public that this application of biotechnology is useful, risk free, or morally acceptable.

What underlies attitudes to biotechnology?

We now turn to perceptions that may underlie people's judgements about applications of biotechnology. Ideally this analysis would explore differences in perceptions between the supporters, risk-tolerant supporters and the opponents. However, with the relatively large percentage of 'don't know' responses, numbers in the three logic groups are too small for reliable statistical analysis. Hence, we contrast the views of those who thought that biotechnology 'would improve our way of life' whom we will call 'optimists' with those who thought biotechnology 'would make things worse' – the 'pessimists'.

There are some striking contrasts in the views of the optimists and pessimists about the moral implications and risks associated with GM foods and the cloning of animals. And beyond these contrasts it is apparent that even the optimists are troubled about the technology. For example, while 87 per cent of pessimists think that 'even if biotechnology has benefits it is fundamentally unnatural', as many as 68 per cent of optimists share the same view. Asked whether 'the risks are acceptable', 78 per cent of pessimists and 44 per cent of optimists say 'no'. Finally to the statement 'biotechnology poses no dangers to future generations', 74 per cent of pessimists and 37 per cent of optimists disagree.

Five questions about risks were combined into a scale called 'risk perception' ($\alpha = 0.79$). The scale maps the position of the application in question on a continuum from perceived 'dread risks' to 'calm risks'. This dimension has been shown to be important in risk acceptability. For cloning animals and GM foods the pessimists perceive the risks as being more 'dreaded' than the optimists. But once again, even the optimists perceive the applications to be in the dreaded end of the dimension.

A consistent pattern of attitudes is evident. On different dimensions of risk and on the moral implications of biotechnology, the greater majority of pessimists express concerns. But perhaps more strikingly these concerns are also shared by many of the optimists. Such concerns were a pronounced feature in our qualitative interviews and they are clearly reflected in the quantitative survey data.

The concerns about GM foods are also reflected in a series of questions about intentions for consumer choices. Respondents were asked if they would 'buy GM foods if they tasted better', 'buy cooking oil that contained a small amount of GM soya', 'eat GM sugar if traces of genetic modification had been removed', and 'eat eggs of chickens fed on GM corn'. A cumulative scale of these four items gives an indication of the strength of behavioural intentions. Of course one must be cautious in extrapolating such answers to actual consumer choices, as intentions are not behaviours, and none of the questions referred to prices. That said, the mean score of 1.7 GM-purchasing intentions for the optimists hardly shows great enthusiasm. Not surprisingly the pessimists are lower at 0.77. But notwithstanding the impact of the British GM food debate, in the context of Europe as a whole the British public are relatively well disposed towards GM consumer products. The UK mean of 1.22 is surpassed only by Sweden and the Netherlands.

It has been argued that what is needed to generate support for GM foods is more trust in the technology and in the regulatory processes. We asked about trust in two ways. First, as in 1996, respondents were asked who they would trust to tell the truth about biotechnology. They were provided with a list of 12 sources and offered multiple choices. In order of public trust were the medical profession (53 per cent), consumer organisations (42 per cent), environmental organisations (39 per cent) and universities (29 per cent). By contrast, national and international bodies each attracted around 11 per cent, an increase from 1996, and industry a mere 3 per cent. As in 1996, it is those who are independent of

and in some cases have campaigned against biotechnology that are trusted to tell the truth.

The second approach to the issue of trust was informed by Luhmann,[13] who argues that trust is part of the taken for granted and to ask about it directly is to call it into question. In the light of this, respondents were asked whether a range of actors were 'doing a good job' or 'not doing a good job for society in relation to biotechnology'.

Of those who expressed an opinion, the government is thought to be doing a good job by 47 per cent, and the comparable figure for industry is 42 per cent. But as in the previous question on who to trust to tell the truth, it is bodies that are independent of biotechnology that are more likely to be seen to be doing a good job, for example consumer organisations (75 per cent), environmental organisations (72 per cent), shops (69 per cent), ethics committees (64 per cent) and newspapers (62 per cent). Although the picture in broad terms is similar for the two ways of asking about trust – there is more trust in bodies independent of government and industry, the form of the question has a considerable impact on the estimated extent of trust.

Finally there is a relation between trust and feelings of optimism and pessimism about biotechnology. For example, the optimists have more trust in industry and government than the pessimists. By contrast the pessimists have more trust in environmental organisations than the optimists. Consumer organisations, shops and the medical profession are trusted by the majority of both optimists and pessimists.

In 1996 we found that gender and education were correlated with support for biotechnology. At that time supporters were more likely to be male and in the better educated groups. Over the last three years the gender difference on optimism and pessimism has become accentuated. Amongst men there has been a decline in optimism from 60 per cent to 53 per cent, with the comparable figures for women of 55 per cent and 39 per cent. Hence the decline in optimism is twice as great in women as in men. This may be the result of the health concerns around GM foods as we also find that women have significantly higher scores on the scale of 'dread risks' for GM foods.

Integrative commentary

For the UK the years of controversy ended in the announcement and publication of the first draft of the human genome sequence, an achievement both widely supported and heavily funded by UK institutions. But leading up to this announcement, in the years 1996–2000 biotechnology has lived up to the connotations of a strategic technology: that of carrying economic prospects and the potential to transform diverse areas of future life. As cloning, xenotransplantation, genetic testing and GM foods moved from theory to reality, each one has been the subject of controversy. The intensity, duration and the breadth of the controversy has varied across these applications, with the most extreme being seen in the case of GM foods. Here, an application of biotechnology became both a party political issue and a topic in the ongoing circulation war of the national press.

Biotechnology's emerging controversial status reflected both direct implications of the technology and associations with other issues and events. The idea of using modern biotechnology in the context of animals and foods raised public anxieties as had been shown in the Eurobarometer of 1996. And at the same time the public had little trust in the regulatory authorities' ability to deal with new technologies with uncertain implications. The advent of Dolly the sheep was taken as a signal that the technology was going to change the world and to do so in ways that many felt were not acceptable. Monsanto's marketing of GM soya attracted the critical attention of environmental groups and the prospect of unlabelled GM products raised consumer concerns. There followed debates about globalisation, the vertical integration of the food chain, and the result was suspicion about the motives of the life-science conglomerates. Biotechnology was not insulated from the continuing BSE crisis which sowed the seeds of doubt in modern agriculture and confirmed worries about the regulatory system.

In the period 1996–2000 the three arenas of the public sphere, policy-making, media coverage and public perceptions, became more interdependent, mutually aware and reflexive.

From a policy orientation that sought to support biotechnology within the context of advice from specialist advisory committees, public concerns have been recognised and now, under the Labour government since 1997,[14] there is a new commitment to greater transparency and public consultation in science and technology. In a radical reappraisal of biotechnology policy, the advisory committee structures have been significantly changed and a new and unprecedented era of openness and transparency in policy deliberations introduced. In broad terms the media have sustained a largely positive and supportive reportage, now tempered by concerns about public accountability and a greater emphasis on risks. But for particular events such as GM foods the media has been sceptical and critical. It is of note that in the GM food debate the media not only took on a campaigning style but relied on political rather than science and technology journalists for the stories. The political era of biotechnology has arrived. Public perceptions are now more differentiated. There is still support for the use of genetic technology in medicine and for genetic testing of inherited diseases, but now GM foods are widely rejected as is the cloning of animals. Sections of the public have been sensitised to possible risks from certain applications of biotechnology and to shortcomings in the policy process.

Whether the Labour government's double strategy of supporting biotechnology as a strategic technology, but at the same time adopting a more participatory approach to accommodate public opinion, will be sustainable is an open question. For example, despite the government's continued commitment to field trials of GM crops in the UK, in November 1999 it conceded to a voluntary moratorium on the commercial plantings of GM crops until 2002. In parallel it also proposed that clauses in the new Anti-Terrorism Bill, announced in December 1999, should include some of the actions of animal-rights campaigners and of environmental protestors who have been destroying fields of GM test-trials. For some, opening up the policy process to a range of stakeholders is a cosmetic exercise designed to gain trust, defuse opposition and allow the technology to progress unhindered. But for others, the Dutch model of participatory technology evaluation[15] is a practical solution to a complex and politically charged problem of providing legitimacy to a new technological development.

Across the three arenas, policy, media and public perceptions, there has been an increasing synchronisation in representations of biotechnology. In each we find a similar bifurcation between medical, so-called 'red', biotechnologies and the 'green' agrifood biotechnologies. The red and green varieties now come under the aegis of different regulatory bodies. Red biotechnologies continue to be viewed positively, based on the imperative of life saving and alleviating illness, while green biotechnologies have run into considerable resistance as a result of their lack of utility and fears of infection. Some applications do not rest easily in either the red/good or the green/bad category. The medical benefits do not outweigh a host of concerns over the cloning of animals. Similar anomalies may arise for xenotransplantation or in the use and protection of diagnostic test data that may infringe privacy. In the regulatory arena the bifurcation is evidenced in the new committee structures for the governance of biotechnology, while the collapse of the life-science vision has led to the separation of red and green clusters of business activities. In the short term this bifurcation may insulate red biotechnologies from public controversy. But will the controversy over GM agrifoods spill over into medical applications of biotechnology? Will novel foods integrating the greengrocer, baker and pharmacist break the 'Chinese wall' between red and green?

For the future, public interest in the implications of the Human Genome Project is likely to grow as its potential for medical research is realised. While genetic testing to catch criminals and to identify inherited diseases is widely supported, extensions of this will raise issues of what information, who would have access to it and for what purposes. For example, the Home Office has recently extended its forensic DNA database beyond convicted criminals to include suspects and those acquitted of crimes. These plans have caused unease amongst civil liberty groups and have prompted the HGC to put the issue on their agenda. The years of controversy are likely to continue and to embrace new issues.

Notes and references

1 Bauer, M W, Durant, J, Gaskell, G, Liakopoulos, M and Bridgman, E, 'United Kingdom', in Durant, J, Bauer, M W and Gaskell, G (eds), *Biotechnology in the Public Sphere: A European Sourcebook* (London: Science Museum, 1998), pp162–76.

2 Human Fertilisation and Embryology Authority and Human Genetics Advisory Commission, *Cloning Issues in Reproduction Science and Medicine* (London, 1998).

3 Nuffield Council on Bioethics, *Stem Cell Therapy: The Ethical Issues* (London, 2000).

4 Chief Medical Officer's Expert Advisory Group On Therapeutic Cloning, *Stem Cell Research: Medical Progress with Responsibility* (London: Department of Health, 2000).

5 Return to an Order of the Honourable the House of Commons dated October 2000 for the report, evidence and supporting papers of the Inquiry into the emergence and identification of Bovine Spongiform Encephalopathy (BSE) and variant Creutzfeldt-Jakob Disease (vCJD) and the action taken in response to it up to 20 March 1996 <http://www.bse.org.uk/index.htm>.

6 Coghlan, A, 'How it all went so horribly wrong', *New Scientist*, 168 (4 November 2000), p4.

7 Durant, J and Lindsey, N, *The Great GM Food Debate: A Report to the House of Lords Select Committee on Science and Technology Sub Committee on Science and Society*, Report 138 (London: HMSO, 1999).

8 Office of Science and Technology, *The Advisory and Regulatory Framework for Biotechnology: Report from the Government's Review* (London: Cabinet Office, 1999).

9 Durant, J and Lindsey, N (see note 7).

10 Bauer, M W *et al.* (see note 1).

11 Leahy, P J and Mazur, A, 'The rise and fall of public opposition in specific social movements', *Social Studies of Science*, 10 (1980), pp259–84.

12 A technical note: in reporting further findings from the survey and in particular comparisons with 1996 we have eliminated all respondents who gave 'don't know' responses. Even before respondents had been asked the awareness filter questions, we find in the 1999 survey that the percentages of 'don't know' responses were almost double the rate obtained in 1996. While this could be interpreted as an increase in uncertainty, we believe it is more likely to be the product of a change in interviewing practice for the two surveys. According to the field work company, in 1999 'don't know' responses were more likely to be accepted without pressing respondents to make a choice from the response alternatives offered.

13 Luhmann, N, *Trust and Power* (Chichester: Wiley, 1979).

14 House of Lords Select Committee on Science and Technology, *Science and Society: Third Report of the Session 1999–2000* (London: The Stationery Office, 2000).

15 Gutteling, J *et al.*, this volume, pp229–236.

Address for correspondence

George Gaskell, Department of Social Psychology, London School of Economics, Houghton St, London WC2A 2AE, UK. E-mail g.gaskell@lse.ac.uk

Biotechnology in the United States of America: mad or moral science?

Toby A Ten Eyck, Paul B Thompson and Susanna H Priest

Introduction

For the most part, biotechnology has never been as controversial in the USA as it has been in Europe. At the same time, between 1975 and 1997, policy activity in the USA was both lively and hotly contested. General trends and events of this 22-year period will be surveyed, and an attempt will be made to trace policy decisions undertaken by the US government. Few Americans outside the leading graduate research programmes in biology would have known much about recombinant DNA in 1975. Although Watson and Crick's discovery of DNA was, by this time, part of every well-educated American's knowledge set, the technological possibilities and the attendant risks and benefits thereof were wholly unknown. This changed with the 1975 Asilomar conference called to debate whether transfer of genes from one organism to another – something that was already known as genetic engineering – was an inherently dangerous activity. The conference attracted some US news media coverage and, within a few years, popular books on genetic engineering began to appear.[1]

Debate over issues raised at the Asilomar conference provided a platform which activist Jeremy Rifkin used to launch a series of attacks on biotechnology. In addition to popular books,[2] Rifkin's public activism during the late 1970s and early 1980s consisted of college speaking engagements, popular magazine and radio interviews, and coalition building with his constituency groups. During these activities, the theme was frequently to highlight the ethical concerns associated with human eugenics, and to suggest that American science was on a slippery slope. In the 1980s, Rifkin formed the Foundation on Economic Trends (FET), which came to bedevil the scientists and companies that were hoping to develop new products of biotechnology. The most successful FET action was a lawsuit that delayed agricultural experiments on ice-nucleating (so-called 'ice-minus') bacteria for several years and tested the US government's entire regulatory apparatus for agricultural biotechnology.[3]

All told, the decade of the 1980s was a time in which a number of Americans were feeling sceptical about biotechnology. It was, however, also a time in which there were no products of agricultural biotechnology that were actually on the market. As such, it was difficult for this sceptical minority to raise much concern among ordinary Americans, who had other problems to worry about. By the mid 1990s, US government agencies had made formal policy decisions for regulating biotechnology, which are described below. Although many of the individuals who were most active in criticising biotechnology between 1985 and 1995 were deeply dissatisfied with the direction of US policy, the decade of workshops and hearings had apparently exhausted the energy and interest of the broader community of politically active US citizens. At the end of this period, many environmental leaders who had questions seem to have decided that, whatever environmental issues might be associated with biotechnology, other problems were more pressing and more worthy of their limited time and effort. Similarly, few NGOs representing consumer interests placed biotechnology on their agenda for public action. By 1995, when products began to appear in large numbers, Rifkin's coalition had apparently had enough of working together. When the US Food and Drug Administration (FDA) announced its intention to implement a policy that would discourage labelling of genetically engineered foods in 1996, few of the groups even bothered to comment. Rifkin himself had gone on to write books about the beef industry and the end of work.[4]

By 2000, this situation had changed in a manner that surprised many scientists, government regulators and the biotechnology industry itself. Rifkin was back with a new book, *The Biotech Century*, in 1998.[5] In 1997 and 1998, a US Department of Agriculture proposal to allow genetically engineered foods to be labelled as 'organic' was soundly criticised, and was the mirror image of FDA's experience in 1996. While Rifkin's personal influence should not be overstated, this action symbolised renewed US attention to these issues.

In 1999, controversy in Europe began to be reported in US newspapers, and this spawned stories questioning biotechnology in virtually every major daily newspaper. Protestors at the 1999 WTO meetings in Seattle were able to put biotechnology on the nightly news, and in late 2000 leading news outlets gave sensational coverage to a report that a leading brand of taco shells contained some genetically engineered maize that was not approved for humans. Below we review the official regulatory policy for biotechnology in the USA, then comment in more detail on policy debates since 1997.

Regulatory policy in the USA under the Coordinated Framework

The USA has never passed any piece of regulatory legislation aimed specifically at biotechnology. Instead, a number of pre-existing US regulatory agencies have established a regulatory protocol under existing laws. Pure research activities are self-regulated by both non-profit research organisations and commercial firms, though these self-regulatory activities are themselves overseen by the primary research funding agencies of the US government. In fact, policy review for human biotechnology is largely confined to the research setting (with the exceptions noted below) and is a function of Institutional Review Boards (IRBs) constituted at each research organisation under guidelines developed by the National Institutes of Health (NIH). Drugs and food technologies are regulated by the FDA, while chemicals or organisms with a potential for environmental impact are regulated by divisions of the Environmental Protection Agency (EPA) and by the Animal and Plant Health Inspection Service (APHIS) of the US Department of Agriculture (USDA). These federal agencies have co-operated under an administrative agreement referred to as the Coordinated Framework for Biotechnology Regulation.

Under the Coordinated Framework, the FDA oversees new product approval for both human and animal drugs and medical therapeutic devices, as well as certifying most questions regarding food safety. Companies hoping for FDA approval submit data demonstrating the safety and, with respect to drugs and therapeutic devices, also the effectiveness of their products. FDA scientists may reject or approve a product or, as is usually the case, will indicate that the product will not be approved until specific questions are addressed. Companies then conduct the requested studies. The process

generally ends with either approval or withdrawal of the request for approval. At present drugs continue to be approved on a case-by-case basis, without regard to whether genetic engineering is used in their development or manufacture. FDA exempts many food products from review under the doctrine of 'substantial equivalence'. The basic idea behind this policy is that review is not necessary when all of the genes involved in the transformation are from foods or have been previously approved by FDA, unless there is further reason to suspect that a specific transformation might have toxic or allergenic properties. All 'enhancements' or transformations that *do* introduce novel gene sequences and their attendant proteins into foods are subject to full FDA review and the standard approval process. Companies *may request* review even for products that would technically be exempt under the doctrine of substantial equivalence. Since US citizens enjoy ample opportunity to hold businesses operating in the USA liable for harm, it is likely that any company developing a product that would be found to be of questionable safety in a liability court would seek voluntary FDA review.[6] The FDA has been sharply criticised in the USA for its policy of substantial equivalence.[7]

With respect to environmental risk, monitoring is shared by two agencies, the EPA and APHIS. Broadly, the division of authority is as follows: EPA regulates plants or microorganisms that have been genetically engineered to serve as agents for the control of insects, fungi or other agricultural pests, except weeds. APHIS has traditionally had the responsibility of protecting US agricultural producers from invasive species brought in from outside US borders. Based on early concerns that genetically engineered crops could become noxious weeds, APHIS undertook regulatory monitoring of environmental impacts not covered by EPA under the Coordinated Framework. APHIS staff reviewed proposals to field test herbicide-tolerant and Bt crops[8] in the late 1980s and early 1990s, but since 1996 these crops have been deregulated. No agency of the USA monitors deregulated GMOs for ecological impact. Critics have questioned whether APHIS's organisational mandate of protecting the interests of US farmers made it an appropriate agency for environmental risk regulation, and also questioned whether there might be gaps in the regulatory framework for environmental monitoring, especially with respect to monitoring.[9]

Although all of these agencies have undertaken almost continuous review of their policies since the establishment of the Coordinated Framework in

1986, there have been no substantive changes in the main regulatory policies of the three agencies since 1996. The FDA has made no changes with respect to drug or food safety policy, and on 29 September 2000, the United States District Court for the District of Columbia dismissed a legal challenge to those policies brought by a coalition of public-interest NGOs. The suit had challenged FDA policy on grounds that the decision not to require labelling of GMOs discriminated against individuals with food allergies, and also against religious minorities who objected to consumption of genetically engineered foods. Throughout 1999, the FDA conducted a series of public hearings to solicit consumer viewpoints on GMOs and in early 2000 announced that it would support a plan for voluntary labelling of non-GMO products. However, the details for such a plan have not been announced.

The EPA endured severe public criticism when research results reported that pollen from Bt crops endangered Monarch butterflies, and when it became clear that Starlink corn, approved by the EPA only for use in animal feeds, had found its way into human diets. Both of these incidents are discussed below. Furthermore, the National Research Council, an organisation that conducts blue-ribbon scientific studies that are meant to have some impact on policy for the US government, issued a report urging more careful EPA monitoring of environmental risks from GMOs developed to control insect pests in the summer of 2000.[10]

The regulatory authority of APHIS was strengthened by passage of the Plant Protection Act in 2000. Although this law does not specifically mention biotechnology, some have argued that it closes regulatory loopholes, and gives APHIS clear authority to regulate all environmental impacts associated with genetically transformed plants.[11] However, APHIS has not announced how the provisions of this Act will or will not be applied in the regulation of GMOs. A National Research Council study team to review APHIS policies on GMOs will issue its report in late 2001 or early 2002.

There are two general characteristics of the US process for regulating biotechnology that are particularly relevant to comparisons with other countries. First, when US government agencies alter their procedures for product approval, notice of the proposed policy change is published in the *US Federal Register*. Parties that are affected by the change may submit comments before the action becomes final. Agencies are required by law to respond to each public comment providing a public

record of the basis on which decisions are made. NGOs representing both industry and citizen interests monitor the *Federal Register* and make frequent comments. Non-industry NGOs have expressed dissatisfaction with the US government's responsiveness to their comments regarding policy for biotechnology in the food and agricultural arena. These criticisms notwithstanding, US procedures for setting policy can be described as both transparent (one may discern the basis on which decisions are made) and responsive to the interests of affected parties, especially when compared to those of many other industrialised countries. Second, a citizen, company or an NGO may bring a civil action against a regulatory agency in an attempt to overturn or reverse an agency's action on a particular issue (though the US government limits the opportunities to bring such action). Agencies permit and even encourage such actions, especially in cases where agency administrators believe that there may be flaws in existing legislation or procedures for conducting regulatory review. One complaint of environmentally oriented NGOs is that US statutes do not provide sufficient grounds for them to challenge regulatory policies established under the Coordinated Framework.[12]

Policy debates 1997–2000

Although there were virtually no changes in US government policy for biotechnology during the four-year period that began on 1 January 1997, there was a steady increase in the quantity and intensity of public debate during that period. The most evident event was the announcement that Scottish scientists had succeeded in cloning an adult sheep in February 1997. In response to questions about the ethics of human cloning, President Clinton gave the National Bioethics Advisory Committee (NBAC) 90 days to produce a report on this issue. The NBAC was not a standing committee of the federal government in the USA, but a special committee that had been appointed to consider issues involving research on human embryos and stem cells. As such, there was some question as to whether the NBAC included the relevant expertise for a study of cloning. Nevertheless, the NBAC conducted extensive hearings, commissioned a number of advisory papers and issued its report in June 1997. The NBAC concluded that application of then extant adult-cell cloning techniques to human beings posed unacceptable risks and recommended a five-year moratorium, at which time the issue could be revisited. The NBAC did not issue any categorical judgments about the ethical acceptability of human cloning.[13] After holding its own hearings, the US Congress failed to act even on the recommended moratorium.

In 1998, a Chicago scientist named Dr Richard Seed announced his intention to proceed with an attempt to clone himself. Seed's announcement sparked a brief resurgence of debate over cloning. But the public quickly became sceptical of Seed's ability to follow through with his plan. Seed continues to appear as a speaker on college campuses, but has not generated serious response at the policy level. In fact, cloning has all but disappeared from political debate subsequent to the NBAC report and the flurry of interest in Dr Seed. Human cloning has not been made into an issue by American religious groups or NGOs, and was entirely absent from the 2000 election debates. Nevertheless, a steady stream of books and scholarly publications have appeared, including a number of readers intended for college classroom applications[14] and a bestselling book by *New York Times* science reporter Gina Kolata.[15]

While human cloning moved from the headlines into the scholarly literature from 1997 to 2000, GM foods went in the opposite direction. Sparked by European resistance to biotechnology, there was widespread policy debate over the food and environmental safety of GM foods throughout 1999 and 2000. This debate has been somewhat diffuse and difficult to classify into discrete themes. One clear strand concerns the potential for allergens in food products derived from genetically transformed organisms. Another more muted strand concerns labelling and consumer consent. With respect to the environment, concern has largely focused on the adequacy of regulatory monitoring under the Coordinated Framework. One may also discern voices expressing concern about the global consequences of gene technology, and a growing sense that development of agricultural biotechnology may not be in the interests of the world's poorest people.

It is perhaps easiest to track this debate not with respect to the substantive policy concerns listed above, but with respect to three specific products of biotechnology: Bt maize, 'golden rice' and Starlink corn. Each sparked substantial press coverage and focused debate on specific issues.

Bt maize. Bt maize, which has been transformed to produce the toxin *Bacillus thuringiensis* in plant tissues, became controversial when a group of researchers at Cornell University announced that

pollen could threaten Monarch butterflies. The announcement promulgated a somewhat confused reaction from the American public and from policymakers. Scientists had long known that Bt maize would be toxic to butterflies and moths. Indeed the entire point of Bt crops is to control these insects in their larval stage. Caterpillars do considerable damage to crops. Monarchs, however, are not crop pests, and there was some scepticism as to whether they would be exposed to significant amounts of the toxin. For the public, however, the story appeared to say that scientists had simply overlooked the possibility of effects on Monarch butterflies, and it appeared as if there were major flaws in the regulatory monitoring of transgenic crops. By 2000, it appeared that each group was about half right. On the one hand, subsequent studies indicated that Bt maize did not pose substantial risks to Monarch butterflies. On the other hand, risk assessments of Bt maize did fail to identify pollen drift as a possible avenue of environmental exposure to non-target insects, and this was regarded as a significant failing of US regulatory review.[16]

Golden rice. The 'golden rice' story broke widely in the spring of 2000. So-called 'golden rice' involves transformations that increase the Vitamin A content of rice. The product was widely touted as a response to nutritional deficiencies among the poorest of the poor. Advocates of biotechnology argued that opponents of the technology were putting forth an elitist view that was contrary to the interests of people in the developing world.[17] This argument contradicted the viewpoint of Indian activist Vandana Shiva,[18] whose books have had a strong influence on public opinion in the USA, especially with the left and with those who have protested US policies toward global free trade and US non-participation in global environmental agreements. In July 2000 a prestigious US group representing the National Academies of Science (NAS) as well as six other science academies around the world again appeared to split the difference between these two points of view. Their report concluded that biotechnology would be an important tool for increasing world food supplies, but also suggested that current trends in the development of this technology did not necessarily favour the interests of poor farmers.[19]

Starlink corn. Starlink corn is a specific variety of Bt maize approved for use as animal feed, but not for human consumption. Debate over genetically engineered food surfaced again in the autumn of 2000 when testing laboratories detected traces of Starlink corn in taco shells and other corn products being marketed in US grocery stores. As with the Monarch case, the Starlink corn incident sparked confusion. Evidence suggested that there was, in fact, no important human health risk associated with the consumption of Starlink. Nevertheless, Starlink was found to be in violation of the FDA's substantial equivalence policy, and the FDA had acquiesced to the EPA's approval of the product only when Aventis, the company that developed Starlink, provided assurances that it would not appear in human diets. The Starlink incident thus reinvigorated debates about the potential for GMOs to elicit allergic reactions from some consumers, the call for labelling of GMOs, and concerns about the potential for communication and regulatory gaps in the US Coordinated Framework. At the same time, advocates of biotechnology insisted that no-one was harmed by the Starlink incident, and that controversy was being blown out of proportion.

Finally, much like the GMO issues and cloning, the effort to sequence the human genome has received a great deal of attention both from US scholars of science and technology policy and from reporters. On the other hand, it has garnered little interest from activists of any sort. In the early 1990s, the genome effort was politely debated as a potential waste of resources and as possibly having an ability to distort the selection of genetics research projects. By the end of the decade, this discussion had given way entirely to coverage of the competition between the NIH group led by Francis Collins and a private group led by Craig Venter. This competition was widely covered in US newspapers and magazines, as was the official resolution of the competition when both agreed to appear with President Clinton to announce the successful completion of the genome project.

Within this context, but in a move quite untypical for US science, the NIH project established a component of their human genome effort to support research and public education efforts associated with many contentious issues arising from human genetics research. This programme, entitled the Ethical, Legal and Social Issues (ELSI) component of the Human Genome Project, began in 1992 under the leadership of James Watson. Through ELSI, the NIH provided more US government funding for research on ethical, legal and socially contentious issues in genetics than was available for all forms of humanities-oriented

research throughout all competitive grant programmes administered by all federal and state governments throughout the USA. Funds available through ELSI continue to dwarf all other available funds for research and education activities associated with contested or controversial science. It is thus not surprising that the number of US scholarly publications and research articles that have been published on various aspects of medical genetics is enormous, and the conferences, workshops and public meetings on this topic are also too numerous to summarise. A two-volume encyclopaedia on such topics was published in 2000 and a more complete and representative sampling of US opinion and reaction to these topics can be found there.[20]

Media coverage in the USA, 1997–99

As mentioned, many of the policy decisions concerning biotechnology have been normalised since the 1975 Asilomar Conference, and especially since 1996, so it is typically the bizarre and controversial decisions, inventions and discoveries that now gain the media spotlight, at least in terms of front-page news, along with promotional messages and activities emanating from the promoters of biotechnology. In the USA these stories are even more important when they appear in *The New York Times* and/or the *Washington Post*. As Gans noted, '[editors] prepare themselves...; before story selection begins, they will have read *The New York Times* and the *Washington Post*... .'[21] We randomly chose 100 articles from both papers for each year under study as a proxy for recent media coverage on biotechnology in the USA.

A preliminary study of biotechnology and genetic issues in these newspapers beginning in 1973 was conducted. Lexis-Nexis was used to search for the keywords biotech(!),[22] genetic(!), genome, and DNA for each year. Figure 1 illustrates the intensity in which these key words appeared in *The New York Times* and *Washington Post* (the *Washington Post* is not available on Lexis-Nexis until 1977). While some decreases do appear within these 27 years, the overall trend is a steady increase in coverage, with most articles appearing in 1998 for both newspapers (665 articles in *The New York Times* and 391 in the *Washington Post*).

Table 1 contains a comparison of articles which treated biotechnology or genetics in more than a cursory or symbolic manner appearing between 1992 and 1996 and between 1997 and 1999. While the progress frame was the most salient frame for

Figure 1. Intensity of articles on biotechnology issues in the US press, 1973–99

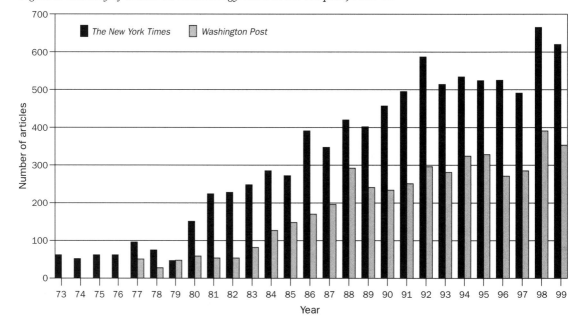

both periods, the higher percentage of progress frames for 1997–99 reflects the fact that many of the technologies which were new and untested in the earlier time period, had become taken for granted. For example, news coverage of the trial of O J Simpson (a well-known retired American-football player who was accused of murdering his ex-wife and her boyfriend in 1993) in 1994 focused heavily on whether or not DNA samples could be used as evidence. By 1997, DNA samples were commonly being used as evidence in court cases. The heavy coverage of the Simpson trial also accounts for the higher percentage of the public accountability frame in the earlier time period, as news coverage focused heavily on judicial proceedings and courtroom antics.

In addition to the Simpson trial, the period 1992–96 was characterised by the movie *Jurassic Park* (1993)[23] and Richard J Herrnstein and Charles Murray's book, *The Bell Curve*.[24] *Jurassic Park* was typically reported as scientific progress, while *The Bell Curve* was often disparaged as a step backward in the debates surrounding race, nature and nurture. The second phase, 1997–99, did not produce the same kinds of cultural icons, though *The Lost World* – the sequel to *Jurassic Park* – was released in 1997. Instead, the focus tended to be on issues such as gene therapy, the identification of genes thought to hold the promise of diagnosing diseases, and the Human Genome Project. In both

periods, the economics of biotechnology and genetics, such as stock-market issues and business transactions, were heavily covered. This is reflected in the finding that business interests appeared in more articles than any other type of actor, including scientists. Finally, biotechnology and genetic news typically enjoyed a positive slant. Between 1992 and 1996, 51.4 per cent of the articles mentioned only the benefits of the technology, and while this fell to 40.8 per cent between 1997 and 1999, this was still a higher percentage than either articles which discussed both risks and benefits (28.0 per cent) or risks only (7.2 per cent).

Figure 2 shows a comparison of four themes which were heavily covered between 1997 and 1999: agriculture and food (108 articles); genetic fingerprinting, e.g. solving crimes through DNA samples (187 articles); medical research (238 articles); and cloning (51 articles). These findings reflect the multivalence of the mass media.[25] Biotechnology and genetic technology applied to agriculture and food issues are very likely to be critically evaluated, while there are nearly two positive evaluations for every negative evaluation for genetic fingerprinting and medical applications. Positive and negative evaluations of cloning are nearly equal, though it should be noted that cloning has a much deeper cultural resonance than the other terms, and can be found in nearly every section of the newspaper, where it is used to define

Table 1. US media profile (threshold for inclusion: 5 per cent)

Phase	1992–96		1997–99	
Frequency (%)[a]	65		35	
Frame (%)	**Progress**	49	**Progress**	63
	Economic	28	Economic	13
	Public accountability	6	Pandora's Box	7
	Nature/nuture	6	Runaway	5
	Ethical	5		
Theme (%)	**Biomedical**	25	**Biomedical**	24
	Genetic identity	16	Genetic indentity	18
	Economic	16	Agrifood	27
	Agrifood	10	Generic research	10
	Generic research	10	Economics	9
	Regulation	8	Regulation	9
	Other	7	Public opionion/policy	6
			Cloning	5
Actor (%)	**Business**	36	**Business**	30
	Independent science	28	Independent science	25
	Politics	20	Politics	22
	Media/published opinion	9	Other	10
			Media/published opinion	8
Benefit/risk (%)	**Benefit only**	51	**Benefit only**	41
	Risk and benefit	26	Risk and benefit	28
	Neither	16	Neither	24
	Risk only	7	Risk only	7
Location (%)	**USA**	81	**USA**	77
	Europe	12	Europe	13
	Other countries	5	Other countries	7
Risk actor (%)	**Business**	39	**Independent science**	36
	Politics	24	Business	33
	Independent science	21	Politics	15
	Media/published opinion	7		
Benefit actor (%)	**Business**	38	**Business**	37
	Independent science	36	Independent science	36
	Politics	19	Politics	19
			Interest groups	5
Valuation of biotechnology (%)	**Positive**	43	**No evaluation**	53
	No evaluation	42	Positive	31
	Balanced	11	Balanced	10
	Negative	4	Negative	4

a Percentage of corpus in the period; $n = 1374$.
b Bold indicates highest frequency within phase.

copies of computers (e.g. PC clones), wishful thinking in the sports section (cloning an prominent athlete or successful season), as well as appearing in reports on the scientific work and debates that surround the cloning of animals and humans. While some would argue that these are completely different issues, it does not detract from the fact that beliefs and attitudes toward cloning in general may be influenced by the widespread use of this term and concept in popular culture, where it often receives positive treatment.

While the quantitative aspects of the US media coverage can offer insights into reporting trends, it is important to discuss these findings from a qualitative perspective. It is known that audience members do not choose which articles to consume based on random sampling, but on particular interests.[26] Two articles, one negative and one

Figure 2. Comparison of themes and evaluations, US media, 1997–1999[a]

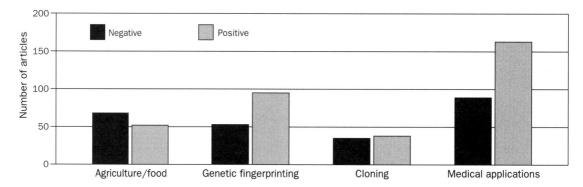

a Some articles contained both positive and negative evaluations. This chart includes all evaluations for both newspapers on all the themes present.

positive, will be chosen from two of the themes presented in Figure 2 – agriculture and medical applications. These articles are not meant to represent all news coverage in the USA, but to offer the reader some understanding of how these issues have been reported.

On 19 November 1997, *The New York Times* published an article in which cotton growers questioned the assertion that GM seeds would bring higher yields. According to the article, cotton growers using Roundup Ready cotton were experiencing reduced cotton yields and were expected to sue Monsanto (the maker of the Roundup Ready seed) for millions of dollars. In the words of *The New York Times*:

> Monsanto calls the genetically engineered cotton it developed with the Delta and Pine Land Company the most successful product introduction in farming history – likely to make cotton the nation's first crop in which genetically altered varieties predominate. But in the Mississippi Delta, the revolution has produced enough casualties that officials are warning farmers to hold off until further testing proves the technology's reliability.[27]

The same commodity received a much different treatment in the *Washington Post* on 3 July 1998. According to this article, a partnership between Monsanto and Grameen Bank was to bring 'exciting advances in biotechnology to Bangladesh'. In fact, '[t]he center's first project is a demonstration farm of about 10 acres where Monsanto will test hybrids of cotton that could increase Bangladesh's cotton yield.'[28] In addition to the introduction of GM cotton, the partnership would also be introducing GM food crops and water-cleaning technologies.

This pattern of seemingly chiastic news stories can also be found around the issues of biotechnology and medicine. For example, in a report on a fatality caused by gene therapy, The New York Times reported on 28 November 1999:

> As far as government officials know, Jesse's death on Sept. 17 was the first directly related to gene therapy… . Jesse's therapy consisted of an infusion of corrective genes, encased in a dose of weakened cold virus, adenovirus, which functioned as what scientists call a vector… . The Penn researchers had tested their vector, at the same dose Jesse got, in mice, monkeys, baboons and one human patient, and had seen expected, flulike side effects, along with some mild liver inflammation, which disappeared on its own. When Jesse got the vector, he suffered a chain reaction that the testing had not predicted – jaundice, a blood-clotting disorder, kidney failure, lung failure and brain death… . The doctors are still investigating; their current hypothesis is that the adenovirus triggered an overwhelming inflammatory reaction – in essence, an immune-system revolt. What they do not understand yet is why.[29]

This recount of a tragedy is a far cry from a report published in the *Washington Post* on 16 March 1999, concerning the mapping of the human genome. According to the article:

> Unraveling big parts of the genetic code is expected to give biotechnology companies a valuable tool for developing new treatments for human disease, and in many instances the companies hope to lock out competitors by patenting genes and other important findings. Government researchers, by contrast, are struggling to make sure as much genetic information

as possible remains in the public domain, to serve as a fundamental resource both for academic research and for private drug-development efforts.[30]

While these contradictory messages do appear in the opinion-leading press in the USA, there seem to be some general trends in covering issues of biotechnology and genetic technology. First, these issues are gaining more coverage in terms of the number of articles appearing each year. Second, a majority of articles are portrayed positively and as progressive. With this in mind, we now turn to public perceptions of biotechnology and genetic technology to examine the differences and similarities between media discourse and public opinion.

Public perceptions

US opinion was assessed in April 2000 through a telephone survey instrument adapted from that used in Canada during the same calendar year, itself adopted from the 1999 Eurobarometer instrument. The survey, conducted by the Public Policy Research Institute at Texas A&M University, was administered to 1002 adults.[31]

Many questions were equivalent to those included on the 1999 Eurobarometer, although there were also a number of questions unique to the US and Canadian instruments. The US sample was large enough to permit overall conclusions to be drawn about opinion distributions in this country, but not large enough to facilitate extensive comparisons to be made among subgroups, such as regional or ethnic divisions. Nevertheless, global conclusions about general characteristics of the opinion climate in the USA are possible on the basis of these data.

US respondents seem to be responsive to perceived moral considerations in their evaluations of biotechnologies. Ranking the six applications according to whether they 'should be encouraged' based on mean responses produces exactly the same order as ranking these applications in order of moral acceptability. Genetic testing is most morally acceptable and most likely to be encouraged, followed by genetically engineering bacteria to produce medicines, genetically modifying crops, food biotechnology generally, producing animal organs for transplantation to humans, and finally cloning animals (such as sheep) that can produce medicines in their milk. Manipulating the genetic characteristics of animals appears to be less acceptable than manipulating the genetic characteristics of plants, which appears to raise

more concerns than manipulating the genetic characteristics of bacteria. This seems to offer a clearer pattern than any preference that might be based on medicinal vs agricultural uses, since both the most and the least controversial technologies (animal cloning and genetic testing, respectively) that were included in this survey were presented as having human medical significance. That genetic testing is the least controversial seemed surprising, given the publicity that has been given to issues of privacy, insurability and even 'designer baby' potentialities. But it is understandable in terms of a hierarchy of acceptability for genetic manipulation, given that testing is the only technology included that does not involve modifying the genetic structure of an organism at all.

Generally speaking, more useful technologies were also rated as more likely to be encouraged, as were less risky technologies. However, regression analysis indicates that in each case (that is, for all six technologies), moral acceptability is a better predictor of encouragement than either risk or usefulness. Further, usefulness is in each case a better predictor than risk. Thus explanations of popular thinking in the USA that rest on the existence of 'public fears' about biotechnology do not appear to be well founded. Morality and usefulness are both stronger predictors than perceived risk, with morality stronger than usefulness.

The generally positive average responses to these and other survey questions may obscure the fact that many of the over 275 million people that make up the US population do have reservations about the new biotechnologies. A majority, 52.8 per cent, of the US population is currently optimistic that genetic engineering will 'improve the quality of life' over the next 20 years, a small increase in the number reported for 1997 at 50.4 per cent (see other time-series information below). But at the same time, 30.1 per cent expect the technology to 'make things worse', a noticeable longer-term increase from the 16 per cent that the US Office of Technology Assessment found answered a similar question this way in 1982.[32] This is nearly comparable to the 32.4 per cent in the current survey who felt the same way about nuclear power, a technology more commonly recognised as controversial. (Compare this to the 1.6 per cent who felt solar energy would make things worse, for example, or the 5.2 per cent for telecommunications.) Generally positive US press reports, often based on information provided by industry and university sources who are interested in promoting biotechnology, may have obscured the fact that substantive disagreement on these issues certainly exists in this country just as it does in much of the rest of the world.[33]

Although a complete time-series comparison is not presently feasible, some data from a comparable 1997 survey are available and suggest that biotechnology-related opinion in the USA has remained largely stable in recent years when overall means are considered.[34] However, some increase in polarisation is apparent for all four of the technologies for which time-series comparisons have been made. These four are food biotechnology generally, genetic modification of crops, genetically engineering bacteria to produce human medicines, and genetically engineering animals to produce organs for transplantation into humans. In each case, mean responses to questions about whether each of these technologies 'should be encouraged', measured on a four-point scale from 'strongly disagree' to 'strongly agree', budged very little; the greatest change was that for xenotransplantation, for which the mean moved from 2.38 to 2.64, while the mean for food biotechnology remained exactly unchanged at 2.75. But in almost every case, the proportions of respondents choosing 'strongly disagree' or 'strongly agree' increased, while the proportions choosing 'disagree' or 'agree' decreased.[35]

These data are consistent with the nature of distributions reported elsewhere[36] for the five global questions on the US survey about GM foods: whether they will bring benefits, whether associated risks are acceptable, whether they are 'against nature', their disaster potential, and the adequacy of current regulations. While noticeably more people lean toward positive (pro-biotechnology) than negative (anti-biotechnology) opinions on these questions, assessed using a five-point scale from 'strongly disagree' to 'strongly agree' and including a neutral option, relatively few chose the neutral response to any of these questions. This is quite likely another indicator that the US population has formed rather definite opinions in this area, in comparison to an earlier period when the topic was so new that few respondents were believed to be in a position to have informed views.

Current industry public-relations efforts, such as those sponsored by the Council for Biotechnology Information, appear to be based in part on the assumption that opposition to biotechnology is a function of incomplete knowledge or miseducation. Certainly intensified public education efforts are appropriate and will undoubtedly help to stimulate broader public debate in an increasingly polarised

USA, an indication of a healthy democracy and probably a necessary precursor to public acceptance. However, the relationship between either levels of education or levels of relevant biological knowledge and encouragement of these technologies is in fact rather weak.[37] In other words, these efforts cannot necessarily be counted on to turn public opinion in a predictable direction. Nevertheless, faith in the groups and institutions responsible for biotechnology's development appears to remain high among the US population.

Finally, the furore surrounding the Human Genome Project in the USA, including the dramatic race between the publicly funded effort of Francis Collins at the NIH and the privately funded effort of Craig Venter at Celera Genomics, may be most visible to those in the scientific and science policy communities. Most recently, both team leaders announced their current results – widely billed as 'cracking the code' of the human genome – at the 2001 meeting of the American Association for the Advancement of Science in San Francisco, with simultaneous, 'hot-off-the-presses' special issues of the prestigious journals *Nature* and *Science*, containing the respective papers, also vying for attention. The impact of all this on public opinion may be negligible, and this particular event took place after this survey was conducted. But the publicity surrounding the project both reflects and contributes to a political culture in which science is both highly privileged and widely regarded as the source of economic prosperity and the solutions to most human problems.

Conclusions

The move to normalise policy decisions concerning biotechnology over the past three decades has not kept the issue from becoming front-page news, as activists, industry and others compete for the coveted attention of the mass media. Reporters, in turn, seek to produce news that will sell papers (and broadcasts), and make editors and producers happy. While a slight majority of audience members tend to approve of biotechnology and genetic technologies, they are becoming more polarised on the issues. This seems to echo practices of the media (at least *The New York Times* and *Washington Post*), as more attention is focused on the negative aspects of these technologies, while other stories still provide information on the positive qualities. These trends point to a future in which new inventions and discoveries in the fields of biotechnology and genetic engineering may be met by various audiences with more clearly defined stakes in publicising and framing stories which support their world views. Each side has a spokesperson whose legitimacy relies on their ability to keep frames of discourse on a specific track and in the limelight, which will have some impact on policy decisions and public opinion. At this point, it is far too early to declare a winner or even a favourite in the battle over biotechnology. Both sides will continue to portray themselves as the moral guardians of science and the public interest, while damning their adversaries as 'mad scientists'.

Notes and references

1 Goodfield, J, *Playing God: Genetic Engineering and the Manipulation of Life* (New York: Random House, 1977); Krimsky, S, *Genetic Alchemy: The Social History of the Recombinant DNA Controversy* (Cambridge, MA: MIT Press, 1982).

2 Rifkin, J with Perlas, N, *Algeny: A New Word; a New World* (New York: Viking Press, 1983); Rifkin, J, *Declaration of a Heretic* (Boston: Routledge & Kegan Paul, 1985).

3 Krimsky, S and Wrubel, R, *Agricultural Biotechnology and the Environment: Science, Policy and Social Issues* (Urbana, IL: University of Illinois Press, 1996).

4 Thompson, P B, *Food Biotechnology in Ethical Perspective* (London: Blackie, 1997).

5 Rifkin, J, *The Biotech Century: Harnessing the Gene and Remaking the World* (New York: Jeremy P Tarcher, 1998).

6 Malinowski, M J, 'Biotechnology in the USA: responsive regulation in the life science industry', *International Journal of Biotechnology*, 2 (2000), pp6–25.

7 Krimsky, S, 'Risk assessment and regulation of bioengineered food products', *International Journal of Biotechnology*, 2 (2000), pp231–8.

8 Bt crops are those containing genes from the biopesticide soil organism *Bacillus thuringiensis*.

9 MacKenzie, D, 'Agricultural Biotechnology, Law, APHIS Regulation', in Murray, T H and Mehlman, M J, *Encyclopedia of Ethical, Legal and Policy Issues in Biotechnology* (New York: John Wiley and Sons, 2000), pp56–66.

10 National Research Council, *Genetically Modified Pest-Protected Plants: Science and Regulation* (Washington, DC: National Academy Press, 2000).

11 Abramson, S, 'USDA's legal authority and perspectives on assessment of environmental effect', presentation at the Workshop to Assess the Regulatory Oversight of GM Crops and the Next Generation of Genetic Modifications for Crop Plants, National Research Council, Washington, DC, 13 October 2000.

12 Adelman, D, 'Forward-looking regulation of agricultural biotechnology', presentation at the Workshop to Assess the Regulatory Oversight of GM Crops and the Next Generation of Genetic Modifications for Crop Plants (see note 11).

13 National Bioethics Advisory Commission, *Cloning Human Beings* (Rockville, MD: NBAC), 2 vols, 1997.

14 Pence, G E (ed.), *Flesh of My Flesh: The Ethics of Cloning Humans* (New York: Rowman and Littlefield, 1998); McGee, G (ed.), *The Human Cloning Debate* (Berkeley, CA: Berkeley Hills Books, 1998).

15 Kolata, G, *Clone: The Road to Dolly and the Path Ahead* (New York: Wm Morrow, 1998).

16 National Research Council (see note 10).

17 Nash, J M, 'Grains of hope', *Time*, 156 (13 July 2000), pp38–46; Meredith, J, 'Biotech foes eat well while others starve', *Des Moines Register* (21 August 2000).

18 Shiva, V, *Monocultures of the Mind: Perspectives on Biodiversity and Biotechnology* (London: Zed Books, 1993); Shiva, V, *Biopiracy: The Plunder of Nature and Knowledge* (Boston, MA: South End Press, 1997); Shiva, V, *Stolen Harvest: The Hijacking of the Global Food Supply* (Cambridge, MA: South End Press, 2000).

19 National Academies of Science, *Transgenic Plants and World Agriculture* (Washington, DC: National Academy Press, 2000).

20 Murray, T J and Mehlman, M J (eds), *Encyclopedia of Ethical, Legal and Policy Issues in Biotechnology* (New York: John Wiley and Sons, 2000), 2 vols.

21 Gans, H J, *Deciding What's News* (New York: Vintage Books, 1979), p91.

22 The exclamation mark represents a wild-card character.

23 The film *Jurassic Park* is based on a novel by Michael Crichton and directed by Stephen Spielberg. It portrays dinosaurs cloned from DNA extracted from the blood of mosquitoes encased in amber from the Jurassic period.

24 Herrnstein, R J and Murray, C, *The Bell Curve: Intelligence and Class Structure in American Life* (New York: Free Press, 1994).

25 Gamson, W A, Croteau, D, Hoynes, W and Sasson, T, 'Media images and the social construction of reality', *Annual Review of Sociology*, 18 (1992), pp373–93.

26 Gans, H J, 'Reopening the black box: toward a limited effects theory', *Journal of Communication*, 43 (1993), pp29–35.

27 Myerson, A R, 'Breeding seeds of discontent; cotton growers say strain cuts yield', *The New York Times* (19 November 1997): D1.

28 Mann, J, 'Partnership takes bioscience to Bangladesh', *Washington Post* (3 July 1998): E3.

29 Stolberg, S G, 'The biotech death of Jesse Gelsinger', *The New York Times* (28 November 1999): section 6, p137.

30 Gillis, J, 'Gene map is on fast track; millions in grants speed up project', *Washington Post* (16 March 1999): A19.

31 The survey sample was generated using widely accepted random-digit dialling techniques, the standard strategy used in the USA because of the country's high rate of telephone ownership and enormous geographic size, which makes representative studies using in-person interviews both expensive and difficult. Random-digit dialling techniques generate potentially valid phone numbers based on the distribution of valid telephone prefixes, minimising the selection of invalid numbers without sacrificing representativeness. This approach reaches publicly listed as well as unlisted numbers, regardless of how recently they were assigned. (It is not limited to persons listed in a current printed phonebook, in other words.) While it does omit persons who do not own telephones at all, the number of such people in the USA is believed to be relatively low (around 6 per cent).

32 US Office of Technology Assessment, 'New developments in biotechnology: public perceptions of biotechnology', NTIS #PB87-2-7544 <www.ota.nap.edu/pubs.html> (1987).

33 Priest, S, *A Grain of Truth: The Media, the Public, and Biotechnology* (Lanham, MD: Rowman & Littlefield, 2001).

34 Comparison based on US data provided from the comparable 1997 survey via personal communication with Dr Edna Einsiedel of the University of Calgary. The 1997 data remain unpublished.

35 The magnitude of these changes ranged from just over 1 per cent to over 12 per cent. Only for xenotransplantation was there any shift at all away from the extremes; in this case the number of persons 'strongly disagreeing' that this technology should be encouraged, dropped modestly from 23.9 to 22.8 per cent.

36 Priest, S, 'US public opinion divided over biotechnology?', *Nature Biotechnology*, 18 (2000), pp939–42.

37 Priest, S (see note 36).

Address for correspondence

Toby Ten Eyck, Department of Sociology / National Food Safety & Toxicology Center, 316 Berkey Hall, Michigan State University, East Lansing, MI 48824-1111, USA. E-mail Toby.Teneyck@ssc.msu.edu

Appendices

Appendix 1. Coding frame for media analysis

For more details and technical information please visit the LSES website at: http://www.lse.ac.uk/lses

The media data corpus

The analysis of the elite press reported in this book is based on two indicators: an indicator of the salience and an indicator of the framing of biotechnology in the various countries.

Salience

The salience is based on a population count of all press articles in the opinion leading outlets of each country making reference to 'biotechnology'. Depending on the availability of press data in the country, this is estimated either on the basis of manual counts, or established by online search using at least these five search strings: biotech*, genetic*, genome, DNA, cloning.

Content framing

The content analysis of the press materials is based a subsample of articles reported in the salience indicator. This sample is either proportional to the salience indicator, or is following a fixed sample design, depending on the sampling practice of the research groups. Only this subsample of articles is coded and enters the final data corpus. The sample size of the content analysis and the salience figure reported in Tables 1 in the national profiles must not be confused.

For the analysis a coding frame was developed (see below for version 2 1997–99). Compared to version published in Durant, Bauer & Gaskell (1998, pp283–88), the new version implements several alterations for the analysis of the period 1997–99 which accommodates shifts in the public debates and concerns over the efficiency of coding: (a) adjustments to v15 (additional themes were added such as 'cloning') v19 and v21 (re-coding of likelihood of risks and benefits), and (b) addition of new variables (v30–37 and v38–43 on the 'actor networks' involved), and (c) we deleted variables v8 (day of month), v10 (verbatim headline) and v24 (verbatim metaphors) for the analysis of the period 1997–99.

1 Basic information

V1 Country

UK / France / Germany / the Netherlands / Austria / Sweden / Spain / Greece / Denmark / Italy / Finland/ Portugal / Ireland / Luxembourg /Japan Switzerland / Poland / Canada / USA / Norway /

V2 Coder [country code + coder]

V3 Item number [country code + 2000]

V4 Newspaper name [country code + 1 digit]

V5 Month [2 digits]

V6 Day of month [2 digits]

V7 Year [2 digits]

2 Attention structuring

V9 Page type / exposition

Information not available / Front page (absolute) / Second or third page / Front page of folder / In the middle / Back page (absolute) / Back page of folder

V11 Size of the article

Small / Medium / Large

3 Contents

3.1 Journalistic features

V12 Newspaper section

Not applicable / Front page or general news / International news / National news / Local news / Other media quotations / Debate / 'Light' page /

Consumer / Editorial page / Culture; Feuilleton / Business pages / Science & technology, environment, medicine / Letters to the editor / Entertainment: TV, radio, film, theatre / Sport / Lifestyle, health / Other

V13 News format

Article with latest news / Investigation, reportage, background / Interview, mainly / Column, commentary (regular) / Editorial (paper's editor) / Commentary from other people (from outside) / Reviews of books, films, etc. / Other

3.2 Authorship

V14 Author

Wire service text, e.g. Reuters
In-house journalist: Political journalist / Science journalist / Other journalist
Sent-in: Other authors: scientists / Other authors: party politician / Other authors: special interests (Consumer / Religious / Industry, business / Patient groups / Environment group / Agricultural, farming / Civil service / Labour union / Regulatory, ethics committee / Military / Judicial, legal voice / Other special interest / General public voice)
No signature, anonymous, unknown

3.3 Biotechnology Events

V15abc Main themes [maximum three codings]

Transgenic: Microorganisms / Plants breeding / Animal breeding / Humans (general) / Human genome research / Gene therapy / Xenotransplanations / GMO release, e.g. field tests of plants

Safety/risks: Laboratory, workers / Environment / Public, local community / GM food
Identification: Genetic 'fingerprinting' for crime / Genetic 'fingerprinting' for other purposes / Diagnosis, testing, predictive medicine / Screening of large populations / Insurance issues / Privacy, protection of genetic information

Other issues: Patenting, property rights / Economic prospects, opportunities / Pharmaceuticals, vaccines / Reproduction, child bearing, e.g. *in vitro* fertilization / DNA, genetic research (unspecific) / Public opinion on genetics, biotechnology / Biodiversity / Legal regulation / Voluntary

regulations / Science policy for biotechnology, genetics / Education, genetic literacy / Human inheritance / Eugenics / Military, defence issues / Ethical issues / Other / Labelling / Animal cloning / Whole human cloning / Human organ cloning / Public protest, public demonstration

V16 Main actor [one coding per article]

Not applicable, unknown

Public sector: Parliament / Government (general) / Government agencies (specific) / Environment / Health / Industry / Agriculture / Government research institutions / Universities (scientists) / Ethics committees / Hospitals / National patent office / Police / Military / Judicial, legal voice / Technology assessment agency / The public, public opinion (also: 'we', 'one') / The media, published opinion

Private sector: Political parties / Religious organisations / Consumer groups / Environmental organisations / Labour unions / Agriculture, farming / Professional organisations: medical, legal etc. / Scientific organisations / Patient groups, lobbies / Industry, producers / Distributors / Scientists in private laboratories / Other
International institutions: Developing countries / European patent office / European Union, E Commission, E Parliament / OECD, EFTA or EEU34 / UN organisations / Other international organisations

Stock exchange
Author of the article

3.4 Contexts

V17 Type of controversy

None

If a controversy, is the report: balanced / imbalanced or advocating a position

V18ab Locations of event [maximum two codings]

Not mentioned

National regions

Location international
EU: Austria / Belgium / Denmark / Finland / France / Germany / Greece / Italy / Ireland /

Netherlands / Luxembourg / Portugal / United Kingdom / Spain / Sweden
Other Europe / USA / Canada / Latin America / USSR, Russian Federation area / Japan / Other East Asia, inclusive of China / Other Asia / North Africa / Sub Saharan Africa / South Africa / Australia / New Zealand / Developing countries, 'Third World' / Not identified place / Switzerland / 'Europe' / 'The world' / Norway / Poland

3.5 Impacts/outcomes

V19ab Likelihood of benefits [maximum two codings]

Not mentioned / Very unlikely / Rather unlikely / Rather likely / Very likely or already present / Mentioned, but likelihood (probability) not quantified

V20ab Type of benefits [maximum two codings]

Not mentioned / Economic growth, development /'Third World' development / Health / Legal / Social equality / Moral, ethical / Environmental, ecological / War and peace, military / Research / Consumer / Other

V20c Responsible actor for first type of benefit (coded in V20a)

Not mentioned / Use list of actors [V16]

V21ab Likelihood if risks/costs [maximum two codings]

Not mentioned / Very unlikely / Rather unlikely / Rather likely / Very likely or already present / Mentioned, but likelihood (probability) not quantified

V22ab Type of risks/costs [maximum two codings]

Not mentioned / Economic growth, development / 'Third World' development' / Health / Legal / Social inequality / Moral, ethical / Environmental, ecological / War and peace, military / Research / Consumer / Other

V22c Responsible actor for first type of risk (as coded in V22a)

Not mentioned / Use list of actors [V16]]

3.6 Demands and evaluations

V30 Type of demand (a)

No demand related to biotechnology / Call for action (do it) / Stop the action (do not do it)

V31 Area of demand (a)

No demand related to biotechnology / Otherwise use list of biotechnology themes [v15]

V32 Author of demand (a)

No demand / Otherwise use list of actors [v16]

V33 Addressee of demand (a)

No demand / Otherwise use list of actors [v16]

V34 Type of demand (b)

No second demand related to biotechnology / Call for action (do it) / Stop the action (do not do it)

V35 Area of demand (b)

No second demand related to biotechnology / Otherwise use list of themes [v15]

V36 Author of demand (b)

No second demand related to biotechnology / Otherwise use list of actors [v16]

V37 Addressee of demand (b)

No second demand related to biotechnology / Use list of actors [v16]

V38 Author of evaluation (a)

No evaluation / Otherwise use list of actors [v16]

V39 Direction of evaluation (a)

No evaluation, neutral / Very negative / Fairly negative / Somewhat negative / Balanced / Somewhat positive / Fairly positive / Very positive

V40 Addressee of evaluation (a)

No evaluation / Otherwise use list of actors [v16]

V41 Author of evaluation (b)

No evaluation / Otherwise use list of actors [v16]

V42 Direction of evaluation (b)

No evaluation, neutral / Very negative / Fairly negative / Somewhat negative / Balanced / Somewhat positive / Fairly positive / Very positive

V43 Addressee of evaluation (b)

No evaluation / Otherwise use list of actors [v16]

4 Ratings, judgements

V23a Negative evaluation of biotechnology, genetic developments

Not applicable / Slightly critical, some discourse of concern / Somewhat critical / Quite critical / Very critical / Extremely critical: discourse of great concern, of doom

V23b Positive valuation of biotechnology, genetic developments

Not applicable / Slightly positive; discourse of promise / Somewhat positive / Quite positive / Very positive / Extremely positive; discourse of great promise, of progress

V24 Use of metaphors [voluntary]

No metaphor / Metaphors used

V25 Focus

Main biotechnology, genetics focus / Other story only with biotechnology or genetic reference / Symbolic or rhetorical usage of biotech, only

V26 Frame [code every article with one frame only]

1 'Progress': celebration of new development, breakthrough; direction of history; conflict between progressive/conservative-reactionary.

2 'Economic prospect': economic potential; prospects for investment and profits; R&D arguments.

3 'Ethical': call upon ethical principles; thresholds; boundaries; distinctions between acceptable/ unacceptable risks in discussions on known risks; dilemmas. Professional ethics.

4 'Pandora's box': [likely before the event] call for restraint in the face of the unknown risk; the 'opening of flood gates' warning; unknown risks as anticipated threats; catastrophe warning.

5 'Runaway': [likely after the event] fatalism after the innovation; having adopted the new technology/ products a price may well have to be paid in the future; no control any more after the event.

6 'Nature/nurture': environmental versus genetic determination; inheritance issues.

7 'Public accountability': call for public control, participation, public involvement; regulatory mechanisms; private versus public interests; openness of procedures; transparency; justification of procedures

8 'Globalisation': call for global perspective; national competitiveness within a global economy; opposite: splendid isolation.

Appendix 2. Focus Group Short Topic Guide

Phase 1, Summer 1999

Section 1

Introduction

Welcome the participants and thank them for coming along, and for their participation in a discussion about new applications of science and technology.

Opening the frame (10–15 minutes)

'There has been a lot of coverage of biotechnology and genetic engineering in the press and on television recently, when you think about biotechnology and genetic engineering, what sort of things come to mind ?'

Awareness and evaluation of the actors involved (10–15 minutes)

'You have mentioned things like x, y, z who do you think is doing all this?'.
'Who do you think should set the limits?'
'What are the limits and what would it mean to go beyond them?'

Evaluation of specific applications (30 minutes)

Cards with the nine applications of biotechnology.
'Now I would like you to put them into piles or groups so that the ones that are similar in some way go together.'

Section 2: topics 5–6 (select one or two applications for each group).

Focus on GM foods (15–20 minutes)

'What do you understand by GM foods?' (description)

Focus on xenotransplantation or cloning (15–20 minutes)

'Can someone tell me what this is all about?'

Section 3: topics 7–9. Further exploration, if required of the dimensions of public concerns

Risk and moral (10 minutes)

'Does the idea of risks and moral issues capture the way you think about these issues?' 'Are these really the same thing in different words, or are they different ideas altogether?'

Trust (10 minutes)

'And taking everything into account, do you think people, like the government, the industry and the environmental and consumer watchdogs are doing the right thing, behaving properly when it comes to genetic engineering?'

The media (10 minutes)

Circulates one or two articles.
'Do you feel the media has done a good job reporting issues like this?'

Section 4: the ending

Phase 2, Autumn 1999

Section 1

1.1 Introduction

Welcome the participants and thank them for coming along, and for their participation in a discussion about new applications of science and technology applications.

1.2 Opening the frame (10–15 minutes)

'There has been a lot of coverage of biotechnology and genetic engineering in the press and on television recently, when you think about biotechnology and genetic engineering, what sort of things come to mind?'

1.3 Evaluation of specific applications (30 minutes)

(Cards with the nine applications of biotechnology.)

Task 1.1 Hand out cards individually
Ask for spontaneous views/reactions from the group.

Task 1.2 All the cards on the table
'Now I would like you to put them into piles or groups so that the ones that are similar in some way go together.'

Task 1.3 Now ask the group to sort the applications on the four criteria of useful/not useful, risky/not risky, morally acceptable/not morally acceptable, is legal/is not legal and is being done today/is not done being done today.

Section 2: topics A and B (select one or two applications for each group)

Topic 2.1 Focus on gm foods (15 minutes)
'What do you understand by gm foods?' (description)

Topic 2.2 Focus on cloning (15 minutes)
'Can someone tell me what this is all about?'

Section 3: regulation and trust (20–30 minutes)

Awareness: How is biotechnology controlled, assessed and monitored, who is controlling and awareness of current controls?
(Cards with relevant actors)

Task 3.1 Hand out cards individually and ask what comes to mind.

Task 3.2 (With all the cards on the table) 'Who should have more say in the control and regulation of biotechnology?'

Task 3.3 Select the cards with the actors who are involved in national biotechnology regulation: exploration of trust, distrust, shared values, comparison with other areas of regulation and national/international dimension.

Section 4: further exploration, if required of the dimensions of public concerns.

Risk, ethical and moral dimensions (10 minutes)
'What does 'ethics' mean?' 'Is there a difference between risk and ethical concerns?'
'Which of these should drive regulation and why?'

Section 5: the ending

Appendix 3. Eurobarometer on Biotechnology (EB52.1); English version

NB (N) refers to new questions, not included in EB46.1 (1996).

To start with, let's talk about science and technology.

Q.2. I am going to read out a list of areas in which new technologies are currently developing. For each of these areas, do you think it will improve our way of life in the next 20 years, it will have no effect, or it will make things worse?

Read out
Solar energy
Computers and information technology
Biotechnology (split ballot A)
Genetic engineering (split ballot B)
Telecommunications
New materials or substances
Space exploration
The internet (N)
Nuclear energy (N)

Q.3 a) Please tell me what comes to your mind when you think about modern biotechnology in a broad sense, that is including genetic engineering? *(Int.: write verbatim in full, prompt: 'anything else?', after each word or sentence)*

Q.3 b) *(Int: read back the responses excluding 'don't know' and ask)*
Do you have a positive, negative or neutral opinion about it?

For the rest of the interview, we are using the term 'modern biotechnology' in the broad sense, that is including genetic engineering.

Q.4 For each of the following statements, please tell me whether you think it is true or false.

Read out
1. There are bacteria which live from waste water
2. Ordinary tomatoes do not contain genes, while genetically modified tomatoes do
3. The cloning of living things produces genetically identical offspring
4. By eating a genetically modified fruit, a person's genes could also become modified

5. It is the father's genes that determine whether a child is a girl (N)
6. Yeast for brewing beer consists of living organisms
7. It is possible to find out in the first few months of pregnancy whether a child will have (Down's Syndrome, trisomy, Mongolism – *use the one or two appropriate terms according to local language*)
8. Genetically modified animals are always bigger than ordinary ones
9. More than half of human genes are identical to those of chimpanzees
10. It is impossible to transfer animal genes into plants

Now we will turn to applications which are coming out of modern biotechnology.

Q.5.a) Please tell me whether you have heard of this application of biotechnology before, or not?
(Int.: show card - read out each application in turn, and tick only if answer is 'yes')
(Show card with item 1, 4 dimensions and scale: ask b, then c, then d, then e.)
(Int. code 1 if respondent says 'definitely agree', code 2 if 'tend to agree', code 3 if 'tend to disagree', code 4, if 'definitely disagree', code 5 if 'don't know')
b) Could you please tell me whether you definitely agree, tend to agree, tend to disagree or definitely disagree that this application is useful for society?
c) And to what extent do you agree that this application is a risk for society?
d) And to what extent do you agree that this application is morally acceptable?
e) And to what extent do you agree that this application should be encouraged?

Q.5.2 *(Show card with item 2, 4 dimensions and scale: ask b, then c, then d, then e; then go to item 3, etc.)*

To what extent do you agree or disagree that ...
b) This application is useful for society?
c) This application is a risk for society?
d) This application is morally acceptable?
e) This application should be encouraged?

Read out

1. Use modern biotechnology in the production of foods, for example to make them higher in protein, keep longer or change the taste

2. Taking genes from plant species and transferring them into crop plants, to make them more resistant to insect pests

3. Introducing human genes into bacteria to produce medicines or vaccines, for example to produce insulin for diabetics

4. Cloning human cells or tissues to replace a patient's diseased cells that are not functioning properly (N)

5. Cloning animals such as sheep to get milk which can be used to make medicines and vaccines (N)

6. Using genetic testing to detect diseases we might have inherited from our parents such as cystic fibrosis, mucoviscidosis, thalassaemia (*use the best known example in each country*)

7. Developing genetically modified bacteria to clean up slicks of oil or dangerous chemicals (N)

Split ballot A

Q.6. Now let's talk about cloning animals, for instance to get milk which can be used to make medicines and vaccines. From now on I am going to call this cloning. Please tell me whether you strongly agree, somewhat agree, neither agree nor disagree, somewhat disagree or strongly disagree with each of the following statements? *(show card with scale)*

Read out top/bottom/top alternately

1. Cloning animals will bring benefits to a lot of people

2. Deciding on the issue of cloning animals is so complex that public consultation about it is a waste of time

3. Cloning animals threatens the natural order of things

4. If the majority of people were in favour of cloning animals, then it should be allowed

5. Cloning animals is simply not necessary

6. The risks from cloning animals are acceptable

7. Whatever the risks from cloning animals, you can avoid them if you really want to

8. Even if cloning animals has benefits it is fundamentally unnatural

9. If anything went wrong with cloning animals, it would be a worldwide catastrophe

10. I dread the idea of cloning animals

11. Cloning animals poses no danger for future generations

12. Of all the risks we face these days, the risk from cloning animals is quite small

13. Even if it means missing out on some of its benefits, cloning should be introduced more gradually

Split ballot B

Q.6. Now let's talk about using modern biotechnology in the production of foods, for example to make them higher in protein, keep longer or change the taste. From now on I am going to call this GM food, that is genetically modified food. Please tell me whether you strongly agree, somewhat agree, neither agree nor disagree, somewhat disagree or strongly disagree with each of the following statements? *(Show card with scale)*

Read out top/bottom/top alternately

1. GM food will bring benefits to a lot of people

2. Deciding on the issue of GM food is so complex that public consultation about it is a waste of time

3. GM food threatens the natural order of things

4. If the majority of people were in favour of GM food then it should be allowed

5. GM food is simply not necessary

6. The risks from GM food are acceptable

7. Whatever the risks from GM food, you can avoid them if you really want to

8. Even if GM food had benefits it is fundamentally unnatural

9. If anything went wrong with GM food it would be a worldwide catastrophe

10. I dread the idea of GM food

11. GM food poses no danger for future generations

12. Of all the risks we face these days, the risk from

13. GM food is quite small

14. Even if it means missing out on some of its benefits, GM food should be introduced more gradually

Ask all

Q.7. For each of the following statements, please tell if you tend to agree or tend to disagree?

Read out top/bottom/top alternately

1. I would buy genetically modified fruits if they tasted better

2. I would pay more for non GM food

3. I would sign a petition against biotechnology

4. I would be prepared to take part in public discussions or hearings about biotechnology

5. I would take time to read articles or watch TV programmes on the advantages and disadvantages of developments in biotechnology

6. I feel sufficiently informed about biotechnology
7. I would be willing to buy cooking oil that contained a small amount of GM soya
8. If they got rid of all traces of the genetic modification from GM sugar cane, I would be happy to eat the sugar
9. I would be willing to eat the eggs of chickens fed on GM corn

Q.8. Now I'm going to ask you about different people and groups involved in various applications of modern biotechnology and genetic engineering. Do you think they are doing a good job for society or not doing a good job for society?

Read out top/bottom/top alternately
1. Newspapers and magazines reporting on biotechnology
2. Industry developing new products with biotechnology
3. Ethics committees looking at the moral aspects of biotechnology
4. Consumer organisations checking products of biotechnology
5. Environmental groups campaigning against biotechnology
6. Our government making regulations on biotechnology
7. Shops making sure our food is safe
8. Farmers deciding which types of crop to grow
9. The churches giving their points of view on biotechnology
10. Medical doctors keeping an eye on the health implications of biotechnology

Q.9. Now I would like to ask you which of the following sources of information, if any, you trust to tell you the truth about modern biotechnology.
a) Please choose the source of information you trust most, if any, from the following list. *(Show card – one answer only)*

b) Please indicate also which other sources, if any, you trust to tell you the truth about modern biotechnology. *(Show same card – several answers possible)*

Read out
1. Consumer organisations
2. Environmental organisations
3. Animal welfare organisations
4. The medical profession
5. Farmer's organisations
6. Religious organisations
7. National government bodies
8. International institutions (not companies)

9. A particular industry (M)
10. Universities
11. Political parties
12. Television and newspapers
None of these *(spontaneous)*
Don't know

Q.10. Before today have you ever talked about modern biotechnology with anyone?

(IF YES) Have you talked about it frequently, occasionally, or only once or twice?

No, never
Yes, frequently
Yes, occasionally
Yes, only once or twice
Don't know

Q.11.a) Which, if any, of the following newspapers or magazines have you read most regularly in the past month? *(Show card – one answer only)*

Q.11.b) *(if 'None', code 10 in Q.11.a)*

And, if you were to read one regularly, which one would you prefer? *(Show same card – one answer only)*

Ask all

Q.12.a) There is a lot of talk these days about what *(our country)*'s goals should be for the next ten or fifteen years. On this card are listed some of the goals that different people say should be given top priority. Would you please say which one of them you, yourself, consider to be most important in the long run? *(show card – one answer only)*

Q.12.b) And what would be your second choice? *(show same card – one answer only)*

Read out

1. Maintaining order in the country
2. Giving the people more say in important government decisions
3. Fighting rising prices
4. Protecting freedom of speech
5. Don't know
6. Demos

D.1. In political matters people talk of 'the left' and 'the right'. How would you place your views on this scale? *(Show card – do not prompt. If contact hesitates, ask to try again)*

Left									Right
1	2	3	4	5	6	7	8	9	10

D.27. Would you describe yourself as…?
(Read out – show card – one answer only)
1. Extremely religious
2. Very religious
3. Somewhat religious
4. Neither religious, nor non-religious
5. Somewhat non-religious
6. Very non-religious
7. Extremely non-religious
8. An agnostic
9. An atheist
10. Anti-religious (N)
11. Don't know

Index

Index

DATE DUE